Aircraft Engine Design

Second Edition

Aircraft Engine Design

Second Edition

Jack D. Mattingly
U.S. Air Force

William H. Heiser
U.S. Air Force Academy

David T. Pratt
University of Washington

EDUCATION SERIES
J. S. Przemieniecki
Series Editor-in-Chief

Published by
American Institute of Aeronautics and Astronautics, Inc.
1801 Alexander Bell Drive, Reston, VA 20191-4344

American Institute of Aeronautics and Astronautics, Inc., Reston, Virginia

6 7 8 9 10

Library of Congress Cataloging-in-Publication Data

Mattingly, Jack D.
    Aircraft engine design / Jack D. Mattingly, William H. Heiser, David T. Pratt. 2nd ed.
        p.   cm. (AIAA education series)
Includes bibliographical references and index.
    1. Aircraft gas-turbines Design and construction.   I. Heiser, William H.   II. Pratt, David T.
III. Title.   IV. Series.
TL709.5.T87 M38   2002   629.134353—dc21   2002013143
ISBN 1-56347-538-3 (alk. paper)

Foreword

The publication of the second edition of *Aircraft Engine Design* is particularly timely because it appears on the eve of the 100th anniversary of the first powered flight by the Wright brothers in 1903 that paved the path to our quest for further development and innovative ideas in aircraft propulsion systems. That path led to the invention of the jet engine and opened the possibility of air travel as standard means of transportation. The three authors of this new volume, Dr. Jack Mattingly, Dr. William Heiser, and Dr. David Pratt produced an outstanding textbook for use not only as a teaching aid but also as a source of design information for practicing propulsion engineers. They all had extensive experience both in teaching the subject in academic institutions and in research and development in U.S. Air Force laboratories and in aerospace manufacturing companies. Their combined talents in refining and expanding the original edition produced one of the best teaching texts in the Education Series.

The 10 chapters in this text are organized essentially along three main themes: 1) The Design Process (Chapters 1 through 3) involving constraint and mission analysis, 2) Engine Selection (Chapters 4 through 6), and 3) Engine Components (Chapters 7 through 10). Thus the present text provides a comprehensive description of the whole design process from the conceptual stages to the final integration of the propulsion system into the aircraft. The text concludes with some 16 appendices on units, conversion factors, material properties, analysis of a variety of engine cycles, and extensive supporting material for concepts used in the textbook. The structure of this text is tailored to the special needs of teaching design and therefore should contribute greatly to the learning of the design process that is the crucial requirement in any aeronautical engineering curricula. At the same time, the wealth of design information in this text and the comprehensive accompanying software will provide useful information for aircraft engine designers.

The AIAA Education Series of textbooks and monographs, inaugurated in 1984, embraces a broad spectrum of theory and application of different disciplines in aeronautics and astronautics, including aerospace design practice. The series includes also texts on defense science, engineering, and management. It serves as teaching texts as well as reference materials for practicing engineers, scientists, and managers. The complete list of textbooks published in the series can be found on the end pages of this volume.

J. S. PRZEMIENIECKI
Editor-in-Chief
AIAA Education Series

Table of Contents

Part I   Engine Cycle Design

Preface

On the eve of the 100th anniversary of powered flight, it is fitting to recall how the first successful aircraft engine came about. In 1902 the Wright brothers wrote to several engine manufacturers requesting a 180-lb gasoline engine that could produce 8 hp. Since none was available, Orville Wright and mechanic Charlie Taylor designed and built their own that produced 12 hp and weighed 200 lbs. How far aircraft engines have come since then! Only a generation later Sir Frank Whittle and Dr. Hans von Ohain, independently, developed the first flight-worthy jet engines. Subsequent advances have produced the high-tech gas turbine engines that power modern aircraft.

Over the past century of progress in propulsion, one constant in aircraft engine development has been the need to respond to changing aircraft requirements. *Aircraft Engine Design, Second Edition* explains how to meet that need. You have in your hands a state-of-the-art textbook that is the distillation of 15 years of improvements since its original publication. Five primary factors prompted this revised and enlarged edition:

1) Altogether new concepts have taken hold in the world of propulsion that require exposition, such as the recognition of throttle ratio as a primary designer engine cycle selection, the development of low pollution combustor design, the application of fracture mechanics to durability analysis, and the recognition of high-cycle fatigue as a leading design issue.

2) Classroom experiences with the original textbook have led to improved methods for explaining many central concepts, such as off-design performance and turbomachinery aerodynamic performance. Also, some concepts deserve further exploration, for example, uninstalled/installed thrust and some analytical demonstrations of engine behavior.

3) Dramatically new software has been developed for constraint, mission, and component analyses, all of which is compatible with modern, user-friendly, menu-driven PC environments. The new software is much more comprehensive, flexible, and powerful, and it greatly facilitates rapid design iteration to convergence.

4) The original authors became acquainted with Dave Pratt, an expert in the daunting field of combustion, and persuaded him to place the material on combustors and afterburners on a sound phenomenological basis. This required entirely new text and computer codes. They were also fortunate to be able to solicit outstanding material on engine life management and engine controls.

5) The authors felt that a second example Request for Proposal (RFP) would add an important dimension to the textbook. Moreover, their experience with a wide variety of example RFPs revealed the need for several new constraint and mission analysis cases.

With more than 100 years of experience in propulsion systems, the authors have each contributed their own particular expertise to this new edition with a resultant synergy that will be apparent to the discerning reader. One experience that the authors have in common is service in the Department of Aeronautics at the U.S. Air Force Academy where I was department head. It was also my privilege to have worked with Bill Heiser and Jack Mattingly as a coauthor on the original edition of *Aircraft Engine Design*. I am pleased that Dave Pratt has joined Bill and Jack to contribute his knowledge of combustion to this new edition. The result is a much improved and very usable textbook that will well serve the next generation of professionals and students.

In preparing this new edition of *Aircraft Engine Design*, the authors have drawn upon their vast experience in academia. Dr. Heiser served 10 years in the Department of Aeronautics of the Air Force Academy and has taught at the University of California, Davis, and the Massachusetts Institute of Technology. Dr. Mattingly taught for seven years at the Air Force Academy. In addition, he has taught at the Air Force Institute of Technology, the University of Washington, the University of Wisconsin, and Seattle University, where he served as Department Chair. Dr. Pratt has been a faculty member at the U.S. Naval Academy, Washington State University, the University of Utah, the University of Michigan, and the University of Washington, including eight years as Department Chair at Michigan and Washington. He also spent a sabbatical at the Air Force Academy. In recognition of their academic contributions, the authors have all been named professors emeriti.

The authors' considerable experience in research and industry also contributed to their revision of *Aircraft Engine Design*. Dr. Heiser began his industrial experience at Pratt and Whitney working on gas turbine technology. Subsequently he was Air Force Chief Scientist of the Wright–Patterson Air Force Base Aero Propulsion Laboratory in Ohio and then at the Arnold Engineering Development Center in Tennessee. Later he directed all advanced engine technology at General Electric. He was the principal propulsion advisor to the Joint Strike Fighter Propulsion Team that was awarded the 2001 Collier Trophy for outstanding achievement in aeronautics. Dr. Heiser was Vice President and Director of the Aerojet Propulsion Research Institute in Sacramento, California, where Dr. Pratt was also a Research Director. Dr. Pratt was a Senior Fulbright Research Fellow at Imperial College in London and spent time at the Los Alamos Laboratories. He has consulted for more than 20 industrial and government agencies. While at the Air Force Aero Propulsion Laboratory, Dr. Mattingly directed exploratory and advanced development programs aimed at improving the performance, reliability, and durability of jet engine components. He also led the combustor technical team for the National AeroSpace Plane program. Dr. Mattingly did research in propulsion and thermal energy systems at AFIT and at the Universities of Washington and Wisconsin.

In addition to this new edition of *Aircraft Engine Design*, the authors have published other significant textbooks and technical publications. Dr. Heiser and Dr. Pratt received the 1999 Summerfield Award for their AIAA Education Series textbook *Hypersonic Airbreathing Propulsion*. Dr. Mattingly is the author of the McGraw-Hill textbook *Elements of Gas Turbine Propulsion* and has published more than 30 technical papers on propulsion and thermal energy. Dr. Heiser has published more than 70 technical papers dealing with propulsion, aerodynamics, and magnetohydrodynamics (MHD). Dr. Pratt has more than 100 publications in pollution formation and control in coal and gas-fired furnaces and gas turbine engines, and in numerical modeling of combustion processes in gas turbine, automotive, ramjet, scramjet, and detonation wave propulsion systems.

Just as important as the depth and breadth of the authors' expertise is their ability to impart their knowledge through this textbook. I am confident that this will become apparent as you use the second edition of *Aircraft Engine Design*.

As we embark on the second century of powered flight, let us recall the words of Austin Miller inscribed on the base of the eagle and fledglings statue at the U.S. Air Force Academy:

"Man's flight through life is sustained by the power of his knowledge."

Brig. Gen. Daniel H. Daley (Retired)
U.S. Air Force
August 2002

Acknowledgments

The writing of the second edition of Aircraft Engine Design began as soon as the first edition was published in 1987. The ensuing 15 years of evolutionary changes have created an altogether new work. This could hardly have been done without the help of many people and organizations, the most important of which will be noted here.

We are especially indebted to Richard J. Hill and William E. Koop of the Turbine Engine Division of the Propulsion Directorate of the U.S. Air Force Wright Laboratories for their financial support and enduring dedication to and guidance for this project. We hope and trust that this textbook fulfills their vision of a fitting contribution of the Wright Laboratories to the celebration of the 100th anniversary of the Wright Brothers' first flight. Our debt in this matter extends to Dr. Aaron R. Byerley of the Department of Aeronautics of the U.S. Air Force Academy for his impressive personal innovative persistence that made it possible to execute an effective contract.

The contributions of uniquely qualified experts provide a valuable new dimension to the Second Edition. These include Appendix N on Turbine Engine Life Management by Dr. William D. Cowie and Appendix O on Engine Controls by Charles A. Skira (with Timothy J. Lewis and Zane D. Gastineau). It is our pleasure to have worked with them and to be able to share their knowledge with the reader.

Many of our insights were generated by and our solutions tested by the hundreds of students that have withstood the infliction of our constantly changing material over the decades. It has been our special privilege to share the classroom with them, many of whom have assumed mythic proportions over time. The second edition is enormously better because of them, and so are we.

The generous Preface was provided by our dear friend and mentor, and coauthor of the first edition, retired U.S. Air Force Brig. Gen. Daniel H. Daley. His inquiring spirit, as well as his love of thermodynamics, still inhabit these pages.

The AIAA Education Series and editorial staff provided essential support to the publication of the second edition. Dr. John S. Przemieniecki, Editor-in-Chief of the AIAA Education Series, who accepted the project, and Rodger S. Williams, publications development, and Jennifer L. Stover, managing editor, who took care of the legal, financial, and production arrangements, are especially deserving of mention. We have been blessed with the steady and comforting support of our constant friend and comrade Norma J. Brennan, publications director.

Finally, we believe it is very important that we record our gratitude to our wives Sheila Mattingly, Leilani Heiser, and Marilyn Pratt. By combining faith, love, patience, and a sense of humor, they have unflaggingly supported us throughout this endeavor and we are eternally in their debt.

Nomenclature (Chapters 1–3)

A = area
AB = afterburner
AOA = angle of attack, Fig. 2.4
AR = aspect ratio
a = speed of sound
a = quantity in quadratic equation
b = quantity in quadratic equation
BCA = best cruise altitude
BCM = best cruise Mach number
C_D = coefficient of drag, Eq. (2.9)
C_D^* = coefficient of drag at maximum L/D, Eq. (3.27a)
C_{DR} = coefficient of additional drags
C_{DRC} = coefficient of drag for drag chute
C_{D0} = coefficient of drag at zero lift
C_L = coefficient of lift, Eq. (2.8)
C_L^* = coefficient of lift at maximum L/D, Eq. (3.27b)
C_1 = coefficient in specific fuel consumption model, Eq. (3.12)
C_2 = coefficient in specific fuel consumption model, Eq. (3.12)
c = quantity in quadratic equation
D = drag
d = infinitesimal change
e = planform efficiency factor
exp = exponential of
f_s = fuel specific work, Eq. (3.8)
g = acceleration
g_c = Newton's gravitational constant
g_0 = acceleration of gravity
h = height
K_1 = coefficient in lift-drag polar equation, Eq. (2.9)
K_2 = coefficient in lift-drag polar equation, Eq. (2.9)
K' = inviscid drag coefficient in lift-drag polar equation, Eq. (2.9)
K'' = viscous drag coefficient in lift-drag polar equation, Eq. (2.9)
k_{obs} = velocity ratio over obstacle, Eq. (2.36)
k_{TD} = velocity ratio at touchdown, $(V_{TD} = k_{TD} V_{STALL})$
k_{TO} = velocity ratio at takeoff, Eq. (2.20)
L = lift
ln = natural logarithm of
M = Mach number
M^* = best cruise Mach number
N = number of turns

n	=	load factor, Eq. (2.6)
P	=	pressure
P_t	=	total pressure, Eq. (1.2)
P_s	=	weight specific excess power, Eq. (2.2b)
q	=	dynamic pressure, Eq. (1.6)
R	=	additional drags; gas constant
r	=	radius
S	=	wing planform area
s	=	distance
T	=	installed thrust; temperature
T_t	=	total temperature, Eq. (1.1)
TR	=	throttle ratio, Eq. (D.6)
$TSFC$	=	installed thrust specific fuel consumption, Eq. (3.10)
t	=	time
u	=	total drag-to-thrust ratio, Eq. (3.5)
V	=	velocity
W	=	weight
z_e	=	energy height, Eq. (2.2a)
α	=	installed thrust lapse, Eq. (2.3)
β	=	instantaneous weight fraction, Eq. (2.4)
Γ	=	empty aircraft weight fraction ($= W_E / W_{TO}$)
γ	=	ratio of specific heats
Δ	=	finite change
δ	=	dimensionless static pressure (see Appendix B)
δ_0	=	dimensionless total pressure, Eq. (2.52b)
ε	=	infinitesimal quantity
θ	=	dimensionless static temperature (see Appendix B)
θ_{CL}	=	angle of climb
θ_0	=	dimensionless total temperature, Eq. (2.52a)
θ_{0break}	=	theta break, θ_0 where engine control system sets simultaneous maxima of T_{t4} and π_c (see Appendix D)
Λ	=	wing sweep angle
μ	=	coefficient of friction
ξ_L	=	drag coefficient for landing, Eq. (2.32)
ξ_{TO}	=	drag coefficient for takeoff, Eq. (2.24)
$\prod_{if}$	=	mission leg weight fraction, Eq. (3.46)
ρ	=	density
Σ	=	summation
σ	=	dimensionless static density (see Appendix B)
φ	=	angle of thrust vector to wing chord line, Fig. 2.4
Ω	=	angular velocity

Subscripts

avg	=	average
B	=	braking
BCA	=	best cruise altitude
CAP	=	combat air patrol

CL	=	climb
$CRIT$	=	critical
$c/4$	=	quarter chord
D	=	drag
dry	=	without afterburning
E	=	empty
F	=	fuel
FR	=	free roll
f	=	final
G	=	ground roll
i	=	initial
L	=	landing; lift
max	=	maximum
mid	=	mid point
min	=	minimum
obs	=	obstacle
P	=	payload
PE	=	expended payload
PP	=	permanent payload
R	=	rotation
SL	=	sea level static
$STALL$	=	corresponding to stall
std	=	standard day
TD	=	touchdown
TO	=	takeoff
TR	=	transition
wet	=	with afterburning
$A \rightarrow J$	=	mission segments
$a \rightarrow c$	=	integration intervals
$1 \rightarrow 14$	=	mission phases

Nomenclature (Chapters 4–10 and Appendices)

A	=	area; pre-exponential factor, Eq. (9.25)
AR	=	aspect ratio; area ratio, Eq. (9.61)
a	=	speed of sound; axial interference factor, Fig. L.4
a	=	constant in swirl velocity equation, Eq. (8.24)
a_i	=	speed of sound at station i
a'	=	rotational interference factor, Fig. L.4
B	=	ratio of Prandtl mixing length to shear later width, Eq. (9.53); afterburner blockage D/H, Eq. (9.87)
BCA	=	best cruise altitude
BCM	=	best cruise Mach number
b	=	constant in swirl velocity equation, Eq. (8.24)
C	=	constant
C_A	=	nozzle angularity coefficient, Eq. (10.24)
C_D	=	coefficient of drag; nozzle discharge coefficient, Eq. (10.22)
C_{fg}	=	nozzle gross thrust coefficient, Eq. (10.21)
C_L	=	coefficient of lift
C_P	=	pressure recovery coefficient, Eq. (9.62); power correlation parameter, Eq. (L.18)
C_P^*	=	ideal power coefficient, Eq. (L.9)
C_T	=	thrust correlation parameter, Eq. (L.17)
C_T^*	=	ideal thrust coefficient, Eq. (L.8)
C_{TOH}	=	power takeoff shaft power coefficient for high-pressure spool, Eq. (4.21b)
C_{TOL}	=	power takeoff shaft power coefficient for low-pressure spool, Eq. (4.22b)
C_V	=	nozzle velocity coefficient, Eq. (10.23)
C_δ	=	shear layer growth constant, Eq. (9.54)
c	=	airfoil chord
c_p	=	specific heat at constant pressure
D	=	diameter; drag; diffusion factor, Eq. (8.1)
D_{add}	=	additive drag, Eq. (6.5)
DSF	=	disk shape factor, Eq. (8.68)
d	=	infinitesimal change
E	=	modulus of elasticity
e_i	=	polytropic efficiency of component i
exp	=	exponential of
F	=	uninstalled thrust, Eq. (4.1)
f	=	fuel-to-air mass flow ratio
g_c	=	Newton's gravitational constant
g_0	=	acceleration of gravity

H	=	height; enthalpy of a mixture of gases, Eq. (9.8)
HP	=	horsepower
h	=	altitude; static enthalpy
h_{PR}	=	Heating value of fuel
h_r	=	height of rim
h_{ti}	=	total enthalpy at station i
I	=	impulse function, Eq. (1.5); air loading, Eq. (9.31)
IMS	=	integral mean slope, Eq. (6.11)
J	=	ratio of jet-to-crossflow momentum flux or dynamic pressure, Eq. (9.40); advance ratio, Eq. (L.20)
$k_{j,}, k_{-j}$	=	forward, reverse rate constant for jth reaction, Eqs. (9.14) and (9.15)
L	=	length
ℓ_n	=	natural logarithm of
M	=	Mach number; mean molecular weight
MFP	=	mass flow parameter, Eq. (1.3)
MF_p	=	static pressure mass flow parameter, Eq. (1.4)
$\dot{m}$	=	mass flow rate
$\dot{m}_{ci}$	=	corrected mass flow rate at station i, Eq. (5.23)
N	=	rotational speed (rpm); number of moles, Eq. (9.26); number of holes, Eq. (9.113) and (9.118); number of nozzle assemblies, Eq. (9.105)
N_B	=	number of blades
N_{ci}	=	corrected engine speed at station i, Eq. (5.24)
N_H	=	rotational speed of high-pressure spool
N_L	=	rotational speed of low-pressure spool
n	=	number; exponent
n_i	=	mass-specific mole number of ith species
n_m	=	sum of mole number in mixture
P	=	pressure; power
P_e	=	external pressure
P_i	=	pressure at station i
P_r	=	reduced pressure, Eq. (4.3c)
P_{TO}	=	shaft power takeoff
P_{ti}	=	total (or stagnation) pressure at station i
P_w	=	wetted perimeter of duct
Q	=	torque
q	=	dynamic pressure, Eq. (1.6)
R	=	gas constant
$\overline{R}$	=	universal gas constant
R_j	=	forward volumetric rate of jth reaction, Eq. (9.14)
RR_f	=	volumetric reaction rate of fuel, Eq. (9.24)
r	=	radius; shear layer velocity ratio, Eq. (9.52)
S	=	uninstalled thrust specific fuel consumption, Eq. (4.2)
S'	=	swirl number of primary air swirler, Eq. (9.48)
s	=	entropy; spacing; shear layer density ratio, Eq. (9.55)
T	=	temperature
T_{AFT}	=	adiabatic flame temperature, Fig. 9.3, Eq. (9.23)

T_{act}	=	activation temperature, Eq. (9.24)
TR	=	throttle ratio, Eq. (D.6)
TSF	=	thrust scale factor (Section 6.3)
T_{ti}	=	total (or stagnation) temperature at station i
t_{BO}	=	residence time or stay time at blowout, Eqs. (9.76) and (9.129)
t_s	=	residence time or stay time, Eqs. (9.76) and (9.129)
U	=	velocity component in direction of flow
u	=	axial or throughflow velocity
V	=	velocity; volume, Eq. (9.19)
V'	=	turbine reference velocity, Eq. (8.38)
v	=	tangential velocity
W	=	weight; thickness; width
$\dot{W}_c$	=	power absorbed by the compressor
$\dot{W}_t$	=	power produced by the turbine
X	=	axial component of distance along jet trajectory, Fig. 9.14, Eq. (9.40)
x	=	axial location
Y	=	radial component of distance along jet trajectory, Fig. 9.14, Eq. (9.40)
Y_i	=	mole fraction of ith species, Eq. (9.25)
Z	=	Zweifel coefficient
α	=	engine bypass ratio, Eq. (4.8a); angle; coefficient of thermal expansion; area fraction, Eq. (9.108)
α'	=	mixer bypass ratio, Eq. (4.8f)
α_{sw}	=	off-axis turning angle of swirler blades, Eq. (9.48)
$\alpha'_{ij}, \alpha''_{ij}$	=	stoichiometric coefficients of ith species in jth reaction, Eq. (9.13)
β	=	bleed air fraction, Eq. (4.8b); angle
β_b	=	blade angle
Γ	=	function defined by Eq. (8.7)
γ	=	ratio of specific heats; angle
Δ	=	finite change
$\Delta h^0_{f_i}$	=	enthalpy of formation of ith species, Eq. (9.7) and Table 9.1
δ	=	small change in; dimensionless static pressure (see Appendix B); time-mean width of shear layer, Figs. 9.12 and 9.19, Eq. (9.54)
δ_c	=	exit deviation of compressor blade, Eq. (8.18)
δ_i	=	dimensionless total pressure at station i, Eq. (5.21)
δ_m	=	time-mean width of mixing layer, Eqs. (9.37) and (9.58)
δ_t	=	exit deviation of turbine blade, Eq. (8.55)
ε	=	combustion reaction progress variable, Eq. (9.21)
ε_T	=	rate of dissipation of turbulence kinetic energy, Eq. (9.74)
ε_1	=	cooling air #1 mass flow rate, Eq. (4.8c)
ε_2	=	cooling air #2 mass flow rate, Eq. (4.8d)
η_i	=	adiabatic efficiency of component i
η_O	=	engine overall efficiency of engine, Eq. (E.3)
η_P	=	engine propulsive efficiency of engine, Eq. (E.4)
η_R	=	inlet total pressure recovery (Section 10.2.3.2)
η_{Rspec}	=	mil spec inlet total pressure recovery, Eq. (4.12b–d)
η_{TH}	=	engine thermal efficiency of engine, Eq. (E.4)

θ	=	dimensionless static temperature ratio (see Appendix B); angle
θ_i	=	dimensionless total temperature at engine station i, Eq. (5.22)
θ_{0break}	=	theta break, θ_0 where engine control system sets simultaneous maxima of T_{t4} and π_c (see Appendix D)
Π	=	weight fraction, Eq. (3.46)
π_i	=	total pressure ratio of component i
π_r	=	isentropic freestream recovery pressure ratio, Eq. (4.5b)
ρ	=	density
σ	=	solidity; stress; static density ratio (see Appendix B); time-mean conical half-angle of round jet, Fig. 9.12, Eq. (9.37)
$\bar{\sigma}_{blade}$	=	average blade stress, Eq. (8.66)
σ_c	=	rotor airfoil centrifugal stress, Eq. (8.62)
σ_D	=	disk stress
σ_R	=	rim stress
σ_{tr}	=	disk thermal differential stress in radial direction, Eq. (8.71)
$\sigma_{t\theta}$	=	disk thermal differential stress in tangential direction, Eq. (8.72)
σ_u	=	ultimate stress
τ	=	enthalpy ratio; temperature ratio
τ_i	=	total enthalpy ratio of component i
τ_r	=	adiabatic freestream recovery enthalpy ratio, Eq. (4.5a)
τ_λ	=	enthalpy ratio of burner, Eq. (4.6c)
$\tau_{\lambda AB}$	=	enthalpy ratio of afterburner, Eq. (4.6d)
Φ	=	cooling effectiveness, Eq. (8.56)
ϕ	=	entropy function, Eq. (4.3b); equivalence ratio, Eq. (9.3)
ϕ_{inlet}	=	inlet external loss coefficient, Eq. (6.2a)
ϕ_{nozzle}	=	nozzle external loss coefficient, Eq. (6.2b)
ψ	=	turbine stage loading coefficient, Eq. (8.57)
Ω	=	dimensionless turbine rotor speed, Eq. (8.38)
ω	=	angular velocity
$°R_c$	=	degree of reaction for compressor stage, Eq. (8.8)
$°R_t$	=	degree of reaction for turbine stage, Eq. (8.36)

Subscripts

A	=	air; annulus
AB	=	afterburner
A/C	=	aircraft
add	=	additive drag
$avail$	=	available
b	=	burner; bleed air
bl	=	boundary layer bleed
bp	=	bypass
$break$	=	location where engine control system has simultaneous maximums of T_{t4} and π_c
C	=	core flow
c	=	compressor; centrifugal; capture; corrected; chord; cooling
cc	=	compressor corrected
ce	=	engine corrected
cH	=	high-pressure compressor

cL	=	low-pressure compressor
$c1$	=	cooling air #1
$c2$	=	cooling air #2
D	=	diffuser
DP	=	pressure drag
DZ	=	dilution
d	=	diffuser or inlet; disk
dd	=	drag divergence
$design$	=	at design value
dr	=	disk rim
ds	=	disk shaft
E	=	existing
e	=	exit; external; exhaust; engine
F	=	bypass flow
f	=	fuel; fan
fAB	=	fuel at afterburner
g	=	gross; gas
h	=	hub; hole
hl	=	highlight
i	=	inlet; ideal; inner; index number
j	=	jet; index number
k	=	index number
L	=	liner
M	=	mixer
MB	=	main burner
m	=	mean; intermediate; micromixing; metal
max	=	maximum
mH	=	mechanical, high-pressure spool
min	=	minimum
mL	=	mechanical, low-pressure spool
mPH	=	mechanical, power takeoff shaft from high-pressure spool
mPL	=	mechanical, power takeoff shaft from low-pressure spool
$m1$	=	coolant mixer 1
$m2$	=	coolant mixer 2
N	=	new (or updated) value of
n	=	nozzle; number of stages
nac	=	nacelle
O	=	overall
o	=	overall; outer
opt	=	optimum
P	=	propulsive
PD	=	preliminary design
PR	=	products to reactants
PZ	=	primary zone
$prop$	=	propeller
R	=	reference; relative; rim
r	=	radial direction
ref	=	reference

rel	=	relative
req	=	required
rm	=	mean radius
S	=	shaft
SZ	=	secondary zone
s	=	stage
sp	=	spillage
spec	=	with respect to reference ram recovery
std	=	standard day sea level property
st	=	stoichiometric
T	=	tip
TH	=	thermal
TO	=	power takeoff
t	=	turbine; total; tip
tH	=	high-pressure turbine
th	=	throat
tL	=	low-pressure turbine
u	=	axial velocity
v	=	tangential velocity
x	=	upstream of normal shock
y	=	downstream of normal shock
$0 \rightarrow 19$	=	station location
θ	=	tangential direction

Superscripts

n	=	power
$()^*$	=	corresponding to $M = 1$; ideal
$(^-)$	=	average

PART I
Engine Cycle Design

1
The Design Process

1.1 Introduction

This is a textbook on *design*. We have attempted to capture the essence of the design process by means of a realistic and complete design experience. In doing this, we have had to bridge the gap between traditional academic textbooks, which emphasize individual concepts and principles, and design handbooks, which provide collections of known solutions. The most challenging and productive activities of the normal engineering career are at neither end of the spectrum, but, instead, require the simultaneous application of many principles for the solution of altogether new problems.

The vehicle employed in order to accomplish our teaching goals is the airbreathing gas turbine engine. This marvelous machine is a pillar of our modern technological society and comes in many familiar forms, such as the turbojet, turbofan, turboprop, and afterburning turbojet. With such a variety of engine configurations, the most appropriate for a given application cannot be determined without going through the design process.

1.2 Designing Is Different

It should be made clear at the outset what is special about the design process, for that is what this textbook will attempt to emphasize. Every designer has an image of what elements constitute the design process, and so our version is not likely to be exhaustive. Nevertheless, the following list contains critical elements with which few would disagree:

1) The design process is both started by and constrained by an identified need.

2) In the case of the design of systems, such as aircraft and engines, many legitimate solutions often exist, and none can be identified as unique or optimum. Systematic methods must be found to identify the most preferred or "best" solutions. The final selection always involves judgment and compromise.

3) The process is inherently iterative, often requiring the return to an earlier step when prior assumptions are found to be invalid.

4) Many technical specialties are interwoven. For example, gas turbine engine design involves at least thermodynamics, aerodynamics, heat transfer, combustion, structures, materials, manufacturing processes, instrumentation, and controls.

5) Above all, the design of a complex system requires active participation and disciplined communication by everyone involved. Because each part of the system influences all of the others, the best solutions can be discovered (and major problems and conflicts avoided) only if the participants share their findings clearly and regularly.

1.3 The Need

Gas turbine engines exert a dominant influence on aircraft performance and must be custom tailored for each specific application. The usual method employed by an aircraft engine user (the customer) for describing the desired performance of an aircraft (or aircraft/engine system) is a requirements document such as a Request for Proposal (RFP). A typical RFP, for the example of an Air-to-Air Fighter (AAF), is included in its entirety in Sec. 1.11 of this chapter. It is apparent that the RFP dwells only upon the final flying characteristics or capabilities of the aircraft and not upon how they shall be achieved.

The RFP is actually a milestone in a sequence of events that started, perhaps, years earlier. During this time, the customer will have worked with potential suppliers to decide what aircraft specifications are likely to be available and affordable as a result of new engineering development programs. Issuance of the RFP implies that there is a reasonable probability of success, but not without risk. Because the cost of development of new aircraft/engine systems as well as the potential future sales are measured in billions of dollars, the competitive system comes to life, and the technological boundaries are pushed to their known limit.

Receipt of the RFP by the suppliers, which in this case would include several airframe companies and several engine companies, is an exciting moment. It marks the end of the preliminary period of study and anticipation and the beginning of the development of a product that will benefit society and provide many with the satisfaction of personal accomplishment. It also marks the time at which the "target" becomes relatively stationary and a truly concerted effort is possible, although changes in the original RFP are occasionally negotiated if the circumstances permit.

A member of an engine company will find his or her situation complicated by a number of things. First, he or she will probably be working with several airframe companies, each of which has a different approach and, therefore, requires a different engine design. This requires some understanding of how the aircraft design influences engine selection, an aspect of engine design that is emphasized in this textbook. All of the engine commonalties possible among competing aircraft designs should be identified in order to prevent resources from being spread too thin. The designer will also experience a natural curiosity to find out what the other engine companies are proposing. This curiosity can be satisfied by a number of legitimate means, notably the free press, but each revelation will only make the designer wonder why the competition is doing it differently and cause his or her management to ask the same question. With experience, the RFP will gradually change in ways not initially anticipated. Slowly but surely, the constraints imposed by each requirement, as well as the possible implications of such constraints, will become evident. When the significance of the constraints can be prioritized, the project will be seen as a whole and the designer will feel comfortable with his choices.

The importance of the last point cannot be overemphasized. Once received, the RFP becomes the touchstone of the entire effort. It must be read very carefully at first so that a start in the right direction is assured. The RFP will be referred to until it becomes ragged, leading to complete familiarity and understanding and, finally, a sense of relaxation.

1.4   Our Approach

To bring as much life as possible to the design process in this textbook, the Air-to-Air Fighter RFP is the basis for a complete preliminary engine design. All of the material required to reach satisfactory final conclusions is included here. Nevertheless, it is strongly encouraged that simultaneous detailed design of the airframe by a parallel group be conducted. The benefits cascade not only because of the technical interchange between the engine and aircraft people, but also because the participants will come to understand professional love-hate relationships in a safe environment!

To make this textbook reasonably self-contained for each step of the design process, a fully usable and (within limits) proper calculation method has been provided. Each method is based on the relevant physical principles, exhibits the correct trends, and has acceptable accuracy. In short, the material in this textbook provides a realistic presentation of the entire design process.

And that is what happens in the case of the AAF engine design as this textbook unfolds. At each step of the design process, the relevant concept is explained, the analytical tools provided, the calculated results displayed, and the consequences discussed. There is no reason that other available tools cannot be substituted, other than the fact that the numbers contained herein will not be exactly reproduced. Moreover, when the detailed design of individual engine components is considered, it will be found that some have been concentrated upon and others passed over. Specific investigations as dictated by interest or curiosity are to be encouraged.

Indeed, when sufficiently familiar with the entire process, it is recommended that the reader consider the Global Range Airlifter (GRA) RFP presented in Appendix P or develop an RFP based on personal interest, such as a supersonic business jet or an unpiloted air vehicle (UAV). The approach and methods of this textbook are also ideally suited to the AIAA Student Engine Design competition, which provides novel challenges annually.

1.5   The Wheel Exists

One of the main reasons that this textbook can be written is that the groundwork for each step has already been developed by previous authors. Our central task has been to tie their material together in a systematic and comprehensive way. It would be inappropriate to repeat such extensive material, and, consequently, the present text leans heavily on available references—in particular, *Aerothermodynamics of Gas Turbine and Rocket Propulsion* by Gordon C. Oates,[1] *Elements of Gas Turbine Propulsion* by Jack D. Mattingly,[2] and *Aircraft Design: A Conceptual Approach* by Daniel P. Raymer.[3] These pioneering contributions share one important characteristic: They have made the difficult easy, and for that we are in their debt.

A persistent problem is that of the often overlapping nomenclature of aerodynamics and propulsion. Because these fields grew more or less independently, the same symbols are frequently used to represent different variables. Faced with this profusion of symbology, the option of graceful surrender was elected, and the traditional conventions of each, as appropriate, are used. The Table of Symbols encompasses all of the aerodynamic and propulsion nomenclature necessary for this textbook, the former applying to Chapters 1–3 and the latter to Chapters 4–10, respectively. Our experience has shown that in most cases readers with appropriate backgrounds will have little difficulty interpreting the symbology and, with practice, recognition will become automatic.

1.6   Charting the Course

There is no absolute roadmap for the design of a gas turbine engine. The steps involved depend, for example, on the experience of the company and the people involved, as well as on the nature of the project. A revolutionary new engine will require more analysis and iteration than the modification of an existing powerplant.

Nevertheless, there are generalized representations of the design process that can be informative and useful. One of these, which depicts the entire development process, is shown in Fig. 1.1. This figure is largely self-explanatory, but it should be noted that the large number of studies, development tests, and iterative loops reveal that it is more representative of what happens to an altogether new engine.

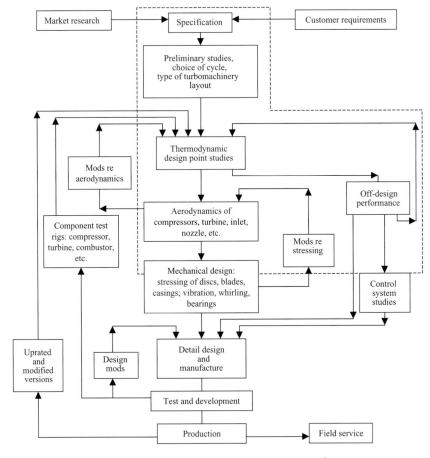

Fig. 1.1   Gas turbine engine design system.[2]

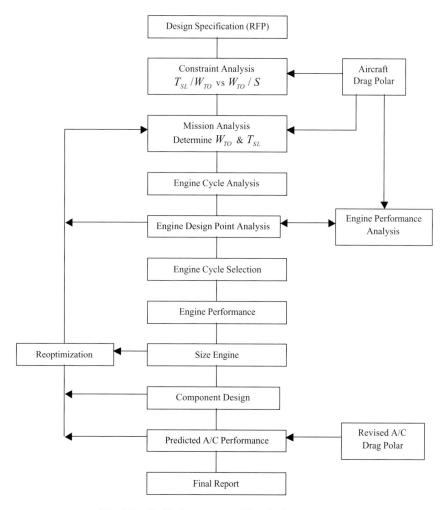

Fig. 1.2   Preliminary propulsion design sequence.

The portion of Fig. 1.1 enclosed by the dashed line is of paramount importance because that is the territory covered by this textbook. Although the boundary can be somewhat altered, for example by including control system studies, it can never encompass the hardware phases, such as manufacturing and testing.

Figure 1.2 shows the sequence of gas turbine engine design steps outlined in this textbook. These steps show more detail, but directly correspond to the territory just noted. They include several opportunities for recapitulation between the engine and airframe companies, each having the chance to influence the other.

It will not be necessary to dwell on Fig. 1.2 at this point because this textbook is built upon this model and the chapters that follow correspond directly to the steps found there.

1.7   Units

Because the British Engineering (BE) system of units is normally found in the published aircraft aerodynamic and propulsion literature, that is the primary system used throughout this textbook. Fortuitously or deliberately, many of the equations and results will be formulated in terms of dimensionless quantities, which places less reliance on conversion factors. Nevertheless, the AEDsys software that accompanies this textbook (see Sec. 1.10.1) automatically translates between BE and SI units, and Appendix A contains a manual conversion table.

When dealing with BE propulsion quantities, it is particularly important to keep in mind the fact that 1 lb force (lbf) is defined as the force of gravity acting on a 1-lb mass (lbm) at standard sea level. Hence, 1 lb mass at (or near) the surface of the Earth "weighs" 1 lb force. Thus, the thrust specific fuel consumption, pounds mass of fuel per hour per pound of thrust, can be regarded as pounds weight of fuel per hour per pound of thrust and traditionally appears with the units of 1/time. Also, specific thrust, pounds of thrust per pound mass of air per second, can be regarded as pounds of thrust per pound weight of air per second. The situation is less complex when dealing with SI units because the acceleration of gravity is not involved in conversion factors.

1.8   The Atmosphere

The properties of the approaching air affect the behavior of both the airplane and the engine. To provide consistency in aerospace analyses, the normal practice is to employ models of the "standard atmosphere" in the form of tables or equations. The equations that describe the standard atmosphere are presented in Appendix B (based on Ref. 4). The properties are presented in terms of the ratio of each property to its sea level reference value. Note that the property values at sea level are also included and are denoted by the subscript "std."

The standard atmosphere is, of course, never found in nature. Consequently, several "nonstandard" atmospheres have been defined in order to allow engine designers to probe the impact of reasonable extremes of "hot" and "cold" days (Ref. 5) on engine behavior. In addition, the "tropical" day (Ref. 6) has been defined for analysis of naval operations. The information in Appendix B or AEDsys software that accompanies this textbook (see Sec. 1.10.1) will allow you to select either the standard, cold, hot, or tropic atmospheres when testing your engines.

1.9   Compressible Flow Relationships

The external and internal aerodynamics of modern aircraft are dominated by compressible flows. To cope with this situation, we will take full advantage throughout this textbook of the analytical and conceptual benefits offered by the classical steady, one-dimensional analysis of the flow of calorically perfect gases (Refs. 1, 2, and 7).

Six of the most prominent compressible flow relationships will now be summarized for later use. Their value to designers and engineers is easily confirmed by their frequent appearance in the literature, as well as by the simple truths they tell and their ease of application. They share the important characteristic that they are evaluated at any point or station in the flow, rather than relating the properties at one point or station to another. The ratio of specific heats γ is constant in this formulation.

1.9.1 Total or Stagnation Temperature

The total or stagnation temperature T_t is the temperature the moving flow would reach if it were brought adiabatically from an initial Mach number M to rest at a stagnation point or in an infinite reservoir. The total temperature is given by the expression

$$T_t = T\left(1 + \frac{\gamma - 1}{2}M^2\right) \tag{1.1}$$

You may find it helpful to know that the term $(\gamma - 1)M^2/2$ that appears in a myriad of compressible flow relationships can be thought of as the ratio of the kinetic energy to the internal energy of the moving flow. Hence, the ratio of total to static temperature increases directly with this energy ratio.

1.9.2 Total or Stagnation Pressure

The total or stagnation pressure P_t is the pressure the moving flow would reach if it were brought isentropically from an initial Mach number M to rest at a stagnation point or in an infinite reservoir. The total pressure is given by the expression

$$P_t = P\left(1 + \frac{\gamma - 1}{2}M^2\right)^{\frac{\gamma}{\gamma-1}} \tag{1.2}$$

This relationship serves as a reminder that the pressure of the flow can be increased merely by slowing it down, reducing the need for mechanical compression. Moreover, because the exponent is rather large for naturally occurring physical processes (e.g., the pressure ratio for air can be as much as 10 when the Mach number is 2.2), no mechanical compression may be required at all. The corresponding propulsion devices are known as ramjets or scramjets because the required pressure ratio results only from decelerating the freestream flow.

1.9.3 Mass Flow Parameter

The mass flow parameter based on total pressure MFP is derived by combining mass flow per unit area with the perfect gas law, the definition of Mach number, the speed of sound, and the equations for total temperature and pressure just given. The resulting expression is

$$MFP = \frac{\dot{m}\sqrt{T_t}}{P_t A} = M\sqrt{\frac{\gamma g_c}{R}}\left(1 + \frac{\gamma - 1}{2}M^2\right)^{\frac{\gamma+1}{2(\gamma-1)}} \tag{1.3}$$

The total pressure mass flow parameter may be used to find any single flow quantity when the other four quantities and the calorically perfect gas constants are known at that station. The MFP is often used, for example, to determine the flow area required to choke a given flow (i.e., at $M = 1$). The MFP can also be used to develop valuable relationships between the flow properties at two different stations, especially when the mass flow is conserved between them.

Because the *MFP* is a function only of the Mach number and the gas properties, it is frequently tabled in textbooks. Unfortunately, each *MFP* corresponds to two Mach numbers, one subsonic and one supersonic, and the complexity of Eq. (1.3) prevents direct algebraic solution for Mach number. Finally, the *MFP* has the familiar maximum at $M = 1$, at which the flow is choked or sonic and the flow per unit area is the greatest.

1.9.4 Static Pressure Mass Flow Parameter

The mass flow parameter based on static pressure *MFp* can be derived by combining Eqs. (1.2) and (1.3). The resulting expression is

$$MFp = \frac{\dot{m}\sqrt{T_t}}{PA} = M\sqrt{\frac{\gamma g_c}{R}\left(1 + \frac{\gamma - 1}{2}M^2\right)} \qquad (1.4)$$

The static pressure mass flow parameter is commonly used by experimentalists, who often find it easier to measure static pressure than total pressure. Fortunately, each MFp corresponds to a single Mach number, and the form of Eq. (1.4) permits direct algebraic solution for Mach number.

1.9.5 Impulse Function

The impulse function I is given by the expression

$$I = PA + \dot{m}V = PA(1 + \gamma M^2) \qquad (1.5)$$

The streamwise axial force exerted on the fluid flowing through a control volume is $I_{exit} - I_{entry}$, while the reaction force exerted by the fluid on the control volume is $I_{entry} - I_{exit}$.

The impulse function makes possible almost unimaginable simplification of the evaluation of forces on aircraft engines and their components. For example, although one could determine the net axial force exerted on the fluid flowing through any device by integrating the axial component of pressure and viscous forces over every infinitesimal element of internal wetted surface area, it is certain that no one ever has. Instead, the integrated result of the forces is obtained with ease and certainty by merely evaluating the change in impulse function across the device.

1.9.6 Dynamic Pressure

Most people are introduced to the concept of dynamic pressure in courses on incompressible flows, where it is the natural reference scale for both inviscid and viscous forces caused by the motion of the fluid. These forces include, for example, stagnation pressure, lift, drag, and boundary layer friction. It is surprising, but nevertheless true, that the dynamic pressure serves the same purpose not only for compressible flows, but for hypersonic flows as well. The renowned and widely used Newtonian hypersonic flow model uses only geometry and the freestream dynamic pressure to estimate the pressures and forces on bodies immersed in flows.

The dynamic pressure q is given by the expression

$$q = \frac{\rho V^2}{2} = \frac{1}{2}\frac{P}{RT}\gamma RTM^2 = \frac{\gamma PM^2}{2} \qquad (1.6)$$

where the equations of state and speed of sound for perfect gases have been substituted. The latter, albeit less familiar, version is greatly preferred for compressible flows because the quantities P and M are more likely to be known or easily found, and because the units are completely straightforward. Consequently, the latter version is predominantly used in this textbook.

1.9.7 Ratio of Specific Heats

The constant ratio of specific heats used in the preceding equations must be judiciously chosen in order to represent the behavior of the gases involved realistically. Because of the temperature and composition changes that take place during the combustion of hydrocarbon fuels, the value of γ within the engine can be considerably different from that of atmospheric air ($\gamma = 1.4$) Two commonly occurring approximations are $\gamma = 1.33$ in the temperature range of 2500–3000°R and $\gamma = 1.30$ in the temperature range 3000–3500°R. The computational capabilities of AEDsys (see Sec. 1.10.1) may also be used in a variety of ways to determine the most appropriate value of γ to be used in any specific situation.

1.10 Looking Ahead

In the following chapters, we have made a substantial effort to reduce intuitive and qualitative judgment as much as possible in favor of sound, flexible, transparent—in short, useful—analytical tools under your control. For example, the next two chapters are based on only two equations of great generality and power. They can be applied to an enormous diversity of situations with successful results.

Even though good analysis can minimize the need for empirical and experimental data, it cannot be altogether avoided in the design of any real device. We have therefore tried to clearly identify when data must be employed, what range of values to chose, and where the data are obtained. We believe that this has the advantage of pinpointing the role of experience in the design process, as well as allowing for sensitivity studies based upon the expected range of variation of parameters.

1.10.1 AEDsys Software

Supplemental material containing an extensive collection of general and specific computational software entitled AEDsys accompanies this textbook. The main purpose of AEDsys is to allow you to avoid the complex, repetitive, tedious calculations that are an inevitable part of the aircraft engine design process and to instead focus on the underlying concepts and their resulting effects. The AEDsys software has been developed and refined with the sometimes involuntary help of captive students from all walks of life over a period of more than 20 years, and it has become a formidable capability. Put simply, the AEDsys software plays an essential role in achieving the pedagogical goals of the authors.

With practice, you will find your own reasons to be fond of AEDsys, but they will probably include the following six. First, the input requirements for any calculation automatically remind you of the complete set of information that must be supplied by the designer. Second, units can be effortlessly converted back and forth between BE and SI, thus evading one of the greatest pitfalls of engineering work. Third, all of the computations are based on physical models and modern algorithms that make them nearly instantaneous. Fourth, many of the most important computational results are presented graphically, allowing visual interpretation of trends and limits. Fifth, they are compatible with modern PC and laptop presentation formats, including menu- and mouse-driven actions. Sixth, and far from least, is the likelihood that you will find uses for the broad capabilities of the AEDsys software far beyond the needs of this textbook.

Because the supplemental material contains a complete user's manual for AEDsys, no explanations will be provided in the printed text. The table of contents is listed next.

1.10.2 AEDsys Table of Contents

AEDsys Program
> This is a comprehensive program that encompasses Chapters 2–7. It includes constraint analysis, aircraft system performance, mission analysis of aircraft system, and engine performance. User can select from the basic engine models of Chapters 2 and 3 or the advanced engine models of Chapter 5 with the installation loss model of Chapter 6 or constant loss. Calculates engine performance at full and partial throttle using the engine models of Chapter 5. Interface quantities can be calculated at engine operating conditions.

ONX Program
> This is a design point and parametric cycle analysis of the following engines based on the models of Chapter 4: single-spool turbojet, dual-spool turbojet with/without afterburner, mixed-flow turbofan with/without afterburner, high bypass turbofan, and turboprop. User can select gas model as one with constant specific heats, variable specific heats, or constant specific heats through all components except for those where combustion occurs where variable specific heats are used. Generates reference engine data for input to AEDsys program.

ATMOS Program
> Calculate properties of the atmosphere for standard, hot, cold, and tropical days.

GASTAB Program
> This is equivalent to traditional compressible flow appendices for the simple flows of calorically perfect gases. This includes isentropic flow; adiabatic, constant area frictional flow (Fanno flow); frictionless, constant area heating and cooling (Rayleigh flow); normal shock waves; oblique shock waves; multiple oblique shock waves; and Prandtl–Meyer flow.

COMPR Program
> This is a preliminary mean-line design of multistage axial-flow compressor. This includes rim and disc stress.

TURBN Program
> This is a preliminary mean-line design of multistage axial-flow turbine. This includes rim and disc stress.

EQL Program
This calculates equilibrium properties and process end states for reactive mixtures of ideal gases, for different problems involving hydrocarbon fuels and air.

KINETX Program
This is a preliminary design tool that models finite-rate combustion kinetics in a simple Bragg combustor consisting of well-stirred reactor, plug-flow reactor, and nonreacting mixer.

MAINBRN Program
This is a preliminary design of main combustor. This includes sizing, air partitioning, and layout.

AFTRBRN Program
This is a preliminary design of afterburner. This includes sizing and layout.

INLET Program
This is a preliminary design and analysis of two-dimensional external compression inlet.

NOZZLE Program
This is a preliminary design and analysis of axisymmetric exhaust nozzle.

The AEDsys Engine Pictures folder also contains numerous digital images of the external and internal appearance of a wide variety of civil and military engines. These are intended to help you visualize the overall layout and the details of components and subsystems of vastly different engine design solutions. You should consult them frequently as a sanity check and/or to reinforce your own learning experience.

1.11   Example Request for Proposal

The following Request for Proposal (RFP) was developed by the authors working with the U.S. Air Force Flight Dynamics Laboratory and has been used in numerous propulsion design course at the U.S. Air Force Academy. This RFP will be used as the specification step in the design process for the example design that is carried through this textbook. The reader is reminded that an RFP for the Global Range Airlifter, an altogether different mission and aircraft, can be found in Appendix P along with the basic elements of a solution found in the supplemental material.

Request for Proposal for the Air-to-Air Fighter (AAF)

A.   Background

Now into the 21st century, both the F-15 and F-16 fighter aircraft are physically aging and using technology that is outdated. Although advances in avionics and weaponry will continue to enhance their performance, a new aircraft will need to be operational by 2020 in order to ensure air superiority in a combat environment. Recent advances in technology such as stealth (detectable signature suppression), controlled configured vehicles (CCV), composites, fly-by-light, vortex flaps, supercruise (supersonic cruise without afterburner operation), etc., offer opportunities for replacing the existing fleets with far superior and more survivable aircraft. The F-22 Raptor will take its place in the fighter inventory by 2010 and capitalize on advanced technologies to provide new standards for fighter aircraft performance.

There will be a pressing need, however, for a smaller, less expensive fighter to complement the F-22 as the low end of a "high/low" fighter mix. It is the purpose of the RFP to solicit design concepts for the Air-to-Air Fighter (AAF) that will incorporate advanced technology in order to meet this need.

B. *Mission*

The AAF will carry two Sidewinder Air Intercept Missiles (AIM-9Ls), two Advanced Medium Range Air-to-Air Missiles (AMRAAMs), and a 25 mm cannon. It shall be capable of performing the following specific mission:

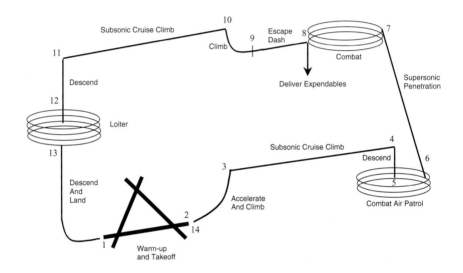

Mission profile by phases[a]

Phase	Description
1–2	Warm-up and takeoff, field is at 2000 ft pressure altitude (PA) with air temperature of 100°F. Fuel allowance is 5 min at idle power for taxi and 1 min at military power (mil power) for warm-up. Takeoff ground roll plus 3 s rotation distance must be $\leq$ 1500 ft on wet, hard surface runway ($\mu_{TO} = 0.05$), $V_{TO} = 1.2\ V_{STALL}$.
2–3	Accelerate to climb speed and perform a minimum time climb in mil power to best cruise Mach number and best cruise altitude conditions (BCM/BCA).
3–4	Subsonic cruise climb at BCM/BCA until total range for climb and cruise climb is 150 n miles.
4–5	Descend to 30,000 ft. No range/fuel/time credit for descent.
5–6	Perform a combat air patrol (CAP) loiter for 20 min at 30,000 ft and Mach number for best endurance.

(continued)

Mission profile by phases[a] (continued)

Phase	Description
6–7	Supersonic penetration at 30,000 ft and $M = 1.5$ to combat arena. Range = 100 n miles. Penetration should be done as a military power (i.e., no afterburning) supercruise if possible.
7–8	Combat is modeled by the following: Fire 2 AMRAAMs Perform one 360 deg, $5g$ sustained turn at 30,000 ft. $M = 1.60$ Perform two 360 deg, $5g$ sustained turns at 30,000 ft. $M = 0.90$ Accelerate from $M = 0.80$ to $M = 1.60$ at 30,000 ft in maximum power (max power) Fire 2 AIM-9Ls and 1/2 of ammunition No range credit is given for combat maneuvers. Conditions at end of combat are $M = 1.5$ at 30,000 ft.
8–9	Escape dash, at $M = 1.5$ and 30,000 ft for 25 n miles. Dash should be done as a mil power supercruise if possible.
9–10	Using mil power, perform a minimum time climb to BCM/BCA. (If the initial energy height exceeds the final, a constant energy height maneuver may be used. No distance credit for the climb.)
10–11	Subsonic cruise climb at BCM/BCA until total range from the end of combat equals 150 n miles.
11–12	Descend to 10,000 ft. No time/fuel/ distance credit.
12–13	Loiter 20 min at 10,000 ft and Mach number for best endurance.
13–14	Descend and land, field is at 2000 ft PA, air temperature is 100°F. A 3 s free roll plus braking distance must be ≤ 1500 ft. On wet, hard surface runway $(\mu_B = 0.18)$, $V_{TD} = 1.15\ V_{STALL}$.

[a]All performance calculations except for takeoff and landing distances should be for a standard day with no wind.

C. Performance Requirements/Constraints

C.1 Performance table

Performance

Item	Requirement
Payload	2 AMRAAM missiles 2 AIM-9L missiles 500 rounds of 25 mm ammunition
Takeoff distance[a]	1500 ft
Landing distance[b]	1500 ft
Max Mach number[c]	1.8M/40 kft
Supercruise requirement[c,d]	1.5M/30 kft

(continued)

Performance (continued)

Item	Requirement
Acceleration[c]	0.8 → 1.6M/30 kft
	$t \leq 50$ s
Sustained g level[c]	$n \geq 5$ at 0.9M/30 kft
	$n \geq 5$ at 1.6M/30 kft

[a]Computed as ground roll plus rotation distance.
[b]Computed as a 3 s free roll plus braking distance to full stop. Aircraft weight will be landing weight after a complete combat mission.
[c]Aircraft is at maneuver weight. Maneuver weight includes 2 AIM-9L missiles, 250 rounds of ammunition, and 50% internal fuel.
[d]The supercruise requirement is designed to establish an efficient supersonic cruise capability. The operational goal is to attain 1.5M at 30,000 ft in mil power; designs capable of meeting this goal will be preferred. As a minimum, the design should achieve the specified speed/altitude condition with reduced afterburner power operation that maximizes fuel efficiency during supercruise.

C.2   Other required/desired capabilities

C.2.1   Crew of one (required).   The cockpit will be designed for single pilot operation. All controls and instruments will be arranged to enhance pilot workload, which includes monitoring all functions necessary for flight safety. Use 200 lb to estimate the weight of the pilot and equipment.

C.2.2   Air refuelable (required).   Compatible with KC-135, KC-10, and HC-130 tankers.

C.2.3   Advanced avionics package.   Per separate RFP.

C.2.4   Maintenance.   A major goal of the design is to allow for easy inspection, access, and removal of primary elements of all major systems.

C.2.5   Structure.   The structure should be designed to withstand 1.5 times the loads (in all directions) that the pilot is expected to be able to safely withstand. The structure should be able to withstand a dynamic pressure of 2133 lbf/ft^2 (1.2M at SL). Primary structures should be designed consistent with requirements for durability, damage tolerance, and repair, and structural carry-throughs should be combined where possible. Primary and secondary structural elements may be fabricated with composite materials of necessary strength. Use of composites in primary and secondary structures should result in substantial weight savings over conventional metal structures. The design will allow for two wing and one centerline wing/fuselage hardpoint for attachment of external stores, in addition to hard points for missile carry.

C.2.6   Fuel/fuel tanks.   The fuel will be standard JP-8 jet engine fuel (required). All fuel tanks will be self-sealing. External fuel, if carried, will be in external 370-gal fuel tanks (JP-8, 6.5 lbf/gal).

C.2.7   Signatures.   Design shall reduce to minimum, practical levels the aircraft's radar, infrared, visual, acoustical, and electromagnetic signatures (desired).

D. Government-Furnished Equipment (GFE)

D.1   Armament/stores
D.1.1   AIM-9L Sidewinder Missile
Launch weight: 191 lbf
D.1.2   AMRAAM
Launch weight: 326 lbf
D.1.3   25 mm cannon
Cannon weight: 270 lbf
Rate of fire: 3600 rpm
Ammunition feed system weight (500 rounds): 405 lbf
Ammunition (25 mm) weight (fired rounds): 550 lbf
Casings weight (returned): 198 lbf

D.2   Drag chute
Diameter, deployed: 15.6 ft
Time from initiation to full deployment (during free roll): 2.5 s

E. Aircraft Jet Engine(s)

The basic engine size will be based on a one- or two-engine installation in the aircraft. Engine operation at mil power is with no afterburning and with the maximum allowable total temperature at the exit of the main burner. Max power is with afterburning and with the maximum allowable total temperatures at the exits of both the main burner and the afterburner. The afterburner shall be capable of both partial and maximum afterburner operations. Each engine shall be capable of providing 1% of the core flow bleed air. The engine(s) shall be capable of providing a total shaft output power of 300 kW at any flight condition. Reverse thrust during landing should be considered as an optional capability in the design.

1.12   Mission Terminology

To identify and classify the many types of flight that must be considered during a given mission, it is important to adhere to a structured set of nomenclature. The starting point for the system employed in this textbook is illustrated in the mission profile of Sec. 1.11B, where the flying that takes place between any two numbered junctions is called "phase" (e.g., Phase 3–4 is a subsonic cruise climb at BCM/BCA). When it happens that more than one clearly identifiable type of flight occurs within a phase, the different types are called "segments" (e.g., combat Phase 7–8 contains two separate turn segments and one acceleration segment). The corollary, of course, is that missions are made up of phases and segments.

During the derivations that will be carried out in order to support mission analyses, the term used to describe generic conditions of flight is "leg" (e.g., constant speed cruise leg and horizontal acceleration leg). Hence, a leg can be either a phase or a segment. Because of the long and varied history of aviation, every type of flight or leg has a number of widely recognized titles. For example, constant speed cruise includes dash and supersonic penetration, and loiter includes combat air patrol.

In the derivations of design tools, the most recognizable, general, and correct title for the type of flight is selected. In the example based upon the RFP, reality dictated the use of the contemporary name (or jargon) for each leg. However, the general case it corresponds to is clearly identified.

References

[1] Oates, G. C., *The Aerothermodynamics of Gas Turbine and Rocket Propulsion*, 3rd ed., AIAA Education Series, AIAA, Reston, VA, 1997.

[2] Mattingly, J. D., *Elements of Gas Turbine Propulsion*, McGraw–Hill, New York, 1996.

[3] Raymer, D. P., *Aircraft Design: A Conceptual Approach*, 3rd ed., AIAA Education Series, AIAA, Reston, VA, 2000.

[4] *U.S. Standard Atmosphere, 1976*, U.S. Government Printing Office, Washington, DC, Oct. 1976.

[5] U.S. Dept. of Defense, "Climatic Information to Determine Design and Test Requirements for Military Equipment," MIL-STD-210C, Rev C, Washington, DC, Jan. 1997.

[6] U.S. Dept. of Defense, "Climatic Information to Determine Design and Test Requirements for Military Equipment," MIL-STD-210A, Washington, DC, Nov. 1958.

[7] Shapiro, A. H., *The Dynamics and Thermodynamics of Compressible Fluid Flow*, Ronald, New York, 1953.

2
Constraint Analysis

2.1 Concept

The design process starts by considering the forces that act on the aircraft, namely, lift, drag, thrust, and weight. This approach will lead to the fortunate discovery that several of the leading performance requirements of the Request for Proposal (RFP) can be translated into functional relationships between the minimum thrust-to-weight or thrust loading at sea-level takeoff (T_{SL}/W_{TO}) and wing loading at takeoff (W_{TO}/S). The keys to the development of these relationships, and a typical step in any design process, are reasonable assumptions for the aircraft lift-drag polar and the lapse of the engine thrust with flight altitude and Mach number. It is not necessary that these assumptions be exact, but greater accuracy reduces the need for iteration. It is possible to satisfy these aircraft/engine system requirements as long as the thrust loading at least equals the largest value found at the selected wing loading. Notice that the more detailed aspects of design, such as stability, control, configuration layout, and structures, are set aside for later consideration by aircraft system designers.

An example of the results of a typical constraint analysis is portrayed in Fig. 2.1. Shown there are the minimum T_{SL}/W_{TO} as a function of W_{TO}/S needed for the following: 1) takeoff from a runway of given length; 2) flight at a given altitude and required speed; 3) turn at a given altitude, speed, and required rate; and 4) landing without reverse thrust on a runway of given length. Any of the trends that are not familiar will be made clear by the analysis of the next section.

What is important to realize about Fig. 2.1 is that any combination of T_{SL}/W_{TO} and W_{TO}/S that falls in the "solution space" shown there automatically meets all of the constraints considered. For better or for worse, there are many acceptable solutions available at this point. It is important to identify which is "best" and why.

It is possible to include many other performance constraints, such as required service ceiling and acceleration time, on the same diagram. By incorporating all known constraints, the range of acceptable loading parameters (that is, the solution space) will be appropriately restricted.

A look at example records of thrust loading vs wing loading at takeoff is quite interesting. Figures 2.2 and 2.3 represent collections of the design points for jet engine powered transport-type and fighter-type aircraft, respectively. The thing that leaps out of these figures is the diversity of design points. The selected design point is very sensitive to the application and the preferences of the designer. Pick out some of your favorite airplanes and see if you can explain their location on the constraint diagram. For example, the low wing loadings of the C-20A and C-21A are probably caused by short takeoff length requirements, whereas the high thrust loading and low wing loading of the YF-22 and MIG-31 are probably caused by requirements for specific combat performance in both the subsonic and supersonic

19

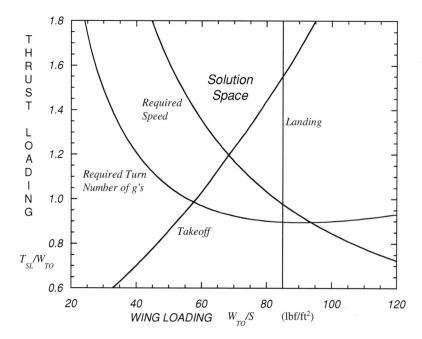

Fig. 2.1   Constraint analysis—thrust loading vs wing loading.

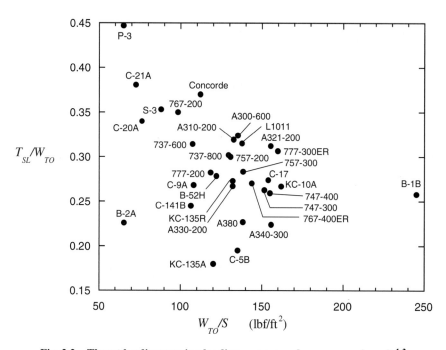

Fig. 2.2   Thrust loading vs wing loading—cargo and passenger aircraft.[1,2]

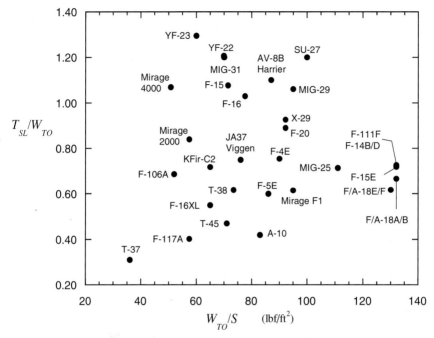

Fig. 2.3 Thrust loading vs wing loading—fighter aircraft.[1,2]

arenas. Where do you think the location would be for the AAF, supersonic business jet, GRA, and UAV?

2.2 Design Tools

A "master equation" for the flight performance of aircraft in terms of takeoff thrust loading (T_{SL}/W_{TO}) and wing loading (W_{TO}/S) can be derived directly from force considerations. We treat the aircraft, shown in Fig. 2.4, as a point mass with a velocity (V) in still air at a flight path angle of θ to the horizon. The velocity of the air ($-V$) has an angle of attack (AOA) to the wing chord line (WCL). The lift

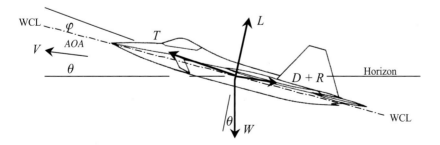

Fig. 2.4 Forces on aircraft.

(L) and drag ($D + R$) forces are normal and parallel to this velocity, respectively. The thrust (T) is at an angle φ to the wing chord line (usually small). Applying Newton's second law to this aircraft we have the following for the accelerations:

Parallel to V:

$$T \cos(AOA + \varphi) - W \sin\theta - (D + R) = \frac{W}{g_0}a_\parallel = \frac{W}{g_0}\frac{dV}{dt} \qquad (2.1a)$$

Perpendicular to V:

$$L + T \sin(AOA + \varphi) - W \cos\theta = \frac{W}{g_0}a_\perp \qquad (2.1b)$$

Multiplying Eq. (2.1a) by the velocity (V), we have the following equation in the direction of flight:

$$\{T \cos(AOA + \varphi) - (D + R)\}V = W\left\{V \sin\theta + \frac{d}{dt}\left(\frac{V^2}{2g_0}\right)\right\} \qquad (i)$$

Note that for most flight conditions the thrust is very nearly aligned with the direction of flight, so that the angle ($AOA + \varphi$) is small and thus $\cos(AOA + \vartheta) \approx 1$. This term will therefore be dropped from the ensuing development, but it could be restored if necessary or desirable. Also, multiplying by velocity has transformed a force relationship into a power, or time rate of change of energy, equation. This will have profound consequences in what follows. Since $V \sin\theta$ is simply the time rate of change of altitude (h) or

$$V \sin\theta = \frac{dh}{dt} \qquad (ii)$$

then combining equations (i) and (ii) and dividing by W gives

$$\frac{T - (D + R)}{W}V = \frac{d}{dt}\left\{h + \frac{V^2}{2g_0}\right\} = \frac{dz_e}{dt} \qquad (2.2a)$$

where $z_e = h + V^2/2g_0$ represents the sum of instantaneous potential and kinetic energies of the aircraft and is frequently referred to as the "energy height." The energy height may be most easily visualized as the altitude the aircraft would attain if its kinetic energy were completely converted into potential energy. Lines of constant energy height are plotted in Fig. 2.5 vs the altitude-velocity axes. The flight condition ($h = 20$ kft and $V = 1134$ fps) marked with a star in Fig. 2.5 corresponds to an energy height of 40 kft. Excess power is required to increase the energy height of the aircraft, and the rate of change is proportional to the amount of excess power.

The left-hand side of Eq. (2.2a) in modern times has become recognized as a dominant property of the aircraft and is called the weight specific excess power

$$P_s = \frac{dz_e}{dt} = \frac{d}{dt}\left\{h + \frac{V^2}{2g}\right\} \qquad (2.2b)$$

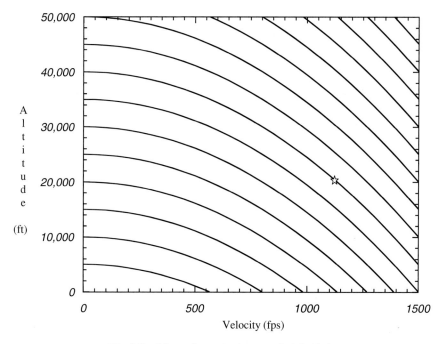

Fig. 2.5   Lines of constant energy height (z_e).

This is a powerful grouping for understanding and predicting the dynamics of flight, including both rate of climb (dh/dt) and acceleration (dV/dt) capabilities. P_s must have the units of velocity.

If we assume that the installed thrust is given by

$$T = \alpha T_{SL} \tag{2.3}$$

where α is the installed full throttle thrust lapse, which depends on altitude, speed, and whether or not an afterburner is operating, and the instantaneous weight is given by

$$W = \beta W_{TO} \tag{2.4}$$

where β depends on how much fuel has been consumed and payload delivered, then Eq. (2.2a) becomes

$$\frac{T_{SL}}{W_{TO}} = \frac{\beta}{\alpha}\left(\frac{D+R}{\beta W_{TO}} + \frac{P_s}{V}\right) \tag{2.5}$$

Note: Definition of α

Particular caution must be exercised in the use of α throughout this textbook because it is intended to be referenced only to the *maximum* thrust or power available for the prevailing engine configuration and flight condition. For example, an afterburning engine will have two possible values of α for any flight condition, one for mil power and one for max power (see Sec. 1.11E of RFP). You must differentiate carefully between them. Lower values of thrust are always available by simply throttling the fuel flow, thrust, or power.

It is equally important to remember that both T and T_{SL} refer to the "installed" engine thrust, which is generally less than the "uninstalled" engine thrust that would be produced if the external flow were ideal and created no drag. The difference between them is the additional drag generated on the external surfaces, which is strongly influenced by the presence of the engine and is not included in the aircraft drag model. The additional drag is usually confined to the inlet and exhaust nozzle surfaces, but in unfavorable circumstances can be found anywhere, including adjacent fuselage, wing, and tail surfaces. The subject of "installed" vs "uninstalled" thrust is dealt with in detail in Chapter 6 and Appendix E.

Now, using the traditional aircraft lift and drag relationships,

$$L = nW = qC_L S \tag{2.6}$$

where n = load factor = number of g's ($g = g_0$) $\perp$ to $V (n = 1$ for straight and level flight even when $dV/dt \neq 0$),

$$D = qC_D S \tag{2.7a}$$

and

$$R = qC_{DR} S \tag{2.7b}$$

where D and C_D refer to the "clean" or basic aircraft and R and C_{DR} refer to the additional drag caused, for example, by external stores, braking parachutes or flaps, or temporary external hardware. Then

$$C_L = \frac{nW}{qS} = \frac{n\beta}{q}\left(\frac{W_{TO}}{S}\right) \tag{2.8}$$

Further, assuming the lift-drag polar relationship,

$$C_D = K_1 C_L^2 + K_2 C_L + C_{D0} \tag{2.9}$$

Equations (2.7–2.9) can be combined to yield

$$D + R = qS\left\{K_1\left(\frac{n\beta}{q}\frac{W_{TO}}{S}\right)^2 + K_2\left(\frac{n\beta}{q}\frac{W_{TO}}{S}\right) + C_{D0} + C_{DR}\right\} \tag{2.10}$$

Finally, Eq. (2.10) may be substituted into Eq. (2.5) to produce the general form of the "master equation"

$$\frac{T_{SL}}{W_{TO}} = \frac{\beta}{\alpha}\left\{\frac{qS}{\beta W_{TO}}\left[K_1\left(\frac{n\beta}{q}\frac{W_{TO}}{S}\right)^2 + K_2\left(\frac{n\beta}{q}\frac{W_{TO}}{S}\right) + C_{D0} + C_{DR}\right] + \frac{P_s}{V}\right\} \tag{2.11}$$

It should be clear that Eq. (2.11) will provide the desired relationships between T_{SL}/W_{TO} and W_{TO}/S that become constraint diagram boundaries. It should also be evident that the general form of Eq. (2.11) is such that there is one value of

W_{TO}/S for which T_{SL}/W_{TO} is minimized, as seen in Fig. 2.1. This important fact will be elaborated upon in the example cases that follow.

Note: Lift-drag polar equation
The conventional form of the lift-drag polar equation is[3]

$$C_D = C_{D\min} + K'C_L^2 + K''(C_L - C_{L\min})^2$$

where K' is the inviscid drag due to lift (induced drag) and K'' is the viscous drag due to lift (skin friction and pressure drag). Expanding and collecting like terms shows that the lift-drag polar equation may also be written

$$C_D = (K' + K'')C_L^2 - (2K''C_{L\min})C_L + \left(C_{D\min} + K''C_{L\min}^2\right)$$

or

$$C_D = K_1 C_L^2 + K_2 C_L + C_{D0} \tag{2.9}$$

where

$$K_1 = K' + K''$$

$$K_2 = -2K''C_{L\min}$$

$$C_{D0} = C_{D\min} + K''C_{L\min}^2$$

Note that the physical interpretation of C_{D0} is the drag coefficient at zero lift. Also, for most high-performance aircraft $C_{L\min} \approx 0$, so that $K_2 \approx 0$.

A large number and variety of special cases of Eq. (2.11) will be developed in order both to illustrate its behavior and to provide more specific design tools for constraint analysis. In all of the example cases that follow, it is assumed that the α of Eq. (2.3), the β of Eq. (2.4), and the K_1, K_2, and C_{D0} of Eq. (2.9) are known. If they change significantly over the period of flight being analyzed, either piecewise solution or use of representative working averages should be considered.

2.2.1 Case 1: Constant Altitude/Speed Cruise ($P_s = 0$)

Given: $dh/dt = 0$, $dV/dt = 0$, $n = 1$ ($L = W$), and values of h and V (i.e., q). Under these conditions Eq. (2.11) becomes

$$\frac{T_{SL}}{W_{TO}} = \frac{\beta}{\alpha}\left\{K_1\frac{\beta}{q}\left(\frac{W_{TO}}{S}\right) + K_2 + \frac{C_{D0} + C_{DR}}{\beta/q(W_{TO}/S)}\right\} \tag{2.12}$$

This relationship is quite complex because T_{SL}/W_{TO} grows indefinitely large as W_{TO}/S becomes very large *or* very small. The location of the minimum for T_{SL}/W_{TO} can be found by differentiating Eq. (2.12) with respect to W_{TO}/S and setting the result equal to zero. This leads to

$$\left[\frac{W_{TO}}{S}\right]_{\min T/W} = \frac{q}{\beta}\sqrt{\frac{C_{D0} + C_{DR}}{K_1}}$$

and

$$\left[\frac{T_{SL}}{W_{TO}}\right]_{min} = \frac{\beta}{\alpha}\left\{2\sqrt{(C_{D0} + C_{DR})K_1} + K_2\right\}$$

This condition produces the minimum thrust and drag for the aircraft and generally corresponds to maximum range.

Also of special note is the frequently encountered situation where the required q is so large that

$$\frac{T_{SL}}{W_{TO}} = \frac{\beta}{\alpha}\frac{C_{D0} + C_{DR}}{\beta/q(W_{TO}/S)}$$

or

$$\left(\frac{T_{SL}}{W_{TO}}\right)\left(\frac{W_{TO}}{S}\right) = \frac{q(C_{D0} + C_{DR})}{\alpha} \qquad (2.13)$$

This limiting case, which corresponds to $C_D = C_{D0} + C_{DR}$, therefore displays a hyperbolic relationship between T_{SL}/W_{TO} and W_{TO}/S.

2.2.2   Case 2: Constant Speed Climb ($P_s = dh/dt$)

Given: $dV/dt = 0$, $n \approx 1$, $(L \approx W)$, and values of h, $dh/dt > 0$, and V (i.e., q). Under these conditions Eq. (2.11) becomes

$$\frac{T_{SL}}{W_{TO}} = \frac{\beta}{\alpha}\left\{K_1\frac{\beta}{q}\left(\frac{W_{TO}}{S}\right) + K_2 + \frac{C_{D0} + C_{DR}}{\beta/q(W_{TO}/S)} + \frac{1}{V}\frac{dh}{dt}\right\} \qquad (2.14)$$

Since $(1/V)(dh/dt)$ is a constant, the behavior of this equation is not only the same as that of Eq. (2.12), but the minimum value of T_{SL}/W_{TO} occurs again at

$$\left[\frac{W_{TO}}{S}\right]_{min\,T/W} = \frac{q}{\beta}\sqrt{\frac{C_{D0} + C_{DR}}{K_1}}$$

and

$$\left[\frac{T_{SL}}{W_{TO}}\right]_{min} = \frac{\beta}{\alpha}\left\{2\sqrt{(C_{D0} + C_{DR})K_1} + K_2 + \frac{1}{V}\frac{dh}{dt}\right\}$$

2.2.3   Case 3: Constant Altitude/Speed Turn ($P_s = 0$)

Given: $dh/dt = 0$, $dV/dt = 0$, and values of h, V (i.e., q), and $n > 1$. Under these conditions Eq. (2.11) becomes

$$\frac{T_{SL}}{W_{TO}} = \frac{\beta}{\alpha}\left\{K_1 n^2\frac{\beta}{q}\left(\frac{W_{TO}}{S}\right) + K_2 n + \frac{C_{D0} + C_{DR}}{\beta/q(W_{TO}/S)}\right\} \qquad (2.15)$$

Again, the behavior of this equation is the same as that of Eq. (2.12), the minimum of T_{SL}/W_{TO} occurring at

$$\left[\frac{W_{TO}}{S}\right]_{min\,T/W} = \frac{q}{n\beta}\sqrt{\frac{C_{D0} + C_{DR}}{K_1}}$$

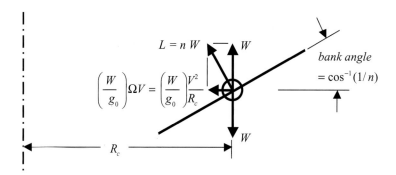

Fig. 2.6   Forces on aircraft in turn.

and

$$\left[\frac{T_{SL}}{W_{TO}}\right]_{min} = \frac{n\beta}{\alpha}\left\{2\sqrt{(C_{D0}+C_{DR})K_1}+K_2\right\}$$

Occasionally n is stipulated in terms of other quantities. In the case of a level, constant velocity turn, for example, where the vertical component of lift balances the weight and the horizontal component is the centripetal force, n is as shown in Fig. 2.6.

It follows from the Pythagorean Theorem that

$$n = \sqrt{1+\left(\frac{\Omega V}{g_0}\right)^2} \tag{2.16}$$

and

$$n = \sqrt{1+\left(\frac{V^2}{g_0 R_c}\right)^2} \tag{2.17}$$

which can be used when the rotation rate (Ω) or the radius of curvature (R_c) is given rather than the load factor (n).

2.2.4   Case 4: Horizontal Acceleration [$P_s = (V/g_0)(dV/dt)$]

Given: $dh/dt = 0$, $n = 1$ ($L = W$) and values of h, $V_{initial}$, V_{final}, and $\Delta t_{allowable}$. Under these conditions Eq. (2.11) becomes

$$\frac{T_{SL}}{W_{TO}} = \frac{\beta}{\alpha}\left\{K_1\frac{\beta}{q}\left(\frac{W_{TO}}{S}\right)+K_2+\frac{C_{D0}+C_{DR}}{\beta/q(W_{TO}/S)}+\frac{1}{g_0}\frac{dV}{dt}\right\} \tag{2.18a}$$

which can be rearranged to yield

$$\frac{1}{g_0}\frac{dV}{dt} = \frac{\alpha}{\beta}\frac{T_{SL}}{W_{TO}}-\left\{K_1\frac{\beta}{q}\left(\frac{W_{TO}}{S}\right)+K_2+\frac{C_{D0}+C_{DR}}{\beta/q(W_{TO}/S)}\right\} \tag{2.18b}$$

Strictly speaking, Eq. (2.18b) must be integrated from $V_{initial}$ to V_{final} in order to find combinations of thrust loading and wing loading that satisfy the acceleration time criterion. A useful approximation, however, is to select some point between $V_{initial}$ and V_{final} at which the quantities in Eq. (2.18a) approximate their working average over that range, and set

$$\frac{1}{g_0} \frac{dV}{dt} = \frac{1}{g_0} \left(\frac{V_{final} - V_{initial}}{\Delta t_{allowable}} \right)$$

In this case the constraint curve is obtained from Eq. (2.18a), which again has the properties of Eq. (2.12) including the location of the minimum T_{SL}/W_{TO}.

Equation (2.18b) can be numerically integrated by first recasting the equation as

$$\Delta t_{allowable} = \frac{1}{g_0} \int_{V_{initial}}^{V_{final}} \frac{V \, dV}{P_s} = \frac{1}{2g_0} \int_{V_{initial}^2}^{V_{final}^2} \frac{dV^2}{P_s} \qquad (2.19a)$$

where

$$P_s = V \left\{ \frac{\alpha}{\beta} \frac{T_{SL}}{W_{TO}} - \left[K_1 \frac{\beta}{q} \left(\frac{W_{TO}}{S} \right) + K_2 + \frac{C_{D0} + C_{DR}}{\beta/q(W_{TO}/S)} \right] \right\} \qquad (2.19b)$$

The solution of the required thrust loading (T_{SL}/W_{TO}) for each wing loading (W_{TO}/S) can be obtained by the following procedure:

1) Divide the change in kinetic energy into even sized increments, and calculate the minimum thrust loading [maximum T_{SL}/W_{TO} corresponding to $P_s = 0$ in Eq. (2.19b) for all kinetic energy states].

2) Select a thrust loading larger than the minimum and calculate the acceleration time (Δt) using Eqs. (2.19a) and (2.19b). Compare resulting acceleration time with $\Delta t_{allowable}$. Change the thrust loading and recalculate the acceleration time until it matches $\Delta t_{allowable}$.

2.2.5   Case 5: Takeoff Ground Roll (s_G), when $T_{SL} \gg (D + R)$

Given: $dh/dt = 0$ and values of s_G, ρ, $C_{L\,max}$, and $V_{TO} = k_{TO} V_{STALL}$. Under these conditions Eq. (2.5) reduces to

$$\frac{T_{SL}}{W_{TO}} = \frac{\beta}{\alpha g_0} \frac{dV}{dt} = \frac{\beta}{\alpha g_0} \frac{dV}{ds/V}$$

which can be rearranged to yield

$$ds = \frac{\beta}{\alpha g_0} \left(\frac{W_{TO}}{T_{SL}} \right) V \, dV$$

and integrated from $s = 0$ and $V = 0$ to takeoff, where $s = s_G$ and $V = V_{TO}$, with the result that

$$s_G = \frac{\beta}{\alpha} \left(\frac{W_{TO}}{T_{SL}} \right) \frac{V_{TO}^2}{2g_0}$$

provided that representative takeoff values of α and β are used. Defining

$$V_{TO} = k_{TO} V_{STALL} \qquad (2.20)$$

where k_{TO} is a constant greater than one (generally specified by appropriate flying regulations) and V_{STALL} is the minimum speed at which the airplane flies at $C_{L\,max}$, then

$$q C_{L\,max} S = \tfrac{1}{2}\rho V_{STALL}^2 C_{L\,max} S = \beta W_{TO}$$

or

$$\frac{V_{TO}^2}{2} = k_{TO}^2 \frac{V_{STALL}^2}{2} = \frac{\beta k_{TO}^2}{\rho C_{L\,max}}\left(\frac{W_{TO}}{S}\right) \tag{2.21}$$

with the final result that

$$\frac{T_{SL}}{W_{TO}} = \frac{\beta^2}{\alpha}\frac{k_{TO}^2}{s_G \rho g_0 C_{L\,max}}\left(\frac{W_{TO}}{S}\right) \tag{2.22}$$

For this limiting case T_{SL}/W_{TO} is directly proportional to W_{TO}/S and inversely proportional to s_G.

2.2.6 Case 6: Takeoff Ground Roll (s_G)

Given: $dh/dt = 0$ and values of ρ, $D = q C_D S$, $C_{L\,max}$, $V_{TO} = k_{TO} V_{STALL}$, and $R = q C_{DR} S + \mu_{TO}(\beta W_{TO} - q C_L S)$.

Under these conditions

$$\frac{D + R}{\beta W_{TO}} = \frac{(C_D + C_{DR} - \mu_{TO} C_L)q S + \mu_{TO}\beta W_{TO}}{\beta W_{TO}}$$

so that Eq. (2.5) becomes

$$\frac{T_{SL}}{W_{TO}} = \frac{\beta}{\alpha}\left\{\xi_{TO}\frac{q}{\beta}\left(\frac{S}{W_{TO}}\right) + \mu_{TO} + \frac{1}{g_0}\frac{dV}{dt}\right\} \tag{2.23}$$

where

$$\xi_{TO} = C_D + C_{DR} - \mu_{TO} C_L \tag{2.24}$$

which can be rearranged and integrated, as in Case 5, to yield

$$s_G = -\frac{\beta(W_{TO}/S)}{\rho g_0 \xi_{TO}}\ln\left\{1 - \xi_{TO}\middle/\left[\left(\frac{\alpha}{\beta}\frac{T_{SL}}{W_{TO}} - \mu_{TO}\right)\frac{C_{L\,max}}{k_{TO}^2}\right]\right\} \tag{2.25}$$

provided that representative takeoff values of α and β are used.

For this case T_{SL}/W_{TO} must increase continuously with W_{TO}/S, but in a more complex manner than in Case 5. That result is again obtained in the limit as all terms in ξ_{TO} approach zero and $\ln(1 - \varepsilon)$ approaches $-\varepsilon$, whence

$$s_G \to \frac{\beta(W_{TO}/S)}{\rho g_0 \xi_{TO}}\frac{\xi_{TO}}{(\alpha/\beta)(T_{SL}/W_{TO})C_{L\,max}/k_{TO}^2}$$

or

$$\frac{T_{SL}}{W_{TO}} \to \frac{\beta^2}{\alpha}\frac{k_{TO}^2}{s_G \rho g_0 C_{L\,max}}\left(\frac{W_{TO}}{S}\right) \tag{2.22}$$

a)

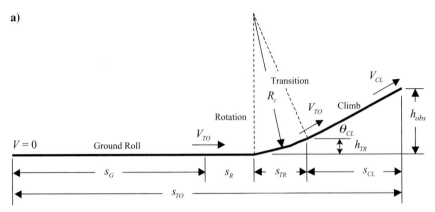

Fig. 2.7a   Takeoff terminology ($h_{TR} < h_{obs}$).

Note: Total takeoff distance
Two cases arise:
Case A (Fig. 2.7a): The total takeoff distance (s_{TO}) can be analyzed as ground roll (s_G) plus three other distances: the first (s_R) to rotate the aircraft to the takeoff lift condition (traditionally $C_L = 0.8C_{L\,max}$) while still on the ground; the second (s_{TR}) to transit to the angle of climb direction; and the last (s_{CL}) to clear an obstacle of given height. These distances may be estimated as follows[1]:

$$s_R = t_R V_{TO} = t_R k_{TO} \sqrt{\{2\beta/(\rho C_{L\,max})\}(W_{TO}/S)} \tag{2.26}$$

where t_R is a total aircraft rotation time based on experience (normally 3 s),

$$s_{TR} = R_c \sin\theta_{CL} = \frac{V_{TO}^2 \sin\theta_{CL}}{g_0(n-1)}$$

$$s_{TR} = \frac{V_{TO}^2 \sin\theta_{CL}}{g_0(0.8k_{TO}^2 - 1)} = \frac{k_{TO}^2 \sin\theta_{CL}}{g_0(0.8k_{TO}^2 - 1)} \frac{2\beta}{\rho C_{L\,max}} \left(\frac{W_{TO}}{S}\right) \tag{2.27}$$

where θ_{CL} is the angle of climb, which can in turn be obtained from Eq. (2.2a) as

$$\frac{1}{V}\frac{dh}{dt} = \sin\theta_{CL} = \frac{T-D}{W}$$

and, if $h_{obs} > h_{TR}$

$$s_{CL} = \frac{h_{obs} - h_{TR}}{\tan\theta_{CL}} \tag{2.28}$$

where h_{obs} is the required clearance height and h_{TR} is given by the following expression, provided that $h_{obs} > h_{TR}$:

$$h_{TR} = \frac{V_{TO}^2(1 - \cos\theta_{CL})}{g_0(0.8k_{TO}^2 - 1)} = \frac{k_{TO}^2(1 - \cos\theta_{CL})}{g_0(0.8k_{TO}^2 - 1)} \frac{2\beta}{\rho C_{L\,max}} \left(\frac{W_{TO}}{S}\right) \tag{2.29}$$

b)

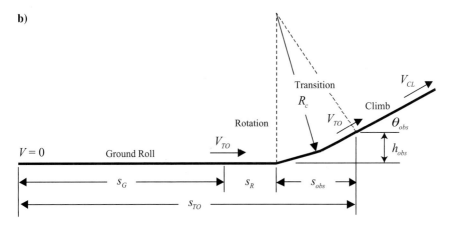

Fig. 2.7b Takeoff terminology ($h_{TR} > h_{obs}$).

Case B (Fig. 2.7b): The distances s_G and s_R are the same as in case A, but the obstacle is cleared during transition so $s_{TO} = s_G + s_R + s_{obs}$ where s_{obs} is the distance from the end of rotation to the point where the height h_{obs} is attained. There follows

$$s_{obs} = R_c \sin\theta_{obs} = \frac{V_{TO}^2 \sin\theta_{obs}}{g_0(0.8k_{TO}^2 - 1)} \tag{2.30}$$

where

$$\theta_{obs} = \cos^{-1}\left(1 - \frac{h_{obs}}{R_c}\right)$$

2.2.7 Case 7: Braking Roll (s_B)

Given: $\alpha \leq 0$ (reverse thrust), $dh/dt = 0$ and values of ρ, $V_{TD} = k_{TD}V_{STALL}$, $D = qC_DS$, and $R = qC_{DR}S + \mu_B(\beta W_{TO} - qC_LS)$.
Under these conditions

$$\frac{D+R}{\beta W_{TO}} = \frac{(C_D + C_{DR} - \mu_BC_L)q + \mu_B\beta W_{TO}}{\beta W_{TO}}$$

so that Eq. (2.5) becomes

$$\frac{T_{SL}}{W_{TO}} = \frac{\beta}{\alpha}\left\{\xi_L\frac{q}{\beta}\left(\frac{S}{W_{TO}}\right) + \mu_B + \frac{1}{g_0}\frac{dV}{dt}\right\} \tag{2.31}$$

where

$$\xi_L = C_D + C_{DR} - \mu_BC_L \tag{2.32}$$

which can be rearranged and integrated, as in Case 6, to yield

$$s_G = \frac{\beta(W_{TO}/S)}{\rho g_0\xi_L}\ln\left\{1 + \xi_L\bigg/\left[\left(\mu_B + \frac{(-\alpha)}{\beta}\frac{T_{SL}}{W_{TO}}\right)\frac{C_{L\,max}}{k_{TD}^2}\right]\right\} \tag{2.33}$$

provided that representative landing values of α and β are used and where k_{TD} is a constant greater than one (generally specified by appropriate flying regulations).

For this case reverse thrust can be used to great advantage. If the second term in the bracket of Eq. (2.33) is made much less than one by making $(-\alpha)$ very large, then

$$s_B \rightarrow \frac{\beta(W_{TO}/S)}{\rho g_0 \xi_L} \frac{\xi_L}{[(-\alpha)/\beta](T_{SL}/W_{TO})\left(C_{L\,max}/k_{TD}^2\right)}$$

or

$$\frac{T_{SL}}{W_{TO}} \rightarrow \frac{\beta^2}{(-\alpha)} \frac{k_{TD}^2}{s_B \rho g_0 C_{L\,max}} \left(\frac{W_{TO}}{S}\right) \tag{2.34}$$

Note: Total landing distance

The total landing distance (s_L) can be analyzed as braking roll (s_B) plus two other distances (see Fig. 2.8): the first (s_A) to clear an obstacle of given height and the second (s_{FR}) a free roll traversed before the brakes are fully applied. These distances may be estimated as follows:[1]

$$s_A = \frac{2\beta}{\rho g_0(C_D + C_{DR})} \left(\frac{W_{TO}}{S}\right)\left(\frac{k_{obs}^2 - k_{TD}^2}{k_{obs}^2 + k_{TD}^2}\right) + \frac{C_{L\,max}}{(C_D + C_{DR})} \frac{2h_{obs}}{\left(k_{obs}^2 + k_{TD}^2\right)} \tag{2.35}$$

where h_{obs} is the height of the obstacle and the velocity at the obstacle is

$$V_{obs} = k_{obs} V_{STALL} \tag{2.36}$$

and

$$s_{FR} = t_{FR} V_{TD} = t_{FR} k_{TD} \sqrt{\{2\beta/(\rho C_{L\,max})\}(W_{TO}/S)} \tag{2.37}$$

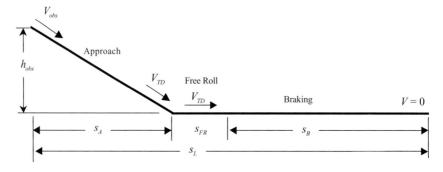

Fig. 2.8   Landing terminology.

where t_{FR} is a total system reaction time based on experience (normally 3 s) that allows for the deployment of a parachute or thrust reverser.

2.2.8 Case 8: Service Ceiling ($P_s = dh/dt$)

Given: $dV/dt = 0, n = 1 (L = W)$, and the values of h (i.e., α), $dh/dt > 0$, and C_L.

Under these conditions Eq. (2.11) becomes

$$\frac{T_{SL}}{W_{TO}} = \frac{\beta}{\alpha} \left\{ K_1 \frac{\beta}{q} \left(\frac{W_{TO}}{S} \right) + K_2 + \frac{C_{D0} + C_{DR}}{\beta/q(W_{TO}/S)} + \frac{1}{V} \frac{dh}{dt} \right\} \qquad (2.38)$$

where

$$qC_L S = \beta W_{TO}$$

or

$$C_L = \frac{\beta}{q} \left(\frac{W_{TO}}{S} \right) \qquad (2.39)$$

and

$$q = \frac{\rho V^2}{2} = \frac{\beta}{C_L} \left(\frac{W_{TO}}{S} \right)$$

or

$$V = \sqrt{\frac{2\beta}{\sigma \rho_{SL} C_L} \left(\frac{W_{TO}}{S} \right)} \qquad (2.40)$$

so that

$$\frac{T_{SL}}{W_{TO}} = \frac{\beta}{\alpha} \left\{ K_1 C_L + K_2 + \frac{C_{D0} + C_{DR}}{C_L} + \frac{1}{V} \frac{dh}{dt} \right\} \qquad (2.41)$$

2.2.9 Case 9: Takeoff Climb Angle

Given: $\theta, n = 1 (L = W), dV/dt = 0, C_{DR}, C_{L\,max}, k_{TO}$, and the values of h and σ.

Under these conditions Eq. (2.11) becomes

$$\frac{T_{SL}}{W_{TO}} = \frac{\beta}{\alpha} \left\{ K_1 \left(\frac{\beta W_{TO}}{qS} \right) + K_2 + \frac{C_{D0} + C_{DR}}{(\beta W_{TO}/qS)} + \sin \theta \right\} \qquad (2.42)$$

Since

$$C_L = \frac{C_{L\,max}}{k_{TO}^2} = \frac{W}{qS} = \frac{\beta}{q} \left(\frac{W_{TO}}{S} \right)$$

then

$$\frac{T_{SL}}{W_{TO}} = \frac{\beta}{\alpha} \left\{ K_1 \frac{C_{L\,max}}{k_{TO}^2} + K_2 + \frac{C_{D0} + C_{DR}}{C_{L\,max}/k_{TO}^2} + \sin \theta \right\} \qquad (2.43)$$

and

$$V = V_{TO} = \sqrt{\frac{2\beta k_{TO}^2}{\sigma \rho_{SL} C_{L\,max}} \left(\frac{W_{TO}}{S} \right)} \qquad (2.44)$$

is employed to find M_{TO} for a given W_{TO}/S and thus the applicable values of α, K_1, K_2, and C_{D0}. Because they vary slowly with W_{TO}/S, the constraint boundary is a line of almost constant T_{SL}/W_{TO}.

2.2.10 Case 10: Carrier Takeoff

Given: $n = 1$ ($L = W$), V_{TO}, dV/dt, $C_{L\,max}$, k_{TO}, β, and the values of h and σ. Solving Eq. (2.44) for wing loading gives

$$\left[\frac{W_{TO}}{S} \right]_{max} = \frac{\sigma \rho_{SL} C_{L\,max} V_{TO}^2}{2\beta k_{TO}^2} \qquad (2.45)$$

where the takeoff velocity (V_{TO}) is the sum of the catapult end speed (V_{end}) and the wind-over-deck (V_{wod}) or

$$V_{TO} = V_{end} + V_{wod} \qquad (2.46)$$

A typical value of k_{TO} is 1.1 and of V_{end} is 120 kn (nautical miles per hour). Wind-over-deck can be 20 to 40 kn, but design specifications may require launch with zero wind-over-deck or even a negative value to ensure launch at anchor. This constraint boundary is simply a vertical line on a plot of thrust loading vs wing loading with the minimum thrust loading given, as already seen in Eq. (2.43), by

$$\left[\frac{T_{SL}}{W_{TO}} \right]_{min} = \frac{\beta}{\alpha} \left\{ K_1 \frac{C_{L\,max}}{k_{TO}^2} + K_2 + \frac{C_{D0} + C_{DR}}{C_{L\,max}/k_{TO}^2} + \frac{1}{g_0} \frac{dV}{dt} \right\} \qquad (2.47)$$

where α, K_1, K_2, and C_{D0} are evaluated at static conditions. A typical value of the required minimum horizontal acceleration at the end of the catapult (dV/dt) is $0.3\ g_0$.

2.2.11 Case 11: Carrier Landing

Given: $n = 1$ ($L = W$), V_{TD}, $C_{L\,max}$, k_{TD}, β, and the values of h and σ. Rewriting Eq. (2.45) for the touchdown condition gives

$$\left[\frac{W_{TO}}{S} \right]_{max} = \frac{\sigma \rho_{SL} C_{L\,max} V_{TD}^2}{2\beta k_{TD}^2} \qquad (2.48)$$

where the touchdown velocity (V_{TD}) is the sum of the engagement speed (V_{eng}, the speed of the aircraft relative to the carrier) and the wind-over-deck (V_{wod}), or

$$V_{TD} = V_{eng} + V_{wod}$$

A typical value of k_{TD} is 1.15 and of V_{eng} is 140 kn (nautical miles per hour). As in Case 10, this constraint boundary is simply a vertical line on a plot of thrust loading vs wing loading. The minimum thrust loading is given by Eq. (2.49):

$$\left[\frac{T_{SL}}{W_{TO}}\right]_{min} = \frac{\beta}{\alpha}\left\{K_1\frac{C_{L\,max}}{k_{TD}^2} + K_2 + \frac{C_{D0} + C_{DR}}{C_{L\,max}/k_{TD}^2} + \sin\theta\right\} \qquad (2.49)$$

where $-\theta$ is the glide-slope angle.

2.2.12 Case 12: Carrier Approach (Wave-off)

Given: $\theta, n = 1 (L = W)$, V_{TD}, dV/dt, α, β, C_{DR}, $C_{L\,max}$, k_{TD}, and the values of h and σ.

Because carrier pilots do not flare and slow down for landing but fly right into the carrier deck in order to make certain the tail hook catches the landing cable, the approach speed is the same as the touchdown speed (V_{TD}). Rewriting Eq. (2.48) for the approach condition gives

$$\left[\frac{W_{TO}}{S}\right]_{max} = \frac{\sigma\rho_{SL}C_{L\,max}V_{TD}^2}{2\beta k_{TD}^2} \qquad (2.50)$$

As in Cases 10 and 11, this constraint boundary is simply a vertical line on a plot of thrust loading vs wing loading.

Under these conditions Eq. (2.11) becomes

$$\left[\frac{T_{SL}}{W_{TO}}\right]_{min} = \frac{\beta}{\alpha}\left\{K_1\frac{C_{L\,max}}{k_{TD}^2} + K_2 + \frac{C_{D0} + C_{DR}}{C_{L\,max}/k_{TD}^2} + \sin\theta + \frac{1}{g_0}\frac{dV}{dt}\right\} \qquad (2.51)$$

where $-\theta$ is the glide-slope angle and α, K_1, K_2, and C_{D0} are evaluated at static conditions. Typical wave-off requirements are an acceleration of $1/8\,g_0$ while on a glide-slope of 4 deg.

2.3 Preliminary Estimates for Constraint Analysis

Preliminary estimates of the aerodynamic characteristics of the airframe and of the installed engine thrust lapse are required before the constraint analysis can be done. The following material is provided to help obtain these preliminary estimates.

2.3.1 Aerodynamics

The maximum coefficient of lift ($C_{L\,max}$) enters into the constraint analysis during the takeoff and landing phases. Typical ranges for $C_{L\,max}$ divided by the cosine of the sweep angle at the quarter chord ($\Lambda_{c/4}$) are presented in Table 2.1, which is taken from Ref. 4. This table provides typical $C_{L\,max}$ for cargo- and passenger-type aircraft. For fighter-type aircraft a clean wing will have $C_{L\,max} \sim 1.0 \rightarrow 1.2$ and a wing with a leading edge slat will have $C_{L\,max} \sim 1.2 \rightarrow 1.6$. The takeoff maximum lift coefficient is typically 80% of the landing value.

Table 2.1 $C_{L\,max}$ **for high lift devices[4]**

High lift device		Typical flap angle, deg		$C_{L\,max}/\cos(\Lambda_{c/4})$	
Trailing edge	Leading edge	Takeoff	Landing	Takeoff	Landing
Plain	——	20	60	1.4 → 1.6	1.7 → 2.0
Single slot	——	20	40	1.5 → 1.7	1.8 → 2.2
Fowler	——	15	40	2.0 → 2.2	2.5 → 2.9
Double sltd.	——	20	50	1.7 → 2.0	2.3 → 2.7
Double sltd.	Slat	20	50	2.3 → 2.6	2.8 → 3.2
Triple sltd.	Slat	20	40	2.4 → 2.7	3.2 → 3.5

The lift-drag polar for most large cargo and passenger aircraft can be estimated (Ref. 5) by using Fig. 2.9 and Eq. (2.9) with

$$0.001 \le K'' \le 0.03, \quad 0.1 \le C_{L\,min} \le 0.3, \quad K' = \frac{1}{\pi A R e}$$

where the wing aspect ratio (AR) is between 7 and 10 and the wing planform efficiency factor (e) is between 0.75 and 0.85. Note that

$$K_1 = K' + K'', \quad C_{D0} = C_{D\,min} + K'' C_{L\,min}^2, \quad K_2 = -2K'' C_{L\,min}$$

The lift-drag polar for high-performance fighter-type aircraft can be estimated (Ref. 5) using Eq. (2.9), $K_2 = 0$, and Figs. 2.10 and 2.11.

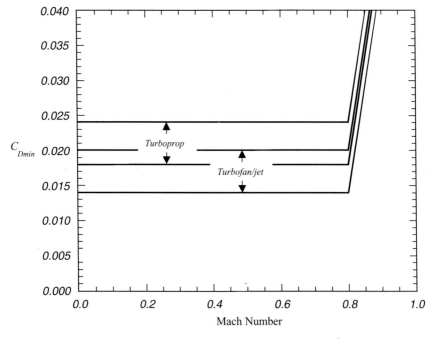

Fig. 2.9 $C_{D\,min}$ **for cargo and passenger aircraft.[5]**

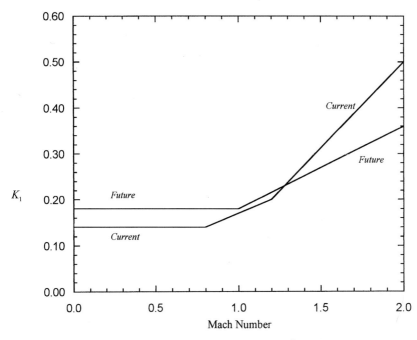

Fig. 2.10 K_1 for fighter aircraft.[5]

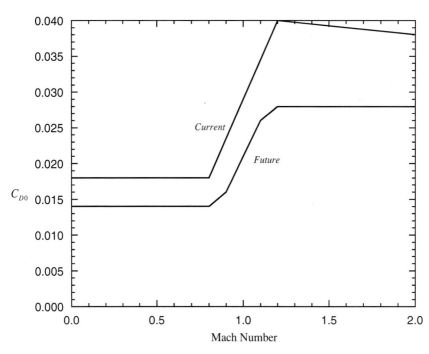

Fig. 2.11 C_{D0} for fighter aircraft.[5]

2.3.2 Propulsion

The variation of installed engine thrust with Mach number, altitude, and after-burner operation can be estimated by developing a simple algebraic equation that has been fit to either existing data of company-published performance curves or predicted data based on the output of performance cycle analysis (see Chapter 5) with estimates made for installation losses. The following algebraic equations for installed engine thrust lapse are based on the expected performance of advanced engines in the 2000 era and beyond. These models use the nondimensional temperature (θ and θ_0) and nondimensional pressure (δ and δ_0), defined next, and the throttle ratio (TR) described in Appendix D. The rationale for these models has a sound, fundamental basis that is developed in Mattingly[6] and confirmed by the analysis of Appendix D.

$$\theta = T/T_{std} \quad \text{and} \quad \theta_0 = T_t/T_{std} = \theta \left(1 + \frac{\gamma - 1}{2} M_0^2\right) \tag{2.52a}$$

$$\delta = P/P_{std} \quad \text{and} \quad \delta_0 = P_t/P_{std} = \delta \left(1 + \frac{\gamma - 1}{2} M_0^2\right)^{\frac{\gamma}{\gamma-1}} \tag{2.52b}$$

High bypass ratio turbofan ($M_0 < 0.9$)

$$\theta_0 \leq TR \quad \alpha = \delta_0 \{1 - 0.49\sqrt{M_0}\}$$

$$\theta_0 > TR \quad \alpha = \delta_0 \left\{1 - 0.49\sqrt{M_0} - \frac{3(\theta_0 - TR)}{1.5 + M_0}\right\} \tag{2.53}$$

Low bypass ratio, mixed flow turbofan
Maximum power:

$$\theta_0 \leq TR \quad \alpha = \delta_0$$

$$\theta_0 > TR \quad \alpha = \delta_0 \{1 - 3.5(\theta_0 - TR)/\theta_0\} \tag{2.54a}$$

Military power:

$$\theta_0 \leq TR \quad \alpha = 0.6\delta_0$$

$$\theta_0 > TR \quad \alpha = 0.6\delta_0 \{1 - 3.8(\theta_0 - TR)/\theta_0\} \tag{2.54b}$$

Turbojet
Maximum power:

$$\theta_0 \leq TR \quad \alpha = \delta_0 \{1 - 0.3(\theta_0 - 1) - 0.1\sqrt{M_0}\}$$

$$\theta_0 > TR \quad \alpha = \delta_0 \left\{1 - 0.3(\theta_0 - 1) - 0.1\sqrt{M_0} - \frac{1.5(\theta_0 - TR)}{\theta_0}\right\} \tag{2.55a}$$

Military power:

$$\theta_0 \leq TR \quad \alpha = 0.8\delta_0 \{1 - 0.16\sqrt{M_0}\}$$

$$\theta_0 > TR \quad \alpha = 0.8\delta_0 \left\{1 - 0.16\sqrt{M_0} - \frac{24(\theta_0 - TR)}{(9 + M_0)\theta_0}\right\} \tag{2.55b}$$

Turboprop

$$M_0 \leq 0.1 \quad \alpha = \delta_0$$

$$\theta_0 \leq TR \quad \alpha = \delta_0\{1 - 0.96(M_0 - 1)^{1/4}\}$$

$$\theta_0 > TR \quad \alpha = \delta_0\left\{1 - 0.96(M_0 - 1)^{1/4} - \frac{3(\theta_0 - TR)}{8.13(M_0 - 0.1)}\right\} \quad (2.56)$$

2.3.3 Weight Fraction

In the computation of every constraint, the instantaneous weight fraction (β) of the aircraft is required. An initial numerical estimate for this weight fraction at each mission junction must be based on experience. To provide you with guidance for these estimates, the instantaneous weight fraction along the mission of two typical aircraft, a fighter aircraft and a cargo or passenger aircraft, are shown in Figs. 2.12 and 2.13, respectively.

2.4 Example Constraint Analysis

The performance requirements of the Air-to-Air Fighter (AAF) aircraft Request for Proposal (RFP) in Chapter 1 that might constrain the permissible aircraft takeoff thrust loading (T_{SL}/W_{TO}) and wing loading (W_{TO}/S) are listed in Table 2.E1. In this example, we shall translate each of these performance requirements into a constraint boundary on a diagram of takeoff thrust loading vs wing loading. This will be accomplished with each requirement by developing an equation for the limiting allowable loadings in the form

$$f\{(T_{SL}/W_{TO}), (W_{TO}/S)\} = 0$$

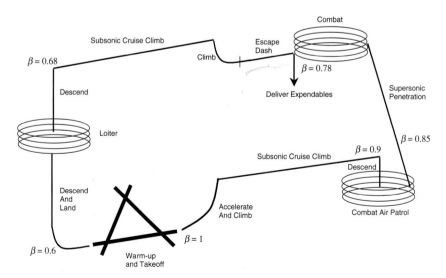

Fig. 2.12 Instantaneous weight fraction: typical fighter aircraft.

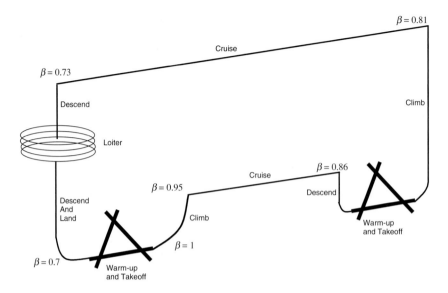

Fig. 2.13   Instantaneous weight fraction—typical cargo and passenger aircraft.

Finally, with the help of the constraint diagram so constructed, we shall select initial values of (T_{SL}/W_{TO}) and (W_{TO}/S) for the AAF.

2.4.1   Constraint Boundary Analysis

To proceed, it is necessary to have preliminary estimates for $C_{L\,\mathrm{max}}$, the lift-drag polar, and engine performance data. These data are based on current technology

Table 2.E1   Selected AAF specifications

Mission phases and segments		Performance requirement
1–2	*Takeoff*	2000 ft PA, 100°F, $s_{TO} = s_G + s_R \le 1500$ ft
	Acceleration	$k_{TO} = 1.2$, $\mu_{TO} = 0.05$, max power
	Rotation	V_{TO}, $t_R = 3$ s, max power
6–7 and 8–9	Supersonic penetration and escape dash	1.5M/30 kft, no afterburning (if possible)
7–8	Combat	30,000 ft
	Turn 1	1.6M, one 360 deg 5g sustained turn, with afterburning
	Turn 2	0.9M, two 360 deg 5g sustained turn, with afterburning
	Acceleration	$0.8 \rightarrow 1.6$M, $\Delta t \le 50$ s, max power
13–14	Landing	2000 ft PA, 100°F, $s_L = s_{FR} + s_{BR} \le 1500$ ft
	Free roll	$k_{TD} = 1.15$, $t_{FR} = 3$ s, $\mu_B = 0.18$
	Braking	Drag chute diameter 15.6 ft, deployment ≤ 2.5 s
Max Mach number RFP para. C.1		1.8M/40 kft, max power

for fighter-type aircraft and engines. The variation of thrust with Mach number and density is shown in Fig. 2.E1b that depicts the so-called engine thrust lapse of Eqs. (2.54a) and (2.54b) for three typical values of the throttle ratio (TR). In addition, the instantaneous weight fraction (β) must be estimated for each item of Table 2.E1. Reasonable estimates (see Figs. 2.12 and 2.13) will fall between 1.0 at takeoff and 0.5, say, at landing.

The aerodynamic data of Fig. 2.E1a provide the initial estimates of $C_{L\max}$, K_1, and C_{D0} required by Eq. (2.11b) and its descendants. Please note that the AAF is at first assumed to have an uncambered airfoil, for which $K_2 = 0$. The following AAF calculations will therefore use the relevant equations with K_2 set equal to zero. Note that $C_{L\max} = 2$ was arrived at after many values of $C_{L\max}$ were examined, such that takeoff would not overconstrain the problem. According to Table 2.1, this requires a fighter with very low wing sweep (improbable, especially in this case with supercruise requirements) or augmented high lift (such as achieved by using vortex lift created by leading edge extensions, etc.). This challenges the aircraft designer to join in the effort by using advanced technology for this requirement.

The installed propulsion data of a low bypass ratio, mixed flow turbofan engine are selected and plotted in Fig. 2.E1b based on Eqs. (2.54a) and (2.54b). A range of TR from 1.0 to 1.08 is shown because the hot day takeoff and supercruise requirements desire a TR greater than 1.0 (see Appendix D). It is important to have a good first estimate of the installed engine thrust lapse, which is usually obtained from such open literature information as company brochures, technical papers, and textbooks.[1,2] Another very effective method for obtaining engine thrust lapse is simply to run the performance computer portion of the AEDsys program supplied with this textbook for an initial guess of the engine design point. That was the origin of the engine thrust lapse equations of Sec. 2.3.2.

The computations and data required to construct each boundary in the complete constraint diagram of the AAF are contained in the Sec. 2.4.3. The Constraint Analysis software in the AEDsys program makes these calculations effortless.

Before determining the constraint for each item of Table 2.E1 in detail, we will first illustrate the procedure with the takeoff distance and supercruise phases. This will also help us appreciate the role of the engine TR and select a value capable of meeting these two constraints.

Takeoff. For this illustrative case we consider the airplane accelerated by thrust with no resisting forces whatever in the ground roll. The thrust is balanced by drag forces during the constant velocity rotation. Under these conditions our takeoff constraint boundary equation comes from Case 5, Eq. (2.22), solved for s_G, and Eq. (2.26), where $s_{TO} = s_G + s_R$, or

$$s_{TO} = \left\{ \frac{k_{TO}^2 \beta^2}{\rho g_0 C_{L\max} \alpha_{wet}(T_{SL}/W_{TO})} \right\} \left(\frac{W_{TO}}{S} \right) + \left\{ t_R k_{TO} \sqrt{\frac{2\beta}{\rho C_{L\max}}} \right\} \sqrt{\frac{W_{TO}}{S}}$$

$$(2.E1)$$

which is in the form

$$a\left(\frac{W_{TO}}{S} \right) + b\sqrt{\frac{W_{TO}}{S}} - c = 0$$

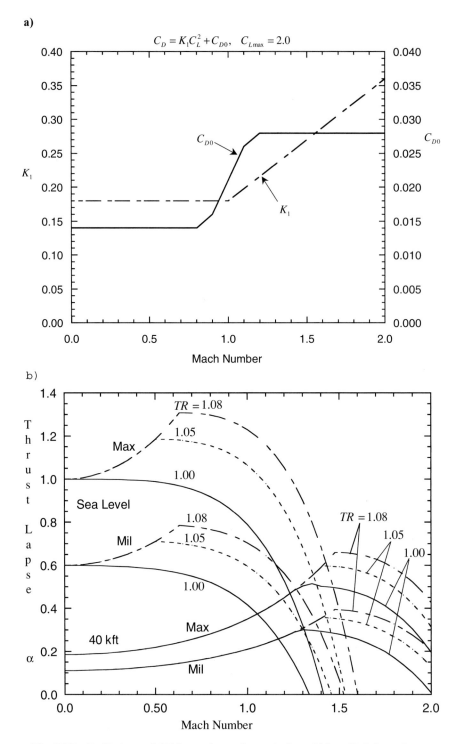

Fig. 2.E1   Preliminary AAF data: a) aerodynamic data; b) installed thrust lapse.

**Table 2.E2   Thrust lapse variation
with throttle ratio-AB on**

TR	α_{wet}
1.00	0.6885
1.05	0.8400
1.06	0.8703
1.07	0.9006
1.08	0.9309

From item 1 of Table 2.E1, Fig. 2.E1, and the standard atmosphere of Appendix B, we have

$k_{TO} = 1.2$ $\beta = 1.0$ $\theta = 1.0796$ $(\theta_0)_{M=0.1} = 1.0818$

$M_{TO} = 0.1$ $C_{L\,max} = 2.0$ $\delta = 0.9298$ $(\delta_0)_{M=0.1} = 0.9363$

$\sigma = \delta/\theta = 0.8612$ $\rho = 0.002047$ sl/ft^3 $t_R = 3.0$ s $s_{TO} = 1500$ ft

$g_0 = 32.17$ ft/s^2

For the range of TR the corresponding thrust lapses (α) from Eq. (2.54a) are shown in Table 2.E2.

With these values we can evaluate the coefficients a, b, and c in Eq. (2.E1), which, for computational convenience, we solve for W_{TO}/S in order to obtain

$$\left(\frac{W_{TO}}{S}\right) = \left\{\frac{-b + \sqrt{b^2 + 4ac}}{2a}\right\}^2 \qquad (2.E2)$$

where

$$a = \frac{10.93}{\alpha_{wet}(T_{SL}/W_{TO})} \quad b = 79.57 \quad c = 1500$$

whence we obtain the matrix of results for W_{TO}/S:

TR	T_{SL}/W_{TO}	0.4	0.8	1.2	1.6	2.0	2.4
1.00	W_{TO}/S (lbf/ft^2)	27.3	47.9	64.9	79.6	92.5	104
1.05	W_{TO}/S (lbf/ft^2)	32.2	55.7	74.8	91.1	105	118
1.06	W_{TO}/S (lbf/ft^2)	33.2	57.2	76.7	93.2	107	120
1.07	W_{TO}/S (lbf/ft^2)	34.1	58.7	78.6	95.33	110	122
1.08	W_{TO}/S (lbf/ft^2)	35.1	60.2	80.4	97.4	112	125

The takeoff constraint boundaries for this range of throttle ratios are shown in Fig. 2.E2. An airplane with thrust and wing loadings in the region to the left of the boundary can take off within the specified constraints, but those to the right cannot.

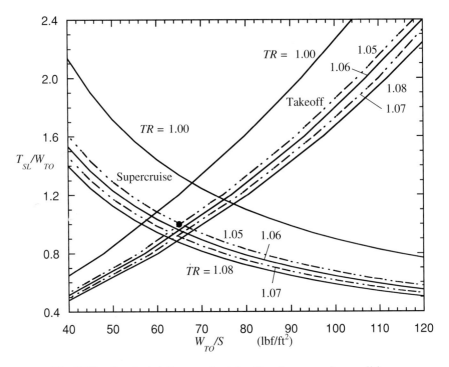

Fig. 2.E2   Constraint diagram for takeoff and supercruise conditions.

Supercruise.   For constant altitude/speed cruise, Case 1, Eq. (2.12), with $C_{DR} = K_2 = 0$ gives

$$\left(\frac{T_{SL}}{W_{TO}}\right) = \frac{\beta}{\alpha}\left\{K_1\frac{\beta}{q}\left(\frac{W_{TO}}{S}\right) + \frac{C_{D0}}{\beta/q\,(W_{TO}/S)}\right\}$$

From item 2 of Table 2.E1, Fig. 2.E1, and the standard atmosphere of Appendix B, we have

$\theta = 0.7940$ $(\theta_0)_{M=1.5} = 1.1513$ $\delta = 0.2975$ $(\delta_0)_{M=1.5} = 1.0921$

$K_1 = 0.27$ $C_{D0} = 0.028$ $\beta = 0.78$

$q = 991.6\ \text{lbf/ft}^2$

The supercruise constraint boundary equation is, therefore,

$$\left(\frac{T_{SL}}{W_{TO}}\right) = \frac{0.78}{\alpha}\left\{2.12 \times 10^{-4}\left(\frac{W_{TO}}{S}\right) + \frac{35.6}{(W_{TO}/S)}\right\} \qquad (2.E3)$$

**Table 2.E3   Thrust lapse variation
with throttle ratio-AB off**

TR	α_{dry}
1.00	0.3278
1.05	0.4359
1.06	0.4576
1.07	0.4792
1.08	0.5008

with $\alpha = \alpha_{dry}$ as a function of TR from Eq. (2.54b), as shown in Table 2.E3, whence we obtain the matrix of results for T_{SL}/W_{TO}:

TR	W_{TO}/S (lbf/ft^2)	20	40	60	80	100	120
1.00	T_{SL}/W_{TO}	4.25	2.14	1.44	1.10	0.898	0.767
1.05	T_{SL}/W_{TO}	3.19	1.61	1.08	0.827	0.675	0.576
1.06	T_{SL}/W_{TO}	3.04	1.53	1.03	0.788	0.643	0.549
1.07	T_{SL}/W_{TO}	2.90	1.46	0.986	0.752	0.614	0.524
1.08	T_{SL}/W_{TO}	2.80	1.40	0.944	0.720	0.588	0.502

As shown in Fig. 2.E2, this constraint boundary places a lower limit on the allowable wing loading and, together with the takeoff constraint boundary, encloses the "solution space" of allowable combinations of thrust and wing loadings that satisfy the two performance requirements considered here. The main consequence of increased throttle ratio, as expected, is to reduce T_{SL}/W_{TO} by sustaining thrust to higher values of M_0 and θ_0 (see Fig. 2.E1b).

The selection of a thrust loading and wing loading from Fig. 2.E2 is a compromise of many factors. For a given W_{TO}, a low (W_{TO}/S) value means large wing area while a high value of (T_{SL}/W_{TO}) results in a large thrust requirement. In addition, a low wing loading reduces the airplane riding qualities and range and can increase the aircraft radar cross section. We would prefer, therefore, relatively low thrust and high wing loadings. We might, based on the constraint diagram of Fig. 2.E2, select 1.0 and 64 lbf/ft^2 for our AAF thrust and wing loadings and an engine throttle ratio of 1.07. However, we must take into account all performance requirements as well as the takeoff ground roll drag in constructing the fighter's complete constraint diagram.

When this is done, we employ the AEDsys Constraint Analysis software to obtain and construct Fig. 2.E3, which is the complete constraint diagram we seek in order to make a judicious selection of (T_{SL}/W_{TO}) and (W_{TO}/S) for the AAF. Notice that the solution space in the diagram is bounded with constraints formed by the supercruise, 0.9M/5g combat turn, takeoff, and landing RFP requirements. It is interesting to superimpose the AAF solution space of Fig. 2.E3 on Fig. 2.3, which contains the wing and thrust loadings of 22 fighter-type airplanes, as is done in the composite Fig. 2.E4. We see that none of the contemporary fighters meets all of the RFP requirements for the AAF, thus the need for a new airplane. However, the larger YF-22 and YF-23 have similar thrust and wing loadings, which might be expected because they have similar requirements.

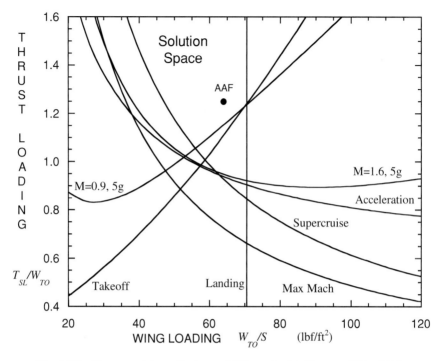

Fig. 2.E3   The complete preliminary AAF constraint diagram ($TR = 1.07$).

2.4.2   Selection of the Preliminary Air-to-Air Fighter Design Point

We are now in a position to make a preliminary selection of the thrust loading and wing loading that will guarantee that all the flight constraints are met. To do this, we will refer repeatedly to the constraint diagram of Fig. 2.E3. You will find that the tools are provided to allow the solution to be iterated and refined as better information becomes available, until a final converged solution is obtained.

As you can see from Fig. 2.E3, the limits imposed by the sustained 1.6M/5g combat turn, the acceleration requirement, and the maximum Mach are, for this aircraft, not important. Please bear in mind, however, that this will not be the case for aircraft designed for other applications and may not even remain true for the AAF if the underlying assumptions change (e.g., if the afterburner is not used during sustained combat turns). For the time being, then, we will concentrate on the four flight conditions that do form the boundaries of the AAF solution space, namely, supercruise, 0.9M/5g combat turn, takeoff, and landing.

At this stage of the design process, the constraint analysis also can be used to bring down the ultimate takeoff weight (and cost) of the AAF. On the one hand, lower thrust loadings lead to smaller engines and greater wing loadings lead to smaller wings. On the other hand, as you will see in Sec. 3.2.7, the fuel consumed in supercruise can be reduced by selecting a wing loading closer to the minimum thrust loading, which is evidently to the right of the solution space. This means that we must focus on design points on the right side of the "bucket" formed

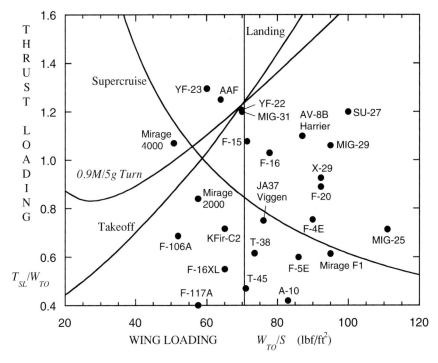

Fig. 2.E4 Composite thrust loading vs wing loading—fighter aircraft and preliminary AAF.

near the juncture of the three constraining lines, preferably those near to the region of previous thrust loading experience, which extends to about $T_{SL}/W_{TO} = 1.2$ according to Fig. 2.E4. Fortunately, the wing loadings in the region are well within the design experience of the industry, as seen in Fig. 2.E4, and high enough to assure good handling qualities.[3] It is equally important to avoid trying to put too fine a point on our choice, lest the movement of any of the constraining lines caused by improved estimates of aircraft and/or engine performance render it useless. Following this logic, it appears that the preliminary design point

$$T_{SL}/W_{TO} = 1.25$$

$$W_{TO}/S = 64 \text{ lbf/ft}^2$$

$$TR = 1.07$$

as indicated on Figs. 2.E3 and 2.E4, is a reasonable first choice, and this shall be used as our decision. A host of interesting observations evolve, the most important of which are the following:

1) The "new" capabilities of the AAF, namely short takeoff and landing, and nonafterburning supercruise have "driven" the design.

2) Relieving the takeoff constraint (by increasing s_{TO} or $C_{L\,max}$), the landing constraint (by increasing s_L or providing reverse thrust), the 0.9M combat turn (by

decreasing the number of gs), and the supercruise constraint (by decreasing the supercruise Mach number) simultaneously would do little to reduce the required T_{SL}/W_{TO} because of the bunching of the other constraints in the same neighborhood. The good side of this situation is that the resulting engine will be running near its full thrust at many flight conditions, so that its size will not be made excessively large by any single requirement, and its performance is liable to remain high over the entire mission. This often happens when the RFP is the result of thoughtful consideration and balancing of the requirements.

3) The drag chute is a bargain. Without it T_{SL}/W_{TO} would increase beyond any reasonable limit because $W_{TO}/S = 50.8$ lbf/ft^2 with no drag chute.

4) The throttle ratio has migrated in the direction of the supercruise $\theta_0 = 1.15$ (see Appendix D).

Evaluating P_s. At this point in the design process, it may surprise you to find that a great deal of preliminary information is already available about the AAF. For example, once T_{SL}/W_{TO} and W_{TO}/S are selected, it is possible to compute the weight specific excess power (P_s) for flight at any chosen β, n, altitude, and velocity. To see this, combine Eqs. (2.2b) and (2.11) with $R = 0$ to find that

$$P_s = V \left\{ \frac{\alpha}{\beta} \left(\frac{T_{SL}}{W_{TO}} \right) - K_1 n^2 \frac{\beta}{q} \left(\frac{W_{TO}}{S} \right) - K_2 n - \frac{C_{D0}}{\beta/q(W_{TO}/S)} \right\} \quad (2.E4)$$

Equation (2.E4) was used in AEDsys to compute the contours of constant P_s for the preliminary AAF of Fig. 2.E3 at military power with $n = 1$ and $\beta = 0.97$. The results, which are displayed in Fig. 2.E5, are remarkably similar to that of "real" airplanes and contain useful guidance for future pilots of the AAF, as well

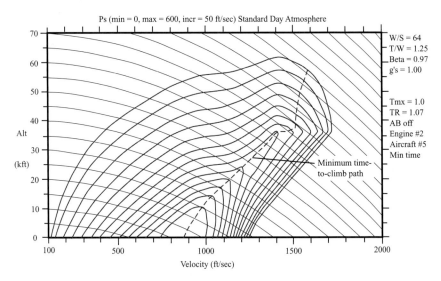

Fig. 2.E5 Preliminary AAF P_s contours at military power with minimum time-to-climb path.

as for analyses. Fighter pilots routinely compare these P_s diagrams for their aircraft with those of their potential adversaries in order to determine where in the flight envelope they enjoy the greatest combat advantage.

Further, Fig. 2.E5 provides a graphic method for determining the minimum time-to-climb flight path from a lower to a higher energy height. Equation (2.2b) rewritten as

$$\Delta t = \int_1^2 dt = \int_{z_{e1}}^{z_{e2}} \frac{dz_e}{P_s} \qquad (2.E5)$$

shows that the minimum time-to-climb from $z_{e1}(h_1, V_1)$ to the higher energy level $z_{e2}(h_2, V_2)$ corresponds to the flight path that produces the maximum specific excess power P_s at each z_e. This maximum occurs at the point of tangency between a line of constant energy height and the contour line of the maximum P_s attainable for that energy height. For $z_e = 70$ kft, for example, this tangency occurs at $P_s = 320$ ft/s, $V = 1480$ ft/s, and $h = 36$ kft. Continuing in this vein, one can find the minimum time-to-climb flight path, from z_e of 13 kft at sea level to a z_e of 96 kft at an altitude of 57 kft, as shown in Fig. 2.E5.

These preliminary quantitative results will, of course, change once the final selection of the AAF design point has been made and as improved models of the aircraft and engine performance are developed and used.

There are several other features of the P_s contours of Fig. 2.E5 that are striking and noteworthy, and they can be usefully generalized to applications beyond the AAF. First, the theta break line of 1.07 at the peak of each contour is clearly visible, and the value of moving it nearer to the supercruise flight condition is evident. Second, the dip of each contour caused by the transonic drag rise near $M = 1$ is also clearly visible. Third, the discontinuity on the right-hand side of each contour marks the atmospheric tropopause. Finally, the minimum time-to-climb path is quite similar to the theta break line because of the dominant influence of engine thrust on P_s, but not identical because aircraft drag also contributes to the calculation [see Eq. (2.E4)].

2.4.3 Complete AAF Constraint Boundary Computations

The constraint computational procedure and results for the performance requirements in Table 2.E1 follow. The same procedure is used in each constraint boundary calculation. First, the applicable constraint boundary equation from Sec. 2.2 is written. Next, data to determine the values of all constants as they appear from left to right in the equation are listed. This is followed by the specific constraint boundary equation resulting from the given data. Finally, some solution sets of this equation are tabulated. These are the data plotted in Figs. 2.E3 and 2.E4. The same calculations can be performed and the boundaries plotted much more rapidly using the Constraint Analysis portion of the AEDsys software included with this textbook. An additional benefit of the software is that it constitutes a checklist of the quantities required for the calculation of any chosen constraint boundary. The individual values were obtained as described in Sec. 2.4.1, but it must be emphasized that they can be altered for the purpose of exploration at the discretion of the reader.

Careful note should be taken of the fact that these hand calculations completely duplicate the AEDsys Constraint Analysis computations obtained by using the AAF.AED file. Any minor differences are simply the result of the cumulative effects of rounding off. Thus we see that one of the motivating forces for carrying four significant figures is to minimize the impact of these small imperfections on the overall results.

Mission phase 1–2: Takeoff, no obstacle.   2000 ft PA, 100°F, $k_{TO} = 1.2$, $\mu_{TO} = 0.05$, $t_R = 3$ s, $s_{TO} = s_G + s_R \leq 1500$ ft, max power.
    From Case 6, Eqs. (2.25) and (2.26) with $s_{TO} = s_G + s_R$

$$\left(\frac{W_{TO}}{S}\right) = \left\{\frac{-b + \sqrt{b_4^2 + 4ac}}{2a}\right\}^2$$

where

$$a = -\frac{\beta}{\rho g_0 \xi_{TO}} \ln\left\{1 - \xi_{TO} \bigg/ \left[\left(\frac{\alpha}{\beta}\frac{T_{SL}}{W_{TO}} - \mu_{TO}\right)\frac{C_{L\,max}}{k_{TO}^2}\right]\right\}$$

$$b = t_R k_{TO}\sqrt{2\beta/(\rho C_{L\,max})} \quad c = s_{TO}$$

We estimate α and β to be constant at appropriate mean values. A conservative estimate for ξ_{TO} for the AAF is obtained by assuming $(C_{DR} - \mu_{TO}C_L) = 0$ and evaluating C_D at $C_L = C_{L\,max}/k_{TO}^2$. With

$\beta = 1.0$	$\rho = 0.002047$ slug/ft^3	$C_{L\,max} = 2.0$	$C_L = 1.389$
$K_1 = 0.18$	$C_{D0} = 0.014$	$\xi_{TO} = 0.3612$	
$\sigma = 0.8613$	$\theta = 1.0796$	$\delta = 0.9298$	$TR = 1.07$
$M_{TO} = 0.1$	$(\theta_0)_{M=0.1} = 1.0818$	$(\delta_0)_{M=0.1} = 0.9363$	$(a_{wet})_{M=0.1} = 0.9006$
$s_{TO} = 1500$ ft			

then

$$a = -42.06\ln\left\{1 - 0.2599 \bigg/ \left[0.9006\left(\frac{T_{SL}}{W_{TO}}\right) - 0.05\right]\right\} \quad b = 79.57 \quad c = 1500$$

whence

T_{SL}/W_{TO}	W_{TO}/S, lbf/ft^2
0.4	15.5
0.8	46.4
1.2	68.7
1.6	86.9
2.0	103

Mission phases 6–7 and 8–9: Supersonic penetration and escape dash.
1.5M/30 kft, no afterburning.

From Case 1, Eq. (2.12), with C_{DR} and $K_2 = 0$

$$\frac{T_{SL}}{W_{TO}} = \frac{\beta}{\alpha}\left\{K_1\frac{\beta}{q}\left(\frac{W_{TO}}{S}\right) + \frac{C_{D0}}{\beta/q(W_{TO}/S)}\right\}$$

With

$$\beta = 0.78 \qquad \theta = 0.7940 \qquad \theta_0 = 1.1513 \qquad \delta = 0.2975$$

$$\delta_0 = 1.0921 \quad TR = 1.07 \qquad a_{dry} = 0.4792 \quad q = 991.6 \text{ lbf/ft}^2$$

$$K_1 = 0.27 \qquad C_{D0} = 0.028$$

then

$$\left(\frac{T_{SL}}{W_{TO}}\right) = 3.457 \times 10^{-4}\left(\frac{W_{TO}}{S}\right) + \frac{57.94}{(W_{TO}/S)}$$

whence

W_{TO}/S, lbf/ft^2	T_{SL}/W_{TO}
20	2.90
40	1.46
60	0.986
80	0.752
100	0.614
120	0.524

Mission phase 7–8: Combat turn 1. 1.6M/30 kft, one 360 deg 5g sustained turn, with afterburning.

From Case 3, Eq. (2.15), with C_{DR} and $K_2 = 0$

$$\frac{T_{SL}}{W_{TO}} = \frac{\beta}{\alpha}\left\{K_1 n^2 \frac{\beta}{q}\left(\frac{W_{TO}}{S}\right) + \frac{C_{D0}}{\beta/q(W_{TO}/S)}\right\}$$

With

$$\beta = 0.78 \qquad \theta = 0.7940 \quad \theta_0 = 1.2005 \qquad \delta = 0.2975$$

$$\delta_0 = 1.2645 \quad TR = 1.07 \qquad \alpha_{wet} = 0.7829 \quad q = 1128 \text{ lbf/ft}^2$$

$$C_{D0} = 0.028 \quad K_1 = 0.288$$

then

$$\left(\frac{T_{SL}}{W_{TO}}\right) = 4.960 \times 10^{-3}\left(\frac{W_{TO}}{S}\right) + \frac{40.34}{(W_{TO}/S)}$$

whence

W_{TO}/S, lbf/ft^2	T_{SL}/W_{TO}
20	2.12
40	1.21
60	0.970
80	0.901
100	0.899
120	0.931

Mission phase 7–8: Combat turn 2.   0.9M/30 kft, two 360 deg 5g sustained turns, with afterburning.

From Case 3, Eq. (2.15), with C_{DR} and $K_2 = 0$

$$\frac{T_{SL}}{W_{TO}} = \frac{\beta}{\alpha}\left\{ K_1 n^2 \frac{\beta}{q}\left(\frac{W_{TO}}{S}\right) + \frac{C_{D0}}{\beta/q(W_{TO}/S)} \right\}$$

With

$$\beta = 0.78 \qquad \theta = 0.7940 \quad \theta_0 = 0.9226 \qquad \delta = 0.2975$$

$$\delta_0 = 0.5032 \qquad TR = 1.07 \quad \alpha_{wet} = 0.5033 \quad q = 357.0 \text{ lbf/ft}^2$$

$$C_{D0} = 0.016 \quad K_1 = 0.18$$

then

$$\left(\frac{T_{SL}}{W_{TO}}\right) = 0.01524\left(\frac{W_{TO}}{S}\right) + \frac{11.35}{(W_{TO}/S)}$$

whence

W_{TO}/S, lbf/ft^2	T_{SL}/W_{TO}
20	0.872
40	0.893
60	1.10
80	1.36
100	1.64
120	1.92

Mission phase 7–8: Horizontal acceleration. $0.8 \to 1.6$M/30 kft, at $\Delta t \le$ 50 s, max power.

From Case 4, Eq. (2.18a), with C_{DR} and $K_2 = 0$

$$\frac{T_{SL}}{W_{TO}} = \frac{\beta}{\alpha}\left\{ K_1 \frac{\beta}{q}\left(\frac{W_{TO}}{S}\right) + \frac{C_{D0}}{\beta/q(W_{TO}/S)} + \frac{a\Delta M}{g_0 \Delta t} \right\}$$

We obtain approximate constant values of q, K_1, C_{D0}, and α at a mean Mach number of 1.2.

With

$$\beta = 0.78 \qquad \theta = 0.7940 \qquad \theta_0 = 1.0227 \qquad \delta = 0.2975$$

$$\delta_0 = 0.7215 \qquad TR = 1.07 \qquad \alpha_{wet} = 0.7216 \qquad q = 634.6 \text{ lbf/ft}^2$$

$$C_{D0} = 0.028 \qquad K_1 = 0.216 \qquad a = 994.8 \text{ ft/s} \qquad \Delta M = 0.8$$

$$\Delta t = 50 \text{ s}$$

then

$$\frac{T_{SL}}{W_{TO}} = 2.870 \times 10^{-4} \left(\frac{W_{TO}}{S} \right) + \frac{24.62}{(W_{TO}/S)} + 0.5348$$

whence

W_{TO}/S, lbf/ft^2	T_{SL}/W_{TO}
20	1.77
40	1.16
60	0.963
80	0.866
100	0.810
120	0.775

Mission phase 13–14: Landing, no reverse thrust. 2000 ft PA, 100°F, $k_{TD} = 1.15$, $t_{FR} = 3$ s, $\mu_B = 0.18$, $s_L = s_{FR} + s_B \leq 1500$ ft, GFE drag chute, diameter 15.6 ft, deploymemt ≤ 2.5 s.

From Case 7, Eqs. (2.33) and (2.37) with $s_L = s_{FR} + s_B$

$$\left(\frac{W_{TO}}{S} \right) = \left\{ \frac{-b + \sqrt{b^2 + 4ac}}{2a} \right\}^2$$

where

$$a = \frac{\beta}{\rho g_0 \xi_L} \ln \left\{ 1 + \xi_L \Big/ \left[\left(\mu_B + \frac{(-\alpha)}{\beta} \frac{T_{SL}}{W_{TO}} \right) \frac{C_{L\,max}}{k_{TD}^2} \right] \right\}$$

$$b = t_{FR} k_{TD} \sqrt{2\beta/(\rho C_{L\,max})} \qquad c = S_L$$

We assume a drag chute drag coefficient of 1.4 based on the RFP chute area of 191 ft^2. Estimating the airplane wing area to be about 500 ft^2, the chute drag coefficent (C_{DR_c}) is 0.5348 referred to the wing area. A conservative estimate of ξ_L for the AAF is obtained by evaluating C_D at 0.8 of the touchdown lift coefficient ($C_{L\,max}/k_{TD}^2$) and by assuming ($C_{DR} - \mu_B C_L$) = 0.

With

$$\beta = 0.56 \qquad \rho = 0.002047 \text{ slug/ft}^3 \qquad C_{L\,max} = 2.0 \qquad C_{DR_c} = 0.5348$$

$$C_L = 1.210 \qquad K_1 = 0.18 \qquad C_{D0} = 0.014 \qquad C_D = 0.2775$$

$$\xi_L = 0.8123 \qquad \alpha = 0 \qquad s_L = 1500 \text{ ft}$$

then

$$a = 14.47 \quad b = 57.06 \quad c = 1500$$

whence

$$W_{TO}/S = 70.6 \text{ lbf/ft}^2$$

With no drag chute, the same assumptions and computational methods yield a wing loading constraint of 50.8 lbf/ft^2.

Maximum Mach number. $M = 1.8$ at 40,000 ft, max power. From Case 1, Eq. (2.12), with C_{DR} and $K_2 = 0$

$$\frac{T_{SL}}{W_{TO}} = \frac{\beta}{\alpha} \left\{ K_1 \frac{\beta}{q} \left(\frac{W_{TO}}{S} \right) + \frac{C_{D0}}{\beta/q(W_{TO}/S)} \right\}$$

With

$\beta = 0.78$ $\qquad\qquad \theta = 0.7519$ $\qquad (\theta_0)_{M=1.8} = 1.2391$ $\quad \delta = 0.1858$

$(\delta_0)_{M=1.8} = 1.0676$ $\quad TR = 1.07$ $\qquad \alpha_{wet} = 0.5575$ $\qquad q = 891.8 \text{ lbf/ft}^2$

$K_1 = 0.324$ $\qquad\qquad C_{D0} = 0.028$

then

$$\left(\frac{T_{SL}}{W_{TO}} \right) = 3.965 \times 10^{-4} \left(\frac{W_{TO}}{S} \right) + \frac{44.79}{(W_{TO}/S)}$$

whence

W_{TO}/S, lbf/ft^2	T_{SL}/W_{TO}
20	2.25
40	1.14
60	0.770
80	0.592
100	0.487
120	0.421

References

[1] "2002 Aerospace Source Book," *Aviation Week and Space Technology*, 14 Jan. 2002.

[2] *Jane's All the World's Aircraft, 2000–2001*, Jane's Yearbooks, Franklin Watts, Inc., New York, 2000.

[3] Raymer, D. P., *Aircraft Design: A Conceptual Approach*, 3rd ed., AIAA Education Series, AIAA, Reston, VA, 2000.

[4] Torenbeek, E., *Synthesis of Subsonic Airplane Design*, Delft Univ. Press, Delft, the Netherlands, 1976.

[5] Jonas, F., *Aircraft Design Lecture Notes*, U.S. Air Force Academy, Colorado Springs, CO, 1984.

[6] Mattingly, J. D., *Elements of Gas Turbine Propulsion*, McGraw–Hill, New York, 1996.

3
Mission Analysis

3.1 Concept

With preliminary design values of takeoff thrust loading (T_{SL}/W_{TO}) and wing loading (W_{TO}/S) now in hand, the next step is to establish the scale of the aircraft via the estimation of gross takeoff weight (W_{TO}). This will be accomplished by flying the aircraft through its entire mission on paper.

The key fact is that W_{TO} is simply the sum of the payload weight (W_P), the empty weight (W_E), and the required fuel weight (W_F), or

$$W_{TO} = W_P + W_E + W_F \qquad (3.1)$$

These will now be considered in turn.

W_P is specified in the Request for Proposal (RFP) and comes in two parts. The first is the expendable payload weight, which is delivered during the trip (W_{PE}), such as cargo or ammunition. The second is the permanent payload weight, which is carried the entire mission (W_{PP}), such as the crew and passengers and their personal equipment.

W_E consists of the basic aircraft structure plus any equipment that is permanently attached, such as the engines, the avionics, the wheels, and the seats. In short, W_E includes everything except W_P and W_F. W_E can be estimated as a fraction of W_{TO}, as shown in Figs. 3.1 and 3.2, which correspond to conventional, lightweight metal construction. The ratio of W_E to W_{TO} has obviously depended on the type of aircraft and its size, but the range of this parameter is not wide. Because W_E/W_{TO} varies slowly with W_{TO}, an initial value may be obtained from an initial estimate of W_{TO} and any necessary correction made when W_{TO} becomes more accurately known.

When one contemplates the enormous range of ages and types of aircraft displayed in Figs. 3.1 and 3.2, and the relatively narrow range of W_E/W_{TO}, it is possible to conclude that "practical" aircraft have "natural" empty weight fractions that provide reliable future projections. This observation should increase your confidence in their validity.

W_F represents the fuel gradually consumed during the entire mission. Except for the instantaneous release of W_{PE}, the aircraft weight decreases at exactly the same rate at which fuel is burned in the engine. The rate of fuel consumption, in turn, is simply the product of installed engine thrust (T) and installed engine thrust specific fuel consumption ($TSFC$). T can be found from whatever version of Eq. (2.1) is most convenient, while $TSFC$ depends on the engine cycle, flight conditions, and throttle setting and must initially be estimated on the basis of experience.

The fuel consumption analysis has several fortunate benefits. For one thing, it results in calculations based on relatively little information. For another, it reveals

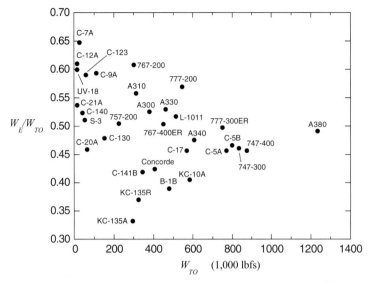

Fig. 3.1   Weight fractions of cargo and passenger aircraft.[1,2]

the "best" way to fly certain legs for minimum fuel usage. Finally, it shows that the fuel burned during each mission leg is a fraction of the aircraft weight starting the leg, whence W_F becomes a calculable fraction of W_{TO}. Most of the analysis below is devoted to the development of the "weight fraction" equations needed for the many possible kinds of mission legs.

Substitution of the derived results for W_E/W_{TO} and W_F/W_{TO} into Eq. (3.1) yields an unambiguous value for W_{TO} as a function of W_{PP} and W_{PE} (see

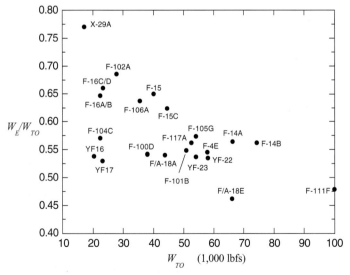

Fig. 3.2   Weight fractions of fighter aircraft.[1,2]

Sec. 3.2.12). Then T_{SL} and S are found by multiplying W_{TO} by thrust loading and wing loading, respectively.

3.2 Design Tools

The following material might very well be called the "thermodynamics of flight" because it deals largely with the way the thrust work of the engine is used by the aircraft. We expect that it should have a special appeal to engine designers, who always deal with the conversion of energy from one form to another, but seldom see aircraft treated in this manner.

We begin by considering the rate at which aircraft weight is diminishing as a result of the consumption of fuel, namely

$$\frac{\mathrm{d}W}{\mathrm{d}t} = -\frac{\mathrm{d}W_F}{\mathrm{d}t} = -TSFC \times T \qquad (3.2)$$

which may be rewritten as

$$\frac{\mathrm{d}W}{W} = -TSFC\frac{T}{W}\,\mathrm{d}t \qquad (3.3)$$

Note again that T is the installed thrust and $TSFC$ is the installed thrust specific fuel consumption. Also, since

$$\frac{T}{W}\,\mathrm{d}t = \frac{T}{W}\frac{\mathrm{d}t}{\mathrm{d}s}\,\mathrm{d}s = \frac{T}{W}\frac{\mathrm{d}s}{V}$$

then this portion of Eq. (3.3) represents the incremental weight-velocity specific engine thrust work done as the amount of fuel $\mathrm{d}W_F$ is consumed. Just as it is with any other thermodynamic situation, this engine thrust work will be partly invested in the mechanical energy (potential plus kinetic) of the airplane mass and partly "dissipated" into the nonmechanical energy of the airplane/atmosphere system (e.g., wing tip vortices, turbulence, and aerodynamic heating). The ratio of mechanical energy to "dissipation" will, of course, depend on the type of flight under consideration, as will be seen in what follows.

The main work of this section will be to determine how Eq. (3.3) can be integrated in order to obtain "weight fractions"

$$\frac{W_{final}}{W_{initial}} \doteq \frac{W_f}{W_i}$$

for a variety of mission legs of practical interest. From a mathematical point of view, proper integration of Eq. (3.3) requires a knowledge of the behavior of the thrust specific fuel consumption and the "instantaneous thrust loading" $\{T/W = (\alpha/\beta)(T_{SL}/W_{TO})\}$ as a function of time along the flight path. Experience indicates that the integration can be separated into two distinct classes, corresponding to $P_s > 0$ (type A) and $P_s = 0$ (type B). These will now be considered in turn.

Instantaneous thrust loading behavior: type A, $P_s > 0$. When $P_s > 0$, some of the thrust work is invested in mechanical energy. Also, it is generally true that specific information is given regarding the amount of installed thrust applied, as well as the total changes in altitude (h) and velocity (V) that take place, but not the time or distance involved. In fact, the usual specification for thrust is the maximum available for the flight condition, or $T = \alpha T_{SL}$. Examples of type A are found as Cases 1–4: 1) constant speed climb, 2) horizontal acceleration, 3) climb and acceleration, and 4) takeoff acceleration.

Progress toward a solution may now be made by using Eq. (2.2a) in the form

$$\frac{T}{W} V \, dt = \frac{T}{W} \, ds = \frac{d(h + V^2/2g_0)}{1 - u} = \frac{dz_e}{1 - u} \tag{3.4}$$

where

$$u = \frac{D + R}{T} \tag{3.5}$$

whence, combining Eqs. (3.3) and (3.4),

$$\frac{dW}{W} = -\frac{TSFC}{V(1 - u)} \, d(h + V^2/2g_0) \tag{3.6a}$$

or

$$\frac{dW}{W} = -\frac{TSFC}{V(1 - u)} \, dz_e \tag{3.6b}$$

The quantity u determines how the total engine thrust work is distributed between mechanical energy and dissipation. More precisely, Eq. (3.5) shows that u is the fraction of the engine thrust work that is dissipated, so that $(1 - u)$ must be the fraction of the engine thrust work invested in mechanical energy. This is further confirmed by Eq. (3.4), which reveals that $(1 - u)$ equals the change in mechanical energy ($W \, dz_e$) divided by the total engine thrust work $T \, ds$. Note that when $T = D + R$ and $u = 1$, all of the thrust work is dissipated, and the type A analysis yields no useful results.

The actual integration of Eq. (3.6a) is straightforward and depends only upon the variation of $\{TSFC/V(1 - u)\}$ with altitude and velocity. When this quantity remains relatively constant over the flight leg, as it frequently does, the result is

$$\frac{W_f}{W_i} = \exp\left\{ -\frac{TSFC}{V(1 - u)} \Delta \left(h + \frac{V^2}{2g_0} \right) \right\} \tag{3.7a}$$

or

$$\frac{W_f}{W_i} = \exp\left\{ -\frac{TSFC}{V(1 - u)} \Delta z_e \right\} \tag{3.7b}$$

where Δz_e is the total change in energy height. Otherwise, the integration can be accomplished by breaking the leg into several smaller intervals and applyng Eq. (3.7) to each. The overall W_f/W_i will then be the product of the results for the separate intervals.

Equations (3.6) and (3.7) highlight the fact that, within certain limits, potential energy and kinetic energy can be interchanged or "traded." For example, if there were no drag ($u = 0$) and z_e were constant, as in an unpowered dive or zoom climb, no fuel would be consumed and $dW = 0$ or $W_f = W_i$. This, in turn, reveals the forbidden solutions of Eqs. (3.2), (3.6), and (3.7) for which W would increase during the flight leg and which correspond to $T < 0$ and $dz_e < 0$. Lacking special devices onboard the aircraft that could convert aircraft potential and/or kinetic energy into "fuel," it must be true for any condition of flight that $dW \leq 0$ and $W_f \leq W_i$.

f_s and the minimum fuel path. As already mentioned, the fuel consumption analysis also reveals the "best" way to fly type A legs for minimum fuel usage. Equations (3.2), (2.2b), and (2.3) may be combined to yield

$$dW_F = T \times TSFC \times dt = T_{SL} \frac{\alpha\, TSFC}{P_s} dz_e$$

where

$$P_s = \left\{ \frac{T - (D + R)}{W} \right\} V = \frac{T}{W}(1 - u)V$$

Defining the fuel consumed specific work (f_s) as

$$f_s \doteq \frac{P_s}{\alpha\, TSFC} = \frac{T_{SL}\, dz_e}{dW_F} \tag{3.8}$$

then

$$W_{F_{1-2}} = \int_1^2 dW_F = T_{SL} \int_{z_{e1}}^{z_{e2}} \frac{dz_e}{f_s} \tag{3.9}$$

Equation (3.9) shows that the minimum fuel-to-climb flight from z_{e1} (h_1, V_1) to z_{e2} (h_2, V_2) corresponds to a flight path, that produces the maximum thrust work per unit weight of fuel consumed at each energy height level in the climb, i.e., the maximum value of f_s at each z_e. As you can see from Eq. (3.8), the units of f_s are feet.

Constant f_s and z_e contours in the altitude-velocity plane (e.g., see Fig. 3.E6 in Sec. 3.4.4) provide a graphical method for finding the maximum f_s at any z_e and hence the minimum fuel-to-climb path from z_{e1} to z_{e2}. This is analogous to using the P_s and z_e contours of Fig. 2.E5 to find the minimum time-to-climb path in conjunction with the time-to-climb equation from Eq. (2.2b).

$$\Delta t = \int_1^2 dt = \int_{z_{e1}}^{z_{e2}} \frac{dz_e}{P_s}$$

Because f_s and P_s are closely related through Eq. (3.8), it should not be surprising to find that the minimum fuel-to-climb and time-to-climb paths are similar. This is a fortuitous result because there is little conflict between the alternatives.

Instantaneous thrust loading behavior: type B, $P_s = 0$. When $P_s = 0$, all of the thrust work is dissipated. Also, it is generally true that the speed and altitude are essentially constant, and specific information is given regarding the total amount of time (Δt or $\Delta s/V$), which elapses. Examples of type B are found as Cases 5–11: 5) constant speed cruise, 6) constant speed turn, 7) best cruise Mach number and altitude, 8) loiter, 9) warm-up, 10) takeoff rotation, and 11) constant energy height maneuver.

For this type of flight, the required thrust may not be known in advance. The thrust is modulated or throttled so that $T = (D + R)$, or $u = 1$ by Eq. (3.5), and $dz_e = 0$ by Eq. (3.4).

Using Eq. (3.3), it follows immediately that

$$\frac{dW}{W} = -TSFC\left(\frac{D+R}{W}\right) dt \qquad (3.10)$$

It is often found that the quantity $\{TSFC(D+R)/W\}$ remains relatively unchanged over the flight leg, and Eq. (3.10) can be integrated to yield

$$\frac{W_f}{W_i} = \exp\left\{-TSFC\left(\frac{D+R}{W}\right)\Delta t\right\} \qquad (3.11)$$

where Δt is the total flight time. If desired, the required thrust may be computed after the fact. Otherwise, the integration of Eq. (3.10) can be accomplished by breaking the leg into several smaller intervals.

TSFC behavior.   The engine installed thrust specific fuel consumption that appears in Eq. (3.3) is a complex function of the combination of the instantaneous altitude, speed, and throttle setting, especially if the engine has the option of afterburning. A satisfactory starting point with sufficient accuracy for this stage of analysis is the approximation that (see Sec. 3.3.2 and Appendix D)

$$TSFC = (C_1 + C_2 M)\sqrt{\theta} \qquad (3.12)$$

where C_1 and C_2 are constants that are known in advance for each type and operation of turbine engine cycle.

It should be emphasized that approximations for *TSFC* different from Eq. (3.12) could be made and the weight fraction analysis continued to completion, but our experience is that this model strikes an excellent balance between accuracy and ease of solution for turbojet, turbofan, and turboprop engines, with or without afterburning.

Summary of weight fraction equations.   Combining Eqs. (3.6), (3.7), (3.10), (3.11), and (3.12) as appropriate, the weight fraction analysis results may be summarized as follows:

Type A ($P_s > 0$, $T = \alpha\, T_{SL}$ given):

$$\frac{dW}{W} = -\frac{(C_1/M + C_2)}{a_{std}(1-u)} d\left(h + \frac{V^2}{2g_0}\right) \qquad \text{(Instantaneously exact)} \qquad (3.13)$$

where

$$u = \frac{D+R}{T}$$

$$\frac{W_f}{W_i} = \exp\left\{-\frac{(C_1/M + C_2)}{a_{std}(1-u)}\Delta\left(h + \frac{V^2}{2g_0}\right)\right\} \qquad \{\text{Exact when} \qquad (3.14)$$

$$[(C_1/M + C_2)/(1-u)] \text{ is constant.}\}$$

Please note that type A weight fraction analysis is independent of altitude.

Type B ($P_s = 0, T = D + R$):

$$\frac{dW}{W} = -(C_1 + C_2 M)\sqrt{\theta}\left(\frac{D + R}{W}\right) dt \qquad \text{(Instantaneously exact)} \qquad (3.15)$$

$$\frac{W_f}{W_i} = \exp\left\{-(C_1 + C_2 M)\sqrt{\theta}\left(\frac{D + R}{W}\right)\Delta t\right\} \qquad \text{[Exact when} \qquad (3.16)$$

$$(C_1 + C_2 M)\sqrt{\theta}(D + R)/W \text{ is constant.]}$$

Please note that type B weight fraction analysis depends on altitude through $\sqrt{\theta}$.

A large number and variety of special cases of Eqs. (3.13–3.16) shall now be developed in order both to illustrate their behavior and to provide more specific design tools for weight fraction analysis. Close attention should be paid to the fact that the formulas to follow can be used in two separate ways. First, they are imbedded in the Mission Analysis subroutines of AEDsys as the basis for the fuel consumption computations for legs bearing the same titles. Second, they can be used as they stand to estimate weight fractions or carry out mission analysis by hand.

In all the example cases that follow, it is assumed that the α of Eq. (2.3), the β of Eq. (2.4), the K_1, K_2, and C_{D0} of Eq. (2.9), and the C_1 and C_2 of Eq. (3.12) are known. It may also be helpful to note in the following developments that $n = 1$ and $L = W$ except for Cases 4, 6 ($n > 1$), 9, and 10.

3.2.1 Case 1: Constant Speed Climb (P_s = dh/dt)

Given: $dV/dt = 0$, $n = 1$ ($L = W$), full thrust ($T = \alpha T_{SL}$) and values of $h_{initial}$, h_{final}, and V.

Under these conditions

$$u = \frac{C_D + C_{DR}}{C_L}\frac{\beta}{\alpha}\left(\frac{W_{TO}}{T_{SL}}\right)$$

so that Eq. (3.14) becomes

$$\frac{W_f}{W_i} = \exp\left\{-\frac{(C_1/M + C_2)}{a_{std}}\left[\frac{\Delta h}{1 - [(C_D + C_{DR})/C_L](\beta/\alpha)(W_{TO}/T_{SL})}\right]\right\}$$

$$(3.17)$$

where the level flight relationships

$$\frac{D + R}{W} = \frac{D + R}{L} = \frac{q(C_D + C_{DR})S}{qC_L S} = \frac{C_D + C_{DR}}{C_L} \qquad (3.18)$$

have been used, and

$$\Delta h = h_{final} - h_{initial}$$

Appropriate average values of α, β, θ, M, and $(C_D + C_{DR})/C_L$ for the altitude interval should be used, unless the quantity $(C_1/M + C_2)/(1 - u)$ varies too much for acceptable accuracy. Then the integration is accomplished by breaking the climb into several smaller intervals and applying Eq. (3.17) to each. The overall W_f/W_i is then the product of the separate results.

Please note that, as stated earlier, the term $[(C_D + C_{DR})/C_L](\beta/\alpha)(W_{TO}/T_{SL})$ represents the fraction of the engine thrust work that is dissipated, while $\{1 - [(C_D + C_{DR})/C_L](\beta/\alpha)(W_{TO}/T_{SL})\}$ is the fraction invested in potential energy. Low drag and high thrust are obviously conducive to efficient energy conversion, a theme that recurs in all type A flight. This highlights one path to efficient acceleration and/or climb.

3.2.2   Case 2: Horizontal Acceleration ($P_s = Vd V/g_0$ dt)

Given: $dh/dt = 0$, $n = 1$ ($L = W$), full thrust ($T = \alpha T_{SL}$) and values of h, $V_{initial}$, and V_{final}.

Under these conditions

$$u = \frac{C_D + C_{DR}}{C_L} \frac{\beta}{\alpha}\left(\frac{W_{TO}}{T_{SL}}\right)$$

so that Eq. (3.14) becomes

$$\frac{W_f}{W_i} = \exp\left\{-\frac{(C_1/M + C_2)}{a_{std}}\left[\frac{\Delta(V^2/2g_0)}{1 - [(C_D + C_{DR})/C_L](\beta/\alpha)(W_{TO}/T_{SL})}\right]\right\}$$

$$(3.19)$$

where Eq. (3.18) has been used, and

$$\Delta V^2 = V_{final}^2 - V_{initial}^2$$

Appropriate average values of α, β, θ, V, and $(C_D + C_{DR})/C_L$ for the speed interval should be used, unless the quantity $(C_1/M + C_2)/(1 - u)$ varies too much for acceptable accuracy. Then the integration is accomplished by breaking the acceleration into several smaller intervals and applying Eq. (3.19) to each. The overall W_f/W_i is then the product of the separate results.

Please note that, as stated earlier, the term $(C_D/C_L)(\beta/\alpha)(W_{TO}/T_{SL})$ represents the fraction of the engine thrust work that is dissipated, while $\{1 - (C_D/C_L)(\beta/\alpha) \times (W_{TO}/T_{SL})\}$ is the fraction invested in kinetic energy. Low drag and high thrust are again the ingredients of efficient energy conversion.

3.2.3   Case 3: Climb and Acceleration ($P_s = dh/dt + Vd V/g_0$ dt)

Given: $n = 1$, ($L = W$), full thrust ($T = \alpha T_{SL}$), and values of $h_{initial}$, h_{final}, and V_{final}.

This solution combines those of Cases 1 and 2, with the same qualifying remarks. The result is

$$\frac{W_f}{W_i} = \exp\left\{-\frac{(C_1/M + C_2)}{a_{std}}\left[\frac{\Delta(h + V^2/2g_0)}{1 - [(C_D + C_{DR})/C_L](\beta/\alpha)(W_{TO}/T_{SL})}\right]\right\}$$

$$(3.20)$$

Special care must be taken in the application of Eq. (3.20) because h and V are truly independent of each other until the flight trajectory is chosen. The P_s diagram (e.g., Fig. 2.E5) can provide excellent guidance in the selection of the h vs V path, especially if a maximum P_s trajectory is desired. Also, as already noted, the term $[(C_D + C_{DR})/C_L](\beta/\alpha)(W_{TO}/T_{SL})$ represents the fraction of the engine thrust work that is dissipated, and $\{1 - [(C_D + C_{DR})/C_L](\beta/\alpha)(W_{TO}/T_{SL})\}$ is the fraction that is invested in mechanical energy (i.e., potential plus kinetic) or energy height.

3.2.4 Case 4: Takeoff Acceleration (P_s = Vd V/g₀ dt)

Given: $dh/dt = 0$, full thrust $(T = \alpha T_{SL})$ and values of P, D, $C_{L\max}$, k_{TO}, and R.

Under these conditions Eq. (3.14) becomes

$$\frac{W_f}{W_i} = \exp\left\{-\frac{(C_1 + C_2 M)\sqrt{\theta}}{g_0}\left(\frac{V_{TO}}{1 - u}\right)\right\}$$ (3.21)

where u can be obtained from Eq. (2.21) as

$$u = \left\{\xi_{TO}\left(\frac{q}{\beta}\right)\left(\frac{S}{W_{TO}}\right) + \mu_{TO}\right\}\frac{\beta}{\alpha}\left(\frac{W_{TO}}{T_{SL}}\right)$$ (3.22)

and V_{TO} is given by Eq. (2.20) and M is an average value during takeoff.

3.2.5 Case 5: Constant Altitude/Speed Cruise (P_s = 0)

Given: $dh/dt = 0$, $dV/dt = 0$, $n = 1$ $(L = W)$, and values of h, V, and cruise range Δs.

Under these conditions, and replacing Δt with $\Delta s/V$, Eqs. (3.16) and (3.18) become

$$\frac{W_f}{W_i} = \exp\left\{-\frac{(C_1/M + C_2)}{a_{std}}\left(\frac{C_D + C_{DR}}{C_L}\right)\Delta s\right\}$$ (3.23)

where C_L is obtained by setting lift equal to weight and C_D is computed from Eq. (2.9). Because $(C_D + C_{DR})/C_L$ will vary as fuel is consumed and the weight of the aircraft decreases, this result is not, strictly speaking, exact. Hence, it might become advisable to break the cruise into several intervals and apply Eq. (3.23) to each. The type B Cases 6–10 that follow are, however, exact integrals.

Equation (3.23) and the variants that follow in Case 7 are close relatives of the familiar Breguet range formula.[3] The reciprocal of the collection of terms preceding the range Δs in the exponent is customarily referred to as the range factor (RF). Thus, for a given weight fraction, the range is directly proportional to the RF. The endurance factor (EF) of Case 8 belongs to the same family and enjoys qualities quite similar to those of the RF.

3.2.6 Case 6: Constant Altitude/Speed Turn (P_s = 0)

Given: $dh/dt = 0$, $dV/dt = 0$, and values of h, V, $n > 1$, and number of turns N.

This situation can be treated much the same as Case 5, except that $L = nW$. The duration of the turning can be shown, with the help of Eq. (2.17), to equal

$$\Delta t = \frac{2\pi R_c N}{V} = \frac{2\pi NV}{g_0 \sqrt{n^2 - 1}} \qquad (3.24)$$

Under these conditions Eqs. (3.16) and (3.24) become

$$\frac{W_f}{W_i} = \exp\left\{-(C_1 + C_2 M)\sqrt{\theta}\left(\frac{C_D + C_{DR}}{C_L/n}\right)\frac{2\pi NV}{g_0 \sqrt{n^2 - 1}}\right\} \qquad (3.25)$$

where C_L is obtained from the expression

$$C_L = \frac{n\beta}{q}\left(\frac{W_{TO}}{S}\right)$$

and C_D is computed from Eq. (2.9). Because the duration of the turn is usually a small fraction of the mission, the values in Eq. (3.25) may be regarded as constant.

3.2.7 Case 7: Best Subsonic Cruise Mach Number and Altitude (BCM/BCA) ($P_s = 0$)

Given: $dh/dt = 0$, $dV/dt = 0$, $n = 1$ ($L = W$), and the value of cruise range Δs.

Subsonic cruise is usually the most important portion of any mission because it uses the largest amount of the onboard fuel. Hence, the analysis must be as accurate as possible and the results applied to minimize fuel usage. Under these conditions, and replacing dt with ds/V, Eq. (3.15) becomes

$$\frac{dW}{W} = -\frac{(C_1/M + C_2)}{a_{std}}\left(\frac{C_D + C_{DR}}{C_L}\right)ds \qquad (3.26)$$

where the level flight relationship Eq. (3.18) has been used.

From Eq. (3.26), it is obvious that aircraft weight reduction and fuel consumption are minimized by operating at the lowest possible value of $(C_1/M + C_2) \times [(C_D + C_{DR})/C_L]$. This is known as the "best" cruise condition and the individual parameters associated with it are referred to as C_L^*, C_D^*, and M^*. Finding them for a given aircraft is not difficult, as the following will demonstrate for one of the common type represented by Fig. 2.E1a.

First, note that below the critical drag rise Mach number M_{CRIT}, neither C_L nor C_D depend on M. In this range,

$$\frac{C_D + C_{DR}}{C_L} = \frac{K_1 C_L^2 + K_2 C_L + C_{D0} + C_{DR}}{C_L}$$

A minimum for $(C_D + C_{DR})/C_L$ can be found by differentiating the preceding equation with respect to C_L and setting the result equal to zero. This leads to

$$\left(\frac{C_D + C_{DR}}{C_L}\right)^* = \sqrt{4(C_{D0} + C_{DR})K_1} + K_2 \qquad (3.27a)$$

at

$$C_L^* = \sqrt{(C_{D0} + C_{DR})/K_1} \tag{3.27b}$$

This may be substituted into Eq. (3.27) to yield

$$(C_D + C_{DR})^* = 2(C_{D0} + C_{DR}) + K_2\sqrt{(C_{D0} + C_{DR})/K_1} \tag{3.27c}$$

With practice, you may come to appreciate the fact that Case 7 binds constraint and mission analysis together. Equation (3.27c) is the same condition of minimum thrust and drag discussed in Sec. 2.2.1. The need to minimize subsonic cruise fuel consumption will influence the final choice of W_{TO}/S.

Next, because the lowest achievable value of $(C_D + C_{DR})/C_L$ is constant below M_{CRIT}, it follows that $(C_1/M + C_2)[(C_D + C_{DR})/C_L]$ decreases as M increases. Once the transonic drag rise M_{CRIT} is reached, the situation changes rapidly (see Fig. 2.E1a). Further increases in M cause $[(C_D + C_{DR})/C_L]$ and eventually $(C_1/M + C_2)[(C_D + C_{DR})/C_L]$ to increase. Rather than search for the exact $M > M_{CRIT}$ at which the minimum value of $(C_1/M + C_2)[(C_D + C_{DR})/C_L]$ is reached, it is a slightly conservative and entirely suitable approximation to take $M^* = M_{CRIT} = BCM$, whence

$$\left[(C_1/M + C_2)\frac{C_D + C_{DR}}{C_L}\right]^* = \left(\frac{C_1}{M_{CRIT}} + C_2\right)(\sqrt{4(C_{D0} + C_{DR})K_1} + K_2)$$

which may be substituted into Eq. (3.26) to yield

$$\frac{dW}{W} = -\left\{\left(\frac{C_1}{M_{CRIT}} + C_2\right)(\sqrt{4(C_{D0} + C_{DR})K_1} + K_2)\right\}\frac{ds}{a_{std}} \tag{3.28}$$

This may be directly integrated to yield the equivalent of Eq. (3.16),

$$\frac{W_f}{W_i} = \exp\left\{-\left(\frac{C_1}{M_{CRIT}} + C_2\right)(\sqrt{4(C_{D0} + C_{DR})K_1} + K_2)\frac{\Delta s}{a_{std}}\right\} \tag{3.29}$$

The range factor (RF). The range factor can be employed to more accurately determine the best cruise Mach number and altitude (*BCM/BCA*) when the variation of the drag polar coefficients with Mach number is known. First note that Eq. (3.26) can be written in terms of the range factor as

$$\frac{dW}{W} = -\frac{ds}{RF} \tag{3.30}$$

where

$$RF \doteq \frac{L}{D + R}\frac{V}{TSFC} = \frac{C_L}{C_D + C_{DR}}\frac{a_{std}}{C_1/M + C_2} \tag{3.31}$$

The flight condition with the maximum range factor (*RF*) corresponds is the best cruise Mach number and altitude (*BCM/BCA*). The AEDsys software can calculate and plot contours of range factor (*RF*) for a range of altitudes and velocities (similar to the P_s contours of Fig. 2.E5), making it easy for the user to determine the best cruise conditions. For cruises where the range factor (RF) is essentially constant, Eq. (3.30) can be integrated to obtain

$$\frac{W_f}{W_i} = \exp\left\{-\frac{\Delta s}{RF}\right\} \tag{3.32}$$

BCM flight path.   Finally, because the aircraft must sustain its weight under this condition, the altitude may not be arbitrarily chosen, but is obtained from Eq. (2.6) in the form

$$qC_LS = \frac{\gamma P M^2}{2}C_LS = W$$

or

$$\delta = \frac{P}{P_{std}} = \frac{2\beta}{\gamma P_{std}M_{CRIT}^2}\frac{1}{\sqrt{(C_{D0}+C_{DR})/K_1}}\left(\frac{W_{TO}}{S}\right) \tag{3.33}$$

which is used to find the altitude of "best" cruise or *BCA*. Since β must gradually diminish as the mission progresses, this last result shows that δ must gradually decrease and the altitude must gradually increase. Because the flight Mach number is fixed at M_{CRIT}, it also follows that the speed, which is proportional to $\sqrt{\theta}$, must gradually decrease until the tropopause is reached and the speed becomes constant. In most cases, these changes occur so slowly that the assumption of $P_s = 0$ remains true. You may find these relationships worth contemplating during your next long distance flight.

3.2.8   Case 8: Subsonic Loiter ($P_s = 0$)

Given: $dh/dt = 0$, $dV/dt = 0$, $n = 1$ ($L = W$), and the value of flight duration Δt.

Under these conditions Eq. (3.15) becomes

$$\frac{dW}{W} = -(C_1 + C_2M)\sqrt{\theta}\left(\frac{C_D + C_{DR}}{C_L}\right)dt \tag{3.34}$$

where the level flight relationship of Eq. (3.18) has been used.

The endurance factor (EF).   Even though subsonic loiter does not ordinarily consume a large portion of the onboard fuel, the amount consumed should still be minimized. Equation (3.34) does not lend itself easily to this task, and the "best" solution must be found with the search procedures of the AEDsys software. Equation (3.34) can be written in terms of the endurance factor (EF) as

$$\frac{dW}{W} = -\frac{dt}{EF} \tag{3.35}$$

where

$$EF \doteq \frac{L}{D+R}\frac{1}{TSFC} = \frac{C_L}{C_D+C_{DR}}\frac{1}{(C_1+C_2M)\sqrt{\theta}} \tag{3.36}$$

The flight condition with the maximum endurance factor (EF) corresponds is the best loiter Mach number and altitude. The AEDsys software can calculate and plot contours of endurance factor (EF) for a range of altitudes and velocities (similar to the P_s contours of Fig. 2.E5), making it easy for the user to determine the best loiter conditions. For loiters where the endurance factor (EF) is essentially constant, Eq. (3.35) can be integrated to obtain

$$\frac{W_f}{W_i} = \exp\left\{-\frac{\Delta t}{EF}\right\} \tag{3.37}$$

Approximate solution.   Nevertheless, a suboptimal but useful solution can be found when necessary by hand by assuming that the aircraft is flown at the minimum value of $(C_D + C_{DR})/C_L$ as given by Eq. (3.27a) and employing Eq. (2.6) to find the loiter Mach number

$$M_L^2 = \frac{2\beta}{\gamma\, P_{SL}\delta}\, \frac{1}{\sqrt{(C_{D0} + C_{DR})/K_1}} \left(\frac{W_{TO}}{S}\right) \tag{3.38}$$

whence

$$\frac{\mathrm{d}W}{W} = -(C_1 + C_2 M_L)\sqrt{\theta}\left(\frac{C_D + C_{DR}}{C_L}\right)^* \mathrm{d}t \tag{3.39}$$

and, as in Eq. (3.16)

$$\frac{W_f}{W_i} = \exp\left\{-(C_1 + C_2 M_L)\sqrt{\theta}\left(\frac{C_D + C_{DR}}{C_L}\right)^* \Delta t\right\} \tag{3.40}$$

In general, the countering influences of δ in Eq. (3.38) for M_L and θ render Eqs. (3.39) and (3.40) relatively insensitive to altitude provided that M_L is less than M_{CRIT}. Thus, a reasonable but somewhat conservative estimate of the weight fraction can be obtained by evaluating Eq. (3.40) at an altitude in the range of 20–30 kft. If the flight altitude is *also* given, the foregoing discussion still applies, except that M_L is determined from Eq. (3.38) and cannot be freely chosen.

The two cases that follow belong to type B because $P_s = 0$, even though full thrust ($T = \alpha T_{SL}$) is being applied.

3.2.9   Case 9: Warm-Up ($P_s = 0$)

Given: $\mathrm{d}h/\mathrm{d}t = 0$, $\mathrm{d}V/\mathrm{d}t = 0$, $M = 0$, $D = 0$, $R = T = \alpha T_{SL}$ and values of h and warm-up time Δt.

Under these conditions Eq. (3.15) becomes

$$\mathrm{d}W = -C_1\sqrt{\theta}(\alpha T_{SL})\,\mathrm{d}t \tag{3.41}$$

which may be integrated and rearranged to reach the desired result

$$\frac{W_f}{W_i} = 1 - C_1\sqrt{\theta}\frac{\alpha}{\beta}\left(\frac{T_{SL}}{W_{TO}}\right)\Delta t \tag{3.42}$$

where β is evaluated at the beginning of warm-up.

3.2.10   Case 10: Takeoff Rotation ($P_s = 0$)

Given: $dh/dt = 0$, $dV/dt = 0$, $(D + R) = T = \alpha T_{SL}$ and values of h, M_{TO}, and rotation time t_R.

Under these conditions Eq. (3.15) becomes

$$dW = -(C_1 + C_2 M_{TO})\sqrt{\theta}(\alpha T_{SL})\, dt \tag{3.43}$$

which may be integrated and rearranged to reach the desired result

$$\frac{W_f}{W_i} = 1 - (C_1 + C_2 M_{TO})\sqrt{\theta}\frac{\alpha}{\beta}\left(\frac{T_{SL}}{W_{TO}}\right)t_R \tag{3.44}$$

where β is evaluated at the beginning of rotation.

3.2.11   Case 11: Constant Energy Height Maneuver ($P_s = 0$)

Given: $\Delta z_e = 0$, $n = 1$ ($L = W$), and the values of $h_{initial}$, h_{final}, $V_{initial}$, and V_{final}.

This special case corresponds to the situation in which the potential energy is being exchanged in a climb or a dive for an essentially equal amount of kinetic energy. The required thrust work of the engine is only that necessary to balance the energy dissipated by the aerodynamic drag along the path. Because W_f is not much different from W_i for such flight, it is not necessary to perform an elaborate evaluation of relevant parameters along the complete trajectory. Instead, a common sense estimate of the average values of M, θ, and $(C_D + C_{DR})/C_L$ will suffice.

Under these conditions Eqs. (3.16) and (3.18) become

$$\frac{W_f}{W_i} = \exp\left\{-(C_1 + C_2 M)\sqrt{\theta}\left(\frac{C_D + C_{DR}}{C_L}\right)\Delta t\right\} \tag{3.45}$$

where C_L is obtained by setting lift equal to weight and C_D is computed from Eq. (2.9). All terms in Eq. (3.45) are calculated at the average altitude (h_{avg}) and initial energy height (z_{ei}). The associated velocity is designated as V_{mid} and calculated from the kinetic energy at the average energy state using

$$V_{mid} = \sqrt{2g_0(z_{ei} - h_{avg})}$$

The maneuver time interval Δt is best obtained by recognizing that the maneuver vertical distance is $h_{final} - h_{initial}$ and assuming that the vertical speed is some fraction of the midspeed (V_{mid}).

3.2.12   General Determination of W_{TO}

Equation (3.1) is the most fruitful starting point for evaluating W_{TO}, as well as for understanding the factors that control W_{TO}. Regarding the latter, it is useful and illuminating to rewrite Eq. (3.1) in the form

$$W_{TO} = W_P \bigg/ \left(1 - \frac{W_F}{W_{TO}} - \frac{W_E}{W_{TO}}\right) \tag{3.1a}$$

This relationship reveals that W_{TO} is directly proportional to the W_P (as required by the customer), and inversely proportional to the difference between one and the fuel weight fraction (based on aerodynamic and propulsion technologies) and the structural weight fraction (based on material and structural technologies).

This is a scenario rich with heroes and villains, real and imaginary. To increase your appreciation of the stakes, consider the typical situation where the fuel and structural weight fractions add up to about 0.9, and W_{TO} is therefore about 10 W_P. On the one hand, if the fuel plus structural weight fraction turned out to be only 5% higher than expected, W_{TO} would be more than 18 W_P. On the other hand, if the fuel plus structural weight fraction could be made 5% lower than expected, W_{TO} would be less than 7 W_P. Thus, this highly nonlinear equation magnifies both the cost of failure and the reward of technological advance.

This relationship also explains the attraction of novel aircraft concepts. The unpiloted air vehicle (UAV), for example, has less payload (e.g., no pilot plus equipment) and a smaller structural weight fraction (e.g., no cockpit, canopy, or environmental and protective gear) than its piloted counterpart. The result is a dramatically smaller, lighter, and less expensive vehicle for the same mission.

The Mission Analysis subroutine of AEDsys allows W_{TO} to be determined by an iterative process, as follows. For the given mission profile, W_P, an initial estimate of W_{TO}, and the corresponding allowable W_E/W_{TO} (e.g., Figs. 3.1 and 3.2 or Sec. 3.3.1), the vehicle is flown from takeoff to landing. Any remaining payload or reserve fuel is then removed in order to determine the remaining weight, which equals W_E, and allows the actual W_E/W_{TO} to be calculated. If the latter value exceeds the allowable W_E/W_{TO}, a higher value of W_{TO} must be selected and the process repeated, and vice versa. This process continues until a satisfactory level of convergence is reached. Since W_E/W_{TO} is weakly dependent upon W_{TO} (see Sec. 3.3.1), unexpectedly large changes of W_{TO} are generally required to correct for relatively small differences in W_E/W_{TO}. This is, of course, very good news when the latter is smaller than allowable, but very bad news otherwise.

3.2.13 Algebraic Calculation of W_{TO}

Equation (3.1) may also be used to calculate the takeoff weight algebraically (i.e., by hand). It will be convenient in this derivation to use the terminology

$$\frac{W_f}{W_i} = \prod_{i\,f} \le 1 \tag{3.46}$$

for the weight ratio of mission legs where *only* fuel is consumed. For example, if the consecutive junctions of the mission are labeled with sequential cardinal numbers, such as those of the AAF RFP in Chapter 1, it follows that

$$\frac{W_5}{W_2} = \frac{W_3}{W_2} \times \frac{W_4}{W_3} \times \frac{W_5}{W_4} = \prod_{2\,3} \prod_{3\,4} \prod_{4\,5} = \prod_{2\,5}$$

For the special case where the expendable payload is delivered at some point "j" in the mission, the terminology W_f/W_i or $\prod$ is not used. Write instead

$$\frac{W_j - W_{PE}}{W_j} = 1 - \frac{W_{PE}}{W_j} \tag{3.47}$$

When W_F and W_E are expressed in terms of W_{TO}, Eq. (3.1) in the form

$$W_{TO} = W_F + W_E + W_{PE} + W_{PP} \qquad (3.48a)$$

leads to the desired relationship for W_{TO}. For a mission with n junctions and payload delivery at junction $j(j < n)$, W_F is expressed in terms of W_{TO} by the sum of the aircraft weight decrements between takeoff and junction j and between junction j (after the delivery of W_{PE}) and landing thusly

$$W_F = \left\{ W_{TO} - W_{TO} \prod_{1\,j} \right\} + \left\{ \left(W_{TO} \prod_{1\,j} - W_{PE} \right) - \left(W_{TO} \prod_{1\,j} - W_{PE} \right) \prod_{j\,n} \right\}$$

which reduces to

$$W_F = W_{TO}\left(1 - \prod_{1\,n} \right) - W_{PE}\left(1 - \prod_{j\,n} \right) \qquad (3.48b)$$

The historical correlations of Figs. 3.1 and 3.2 and Sec. 3.3.1 relate W_E to W_{TO} via

$$\Gamma \doteq \frac{W_E}{W_{TO}} = f(W_{TO}) \qquad (3.48c)$$

where $f(W_{TO})$ is given by Eqs. (3.50–3.53). Combining Eqs. (3.48a), (3.48b), and (3.48c) and solving for W_{TO} yields

$$W_{TO} = \frac{W_{PP} + W_{PE} \displaystyle\prod_{j\,n}}{\displaystyle\prod_{1\,n} - \Gamma} \qquad (3.49)$$

This equation carries the same information found in Eq. (3.1a) and allows the straightforward calculation of W_{TO}. Of special note are the facts that W_{PP} matters more than W_{PE} because it is carried the whole way, and that the original form of Eq. (3.1a) is recovered when W_{PE} is zero. This approach also produces useful results when payload is expended at multiple junctions in the mission.

An initial estimate of W_{TO} must be made during this part of the design process in order to place values upon the W_{PE}/W_{TO} of the payload deliveries and the allowable Γ. If the initial estimate of W_{TO} is different from the value given by Eq. (3.46), then the $\prod$s computed after payload deliveries and/or the Γ taken from Fig. 3.1 or 3.2 or Sec. 3.3.1 will be in error and an iterative solution of Eq. (3.49) will be necessary. Because both the $\prod$s and Γ vary slowly with the estimate of W_{TO}, this iteration process converges rapidly.

3.3 Aircraft Weight and Fuel Consumption Data

A preliminary estimate of the ratio of aircraft empty weight (W_E) to takeoff weight (W_{TO}) is required to solve for the aircraft takeoff weight as indicated by Eqs. (3.48c) and (3.49). In addition, the thrust specific fuel consumption (*TSFC*) must be estimated for each phase/segment of the mission to determine its weight fraction [see Eqs. (3.12) and (3.17) or (3.32)]. The following material is provided to help make these preliminary estimates.

3.3.1 Empty Aircraft Weight Fraction (Γ)

As indicated by Figs. 3.1 and 3.2, there is a relationship between aircraft empty weight (W_E), aircraft takeoff weight (W_{TO}), and the type of aircraft. Several authors[3,4] have performed correlations of W_E to W_{TO}, which are the bases of the following results:

Cargo aircraft: $\qquad\qquad \Gamma = 1.26 W_{TO}^{-0.08}$ $\qquad\qquad\qquad\qquad$ (3.50)

Passenger aircraft: $\qquad\quad \Gamma = 1.02 W_{TO}^{-0.06}$ $\qquad\qquad\qquad\qquad$ (3.51)

Fighter aircraft: $\qquad\qquad \Gamma = 2.34 W_{TO}^{-0.13}$ $\qquad\qquad\qquad\qquad$ (3.52)

Twin turboprop aircraft: $\quad \Gamma = 0.96 W_{TO}^{-0.05}$ $\qquad\qquad\qquad\qquad$ (3.53)

3.3.2 Installed Thrust Specific Fuel Consumption (TSFC)

The installed thrust specific fuel consumption of an aircraft engine varies with Mach number, altitude, type of engine, and throttle conditions. Estimates of *TSFC* can be obtained from engine manufacturer's published data or from the output of performance (off-design) cycle analysis (see Chapter 5) compensated by installation losses. Another source is measurements of the airframe/engine system obtained during flight test. The following models of *TSFC* (expected for advanced engines in the 2010 era and beyond) are provided to help these preliminary estimates. The units of *TSFC* are 1/hour (h^{-1}).

High bypass ratio turbofan engine ($M < 0.9$):

$$TSFC = (0.45 + 0.54 M_0)\sqrt{\theta} \qquad\qquad (3.54)$$

Low bypass ratio mixed turbofan engine:

$$TSFC = (0.9 + 0.30 M_0)\sqrt{\theta} \text{ mil power} \qquad\qquad (3.55a)$$

$$TSFC = (1.6 + 0.27 M_0)\sqrt{\theta} \text{ max power} \qquad\qquad (3.55b)$$

Turbojet engine:

$$TSFC = (1.1 + 0.30 M_0)\sqrt{\theta} \text{ mil power} \qquad\qquad (3.56a)$$

$$TSFC = (1.5 + 0.23 M_0)\sqrt{\theta} \text{ max power} \qquad\qquad (3.56b)$$

Turboprop engine:

$$TSFC = (0.18 + 0.8 M_0)\sqrt{\theta} \qquad\qquad (3.57)$$

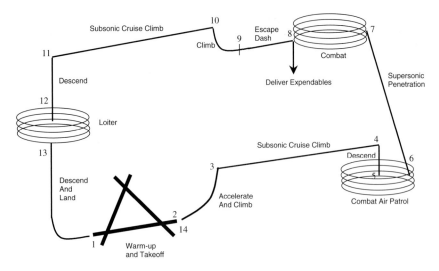

Fig. 3.E1   Mission profile by phases.

3.4   Example Mission Analysis

The Request for Proposal (RFP) mission for the Air-to-Air Fighter (AAF) of Chapter 1 will be flown on paper in this example. The purpose initially is to find the weight fraction (W_f/W_i) of each mission phase and then a takeoff weight (W_{TO}) estimate. Our ultimate goal is to use this estimate of W_{TO} and the value of thrust loading (T_{SL}/W_{TO}) selected in the Chapter 2 example outlined in Sec. 2.4 to determine the AAF installed thrust requirement (T_{SL}). The wing loading (W_{TO}/S) selected and W_{TO} will also give us our first estimate of the AAF wing area. The mission to be flown is depicted in Fig. 3.E1 and is given with more detail in Table 3.E1.

3.4.1   Weight Fraction Analysis

In addition to the design tools of this chapter, certain other information is re-quired to complete the weight fraction calculations. These supportive materials are the AAF preliminary data contained in Figs. 2.E1 and 2.E5, Sec. 3.3, and the standard atmosphere tables in Appendix B. From Eq. (3.55), the thrust specific fuel consumption (*TSFC*) in units of 1/hour is $(1.6 + 0.27\,M_0)\sqrt{\theta}$ for maxi-mum power and $(0.9 + 0.3\,M_0)\sqrt{\theta}$ for military power and lower. Figure 2.E5 was used to determine the minimum time-to-climb path and the result is presented as Fig. 3.E2.

To illustrate the calculation procedure, let us determine the weight fraction of segment E in Mission Phase 2–3 (Table 3.E1). First, please note that we shall round off to four significant digits all numbers recorded for weight fraction calculations in this chapter. However, the recorded numbers are obtained from calculations done by the AEDsys computer program. At times, therefore, you may not reproduce exactly our numbers because of a discrepancy in the significant digits of the input numbers and those used in serial internal calculations.

Table 3.E1   AAF mission

Mission phases	Segments	Condition
1–2	Warm-up and takeoff	2000 ft PA, 100°F
	A—Warm-up	60 s, mil power
	B—Acceleration	$k_{TO} = 1.2$, $\mu_{TO} = 0.05$, max power
	C—Rotation	M_{TO}, $t_R = 3$ s, max power
2–3	Acceleration and climb	Minimum time-to-climb path
	D—Acceleration	M_{TO} to M_{CL}/2000 ft PA, 100°F, mil power
	E—Climb/acceleration	M_{CL}/2000 ft PA, 100°F to BCM/BCA, mil power
3–4	Subsonic cruise climb	BCM/BCA, $\Delta s_{23} + \Delta s_{34} = 150$ n miles
4–5	Descend	BCM/BCA to M_{CAP}/30k ft
5–6	Combat air patrol	30 kft, 20 min
6–7	Supersonic penetration	30,000 ft
	F—Acceleration	M_{CAP} to 1.5M/30k ft, max power
	G—Penetration	1.5M, $\Delta s_F + \Delta s_G = 100$ n miles, no afterburning
7–8	Combat	30,000 ft
	H—Fire AMRAAMs	652 lbf
	I—Turn 1	1.6M, one 360 deg 5g sustained turn, with afterburning
	J—Turn 2	0.9M, two 360 deg 5g sustained turn, with afterburning
	K—Acceleration	0.8 to 1.6M, $\Delta t \le 50$ s, max power
	L—Fire AIM-9Ls & $\frac{1}{2}$ ammo	657 lbf
8–9	Escape dash	1.5M/30 kft, $\Delta s_{89} = 25$ n miles, no afterburning
9–10	Minimum time climb	1.5M/30 kft to BCM/BCA
10–11	Subsonic cruise climb	BCM/BCA, $\Delta s_{10-11} = 150$ n miles
11–12	Descend	BCM/BCA to M_{loiter}/10 kft
12–13	Loiter	M_{loiter}/10 kft, 20 min
13–14	Descend and land	M_{loiter}/10 kft to 2000 ft PA, 100°F

One may question the wisdom of carrying calculations to four significant figures that are based upon numbers often estimated to be correct to a few percent. The underlying reason is that the $\prod$s are generally the difference between unity and a quantity of the order of 0.01, which is calculated from the estimated numbers— often the exponents of Eqs. (3.14) and (3.16). Therefore, in order to be certain that the small quantity is correct to two significant figures, it is necessary to maintain four places in $\prod$. This should also be understood to emphasize the fact that the weight fraction of fuel consumed ($1 - \prod$) for most flight legs is quite small, but the cumulative effect is what matters.

During segment E, the AAF climbs and accelerates at military power to BCM/BCA along the minimum time-to-climb path of Fig. 3.E2 via the following climb schedule of Table 3.E2.

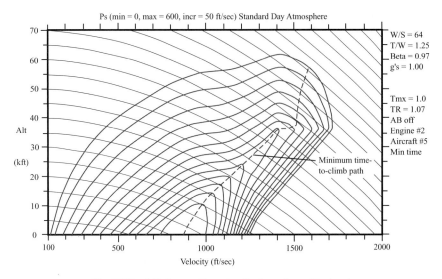

Ps (min = 0, max = 600, incr = 50 ft/sec) Standard Day Atmosphere

W/S = 64
T/W = 1.25
Beta = 0.97
g's = 1.00

Tmx = 1.0
TR = 1.07
AB off
Engine #2
Aircraft #5
Min time

Minimum time-
to-climb path

Alt

(kft)

Velocity (ft/sec)

Fig. 3.E2   Minimum time-to-climb path on P_s chart.

The mid state point is chosen arbitrarily but judiciously in order to obtain reasonable average values. The reader, as ever, is free to vary the mid point selection in order to determine the sensitivity of the results to this choice.

Equation (3.33) of Case 7, with $C_{DR} = 0$, yields the BCA

$$\delta_{BCA} = \frac{P}{P_{std}} = \frac{2\beta(W_{TO}/S)}{\gamma\, P_{std} M_{CRIT}^2}\sqrt{\frac{K_1}{C_{D0}}}$$

where $W_{TO}/S = 64$ lbf/ft^2 and, from Fig. 2.E1a, $M_{CRIT} = 0.9$, $C_{D0} = 0.016$, and $K_1 = 0.18$. From weight fraction calculations preceding segment E, $(\beta_i)_E = 0.9773$, which we can use as an estimate for $\beta = (\beta_i)_E$ so that

$$\delta_{BCA} = 0.1749 \quad \text{and} \quad h \approx 42{,}000 \text{ ft}$$

Table 3.E2   Climb schedule

Altitude, ft	Mach number	Computation interval
2,000 (100°F)	0.70	Initial state point
9,000	0.775	——
16,000	0.85	——
23,000	0.875	Mid state point
30,000	0.90	——
36,000	0.90	——
42,000	0.90	Final state point

Proceeding, then, with the weight fraction calculation for segment E, we have from Case 3, Eq. (3.20), with $C_{DR} = 0$

$$\prod_E = \frac{W_f}{W_i} = \exp\left\{-\frac{(C_1/M + C_2)}{a_{std}}\left[\frac{\Delta(h + V^2/2g_0)}{1 - u}\right]\right\}$$

where

$$u = \frac{C_D}{C_L}\frac{\beta}{\alpha}\left(\frac{W_{TO}}{T_{SL}}\right)$$

For this illustrative calculation we select the single gross interval having the initial, middle, and final state points listed with Table 3.E2. An appropriate average value of u is found using $\beta = \beta_i$ and values C_D/C_L and α at the mid state point. The initial, final, and middle state point values of h and M from Table 3.E2 and $\beta = \beta_i$ are used in conjunction with the following Climb/Acceleration Weight Fraction Calculation Method to find $\prod_E$.

Climb/acceleration weight fraction calculation method

Given:

Initial state point quantities: h_i, M_i, $(a/a_{std})_i$, β_i

Final state point quantities: h_f, M_f, $(a/a_{std})_f$

Middle state point quantities: h, M, θ, δ, θ_0, δ_0, (a/a_{std}), K_1, K_2, C_{D0}

Other quantities: a_{std}, g_0, W_{TO}/S, γ, P_{std}, T_{SL}/W_{TO}, C_1, C_2

Equations:

$$V_i = (a/a_{std})_i a_{std} M_i \qquad u = \frac{C_D}{C_L}\frac{\beta}{\alpha}\left(\frac{W_{TO}}{T_{SL}}\right)$$

$$V_f = (a/a_{std})_f a_{std} M_f \qquad \frac{T\Delta s}{W} = \frac{\Delta z_e}{1 - u}$$

$$\Delta\left(\frac{V^2}{2g_0}\right) = \frac{V_f^2 - V_i^2}{2g_0} \qquad V = (a/a_{std})a_{std} M$$

$$\Delta h = h_f - h_i \qquad \Delta t = \frac{T\Delta s}{W}\frac{1}{V}\frac{\beta}{\alpha}\left(\frac{W_{TO}}{T_{SL}}\right)$$

$$\Delta z_e = \Delta h + \Delta\left(\frac{V^2}{2g_0}\right) \qquad \Delta_s = V\Delta t$$

$$C_L = \frac{2\beta(W_{TO}/S)}{\gamma P_{std}\delta M^2} \qquad \prod_E = \exp\left\{-\frac{(C_1/M + C_2)}{a_{std}}\right.$$

$$\frac{C_D}{C_L} = \frac{K_1 C_L^2 + K_2 C_L + C_{D0}}{C_L} \qquad \left.\times\left[\frac{\Delta(h + V^2/2g_0)}{1 - u}\right]\right\}$$

If max power,

$$\alpha = \alpha_{wet}(\theta_0, TR, \delta_0)$$

If mil power,

$$\alpha = \alpha_{dry}(\theta_0, TR, \delta_0)$$

With

$(a/a_{std})_i = 1.039$	$M = 0.88$	$T_{SL}/W_{TO} = 1.25$
$V_i = 811.7 \, \text{ft/s}$	$C_L = 0.1346$	$u = 0.2780$
$(a/a_{std})_f = 0.8671$	$K_1 = 0.18, K_2 = 0.0$	$T\Delta s/W = 57{,}550 \, \text{ft}$
$V_f = 870.9 \, \text{ft/s}$	$C_{D0} = 0.016$	$(a/a_{std}) = 0.9176$
$(\Delta V^2/2g_0) = 1549 \, \text{ft}$	$C_D = 0.01926$	$V = 901.2 \, \text{ft/s}$
$\Delta h = 40{,}000 \, \text{ft}$	$C_D/C_L = 0.1431$	$\Delta t = 2.068 \, \text{min}$
$\Delta z_e = 41{,}550 \, \text{ft}$	$\theta = 0.8420$	$\Delta s = 18.39 \, \text{n miles}$
$\beta = 0.9773$	$\theta_0 = 0.9724$	$C_1/M + C_2 = 1.323 \, \text{h}^{-1}$
$W_{TO}/S = 64 \, \text{lbf/ft}^2$	$\delta_0 = 0.6706$	
$\delta = 0.4051$	$\alpha_{dry} = 0.4024$	

then

$$\prod_E = 0.9812$$

This weight fraction of 0.9812 means that fuel in the amount $(1 - 0.9812)$ βW_{TO} is consumed as 57,550 ft of weight specific thrust work is produced. The dissipated nonmechanical energy fraction of this work is $u = 0.2780$, while the fraction invested in airplane mechanical energy (Δz_e) is $(1 - u) = 0.7220$, of which 96.27% is potential energy and 3.72% is kinetic energy. The climb time and ground distance covered are 2.068 min and 18.39 n miles, respectively.

At the end of segment E, $\beta_f = \beta_t \prod_E = 0.9589$. Now a new mean value of β for segment E can be estimated and the calculation of $\prod_E$ iterated. When this is done using the average value of $(0.9773 + 0.9589)/2 = 0.9681$, we obtain the same value for $\prod_E$, justifying the use of β_i for β_{avg}. Also the δ_{BCA} calculation can be repeated now using β_f, and we find again that $h \approx 42{,}000$ ft.

This calculation illustrates how a mission leg weight fraction is determined. The results of such calculations for all mission phases are contained in Table 3.E3 and Fig. 3.E3. The detailed computations leading to the data shown there are given in the Sec. 3.4.4 (Complete AAF Weight Fraction Computations).

$$\prod_{1 \, 14} = 0.7152 \quad W_F/W_{TO} = 0.2787$$

$$\prod_{7 \, 14} = 0.8585 \quad \prod_{8 \, 14} = 0.9164$$

Table 3.E3   Summary of results—mission analysis—24,000 lbf W_{TO}

Mission phase	Mission segments	$\beta = W/W_{TO}$ End of leg	$W_f/W_i = \prod\limits_{i\ f}$	Fuel used, lbf	Payload, lbf
1–2 A	Warm-up	0.9895	0.9895	252	——
1–2 B	Takeoff acceleration	0.9853	0.9958	100	——
1–2 C	Takeoff rotation	0.9837	0.9984	39	——
2–3 D	Acceleration	0.9773	0.9935	155	——
2–3 E	Climb/acceleration	0.9584	0.9806	453	——
3–4	Subsonic cruise climb	0.9331	0.9736	607	——
4–5	Descend	0.9331	1.0000	0	——
5–6	Combat air patrol	0.9027	0.9675	729	——
6–7 F	Acceleration	0.8880	0.9837	354	——
6–7 G	Supersonic penetration	0.8331	0.9382	1317	——
7–8 H	Fire AMRAAMs	0.8060	——	0	652
7–8 I	1.6M/5g turn	0.7860	0.9753	478	——
7–8 J	0.9M/5g turns	0.7682	0.9774	427	——
7–8 K	Acceleration	0.7550	0.9828	317	——
7–8 L	Fire AIM-9Ls and $\frac{1}{2}$ ammo	0.7276	——	0	657
8–9	Escape dash	0.7127	0.9795	358	——
9–10	Minimum time climb	0.7106	0.9970	51	——
10–11	Subsonic cruise climb	0.6891	0.9698	516	——
11–12	Descend	0.6891	1.0000	0	——
12–13	Loiter	0.6668	0.9677	535	——
13–14	Descend and land	0.6668	1.0000	0	——
End	Remove permanent payload	0.6106	——	——	1348
Total	——	——	——	6688	2657

3.4.2   Determination of W_{TO}, T_{SL}, and S

The time has come to compute the takeoff weight of the AAF. To do this, information obtained from the RFP, Table 3.E3, and Fig. 3.E4 will be inserted into the equation

$$W_{TO} = \frac{W_{PP} + W_{PE_1}\prod\limits_{7\ 14} + W_{PE_2}\prod\limits_{8\ 14}}{\prod\limits_{1\ 14} - \Gamma}$$

which can be easily recognized as the analytical extension of Eq. (3.49) of Sec. 3.2.12 to this multiple payload release mission.

The quantities appearing on the right-hand side of this equation are evaluated thusly:

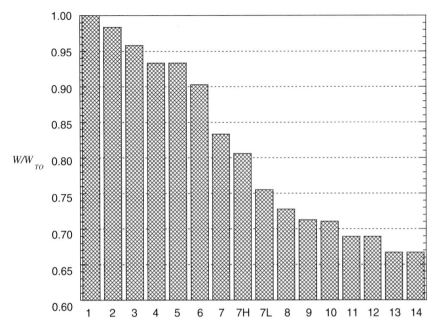

Fig. 3.E3   Fraction of takeoff weight vs mission phase.

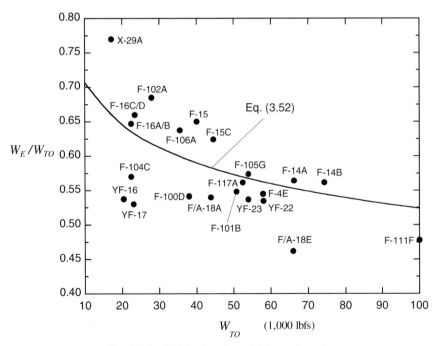

Fig. 3.E4   Weight fraction of fighter aircraft.

W_{PP} = 200 lbf Pilot plus equipment
    270   Cannon
    405   Ammunition feed system
    275   Returning ammunition
    <u>198</u>   Casings weight
  1348 lbf
W_{PE1} = 652 lbf AMRAAMs
W_{PE2} = 382 lbf Sidewinder missiles
    <u>275</u>   Spent ammunition
   657 lbf
 W_P = 2657 lbf
(*Source*: AAF RFP Sec. D.)

$$\prod_{7\,14} = \prod_{7\,8} \cdots \prod_{13\,14} = 0.8585 \qquad \prod_{8\,14} = \prod_{8\,9} \cdots \prod_{13\,14} = 0.9164$$

$$\prod_{1\,14} = \prod_{1\,2} \cdots \prod_{13\,14} = 0.7152$$

(*Source*: Table 3.E3.)
If we assume that W_{TO} = 24,000 lbf, Eq. (3.52) gives

$$\Gamma = W_E/W_{TO} = 0.6306$$

Thus

$$W_{TO} = \frac{1348 + (652)(0.8585) + (657)(0.9164)}{0.7152 - 0.6306} = 29,670\,\text{lbf}$$

This result evidently calls for another iteration, in which the small changes in the $\prod$s after junction 8 are neglected. If we assume that W_{TO} = 28,000 lbf, Eq. (3.32) gives

$$\Gamma = W_E/W_{TO} = 0.6217$$

Thus

$$W_{TO} = \frac{1348 + (652)(0.8585) + (657)(0.9164)}{0.7152 - 0.6217} = 26,840\,\text{lbf}$$

Referring to Fig. 3.2, reproduced here as Fig. 3.E4, it can be seen that this conventional metal version of the AAF would be a little heavier than existing lightweight fighters (e.g., F-16). In the time period of the expected introduction and serial manufacture of the AAF, the available nonmetals that can be used with confidence will reduce Γ for aircraft of this size by approximately 3 to 5%. With this new assumption in hand, W_{TO} is recalculated for the assumed W_{TO} of 24,000 lbf and a conservative estimate of 3% empty weight savings,

$$W_{TO} = \frac{1348 + (652)(0.8585) + (657)(0.9164)}{0.7152 - 0.97 \times 0.6306} = 26,840\,\text{lbf}$$

For an assumed W_{TO} of 24,150 lbf, the resulting W_{TO} is 24,150 lbf.

The conclusion, then, is that the AAF can have a practical (and affordable) size, but only if reliable nonmetallics having competitive strength, durability, and reparability become available according to schedule. Because the choices of $T_{SL}/W_{TO} = 1.25$ and $W_{TO}/S = 64.0$ lbf/ft^2 have already been made, the description of the AAF at this stage of design, in dimensional terms to three significant figures, using $W_F/W_{TO} = 0.2787$, is

$$
\begin{aligned}
W_{TO} &= 24{,}000 \text{ lbf} \\
T_{SL} &= 30{,}000 \text{ lbf} \\
S &= 375 \text{ ft}^2 \\
W_P &= 2660 \text{ lbf} \\
W_E &= 14{,}650 \text{ lbf} \\
W_F &= 6{,}690 \text{ lbf}
\end{aligned}
$$

This information can be used to generate a number of perspectives on the nature and shape of the corresponding aircraft. For example, because afterburning military engines ordinarily have T_{SL} in the range of 15,000–35,000 lbf, the decision may remain open as to whether the AAF is a single- or twin-engine design. Further, if it is assumed that the wing is a delta planform with an aspect ratio of 2, the total wing span will be approximately 27 ft. Because the takeoff payload fraction (W_P/W_{TO}) of fighter aircraft is usually in the range of 0.05–0.10, the AAF value of 0.111 shows that it is quite a workhorse. For further reference, W_P/W_{TO} for the largest cargo and transport aircraft is in the range of only 0.15–0.25.

3.4.3 First Reprise

This is the first opportunity to evaluate some of the key assumptions that have been made along the way. Hopefully, they will be found to be sufficiently accurate that the present results are acceptable. Otherwise, it may be necessary to reiterate the process up to this point with new assumptions.

During the calculation of various other boundaries on the constraint diagram, it was necessary to assume values for the weight fraction (β). In fact, β was taken to be 1.0 at takeoff, 0.56 at landing, and 0.78 everywhere else (an estimate of the aircraft maneuver weight). The maneuver weight (50% fuel, 2 AIM-9Ls, and $\frac{1}{2}$ ammunition) and its associated β can be estimated now that the aircraft takeoff weight has been determined. The easiest method is to subtract the weight of $\frac{1}{2}$ fuel, AMRAAMs, and $\frac{1}{2}$ ammunition from the takeoff weight (W_{TO}) to obtain a maneuver weight of 19,730 lbf or $\beta = 0.8221$. Because this weight fraction is greater than the estimated 0.78 used in the constraint analysis of Chapter 2, the associated constraint lines will require a larger thrust loading for each wing loading. In addition the results of the mission analysis give a better estimate of the takeoff and landing weight fractions (see Table 3.E3). The new estimates for β resulting from the mission analysis and the estimate of the maneuver weight encourage a reconsideration of the legs that bound the solution space of Fig. 2.E3, as summarized next:

1) Takeoff, Mission Phase 1–2: Because the real β must be less than 1.0, the takeoff constraint boundary is conservative and is less critical than originally estimated.

2) Combat Acceleration: The maneuver β value of 0.8221 is greater than the initial estimate of 0.78, and therefore this constraint requires a larger thrust loading of 0.969 at a wing loading of 64 lbf/ft^2, more than originally estimated.

3) Supercruise, Mission Phase 6–7 and Maneuver Weight: Here the initial β value for mission phase 6–7 of 0.8880 is higher than the initial estimate, and the required thrust loading increases to 0.934 at a wing loading of 64 lbf/ft^2, much less than the selected thrust loading of 1.25. The maneuver β value requires a thrust loading of 0.930 at a wing loading of 64 lbf/ft^2, less than that of mission phase 6–7.

4) 5g turn at 0.9M/30 kft, Maneuver Weight: Here the maneuver β value for turn is higher than the initial estimate, and the required thrust loading increases to 1.261 at a wing loading of 64 lbf/ft^2, slightly more than the selected thrust loading of 1.25. If the difference were larger, a reconsideration of the thrust loading would be appropriate, but this small change does not warrant a reselection. Chapter 6 will better define the required thrust loading.

5) 5g turn at 1.6M/30 kft, Maneuver Weight: Here the maneuver β value for turn is higher than the initial estimate, and the required thrust loading increases to 0.931 at a wing loading of 64 lbf/ft^2.

6) Landing, Mission Phase 13–14: In the calculation of landing distance using a drag chute (Sec. 2.4, Mission Phase 13–14), it was assumed that the wing area (S) was 500 ft^2, whereas the presently derived value is 375 ft^2. Substituting the new value would have the effect of increasing the chute drag coefficient to 0.7131. When combined with the new β value of 0.6668, the W_{TO}/S boundary is moved to 64 lbf/ft^2.

7) 1.8M/40 kft, Maneuver Weight: Here the maneuver β value for turn is higher than the initial estimate, and the required thrust loading increases to 0.728 at a wing loading of 64 lbf/ft^2, much less than the selected thrust loading of 1.25.

A revised constraint diagram is given in Fig. 3.E5. Note that the AAF design point is now on the landing constraint line, slightly below the 0.9M/30 kft 5g turn line, and above the other constraint lines. Further work in this textbook will focus on the engine and the design thrust loading (T_{SL}/W_{TO}) may change from its current design value of 1.25. However the wing loading (W_{TO}/S) is assumed to remain at 64 lbf/ft^2.

3.4.4 Complete AAF Weight Fraction Computations

The RFP mission of the AAF is flown in this section to find the weight fraction of each mission segment and phase. These calculations are the source of the data given in Table 3.E3 and Fig. 3.E3. The same procedure is used in each weight fraction calculation. First, the applicable weight fraction equation from Sec. 3.2 is written. Next, data are given to determine the values of all quantities in the order they appear from right to left in the weight fraction equation. Finally, the weight fraction and the accumulated β are calculated. Please note that for all mission legs we shall use β_i for β_{avg} and $K_2 = 0$.

Careful note should be taken of the fact that these hand calculations completely duplicate the AEDsys Mission Analysis computations obtained by using the AAF.AED file. Any minor differences are simply the result of the cumulative

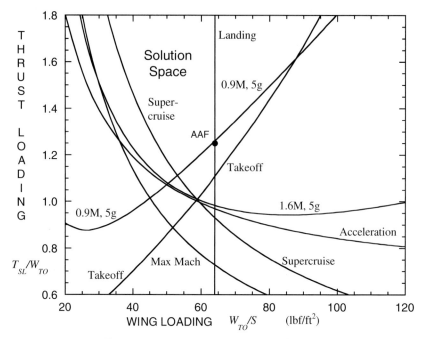

Fig. 3.E5   Revised AAF constraint diagram.

effects of rounding off. Thus we see that one of the motivating forces for carrying four significant figures is to minimize the impact of these small imperfections on the overall results.

Mission phase 1–2: Warm-up and takeoff.   This phase consists of segments A (Warm-up), B (Takeoff Acceleration), and C (Takeoff Rotation).
A) Warm-up.   2000 ft PA, 100°F, 60 s, mil power.
From Case 9, Eq. (3.42)

$$\prod_A = 1 - C_1 \sqrt{\theta} \frac{\alpha}{\beta} \left(\frac{T_{SL}}{W_{TO}} \right) \Delta t$$

With

$\theta = 1.0796 \qquad \delta = 0.9298 \qquad M_0 = 0 \quad \theta_0 = 1.0796 \quad \delta_0 = 0.9298$

$\alpha_{dry} = 0.5390 \quad T_{SL}/W_{TO} = 1.25 \quad \beta = 1.0 \quad \Delta t = 60\,\text{s} \qquad C_1 = 0.9\,\text{h}^{-1}$

then

$$\prod_A = 0.9895$$

$$\beta = 0.9895$$

B) *Takeoff acceleration.* 2000 ft PA, 100°F, $k_{TO} = 1.2$, $\mu_{TO} = 0.05$, $C_{DR} = 0.07$, $C_{L\,max} = 2.0$, $M_{accel} = 0.1$, max power.

From Case 4, Eqs. (3.21) and (3.22)

$$\Pi_B = \exp\left\{\frac{-(C_1 + C_2 M)\sqrt{\theta}}{g_0}\left(\frac{V_{TO}}{1-u}\right)\right\}$$

$$u = \left\{\xi_{TO}\frac{q}{\beta}\left(\frac{S}{W_{TO}}\right) + \mu_{TO}\right\}\frac{\beta}{\alpha}\left(\frac{W_{TO}}{T_{SL}}\right)$$

With V_{TO} evaluated from Eq. (2.21), the takeoff estimate of ξ_{TO} from Chapter 2, Sec. 2.4.3, and α evaluated at M_{accel}, and with

$\beta = 0.9895$	$a = 1160\,\text{ft/s}$	$\mu_{TO} = 0.05$	$M_{accel} = 0.1$
$W_{TO}/S = 64\,\text{lbf/ft}^2$	$C_{L\,max} = 2.0$	$k_{TO} = 1.2$	$V_{TO} = 211.1\,\text{ft/s}$
$M_{TO} = 0.1819$	$\theta = 1.0796$	$\delta = 0.9298$	$q = 45.60\,\text{lbf/ft}^2$
$\theta_0 = 1.0818$	$\delta_0 = 0.9363$	$\alpha_{wet} = 0.9006$	$\xi_{TO} = 0.3612$
$T_{SL}/W_{TO} = 1.25$	$u = 0.2725$	$C_1 + C_2 M = 1.627\,\text{h}^{-1}$	

then

$$\Pi_B = 0.9958$$

$$\beta = 0.9853$$

C) *Takeoff rotation.* $M_{TO}/2000$ ft PA, 100°F, $t_R = 3$ s, max power.

From Case 10, Eq. (3.44)

$$\Pi_C = 1 - (C_1 + C_2 M)\sqrt{\theta}\,\frac{\alpha}{\beta}\left(\frac{T_{SL}}{W_{TO}}\right)t_R$$

With

$t_R = 3\,\text{s}$	$M_{TO} = 0.1819$	$\beta = 0.9853$	$\theta = 1.0796$
$\delta = 0.9298$	$\theta_0 = 1.0867$	$\delta_0 = 0.9515$	$\alpha_{wet} = 0.9003$
$T_{SL}/W_{TO} = 1.25$	$C_1 + C_2 M = 1.649\,\text{h}^{-1}$		

then

$$\Pi_C = 0.9984$$

The weight fraction for mission phases 1–2 is the product of the weight fractions for segments A, B, and C.

$$\Pi_{1\,2} = \Pi_A \Pi_B \Pi_C = 0.9837$$

$$\beta = 0.9837$$

Mission phase 2–3: Accelerate and climb. This phase consists of segments D (Horizontal Acceleration) and E (Climb and Acceleration).

D) Horizontal acceleration. $M_{TO} \rightarrow M_{CL}/2000$ ft PA, 100°F, mil power.

For this Mach number change of 0.1819 to 0.70, a single interval calculation will suffice. The Climb/Acceleration Weight Fraction Calculation Method of Sec. 3.4.1 is used with properties evaluated at the middle state point ($M = 0.4410$, 2000 ft PA, 100°F) and $\beta = \beta_i$.

With

$(a/a_{std})i = 1.039$	$M = 0.4410$	$T_{SL}/W_{TO} = 1.25$
$V_i = 211.1$ ft/s	$C_L = 0.2351$	$u = 0.1524$
$(a/a_{std})_f = 1.039$	$K_1 = 0.18, K_2 = 0.0$	$T\Delta s/W = 11{,}270$ ft
$V_f = 812.0$ ft/s	$C_{D0} = 0.014$	$(a/a_{std}) = 1.039$
$\Delta(V^2/2g_0) = 9555$ ft	$C_D = 0.02395$	$V = 511.5$ ft/s
$\Delta h = 0.0$ ft	$C_D/C_L = 0.1019$	$\Delta t = 32.97$ s
$\Delta z_e \doteq 9555$ ft	$\theta = 1.0796$	$\Delta s = 2.775$ n miles
$\beta = 0.9837$	$\theta_0 = 1.1215$	$C_1/M + C_2 = 2.340\ \mathrm{h}^{-1}$
$W_{TO}/S = 64\ \mathrm{lbf/ft}^2$	$\delta_0 = 1.0627$	
$\delta = 0.9298$	$\alpha_{dry} = 0.5264$	

then

$$\prod{}_D = 0.9935$$

$$\beta = 0.9773$$

Note that $\Delta s_D = 2.775$ n miles and $\Delta t_D = 32.97$ s.

E) Climb and acceleration. $M_{CL}/2000$ ft PA, 100°F $\rightarrow$ BCM/BCA, mil power.

The weight fraction of this mission segment is calculated along the minimum time-to-climb path depicted in Fig. 3.E2. In our illustrative example of Sec. 3.4.1, we found the weight fraction of this segment, using a single gross interval, to be 0.9812. Here we shall use the three successive integration intervals given in Table 3.E4 for our calculations, applying Eq. (3.20) to each. We use $\beta = \beta_i$ and the values of the state properties ($\alpha, \theta, C_D/C_L$, and V) at the mid state point of each interval to obtain an appropriate average value of the required properties. The β_i of each succeeding interval is obtained by multiplying the β_i of the preceding interval by $\prod$. By comparing the final result with that of Sec. 3.4.1, we can determine whether it is necessary for sufficient accuracy to break the climb/acceleration calculations into still smaller intervals.

Following this approach, the Climb/Acceleration Weight Fraction Calculation Method of Sec. 3.4.1 was used to obtain the results given in Table 3.E5.

$$\prod{}_E = \prod{}_a \prod{}_b \prod{}_c = 0.9806$$

Table 3.E4 Segment E—schedule and intervals

Climb schedule		Integration interval (state points)		
Altitude, ft	Mach number	a	b	c
2,000 (100°F)	0.70	Initial	——	——
9,000	0.775	Mid	——	——
16,000	0.85	Final	Initial	——
23,000	0.875	——	Mid	——
30,000	0.90	——	Final	Initial
36,000	0.90	——	——	Mid
42,000	0.90	——	——	Final

This result differs insignificantly from the earlier result of the single gross interval calculations for the illustrative example in Sec. 3.4.1. The amount of fuel consumed for this phase has changed by only 3%. We should therefore not consider breaking this phase into even finer intervals. Summarizing, then, we have the following results for Mission Phase 2–3:

$$\Delta s_{23} = \Delta s_D + \Delta s_E = 23.04 \text{ n miles}$$

$$\Delta t_{23} = \Delta t_D + \Delta t_E = 2.906 \text{ min.}$$

$$\prod_{23} = \prod_D \prod_E = 0.9742$$

$$\beta = 0.9584$$

Mission phase 3–4: Subsonic cruise climb. BCM/BCA, $\Delta s_{23} + \Delta s_{34} = 150$ n miles, mil power.

This is a type B ($P_s = 0$, $T = D + R$) mission leg for which full thrust is not usually applied. Even so, we shall use a conservative full thrust value of *TSFC* from Sec. 3.4.1 for all type B legs in these calculations.

From Case 7, Eq. (3.29), with $C_{DR} = K_2 = 0$

$$\prod_{34} = \exp \left\{ -\frac{\sqrt{4C_{D0}K_1}}{M_{CRIT}} \frac{(C_1 + C_2 M_{CRIT}) \Delta s_{34}}{a_{std}} \right\}$$

Table 3.E5 Segment E—climb/acceleration results

Interval	Δh, ft	$\Delta V^2/2g_c$, ft	Δz_e, ft	C_D/C_L	u	$T\Delta s/W$, ft	Δt, min	Δs, n miles	$C_1/M + C_2$, h^{-1}	$\prod$
a	14,000	2210	16,210	0.1601	0.1962	20,170	0.4915	4.067	1.462	0.9927
b	14,000	2.254	14,000	0.1384	0.2696	19,170	0.6913	6.119	1.329	0.9937
c	12,000	−662.4	11,340	0.1111	0.3755	18,150	1.1728	10.086	1.3	0.9941
Σ	40,000	1550	41,550	——	——	57,490	2.356	20.27	——	——

with

$$\Delta s_{34} = 127.0 \, \text{n miles} \quad K_1 = 0.18 \qquad\qquad C_{D0} = 0.016$$

$$M_{CRIT} = 0.9 \qquad\qquad C_1 + C_2 M_{CRIT} = 1.1700 \, \text{h}^{-1}$$

then

$$\prod_{3\,4} = 0.9736$$

$$\beta = 0.9331$$

Note should be taken of the fact that fuel consumption could be further reduced for this phase by capitalizing on the range factor as described in Sec. 3.2.7, Case 7. Consequently, the preceding result may regarded as conservative.

Mission phase 4–5: Descend. $BCM/BCA \rightarrow M_{CAP}/30$ kft.

$$\prod_{4\,5} = 1.0$$

$$\beta = 0.9331$$

Mission phase 5–6: Combat air patrol.   30 kft, 20 min., mil power. From Case 8, Eq. (3.40), with $C_{DR} = K_2 = 0$

$$\prod_{5\,6} = \exp\{-(C_1 + C_2 M_{CAP})\sqrt{\theta}\sqrt{4C_{D0}K_1}\Delta t\}$$

with

$$\Delta t = 1200 \, \text{s} \qquad \theta = 0.7941 \qquad\qquad \delta = 0.2976$$

$$K_1 = 0.18 \qquad C_{D0} = 0.014 \qquad\qquad C_L^* = 0.2789$$

$$M_{CAP} = 0.6970 \quad C_1 + C_2 M = 1.1091 \, \text{h}^{-1}$$

then

$$\prod_{5\,6} = 0.9675$$

$$\beta = 0.9027$$

At the end of combat air patrol $M_{CAP} = 0.6856$ from Case 8, Eq. (3.38).

Note should be taken of the fact that fuel consumption could be further reduced for this phase by capitalizing on the endurance factor as described in Sec. 3.2.8, Case 8. Consequently, the preceding result may regarded as conservative.

Mission phase 6–7: Supersonic penetration.   This phase consists of segments F (Horizontal Acceleration) and G (Supersonic Penetration).

Table 3.E6   Segment F—horizontal acceleration

Interval	M_i	M_f	M_{avg}	$\Delta z_e,$ ft	C_D/C_L	u	$T\Delta s/W,$ ft	$\Delta t,$ min	$\Delta s,$ n miles	$C_1/M + C_2,$ h^{-1}	$\prod$
a	0.6856	0.95	0.8178	6,652	0.1085	0.1697	8,011	0.2567	2.062	2.227	0.9956
b	0.95	1.23	1.0900	9,389	0.2537	0.2907	13,240	0.2332	2.496	1.738	0.9943
c	1.23	1.5	1.3650	11,340	0.4192	0.3552	17,590	0.1828	2.452	1.442	0.9937
—	—	—	Σ	27,380	—	38,840	—	0.6727	7.010	—	—

F) Horizontal acceleration. $M_{CAP} \rightarrow$ 1.5M/30 kft, max power.

This acceleration calculation is divided into the three intervals shown in Table 3.E6. The initial, final, and average Mach number of each interval and $h = 30,000$ ft are used in the Climb/Acceleration Weight Fraction Calculation Method of Sec. 3.4.1. The calculated results are given in Table 3.E6. Then

$$\prod_F = \prod_a \prod_b \prod_c = 0.9837$$

$$\beta = 0.8880$$

It is interesting to note from Table 3.E6 that the total mission weight specific work is 38,840 ft with 70.49% used to increase the mechanical kinetic energy of the airplane. The remaining 29.51% is dissipated into nonmechanical energy of the airplane/atmosphere system. A single gross interval calculation for this segment gives higher values of total time and total ground distance by 1.16% and 4.22%, respectively, and lower values of weight fraction and specific thrust work by 0.024% and 0.33%, respectively. Also note that $\Delta s_F = 7.01$ n miles.

G) Supersonic penetration.   1.5M/30 kft, $\Delta s_F + \Delta s_G = 100$ n miles, no afterburning.

From Case 5, Eq. (3.23), with $C_{DR} = 0$

$$\prod_G = \exp\left\{-\frac{(C_1/M + C_2)}{a_{std}}\left(\frac{C_D}{C_L}\right)\Delta s_G\right\}$$

with

$\Delta s_G = 92.99$ n miles $C_1/M + C_2 = 0.9\ h^{-1}$ $\delta = 0.2976$

$C_L = 0.05731$ $K_1 = 0.27$ $C_{D0} = 0.028$

$C_D = 0.02889$ $C_D/C_L = 0.5040$

then

$$\prod_G = 0.9382$$

Segments F and G together yield

$$\prod_{67} = \prod_F \prod_G = 0.9231$$

$$\beta = 0.8331$$

Mission phase 7–8: Combat. This phase consists of segments H (Fire AMRAAMs), I (Combat Turn 1), J (Combat Turn 2), K (Horizontal Acceleration), and L (Fire AIM-9Ls and $\frac{1}{2}$ ammo).

H) Fire AMRAAMs. 652 lbf.

From Eq. (3.47), and since $\beta W_{TO} = W_7$ here,

$$\frac{\beta W_{TO} - W_{PE1}}{\beta W_{TO}} = 1 - \frac{W_{PE1}}{\beta W_{TO}}$$

with

$$W_{PE1} = 652\,\text{lbf}$$

$$\beta = 0.8331$$

$$W_{TO} = 24{,}000\,\text{lbf}$$

then

$$\frac{\beta W_{TO} - W_{PE1}}{\beta W_{TO}} = 0.9674 \quad \text{and} \quad \beta = 0.8060$$

I) Combat turn 1. 1.6M/30 kft, one 360 deg 5g sustained turn, with afterburning.

From Case 6, Eq. (3.25), with $C_{DR} = 0$

$$\prod_I = \exp\left\{-(C_1 + C_2 M)\sqrt{\theta}\left(\frac{nC_D}{C_L}\right)\frac{2\pi N V}{g_0\sqrt{n^2 - 1}}\right\}$$

with

$\theta = 0.7941$	$\delta = 0.2976$	$\theta_0 = 1.201$	$\delta_0 = 1.265$

$\alpha = \begin{Bmatrix} 0.7821 \text{ wet} \\ 0.4444 \text{ dry} \end{Bmatrix}$ $C_1 + C_2 M = \begin{Bmatrix} 2.032 \text{ wet} \\ 1.380 \text{ dry} \end{Bmatrix}$ $C_L = 0.2286$

$K_1 = 0.290$ $C_{D0} = 0.028$ $C_D = 0.04305$

$C_D/C_L = 0.1883$ $\alpha_{req} = \beta\dfrac{nC_D/C_L}{T_{SL}/W_{TO}} = 0.6070$ %$AB = 48.15$

$C_1 + C_2 M = 1.693\,\text{h}^{-1}$ linearly interpolated $V = 1592\,\text{ft/s}$

then

$$\prod_I = 0.9753$$

$$\beta = 0.7860$$

J) Combat turn 2. 0.9M/30 kft, two 360 deg 5g sustained turns, with afterburning.

From Case 6, Eq. (3.25), with $C_{DR} = 0$

$$\prod_J = \exp\left\{-(C_1 + C_2 M)\sqrt{\theta}\left(\frac{nC_D}{C_L}\right)\frac{2\pi N V}{g_0\sqrt{n^2 - 1}}\right\}$$

Table 3.E7 Segment J—horizontal acceleration

Interval	M_i	M_f	M_{avg}	Δz_e, ft	C_D/C_L	u	$T\Delta s/W$, ft	Δt, min	Δs, n miles	$C_1/M + C_2$, h^{-1}	$\prod$
a	0.8	1.06	0.930	7,438	0.1589	0.1878	9,158	0.1950	1.781	1.990	0.9955
b	1.06	1.33	1.195	9,925	0.3755	0.3205	14,610	0.1748	2.052	1.609	0.9942
c	1.33	1.6	1.465	12,170	0.5579	0.4086	20,580	0.1723	2.480	1.362	0.9931
—	—	—	Σ	29,530	—	—	44,350	0.5421	6.313	—	—

with

$$\theta = 0.7941 \qquad \delta = 0.2976 \qquad \theta_0 = 0.9228 \qquad \delta_0 = 0.5033$$

$$\alpha = \begin{Bmatrix} 0.5033 \text{ wet} \\ 0.3020 \text{ dry} \end{Bmatrix} \quad C_1 + C_2 M = \begin{Bmatrix} 1.843 \text{ wet} \\ 1.170 \text{ dry} \end{Bmatrix} \quad C_L = 0.7045$$

$$K_1 = 0.18 \qquad C_{D0} = 0.016 \qquad C_D = 0.1053$$

$$C_D/C_L = 0.1495 \qquad \alpha_{req} = \beta \frac{n C_D/C_L}{T_{SL}/W_{TO}} = 0.4700 \quad \%AB = 83.46$$

$$C_1 + C_2 M = 1.732 \text{ h}^{-1} \text{ linearly interpolated} \qquad V = 895.4 \text{ ft/s}$$

then

$$\prod{}_J = 0.9774$$

$$\beta = 0.7682$$

K) Horizontal acceleration. $0.8 \rightarrow 1.6M/30$ kft, max power.
This acceleration calculation is divided into the three intervals shown in Table 3.E7. The initial, final, and average Mach number of each interval and $h = 30{,}000$ ft are used in the Climb/Acceleration Weight Fraction Calculation Method of Sec. 3.4.1. The calculated results are given in Table 3.E7.
Then

$$\prod{}_K = \prod{}_a \prod{}_b \prod{}_c = 0.9828$$

$$\beta = 0.7550$$

The weight specific thrust work of segment K is 44,350 ft with 66.58% going to increase the kinetic energy and 33.43% dissipated into nonmechanical energy by the drag forces.
A single interval calculation for this segment gives essentially the same weight fraction value but lower values of time, distance, and specific thrust work by 4.44%, 3.26%, and 1.78%, respectively.

L) Fire AIM-9Ls and $\frac{1}{2}$ ammunition.   657 lbf.
From Eq. (3.47), and since $W_j = \beta W_{TO}$ here,

$$\frac{\beta W_{TO} - W_{PE2}}{\beta W_{TO}} = 1 - \frac{W_{PE2}}{\beta W_{TO}}$$

with

$$W_{PE2} = 657 \, \text{lbf}$$

$$\beta = 0.7550$$

$$W_{TO} = 24{,}000 \, \text{lbf}$$

then

$$\frac{\beta W_{TO} - W_{PE2}}{\beta W_{TO}} = 0.9637 \quad \text{and} \quad \beta = 0.7276$$

For mission phase 7–8 we have

$$\prod_{7\,8} = 0.8734$$

$$\beta = 0.7276$$

Mission phase 8–9: Escape dash. 1.5M/30 kft, $\Delta s_{89} = 25$ n miles, no afterburning.

The computational procedure is identical with that of segment G. Here the distance is smaller (25 n miles vs 92.99 n miles) and the fraction of takeoff weight (β) is less (0.7276 vs 0.8880), making C_L smaller (0.04696 vs 0.05731) and C_D/C_L greater (0.6090 vs 0.5041). The net effect is a higher weight fraction for this leg (0.9795 vs 0.9382) and less fuel consumed, as

$$\prod_{8\,9} = 0.9795$$

$$\beta = 0.7127$$

Mission phase 9–10: Minimum time climb. 1.5M/30 kft $\rightarrow$ BCM/BCA, mil power.

In this leg kinetic energy is exchanged for potential energy as the airplane climbs from 30,000 ft to the Case 7 48,000 ft (*BCA*) and the Mach number is reduced from 1.5 to 0.9 (*BCM*). Using the initial and final values of h and V in the following listing, we find that the energy height diminishes by 4800 ft. We assume, therefore, in accordance with the RFP, a constant energy height maneuver for the weight fraction calculation of this phase.

From Case 11, Eq. (3.42), with $C_{DR} = 0$

$$\prod_{9\,10} = \exp\left\{ -(C_1 + C_2 M)\sqrt{\theta}\left(\frac{C_D}{C_L}\right)\Delta t \right\}$$

with (assuming the vertical speed is 0.5 of V_{mid})

$$\Delta t = \frac{\Delta h}{0.5 V_{mid}} \qquad \frac{V_{mid}^2}{2 g_0} = z_{ei} - h_{avg}$$

and

$$\theta_t = 0.7941 \qquad \Delta z_e = -4800\,\text{ft} \qquad K_{1mid} = 0.2387$$

$$V_i = 1492\,\text{ft/s} \qquad h_{avg} = 39,000\,\text{ft} \qquad K_{2mid} = 0$$

$$h_i = 30,000\,\text{ft} \qquad V_{mid} = 1284\,\text{ft/s} \qquad C_{D0mid} = 0.028$$

$$z_{ei} = 64,600\,\text{ft} \qquad \Delta_t = 28.04\,\text{s} \qquad C_{Dmid} = 0.2993$$

$$h_f = 48,000\,\text{ft} \qquad \theta_{mid} = 0.7519 \qquad (C_D/C_L)_{mid} = 0.3330$$

$$\theta_f = 0.7519 \qquad M_{mid} = 1.326 \qquad C_1 + C_2 M_{mid} = 1.298\,\text{h}^{-1}$$

$$V_f = 871.2\,\text{ft/s} \qquad \delta_{mid} = 0.1949 \qquad \Delta s = 5.131\,\text{n miles}$$

$$z_{ef} = 59,800\,\text{ft} \qquad C_{Lmid} = 0.08986$$

Then,

$$\prod_{9\ 10} = 0.9971$$

$$\beta = 0.7106$$

This is a conservative estimate in as much as $\Delta z_e = -4800\,\text{ft} < 0$.

Mission phase 10–11: Subsonic cruise climb. BCM/BCA, $\Delta s_{10-11} = 150$ n miles, mil power.

Refer to the outbound subsonic cruise climb leg data, mission phase 3–4. The weight fraction of this leg is lower (0.9698 vs 0.9736) due only to a higher cruise distance (144.9 vs 127.0 n miles). The starting BCA is higher (48,000 ft vs 42,000 ft) because of the airplane's lower weight (0.7106 W_{TO} vs 0.9584 W_{TO}). Then,

$$\prod_{10\ 11} = 0.9698$$

$$\beta = 0.6891$$

Mission phase 11–12: Descend. BCM/BCA $\rightarrow M_{loiter}/10$ kft.

$$\prod_{11\ 12} = 1.0$$

$$\beta = 0.6891$$

Mission phase 12–13: Loiter. $M_{loiter}/10$ kft, 20 min., mil power.

Refer to data for the combat air patrol loiter leg, mission phase 5–6. Compared to that leg the weight fraction of this leg is about the same (0.9677 vs 0.9675) because the offsetting effects of the dimensionless temperature θ (0.9312 vs 0.7941) and Mach number (0.3940 vs 0.6970). Because of the lower vehicle weight and altitude of this leg, the loiter Mach number is much less than that of the CAP leg. Then,

$$\prod_{12\ 13} = 0.9677$$

$$\beta = 0.6668$$

Mission phase 13–14: Descend and land. $M_{loiter}/10$ kft $\rightarrow$ 2000 ft PA, 100°F.

$$\prod_{13\ 14} = 1.0$$

$$\beta = 0.6668$$

The results of all of the AAF weight fraction computations in the preceding are summarized in Table 3.E3 and Fig. 3.E3.

Minimum fuel-to-climb path.   Although the AAF is not required by the RFP to fly a minimum fuel climb, this section is included to show the application of the material on minimum fuel path included as a note in Sec. 3.2 and for comparison with the minimum time path of Fig. 3.E2. Values of fuel consumed specific work (f_s) were calculated for the AAF at military power using Eq. (3.8) for the following data:

$$T_{SL}/W_{TO} = 1.25 \quad W_{TO}/S = 64\,\mathrm{lbf/ft}^2 \quad \beta = 0.97 \quad C_1 + C_2 M = 0.9 + 0.3M$$

The results of these calculations are presented in Fig. 3.E6 as contours of constant fuel consumed specific work (f_s) plotted in the velocity-altitude space with contours of constant energy height (z_e). The minimum fuel-to-climb path from energy

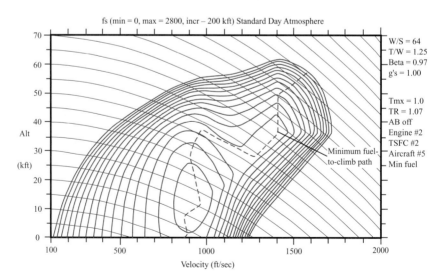

Fig. 3.E6   Minimum fuel-to-climb path on f_s chart.

height $z_{e1}(h_1, V_1)$ to energy height $z_{e2}(h_2, V_2)$ corresponds to a path having a maximum value of f_s at each z_e. The resulting minimum fuel-to-climb path from a z_e of 12 kft at sea level (where $V_1 = 879$ ft/s) to a z_e of 95 kft at 57 kft altitude (where $V_2 = 1564$ ft/s) is also shown on Fig. 3.E6.

Based on the comparison of Figs. 3.E2 and 3.E6, the following comments can be made:

1) The contours $P_s = 0$ and $f_s = 0$ are the same. This follows from the definition of f_s given in Eq. (3.8).

2) The minimum fuel-to-climb path is similar but different from the minimum time-to-climb path for evident reasons [see Eq. (3.8)].

3) The minimum fuel-to-climb path stays subsonic to a higher altitude (about 37 kft) than that of the minimum time-to-climb (about 15 kft).

You may find it useful to know that the weight fraction for a type A flight path can be expressed conveniently in terms of T_{SL}/W_{TO}, f_s, z_e, and β by dividing Eq. (3.9) by the aircraft weight at the start $W_1(= \beta W_{TO})$, noting that $W_{F_{1-2}} = W_1 - W_2$, and using the definition of $\prod_{1\,2}(= W_2/W_1)$. Making these substitutions gives

$$\frac{W_{F_{1-2}}}{W_1} = 1 - \prod_{1\,2} = \frac{T_{SL}}{\beta W_{TO}} \int_{z_{e1}}^{z_{e2}} \frac{dz_e}{f_s}$$

The resulting equation for the aircraft weight fraction $\prod_{1\,2}$ is

$$\prod_{1\,2} = 1 - \frac{T_{SL}}{\beta W_{TO}} \int_{z_{e1}}^{z_{e2}} \frac{dz_e}{f_s}$$

Application of this equation to the subsonic portion of the minimum fuel-to-climb path of Fig. 3.E6 ($z_{e1} = 12$ kft, $z_{e2} = 52$ kft) where f_s is approximately 2800 kft gives the following estimate for the weight fraction:

$$\prod_{1\,2} = 0.9815$$

References

[1] "2002 Aerospace Source Book," *Aviation Week and Space Technology*, 14 Jan. 2002.

[2] *Jane's All the World Aircraft, 2000–2001*, Jane's Yearbooks, Franklin Watts, Inc., New York, 2000.

[3] Raymer, D. P., *Aircraft Design: A Conceptual Approach*, 3rd ed., AIAA Education Series, AIAA, Reston, VA, 2000.

[4] Jonas, F., *Aircraft Design Lecture Notes*, U.S. Air Force Academy, Colorado Springs, CO, 1984.

4
Engine Selection: Parametric Cycle Analysis

4.1 Concept

The preparations are now complete to begin the design of the specific engine and airframe that can best perform the prescribed mission. Engine and airframe designers must now part company in order to concentrate intensely on perfecting their own product. They will come together again and share information only after they know a good deal more about their machines.

As engine designers, the required installed sea level static thrust (T_{SL}) of the engine(s) is now known, as well as the assumed behavior of thrust and specific fuel consumption with altitude and Mach number, depending on whether or not an afterburner is operating. Much good work remains to be done before the right engine is known in enough detail to decide how well the task can really be accomplished. Most of that work is based on a comprehensive, efficient method of jet engine cycle analysis pioneered by Frank Marble of the California Institute of Technology and perfected by Gordon Oates of the University of Washington as presented in Ref. 1 and by Jack D. Mattingly of Seattle University as presented in Ref. 2.

The object of parametric cycle analysis is to obtain estimates of the *performance parameters* (primarily specific thrust and thrust specific fuel consumption) in terms of *design limitations* (such as maximum allowable turbine temperature and attainable component efficiencies), the *flight conditions* (the ambient pressure, temperature, and Mach number), and *design choices* (such as compressor pressure ratio, fan pressure ratio, bypass ratio, and theta break). The comparative simplicity of the aerothermodynamic analysis is achieved by treating each stream as the one-dimensional flow of a perfect gas, by representing nonideal component behavior through realistic efficiencies, and by using a compact and intuitively appealing set of nomenclature. Please note that the inclusion of nonideal (or real) component behavior to the degree desired leads to a close imitation of nature, even for very complex configurations.

Engine design starts with parametric cycle analysis, which presumes that all design choices are still under control and that the size of the engine has yet to be chosen. The mental image usually attached to this stage of development is that of a "rubber" engine, whose size is arbitrary and performance is largely known in terms of ratios or "specific" terms. Therefore, each complete set of design choices results in a piece of hardware with its own geometry and operating characteristics.

This stage of design is usually referred to in the literature as "on-design" or "design point" cycle analysis. Our experience has taught us that the term parametric cycle analysis is preferable because it is always difficult and often impossible to identify a single point that dictates the design. The final design of an engine is based on its performance over the entire aircraft mission, and the winner is chosen because of its balanced behavior over the whole flight spectrum and seldom (if ever) matches any one of the mission flight conditions. Consequently, we have learned that it best to refer to the operating point at which all design quantities are known as the "reference point."

Then, why bother with parametric cycle analysis? There are at least three good reasons. *First*, engine performance analysis at conditions away from the reference point, usually referred to in the literature as "off-design" cycle analysis, cannot start until the reference point and the size of the engine have been chosen by some means. *Second*, parametric analysis is much less tedious and time consuming than performance analysis, often providing mathematical optima, that can be directly exploited. *Third*, and most important, identifying the combinations of design choices that provide the best performance at each mission flight condition reveals trends that illuminate the way to the best solution. A reasonable expectation after the completion of the parametric cycle analysis is that the most promising type of cycle has been identified and the possible range of each design choice has been bracketed.

To provide the most potent tools for parametric cycle analysis, relationships will be developed in this chapter for one of the most complex and flexible engine cycles known: the mixed flow, afterburning, cooled, two-spool turbofan engine with bleed air and power extraction. This is done because the behavior of many other cycles can be obtained merely by setting some design choices to trivial values and because this cycle is needed for the AAF example used in this textbook. Be aware that, even though this cycle is not included there, the development closely parallels that in Chapter 7 of Ref. 2. The resulting equations can be solved in many ways, but the most convenient should be to simply use the ONX computer program provided with this textbook. If you wish, you may choose to build your familiarity with and your confidence in this computer program by calculating the design point performance of some simpler cycles. Otherwise, you will have ample opportunity to compare your results with those that go with the following example.

Believing it serves a useful purpose, introductory material from Ref. 2 is reproduced in the derivations, particularly the definitions and notation. From this point on, the nomenclature is shifted entirely to the propulsion nomenclature of the Table of Symbols and Ref. 2.

4.2   Design Tools

The uninstalled engine thrust (F) and the uninstalled thrust specific fuel consumption (S) are the primary measures of the engine's overall performance. The uninstalled thrust (see Appendix E) for a single exhaust stream engine can be written as

$$F = \frac{1}{g_c}(\dot{m}_9 V_9 - \dot{m}_0 V_0) + A_9(P_9 - P_0) \qquad (4.1)$$

where station 0 is far upstream of the engine and station 9 is the engine exit. The term g_c appears in Eq. (4.1) as a reminder that the units must be watched carefully. In this particular case, for example, if the units of $\dot{m}$ are pounds mass/second and V are feet/second, then g_c must be Newton's constant of 32.174 lbm-ft/(lbf-s^2) if F is to be measured in pounds force. If the units of $\dot{m}$ were slug/s instead, then g_c would be unity. Because incorrect dimensions are responsible for more errors than any other thing, careful bookkeeping and double-checking are a worthwhile

Table 4.1   Typical $F/\dot{m}_0$ and S values

Engine type	Compressor pressure ratio (π_c)	Fan pressure ratio (π_f)	Bypass ratio (α)	T_{t7}, °R	T_{t4}, °R	$F/\dot{m}_0$, lbf/lbm/s	S, 1/h
Turbojet no A/B	10–20	——	——	——	2000	54–58	1.0–1.1
					3000	93–96	1.3–1.4
Turbojet with A/B	10–20	——	——	3600	2000	94–101	2.0–2.2
					3000	115–119	1.7–1.8
Turbofan low α no A/B	20–30	2–4	0.2–1	——	2000	23–47	0.85–1.0
					3000	53–84	0.96–1.5
Turbofan low α with A/B	8–30 10–30	2–4	0.2–1	3600	2000	75–98	2.1–2.7
					3000	102–116	1.7–2.0
Turbofan high α no A/B	30–40	1.4–1.6 1.4–4	5–7.5 5–10	——	2000	5.5–12	0.76–0.97
					3000	13–27	0.67–1.03

investment of time. The uninstalled thrust specific fuel consumption (S) is given by

$$S = \frac{\dot{m}_f + \dot{m}_{fAB}}{F} \tag{4.2}$$

where ($\dot{m}_f + \dot{m}_{fAB}$) is the total fuel flow rate to the main burner and afterburner of an engine. Since one pound mass of fuel at (or near) the surface of the Earth weighs one pound force in the British Engineering system, the thrust specific fuel consumption may be regarded as pounds weight of fuel per hour per pound force of thrust, and is traditionally reported in units of 1/h.

Parametric cycle analysis employs the uninstalled thrust per unit mass flow of captured airflow ($F/\dot{m}_0$) or specific thrust and the uninstalled thrust specific fuel consumption (S) as the performance measures of primary interest. Representative values of these parameters for several common but different engine types are given for guidance in Table 4.1.

4.2.1   Station Numbering

Consider the generalized engine shown in Figs. 4.1a and 4.1b. The station numbers of the locations indicated there are in accordance with Aerospace

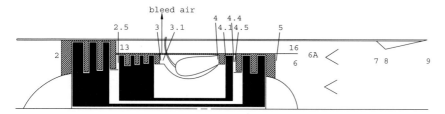

Fig. 4.1a   Reference stations—mixed-flow turbofan engine.

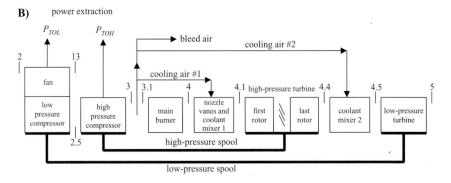

Fig. 4.1b   Reference stations—bleed and turbine cooling airflows.

Recommended Practice (ARP) 755A (Ref. 3) and will be used throughout this textbook, and include:

Station	Location
0	Far upstream or freestream
1	Inlet or diffuser entry
2	Inlet or diffuser exit, fan entry
13	Fan exit
2.5	Low-pressure compressor exit
	High-pressure compressor entry
3	High-pressure compressor exit
3.1	Burner entry
4	Burner exit
	Nozzle vanes entry
	Modeled coolant mixer 1 entry
	High-pressure turbine entry for π_{tH} definition
4.1	Nozzle vanes exit
	Coolant mixer 1 exit
	High-pressure turbine entry for τ_{tH} definition
4.4	High-pressure turbine exit
	Modeled coolant mixer entry
4.5	Coolant mixer 2 exit
	Low-pressure turbine entry
5	Low-pressure turbine exit
6	Core stream mixer entry
16	Fan bypass stream mixer entry
6A	Mixer exit
	Afterburner entry
7	Afterburner exit
	Exhaust nozzle entry
8	Exhaust nozzle throat
9	Exhaust nozzle exit

4.2.2 Gas Model

The air and combustion gases are modeled as perfect gases in thermodynamic equilibrium, and their properties are based on the NASA Glenn thermochemical data and the Gordon–McBride equilibrium algorithm (see Ref. 7). Thus, this gas model includes the variation of specific heat at constant pressure c_p with temperature. In addition, the classical perfect gas model with constant specific heats (also know as a calorically perfect gas) is also included as a limiting case in this analysis.

For the perfect gas with variable specific heats, the required additional thermodynamic definitions (Refs. 1, 2, 4) are

$$h \doteq \int_{T_{ref}}^{T} c_p \, dT \tag{4.3a}$$

$$\phi \doteq \int_{T_{ref}}^{T} c_p \, \frac{dT}{T} \tag{4.3b}$$

$$P_r \doteq \exp\left(\frac{\phi - \phi_0}{R}\right) \tag{4.3c}$$

where ϕ is the temperature dependent portion of entropy (s) and P_r (called the reduced pressure) is the pressure variation corresponding to the temperature change for an isentropic process ($s = $ constant). The differential equation for entropy is the Gibbs equation $T \, ds = dh - v \, dP$, which becomes $T \, ds = dh - RT dP/P$ for a perfect gas (Ref. 4). Integration of this latter equation using the definition of ϕ gives the following relationship for the finite change in entropy between states 1 and 2:

$$s_2 - s_1 = \phi_2 - \phi_1 - R \ln \frac{P_2}{P_1} \tag{4.3d}$$

For an isentropic process, Eq. (4.3d) reduces to

$$\phi_2 - \phi_1 = R \ln \frac{P_2}{P_1} \tag{4.3e}$$

Using Eq. (4.3c) we can express the pressure ratio for an isentropic process in terms of the reduced pressure P_r as

$$\left(\frac{P_2}{P_1}\right)_{s=const} = \frac{P_{r2}}{P_{r1}} \tag{4.3f}$$

We note that for the simplifying case of a calorically perfect gas (CPG) or constant specific heats for the finite change between states 1 and 2

a) Eqs. (4.3a), (4.3b), and (4.3d) become

$$h_2 - h_1 = c_p(T_2 - T_1) \tag{4.3a-CPG}$$

$$\phi_2 - \phi_1 = c_p \ln \frac{T_2}{T_1} \tag{4.3b-CPG}$$

$$s_2 - s_1 = c_p \ln \frac{T_2}{T_1} - R \ln \frac{P_2}{P_1} \tag{4.3d-CPG}$$

Table 4.2   Calling nomenclature for subroutine FAIR

Symbol	Knowns	Unknowns
FAIR(1, f, T, h, P_r, ϕ, c_p, R, γ, a)	f, T	h, P_r, ϕ, c_p, R, γ, a
FAIR(2, f, T, h, P_r, ϕ, c_p, R, γ, a)	f, h	T, P_r, ϕ, c_p, R, γ, a
FAIR(3, f, T, h, P_r, ϕ, c_p, R, γ, a)	f, P_r	T, h, ϕ, c_p, R, γ, a
FAIR(4, f, T, h, P_r, ϕ, c_p, R, γ, a)	f, ϕ	T, h, P_r, c_p, R, γ, a

b) Eq. (4.3f) becomes the familiar isentropic relationship

$$\left(\frac{P_2}{P_1}\right)_{s=const} = \left(\frac{T_2}{T_1}\right)^{\frac{\gamma}{\gamma-1}} \qquad \text{(4.3f-CPG)}$$

The effect of variable gas properties can be easily included in a computer analysis of gas turbine engine cycles, as follows. In addition to the ideal gas equation, two subroutines are needed: 1) a subroutine that can calculate the thermodynamic state of the gas given the fuel/air ratio f and one temperature dependent property; and 2) a subroutine that can calculate the compressible gas relationships T_t/T, P_t/P, and mass flow parameter (MFP) given the Mach number (M), total temperature (T_t), and fuel/air ratio (f).

The subroutine FAIR was developed to calculate the temperature dependent properties given the fuel/air ratio f and one of the following properties: T, h, P_r, or ϕ. Table 4.2 gives the calling nomenclature for the subroutine FAIR. The subroutine also determines the specific heat c_p, the gas constant R, the ratio of specific heats γ, and the speed of sound a.

The compressible flow subroutine RGCOMP was developed to calculate the compressible flow relationships for this gas model with variable specific heats. Table 4.3 gives the calling nomenclature for this subroutine. The equations used in RGCOMP are given in Appendix F.

4.2.3 Total Property Ratios

You will find it very important to be able to swiftly identify and thoroughly grasp the physical meaning of the quantities that are about to be defined in order to understand and manipulate the cycle analysis results. We therefore recommend that you spend enough time to completely familiarize yourself with the material

Table 4.3   Calling nomenclature for subroutine RGCOMP

Symbol	Knowns	Unknowns
RGCOMP(1, T_t, f, M, T_t/T, P_t/P, MFP)	T_t, f, M	T_t/T, P_t/P, MFP
RGCOMP(2, T_t, f, M, T_t/T, P_t/P, MFP)	T_t, f, T_t/T	M, P_t/P, MFP
RGCOMP(3, T_t, f, M, T_t/T, P_t/P, MFP)	T_t, f, P_t/P	M, T_t/T, MFP
RGCOMP(4, T_t, f, M, T_t/T, P_t/P, MFP)	T_t, f, MFP	T_t/T, P_t/P, $M \leq 1$
RGCOMP(5, T_t, f, M, T_t/T, P_t/P, MFP)	T_t, f, MFP	T_t/T, P_t/P, $M > 1$

of Secs. 4.2.3 and 4.2.4, and then mark their location carefully so that you can find them quickly whenever necessary.

The ratio of total (isentropic stagnation) pressures π and total (adiabatic stagnation) enthalpies τ are introduced, where

$$\pi_i \doteq \frac{\text{total pressure leaving component } i}{\text{total pressure entering component } i} \qquad (4.4a)$$

$$\tau_i \doteq \frac{\text{total enthalpy leaving component } i}{\text{total enthalpy entering component } i} \qquad (4.4b)$$

For the case of the calorically perfect gas, we assume a zero reference value of the enthalpy at zero absolute temperature. Thus enthalpies are replaced by the specific heat times the absolute temperature, and τ_i becomes the ratio of total temperatures or

$$\tau_i \doteq \frac{\text{total temperature leaving component } i}{\text{total temperature entering component } i} \qquad (4.4b\text{-CPG})$$

Note should also be taken of the fact that for case of the calorically perfect gas the relationships of Sec. 1.9 apply to Eqs. (4.4a) and (4.4b).

Moreover, the π and τ of each component will be identified by a subscript, as follows:

Subscript	Component	Station
AB	Afterburner	6A → 7
b	Burner	3.1 → 4
c	Compressor	2 → 3
cH	High-pressure compressor	2.5 → 3
cL	Low-pressure compressor	2 → 2.5
d	Diffuser or inlet	0 → 2
f	Fan	2 → 13
—	Fan duct	13 → 16
$m1$	Coolant mixer 1	4 → 4.1
$m2$	Coolant mixer 2	4.4 → 4.5
M	Mixer	6 → 6A
n	Exhaust nozzle	7 → 9
t	Turbine	4 → 5
tH	High-pressure turbine	4 → 4.5
tL	Low-pressure turbine	4.5 → 5

Examples

$$\pi_c, \tau_c = \text{compressor total pressure, temperature ratios}$$

$$\pi_b, \tau_b = \text{burner total pressure, temperature ratios}$$

Exception. τ_r and π_r are related to adiabatic and isentropic freestream recovery, respectively, and are defined by

$$\tau_r \doteq \frac{h_{t0}}{h_0} = \frac{h_0 + V_0^2/(2g_c)}{h_0} \tag{4.5a}$$

$$\pi_r \doteq \frac{P_{t0}}{P_0} = \frac{P_{rt0}}{P_{r0}} \tag{4.5b}$$

Thus, freestream total enthalpy $h_{t0} = h_0 \tau_r$ and freestream total pressure $P_{t0} = P_0 \pi_r$. For the simplifying case of a calorically perfect gas, we have, in accordance with Sec. 1.9,

$$\tau_r = \frac{T_{t0}}{T_0} = 1 + \frac{\gamma - 1}{2} M_0^2 \tag{4.5a-CPG}$$

$$\pi_r = \tau_r^{\frac{\gamma}{\gamma-1}} = \left(1 + \frac{\gamma - 1}{2} M_0^2\right)^{\frac{\gamma}{\gamma-1}} \tag{4.5b-CPG}$$

Further exceptions. It is often desirable to work in terms of design limitations such as the maximum allowable turbine inlet total temperature, T_{t4}. The term τ_λ is thus used and is defined in terms of the enthalpy ratio

$$\tau_\lambda \doteq \frac{h_{t4}}{h_0} \tag{4.6c}$$

Similarly, for the afterburner

$$\tau_{\lambda AB} \doteq \frac{h_{t7}}{h_0} \tag{4.6d}$$

For a calorically perfect gas, Eqs. (4.6c) and (4.6d) become

$$\tau_\lambda = \frac{c_{p4} T_{t4}}{c_{p0} T_0} \tag{4.6c-CPG}$$

$$\tau_{\lambda AB} = \frac{c_{p7} T_{t7}}{c_{p0} T_0} \tag{4.6d-CPG}$$

Component π and τ. A complete compilation of total pressure and total enthalpy ratios follow. Please note in the following that it has been assumed that $P_{t13} = P_{t16}, h_{t13} = h_{t16}$ and $P_{t3} = P_{t3.1}, h_{t3} = h_{t3.1}$.

Diffuser (includes ram recovery):

$$\pi_d = \frac{P_{t2}}{P_{t0}} \qquad \tau_d = \frac{h_{t2}}{h_{t0}} = 1 \tag{4.7a}$$

Fan:

$$\pi_f = \frac{P_{t13}}{P_{t2}} \qquad \tau_f = \frac{h_{t13}}{h_{t2}} \tag{4.7b}$$

Low-pressure compressor:

$$\pi_{cL} = \frac{P_{t2.5}}{P_{t2}} \qquad \tau_{cL} = \frac{h_{t2.5}}{h_{t2}} \tag{4.7c}$$

High-pressure compressor:

$$\pi_{cH} = \frac{P_{t3}}{P_{t2.5}} \qquad \tau_{cH} = \frac{h_{t3}}{h_{t2.5}} \tag{4.7d}$$

Compressor:

$$\pi_c = \frac{P_{t3}}{P_{t2}} = \pi_{cL}\pi_{cH} \qquad \tau_c = \frac{h_{t3}}{h_{t2}} = \tau_{cL}\tau_{cH} \tag{4.7e}$$

Burner:

$$\pi_b = \frac{P_{t4}}{P_{t3}} \qquad \tau_b = \frac{h_{t4}}{h_{t3}} \tag{4.7f}$$

Coolant mixer 1:

$$\pi_{m1} = \frac{P_{t4.1}}{P_{t4}} \qquad \tau_{m1} = \frac{h_{t4.1}}{h_{t4}} \tag{4.7g}$$

High-pressure turbine:

$$\pi_{tH} = \frac{P_{t4.4}}{P_{t4}} = \pi_{m1}\frac{P_{t4.4}}{P_{t4.1}} \qquad \tau_{tH} = \frac{h_{t4.4}}{h_{t4.1}} \tag{4.7h}$$

Coolant mixer 2:

$$\pi_{m2} = \frac{P_{t4.5}}{P_{t4.4}} = 1 \qquad \tau_{m2} = \frac{h_{t4.5}}{h_{t4.4}} \tag{4.7i}$$

Low-pressure turbine:

$$\pi_{tL} = \frac{P_{t5}}{P_{t4.5}} \qquad \tau_{tL} = \frac{h_{t5}}{h_{t4.5}} \tag{4.7j}$$

Mixer:

$$\pi_M = \frac{P_{t6A}}{P_{t6}} \qquad \tau_M = \frac{h_{t6A}}{h_{t6}} \tag{4.7k}$$

Afterburner:

$$\pi_{AB} = \frac{P_{t7}}{P_{t6A}} \qquad \tau_{AB} = \frac{h_{t7}}{h_{t6A}} \tag{4.7l}$$

Exhaust nozzle:

$$\pi_n = \frac{P_{t9}}{P_{t7}} \qquad \tau_n = \frac{h_{t9}}{h_{t7}} = 1 \tag{4.7m}$$

For the calorically perfect gas, all of the component τ except that of the burner and afterburner become total temperature ratios. For example, $\tau_c = T_{t3}/T_{t2}$ and $\tau_{tH} = T_{t4.4}/T_{t4.1}$. The τ for the burner and afterburner become

$$\tau_b = \frac{c_{p4}T_{t4}}{c_{p3}T_{t3}} \tag{4.7f-CPG}$$

$$\tau_{AB} = \frac{c_{p7}T_{t7}}{c_{p6A}T_{t6A}} \tag{4.7l-CPG}$$

4.2.4 Mass Flow Rates

The mixed-flow turbofan engine with afterburning, bleed air, and cooling air is a very complex machine with numerous air and fuel flow rates. The cycle analysis of this engine includes those mass flow rates that have major importance in engine performance and, hence, cycle selection. Please note that the mass flow rate frequently changes between stations as flow is added or removed or fuel is added (see Fig. 4.2). The symbol $\dot{m}$ is used for the mass flow rate with a subscript to denote the type as follows:

Subscript	Description	Station
b	Bleed air	3–3.1
C	Core airflow through engine	2.5, 3
$c1$	Cooling air for high-pressure turbine nozzle vane	3–3.1, 4–4.1
$c2$	Cooling air for remainder of high-pressure turbine	3–3.1, 4.1–4.4
F	Fan air flow through bypass duct	13, 16
f	Fuel flow to main burner	3.1–4
fAB	Fuel flow to afterburner	6A–7
$0 \rightarrow 9$	Flow rate at numbered station	——

Mass flow ratios. In engine cycle analysis, it is often most effective to cast the calculations into dimensionless mass flow ratios. The most useful of these for the engine of Figs. 4.1a, 4.1b, and 4.2 include the following:
Bypass ratio (α):

$$\alpha \doteq \frac{\text{bypass flow}}{\text{core flow}} = \frac{\dot{m}_F}{\dot{m}_C} \tag{4.8a}$$

Bleed air fraction (β):

$$\beta \doteq \frac{\text{bleed flow}}{\text{core flow}} = \frac{\dot{m}_b}{\dot{m}_C} \tag{4.8b}$$

Cooling air fractions (ε_1 and ε_2):

$$\varepsilon_1 \doteq \frac{\dot{m}_{cool1}}{\dot{m}_C} \tag{4.8c}$$

$$\varepsilon_2 \doteq \frac{\dot{m}_{cool2}}{\dot{m}_C} \tag{4.8d}$$

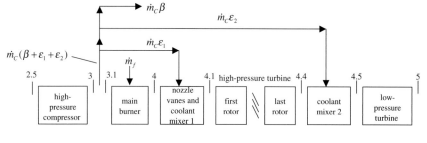

$$\dot{m}_0 = \dot{m}_C + \dot{m}_F = (1+\alpha)\dot{m}_C$$

$$\dot{m}_3 = \dot{m}_C$$

$$\dot{m}_{3.1} = \dot{m}_C (1 - \beta - \varepsilon_1 - \varepsilon_2)$$

$$\dot{m}_4 = \dot{m}_C (1 - \beta - \varepsilon_1 - \varepsilon_2)(1 + f)$$

$$\dot{m}_{4.1} = \dot{m}_{4.4} = \dot{m}_C \{(1 - \beta - \varepsilon_1 - \varepsilon_2)(1 + f) + \varepsilon_1\}$$

$$\dot{m}_{4.5} = \dot{m}_5 = \dot{m}_C \{(1 - \beta - \varepsilon_1 - \varepsilon_2)(1 + f) + \varepsilon_1 + \varepsilon_2\}$$

Fig. 4.2   Reference stations—turbine cooling air.

Burner fuel/air ratio (f):

$$f \doteq \frac{\text{burner fuel flow}}{\text{burner inlet airflow}} = \frac{\dot{m}_f}{\dot{m}_{3.1}} \tag{4.8e}$$

Mixer bypass ratio (α'):

$$\alpha' \doteq \frac{\text{fan air entering mixer}}{\text{turbine gas entering mixer}} = \frac{\dot{m}_{16}}{\dot{m}_6} \tag{4.8f}$$

Afterburner fuel/air ratio (f_{AB}):

$$f_{AB} \doteq \frac{\text{afterburner fuel flow}}{\text{afterburner inlet airflow}} = \frac{\dot{m}_{fAB}}{\dot{m}_C + \dot{m}_F - \dot{m}_b} \tag{4.8g}$$

Overall fuel/air ratio (f_o):

$$f_o \doteq \frac{\text{total fuel flow}}{\text{engine inlet airflow}} = \frac{\dot{m}_f + \dot{m}_{fAB}}{\dot{m}_C + \dot{m}_F} \tag{4.8h}$$

Fuel/air ratio at station 4.1:

$$f_{4.1} = \frac{f}{1 + f + \varepsilon_1/(1 - \beta - \varepsilon_1 - \varepsilon_2)} \tag{4.8i}$$

Fuel/air ratio at station 4.5:

$$f_{4.5} = \frac{f}{1 + f + (\varepsilon_1 + \varepsilon_2)/(1 - \beta - \varepsilon_1 - \varepsilon_2)} \tag{4.8j}$$

Fuel/air ratio at station 6A:

$$f_{6A} = \frac{f_{4.5}(1 - \beta)}{1 + \alpha - \beta} \tag{4.8k}$$

Turbine cooling. The model of turbine cooling incorporated into the engine analysis is shown in Fig. 4.2. Cooling air is drawn off at the compressor exit (station 3). A portion of this cooling air ($\dot{m}_{cool1} = \dot{m}_C \varepsilon_1$) is used to cool the high-pressure turbine nozzle guide vanes. The remainder ($\dot{m}_{cool2} = \dot{m}_C \varepsilon_2$) is used to cool the high-pressure turbine rotor. For cycle purposes, the cooling airflows $\dot{m}_{cool1}$ and $\dot{m}_{cool2}$ are modeled as being introduced and fully mixed in coolant mixer 1 and coolant mixer 2, respectively. No total pressure loss is assumed for coolant mixer 2. No cooling air is included for the low-pressure turbine.

4.2.5 Component Efficiencies

Rotating machinery. For the rotating machinery components it is usually convenient to relate their π to their τ by means of efficiencies, which account for losses or real effects and are based on experience. Two such efficiencies are commonly employed, η corresponding to the overall π and τ and e corresponding to an imaginary process in which π and τ are arbitrarily close to one. The latter efficiency, known as the polytropic efficiency, can be used more broadly because it represents a level of technology rather than the behavior of a given device (as given by η). Table 4.4 gives representative values of the polytropic efficiency for different levels of technology.

Like Refs. 1 and 2, the subscript i is used to represent the exit state or process of a 100% efficient or ideal turbomachinery (such as the compressors and turbines). This ideal exit state or process is used to calculate the overall efficiency (η) from the polytropic efficiency (e) and the dimensionless π or τ. A compilation of relationships for the engine of Figs. 4.1 and 4.2 for variable specific heats are given next. The reduced pressure at the ideal exit state is used to obtain the corresponding temperature and enthalpy.

Fan:

$$\tau_f = \frac{h_{t13}}{h_{t2}}, \quad \pi_f = \left(\frac{P_{rt13}}{P_{rt2}}\right)^{e_f}, \quad P_{rt13i} = \pi_f P_{rt2}, \quad \eta_f = \frac{\tau_{fi} - 1}{\tau_f - 1} \quad (4.9a)$$

Low-pressure compressor:

$$\tau_{cL} = \frac{h_{t2.5}}{h_{t2}}, \quad \pi_{cL} = \left(\frac{P_{rt2.5}}{P_{rt2}}\right)^{e_{cL}}, \quad P_{rt2.5i} = \pi_{cL} P_{rt2}, \quad \eta_{cL} = \frac{\tau_{cLi} - 1}{\tau_{cL} - 1}$$
$$(4.9b)$$

High-pressure compressor:

$$\tau_{cH} = \frac{h_{t3}}{h_{t2.5}}, \quad \pi_{cH} = \left(\frac{P_{rt3}}{P_{rt2.5}}\right)^{e_{cH}}, \quad P_{rt3i} = \pi_{cH} P_{rt2.5}, \quad \eta_{cH} = \frac{\tau_{cHi} - 1}{\tau_{cH} - 1}$$
$$(4.9c)$$

High-pressure turbine:

$$\tau_{tH} = \frac{h_{t4.4}}{h_{t4.1}}, \quad \pi_{tH} = \left(\frac{P_{rt4.4}}{P_{rt4.1}}\right)^{1/e_{tH}}, \quad P_{rt4.4i} = \pi_{tH} P_{rt4.1}, \quad \eta_{tH} = \frac{1 - \tau_{tH}}{1 - \tau_{tHi}}$$
$$(4.9d)$$

Table 4.4   Component polytropic efficiencies and total pressure losses

Component	Figure of merit	Type	Level of technology 1	2	3	4
Diffuser	$\pi_{d\,max}$	A[a]	0.90	0.95	0.98	0.995
		B[b]	0.88	0.93	0.96	0.97
		C[c]	0.85	0.90	0.94	0.96
Compressor	e_c	——	0.80	0.84	0.88	0.90
Fan	e_f	——	0.78	0.82	0.86	0.89
Burner	π_b	——	0.90	0.92	0.94	0.96
	η_b		0.88	0.94	0.99	0.995
Turbine	e_t	Uncooled	0.80	0.85	0.89	0.91
		Cooled		0.83	0.87	0.89
Afterburner	π_{AB}	——	0.90	0.92	0.94	0.95
	η_{AB}		0.85	0.91	0.96	0.97
Nozzle	π_n	D[d]	0.95	0.97	0.98	0.995
		E[e]	0.93	0.96	0.97	0.985
		F[f]	0.90	0.93	0.95	0.98
Maximum T_{t4}		(K)	1110	1390	1780	2000
		(°R)	2000	2500	3200	3600
Maximum T_{t7}		(K)	1390	1670	2000	2220
		(°R)	2500	3000	3600	4000

[a]A = subsonic aircraft with engines in nacelles.
[b]B = subsonic aircraft with engine(s) in airframe.
[c]C = supersonic aircraft with engine(s) in airframe.
[d]D = fixed-area convergent nozzle.
[e]E = variable-area convergent nozzle.
[f]F = variable-area convergent-divergent nozzle.
[g]Stealth may reduce $\pi_{d\,max}$, π_{AB}, and π_n.
Note: The levels of technology can be thought of as representing the technical capability for 20-year increments in time beginning in 1945. Thus level 3 technology presents typical component design values for the time period 1985–2005.

Low-pressure turbine:

$$\tau_{tL} = \frac{h_{t5}}{h_{t4.5}}, \quad \pi_{tL} = \left(\frac{P_{r\,t5}}{P_{r\,t4.5}}\right)^{1/e_{tL}}, \quad P_{r\,t5i} = \pi_{tL}P_{r\,t4.5}, \quad \eta_{tL} = \frac{1 - \tau_{tL}}{1 - \tau_{tLi}}$$

$$(4.9e)$$

A compilation of relationships for the engine of Figs. 4.1 and 4.2 for the case of constant specific heats (calorically perfect gas) includes the following:
Fan:

$$\tau_f = \frac{T_{t13}}{T_{t2}}, \quad \pi_f = \left(\frac{T_{t13}}{T_{t2}}\right)^{\frac{\gamma e_f}{\gamma-1}}, \quad \tau_{fi} = \frac{T_{t13i}}{T_{t2}} = (\pi_f)^{\frac{\gamma-1}{\gamma}}, \quad \eta_f = \frac{\tau_{fi} - 1}{\tau_f - 1}$$

$$(4.9a\text{-CPG})$$

Low-pressure compressor:

$$\tau_{cL} = \frac{T_{t2.5}}{T_{t2}}, \quad \pi_{cL} = \left(\frac{T_{t2.5}}{T_{t2}}\right)^{\frac{\gamma e_{cL}}{\gamma-1}}, \quad \tau_{cLi} = \frac{T_{t2.5i}}{T_{t2}} = (\pi_{cL})^{\frac{\gamma-1}{\gamma}}, \quad \eta_{cL} = \frac{\tau_{cLi}-1}{\tau_{cL}-1}$$

$$\text{(4.9b-CPG)}$$

High-pressure compressor:

$$\tau_{cH} = \frac{T_{t3}}{T_{t2.5}}, \quad \pi_{cH} = \left(\frac{T_{t3}}{T_{t2.5}}\right)^{\frac{\gamma e_{cH}}{\gamma-1}}, \quad \tau_{cHi} = \frac{T_{t3i}}{T_{t2.5}} = (\pi_{cH})^{\frac{\gamma-1}{\gamma}}, \quad \eta_{cH} = \frac{\tau_{cHi}-1}{\tau_{cH}-1}$$

$$\text{(4.9c-CPG)}$$

High-pressure turbine:

$$\tau_{tH} = \frac{T_{t4.4}}{T_{t4.1}}, \quad \pi_{tH} = \left(\frac{T_{t4.4}}{T_{t4.1}}\right)^{\frac{\gamma}{(\gamma-1)e_{tH}}}, \quad \tau_{tHi} = \frac{T_{t4.4i}}{T_{t4.1}} = (\pi_{tH})^{\frac{\gamma-1}{\gamma}}, \quad \eta_{tH} = \frac{1-\tau_{tH}}{1-\tau_{tHi}}$$

$$\text{(4.9d-CPG)}$$

Low-pressure turbine:

$$\tau_{tL} = \frac{T_{t5}}{T_{t4.5}}, \quad \pi_{tL} = \left(\frac{T_{t5}}{T_{t4.5}}\right)^{\frac{\gamma}{(\gamma-1)e_{tL}}}, \quad \tau_{tLi} = \frac{T_{t5i}}{T_{t4.5}} = (\pi_{tL})^{\frac{\gamma-1}{\gamma}}, \quad \eta_{tL} = \frac{1-\tau_{tL}}{1-\tau_{tLi}}$$

$$\text{(4.9e-CPG)}$$

Combustion components.   For those components in which combustion takes place, combustion efficiency is used to characterize the degree to which the chemical reactions have gone to completion. The efficiencies are based upon the ratio of the actual thermal energy rise to the maximum possible thermal energy increase, as represented by the lower heating value of the fuel (h_{PR}, see Table 9.2). Thus, we have the following for a perfect gas with variable specific heats:

Burner:

$$\eta_b = \frac{\dot{m}_4 h_{t4} - \dot{m}_{3.1} h_{t3.1}}{\dot{m}_f h_{PR}} \leq 1 \qquad (4.10a)$$

Afterburner:

$$\eta_{AB} = \frac{\dot{m}_7 h_{t7} - \dot{m}_{6A} h_{t6A}}{\dot{m}_{fAB} h_{PR}} \leq 1 \qquad (4.10b)$$

For the case of the calorically perfect gas, these combustion efficiencies are written as follows:

Burner:

$$\eta_b = \frac{\dot{m}_4 c_{p4} T_{t4} - \dot{m}_{3.1} c_{p3.1} T_{t3.1}}{\dot{m}_f h_{PR}} \leq 1 \qquad (4.10a\text{-CPG})$$

Afterburner:

$$\eta_{AB} = \frac{\dot{m}_7 c_{p7} T_{t7} - \dot{m}_{6A} c_{p6A} T_{t6A}}{\dot{m}_{fAB} h_{PR}} \leq 1 \qquad (4.10b\text{-CPG})$$

Power transmission components. For those components that merely transmit mechanical power by means of shafts, gears, etc., a simple definition of mechanical efficiency is used to account for the losses due, for example, to windage, bearing friction, and seal drag. In such cases

$$\eta_m = \frac{\text{mechanical power output}}{\text{mechanical power input}} \tag{4.11}$$

so that η_{mH}, η_{mL}, η_{mPH}, and η_{mPL} refer to the high-pressure turbine shaft, low-pressure turbine shaft, and power takeoffs from the high-pressure shaft and low-pressure shaft, respectively.

4.2.6 Assumptions

Before proceeding with the analysis, the underlying assumptions to be employed are summarized as follows:

1) The flow is, on the average, steady.

2) The flow is one-dimensional at the entry and exit of each component and at each axial station.

3) The fluid behaves as a perfect gas (but not necessarily calorically perfect) with constant molecular weight across the diffuser, fan, compressor, turbine, nozzle, and connecting ducts.

4) For the case of variable specific heats, the NASA Glenn thermochemical data and the Gordon–McBride equilibrium algorithm are used to obtain thermochemical properties of air and combustion gases at any station (see Chapter 9). For the case of the calorically perfect gas, c_p and γ are assigned one set of values from station 0 through stations 3.1 and 1.6 (denoted as c_{pc} and γ_c), a second set of values from station 4 through 6 (denoted as c_{pt} and γ_t), a third set of values leaving the mixer at 6A (denoted as c_{pM} and γ_M), and a fourth set of values from station 7 through 9 (denoted as c_{pAB} and γ_{AB}).

5) The total pressure ratio of the diffuser or inlet is

$$\pi_d = \pi_{d\,max}\eta_{R\,spec} \tag{4.12a}$$

where $\pi_{d\,max}$ is the total pressure ratio caused only by wall friction effects and $\eta_{R\,spec}$ is the ram recovery of military specification MIL-E-5008B (Ref. 5) as given by

$$\eta_{R\,spec} = 1 \qquad\qquad \text{for } M_0 \leq 1 \quad (4.12b)$$

$$\eta_{R\,spec} = 1 - 0.075(M_0 - 1)^{1.35} \quad \text{for } 1 < M_0 < 5 \quad (4.12c)$$

$$\eta_{R\,spec} = \frac{800}{M_0^4 + 935} \qquad \text{for } 5 < M_0 \quad (4.12d)$$

6) The fan and low-pressure compressor are driven by the low-pressure turbine, which can also provide mechanical power for accessories, P_{TOL}.

7) The high-pressure compressor receives air directly from the low-pressure compressor and is driven by the high-pressure turbine, which can also provide mechanical power for accessories, P_{TOH}.

8) High-pressure bleed air and turbine cooling air are removed between stations 3 and 3.1.

9) The flow in the bypass duct (from station 13 to 16) is isentropic.

10) The effect of cooling on turbine efficiency is accounted for by a reduction of e_{tH} due to $\dot{m}_{cool1}$ and $\dot{m}_{cool2}$.

11) The fan and core streams mix completely in the mixer, the total pressure ratio π_M being

$$\pi_M = \pi_{M\,ideal}\, \pi_{M\,max} \tag{4.13}$$

where $\pi_{M\,ideal}$ is the total pressure ratio across an ideal constant area mixer and $\pi_{M\,max}$ is the total pressure ratio due only to wall friction effects.

4.2.7 Engine Performance Analysis

The definitions and assumptions just catalogued will now be used to analyze the overall and component performance of the engine cycle of Figs. 4.1a, 4.1b, and 4.2. We would like to emphasize the fact that the following solution process may be successfully applied to a wide variety of airbreathing engine cycles. We recommend that you employ the following sequence of steps whenever a new engine cycle is to be studied.

Uninstalled specific thrust $(F/\dot{m}_0)$. Equation (4.1) can be rearranged into the following nondimensional form for the uninstalled specific thrust $(F/\dot{m}_0)$:

$$\frac{F g_c}{\dot{m}_0 a_0} = \left(1 + f_o - \frac{\beta}{1+\alpha}\right)\frac{V_9}{a_0} - M_0 + \left(1 + f_o - \frac{\beta}{1+\alpha}\right)\frac{R_9}{R_0}\frac{T_9/T_0}{V_9/a_0}\frac{(1 - P_0/P_9)}{\gamma_0} \tag{4.14}$$

When the nozzle exit area is chosen for ideal expansion and maximum uninstalled specific thrust, then $P_0 = P_9$, and the last term in the preceding equation vanishes. Otherwise, $P_0/P_9 \neq 1$ is a design choice, and Eq. (4.14) shows that the nondimensional uninstalled specific thrust depends largely upon the velocity ratio V_9/a_0 and the overall static temperature ratio T_9/T_0, which are considered next.

Velocity ratio (V_9/a_0). From $h_t = h + V^2/2g_c$, using Eq. (4.6b) and $h_{t9} = h_{t7}$ gives

$$\left(\frac{V_9}{a_0}\right)^2 = M_0^2 \left(\frac{V_9}{V_0}\right)^2 = M_0^2 \frac{h_{t9} - h_9}{h_{t0} - h_0} = \frac{M_0^2 \tau_{\lambda AB}}{\tau_r - 1}\left\{1 - \frac{h_9}{h_{t9}}\right\} \tag{4.15}$$

where h_{t9}/h_9 is a function of the nozzle total exit state $(t9)$ and the total to static pressure ratio (P_{t9}/P_9) as given by

$$\frac{P_{t9}}{P_9} = \left(\frac{P_0}{P_9}\right)\pi_r\,\pi_d\,\pi_{cL}\,\pi_{cH}\,\pi_b\,\pi_{tH}\,\pi_{tL}\,\pi_M\,\pi_{AB}\,\pi_n \tag{4.16}$$

For the case of a calorically perfect gas, the velocity ratio is given directly by

$$\left(\frac{V_9}{a_0}\right)^2 = \frac{M_0^2 \tau_{\lambda AB}}{\tau_r - 1}\left\{1 - \frac{T_9}{T_{t9}}\right\} = \frac{M_0^2 \tau_{\lambda AB}}{\tau_r - 1}\left\{1 - \left(\frac{P_9}{P_{t9}}\right)^{\frac{\gamma_{AB}-1}{\gamma_{AB}}}\right\} \tag{4.15-CPG}$$

Overall static temperature ratio (T_9/T_0).   The nozzle static exit state (9) can be determined using the isentropic pressure ratio (P_{t9}/P_9) and the nozzle total exit state $(t9)$ because

$$\frac{P_{t9}}{P_9} = \frac{P_{r\,t9}}{P_{r9}} \qquad (4.17)$$

The static temperature ratio (T_9/T_0) directly follows using the reduced pressure at station 9 to obtain the corresponding temperature.

For the case of a calorically perfect gas, the static temperature ratio is given directly by

$$\frac{T_9}{T_0} = \frac{T_{t9}/T_0}{(P_{t9}/P_9)^{\frac{\gamma_{AB}-1}{\gamma_{AB}}}} \qquad (4.17\text{-CPG})$$

Burner fuel/air ratio (f).   Applying the definition of burner efficiency [Eq. (4.10a)] yields

$$\dot{m}_f h_{PR}\eta_b + \dot{m}_{3.1}h_{t3} = \dot{m}_4 h_{t4}$$

which, using the definition of f, Eq. (4.8e), becomes

$$f = \frac{\tau_\lambda - \tau_r \tau_{cL}\tau_{cH}}{h_{PR}\eta_b/h_0 - \tau_\lambda} \qquad (4.18)$$

The equation is written in this form because it is used mainly to compute f from the cycle design parameters. For the case of a calorically perfect gas, $h_0 = c_{pc}T_0$ in Eq. (4.18).

Afterburner fuel/air ratio (f_{AB}).   Applying the definition of afterburner efficiency [Eq. (4.10b)] yields

$$\dot{m}_{fAB}h_{PR}\eta_{AB} + \dot{m}_{6A}h_{t6A} = \dot{m}_7 h_{t7}$$

which, using the definition of f_{AB}, Eq. (4.8g), becomes

$$f_{AB} = \left(1 + f\frac{1 - \beta - \varepsilon_1 - \varepsilon_2}{1 + \alpha - \beta}\right)\frac{\tau_{\lambda AB} - \tau_\lambda \tau_{m1}\tau_{tH}\tau_{m2}\tau_{tL}\tau_M}{h_{PR}\eta_{AB}/h_0 - \tau_{\lambda AB}} \qquad (4.19)$$

Again, Eq. (4.19) is generally used to compute f_{AB} from cycle design parameters. For the case of a calorically perfect gas, $h_0 = c_{pc}T_0$ in Eq. (4.19).

Coolant mixer temperature ratios (τ_{m1}, τ_{m2}).   The first law energy balance of the mixing process from station 4 to 4.1 yields

$$\tau_{m1} = \frac{(1 - \beta - \varepsilon_1 - \varepsilon_2)(1 + f) + \varepsilon_1\tau_r\tau_{cH}\tau_{cH}^{\llcorner}/\tau_\lambda}{(1 - \beta - \varepsilon_1 - \varepsilon_2)(1 + f) + \varepsilon_1} \qquad (4.20a)$$

Likewise, the first law energy balance of the mixing process from station 4.4 to 4.5 gives

$$\tau_{m2} = \frac{(1 - \beta - \varepsilon_1 - \varepsilon_2)(1 + f) + \varepsilon_1 + \varepsilon_2\{\tau_r\tau_{cH}\tau_{cH}^{\llcorner}/(\tau_\lambda\tau_{m1}\tau_{tH})\}}{(1 - \beta - \varepsilon_1 - \varepsilon_2)(1 + f) + \varepsilon_1 + \varepsilon_2} \qquad (4.20b)$$

Equations (4.20a) and (4.20b) are unchanged for the case of a calorically perfect gas.

High-pressure turbine total temperature ratio (τ_{tH}). A power balance on the high-pressure spool gives

$$\dot{m}_{4.1}(h_{t4.1} - h_{t4.4})\eta_{mH} = \dot{m}_C(h_{t3} - h_{t2.5}) + P_{TOH}/\eta_{mPH}$$

which allows the calculation of the high-pressure turbine total temperature ratio

$$\tau_{tH} = 1 - \frac{\tau_r\tau_{cL}(\tau_{cH} - 1) + (1 + \alpha)C_{TOH}/\eta_{mPH}}{\eta_{mH}\tau_\lambda\{(1 - \beta - \varepsilon_1 - \varepsilon_2)(1 + f) + \varepsilon_1\tau_r\tau_{cL}\tau_{cH}/\tau_\lambda\}} \qquad (4.21a)$$

where

$$C_{TOH} = P_{TOH}/(\dot{m}_0 h_0) \qquad (4.21b)$$

For a calorically perfect gas, Eq. (4.21a) is unchanged, and $h_0 = c_{pc}T_0$ in Eq. (4.21b).

For the special case of no bleed air, no turbine cooling, and no power takeoff, Eq. (4.21a) reduces to

$$\tau_{tH} = 1 - \frac{\tau_r\tau_{cL}(\tau_{cH} - 1)}{\eta_{mH}\tau_\lambda(1 + f)} \qquad (4.21c)$$

Low-pressure turbine total temperature ratio (τ_{tL}). A power balance on the low-pressure spool gives

$$\dot{m}_{4.5}(h_{t4.5} - h_{t5})\eta_{mL} = \dot{m}_C(h_{t2.5} - h_{t2}) + \dot{m}_F(h_{t13} - h_{t2}) + P_{TOL}/\eta_{mPL}$$

which allows calculation of the low-pressure turbine total temperature ratio

$$\tau_{tL} = 1 - \frac{\tau_r\{(\tau_{cL} - 1) + \alpha(\tau_f - 1)\} + (1 + \alpha)C_{TOL}/\eta_{mPL}}{\eta_{mH}\tau_\lambda\tau_{tH}\{(1 - \beta - \varepsilon_1 - \varepsilon_2)(1 + f) + (\varepsilon_1 + \varepsilon_2/\tau_{tH})\tau_r\tau_{cL}\tau_{cH}/\tau_\lambda\}} \qquad (4.22a)$$

where

$$C_{TOL} = P_{TOL}/(\dot{m}_0 h_0) \qquad (4.22b)$$

For a calorically perfect gas, Eq. (4.22a) is unchanged, and $h_0 = c_{pc}T_0$ in Eq. (4.22b).

For the special case of no bleed air, no turbine cooling, and no power takeoff, Eq. (4.22a) reduces to

$$\tau_{tL} = 1 - \frac{\tau_r\{(\tau_{cL} - 1) + \alpha(\tau_f - 1)\}}{\eta_{mH}\tau_\lambda\tau_{tH}} \qquad (4.22c)$$

The mixer.   Application of the conservation equations to a mixer with no wall friction is a relatively straightforward task. When the fan and core streams have the same gas properties (i.e., c_p, c_v, R, and γ), closed-form algebraic solutions are possible for the cases of the constant area mixer and the constant pressure mixer, as shown in Ref. 1. For the more general case, where the fan and the core streams have quite different gas properties and the area or static pressure is not held constant, a more complex solution is required. Because the constant area mixer provides a close approximation to the behavior of existing aircraft engine mixers, it is used in our engine performance analysis. The solution for constant area mixer behavior is included in its entirety in Appendix G, and it is outlined next for the general case of a gas with variable specific heats.

There are several important things to keep in mind about the role of the mixer in the turbofan cycle analysis. To begin with, the solution of the mixer equations simply reveals the properties of the completely mixed flow at station 6A (i.e., $\dot{m}_{6A}$, P_{t6A}, h_{t6A}, M_{6A}, c_{p6A}, and γ_{6A}) when the same properties are known for the fan flow at station 16 and the core flow at station 6. Furthermore, the solution depends on the design selection of A_6/A_{16}, which is the equivalent of choosing either M_6, M_{16}, or P_6 (provided that $P_6 = P_{16}$). Finally, and most importantly in the long run, the mixer can have a first-order effect on cycle properties and should not be regarded as a passive device despite its harmless appearance (see Sec. 4.3.4). In many cases, M_6 can be chosen to optimize cycle performance at a chosen reference point, and it is shown in Ref. 6 that the mixer *by itself* can compensate for wide ranges in fan pressure ratio (π_f) to provide almost constant performance for turbofans without afterburners. Conversely, the presence of the mixer can restrict the achievable range of engine operating conditions, as will be seen in the AAF example used in this textbook. The solution is now given in outline form for the total temperature and pressure ratios of a frictionless constant area mixer as presented in Appendix G.

Using the results of the engine performance analysis to this point, values of $\dot{m}_{16}/\dot{m}_6$ (α'), P_{t16}/P_{t6}, and h_{t16}/h_{t6} are easily found from Eqs. (G.1), (G.2), and (G.3) of Appendix G. A first law energy balance across the mixer then directly gives Eq. (G.4), the desired mixer total temperature ratio

$$\tau_M \equiv \frac{h_{t6A}}{h_{t6}} = \frac{1 + \alpha' h_{t16}/h_{t6}}{1 + \alpha'} \tag{4.23}$$

Now all that remains is to find P_{t6A}/P_{t6}. From the definition of the mass flow parameter *MFP* (see Sec. 1.9.3),

$$MFP = \frac{\dot{m}\sqrt{T_t}}{P_t A} = \rho V \frac{\sqrt{T_t}}{P_t} = \frac{M\sqrt{\gamma g_c RT}}{RT} \frac{\sqrt{T_t}}{P_t/P} = M \sqrt{\frac{\gamma g_c}{R}} \frac{\sqrt{T_t/T}}{P_t/P}$$

where R is a function of the fuel/air ratio f and the terms γ, T_t/T, and P_t/P are functions of the Mach number (M), the static or total temperature (T or T_t), and the fuel/air ratio (f). For convenience, we choose the total temperature (T_t) for expressing the mass flow parameter in its functional form, and we write

$$MFP = \frac{\dot{m}\sqrt{T_t}}{P_t A} = M \sqrt{\frac{\gamma g_c}{R}} \frac{\sqrt{T_t/T}}{P_t/P} = MFP(M, T_t, f) \tag{4.24}$$

Solving Eq. (4.24) for P_t and forming the ratio P_{t6A}/P_{t6}, the mixture total pressure ratio is

$$\pi_{M\,ideal} = \frac{P_{t6A}}{P_{t6}} = (1 + \alpha')\sqrt{\tau_M}\,\frac{A_6}{A_{6A}}\,\frac{MFP(M_6, T_{t6}, f_6)}{MFP(M_{6A}, T_{t6A}, f_{6A})} \tag{4.25}$$

where $(1 + \alpha') = \dot{m}_{6A}/\dot{m}_6$. For a constant area mixer with M_6 specified, only M_{6A} need be determined to find $\pi_{M\,ideal}$ from Eq. (4.25) because M_{16}, and hence A_{16}/A_6 and A_6/A_{6A}, result directly from satisfying the Kutta condition at the end of the splitter plate ($P_6 = P_{16}$).

For an ideal (no wall friction) constant area mixer, application of the momentum equation provides an algebraic solution for M_{6A} and, hence, for $\pi_{M\,ideal}$. The momentum equation in terms of the impulse function I (see Sec. 1.9.5) is, for an ideal constant area mixer,

$$I_6 + I_{16} = I_{6A} \tag{4.26}$$

where

$$I \equiv PA(1 + \gamma M^2) \tag{4.27}$$

The product PA in Eq. (4.27) can be replaced by

$$PA = \frac{\dot{m}}{M}\sqrt{\frac{RT}{\gamma g_c}} \tag{4.28}$$

which follows from $\dot{m} = \rho AV$, $P = \rho RT$, and $V = M\sqrt{\gamma g_c RT}$, to give

$$\sqrt{\frac{R_{6A}T_{6A}}{\gamma_{6A}}}\,\frac{1 + \gamma_{6A}M_{6A}^2}{M_{6A}} = \sqrt{\frac{R_6 T_6}{\gamma_6}}\,\frac{(1 + \gamma_6 M_6^2) + A_{16}/A_6(1 + \gamma_{16}M_{16}^2)}{M_6(1 + \alpha')} \tag{4.29}$$

where the right hand side is a known constant. This is a nonlinear equation for M_{6A} that can be solved by functional iteration in combination with the compressible flow functions (f, T_t, and M_{6A} known; find T_{6A}). The resulting value of M_{6A} is placed in Eq. (4.25) to give $\pi_{M\,ideal}$ and, finally,

$$\pi_M = \pi_{M\,max}\,\pi_{M\,ideal} \tag{4.30}$$

where $\pi_{M\,max}$ is the mixer total pressure ratio caused by wall friction only (no mixing losses).

Uninstalled thrust specific fuel consumption (S). Equation (4.2) can be rearranged into the following forms for the uninstalled thrust specific fuel consumption:

$$S = \frac{\dot{m}_f + \dot{m}_{fAB}}{F} = \frac{(\dot{m}_f + \dot{m}_{fAB})/\dot{m}_0}{F/\dot{m}_0} = \frac{f_o}{F/\dot{m}_0} \tag{4.31}$$

The input for this equation is derived from Eqs. (4.14), (4.8h), (4.18), and (4.19).

Propulsive efficiency (η_P), thermal efficiency (η_{TH}), and overall efficiency (η_o). Three cycle concepts usually presented early in the development of propulsion theory are propulsive efficiency (the ratio of thrust power to the rate of kinetic energy generation of the engine gas flow), thermal efficiency (the ratio of the rate of kinetic energy generation of the engine gas flow plus shaft takeoff power to the rate at which thermal energy is made available by the fuel), and overall efficiency (the ratio of the thrust power to the rate at which thermal energy is made available by the fuel). Since these concepts retain much of their original meaning even for the most complex cycles, they are included in our calculations. They are described and examined in detail for the classical case of no bleed air extraction or shaft takeoff power in Appendix E. For the general case,

$$\eta_P = 2\left(\frac{Fg_c}{\dot{m}_0 V_0}\right)\bigg/\left\{\left[1 + f_o - \left(\frac{\beta}{1+\alpha}\right)\right]\left(\frac{V_9}{V_0}\right)^2 - 1\right\} \qquad (4.32a)$$

and

$$\eta_{TH} = \left(\frac{V_0^2}{2g_c}\left\{\left[1 + f_o - \left(\frac{\beta}{1+\alpha}\right)\right]\left(\frac{V_9}{V_0}\right)^2 - 1\right\} + \frac{P_{TOL} + P_{TOH}}{\dot{m}_0}\right)\bigg/ f_o h_{PR}$$

$$(4.32b)$$

and

$$\eta_o = \frac{V_0(F/\dot{m}_0)}{f_o h_{PR}} = \frac{V_0}{h_{PR}}\frac{1}{S} \qquad (4.32c)$$

4.2.8 Computational Inputs and Outputs

It is only reasonable to assume that many design parameters must be selected before the cycle performance equations may be solved in the sequence just outlined and detailed in Appendix H and the parametric performance of the corresponding engine predicted. This is, of course, what makes engine design both fascinating and perplexing, for finding the right combination for a given task requires ingenuity and persistence. At the outset, it is not even certain that a successful combination can be found.

The greatest ally in this potentially overwhelming situation is the AEDsys software, which enables your computer to execute the job of repetitive, complex calculations without delay or error. The parametric design computer program ONX is arranged to accept a traditional list of inputs and provide all of the necessary engine performance outputs. You should be able to convince yourself that the inputs listed as follows, with the help of the definitions and efficiency relationships given in this chapter, will indeed allow the system of equations listed in Appendix H to be solved. Please notice that Table 4.1 and Eq. (4.1) can be used to make an initial estimate for $\dot{m}_0$, which is required for the power extraction input term.

The AEDsys cycle analysis programs have three different models of the gas properties available for your use. In increasing order of complexity, accuracy, and computational time they are the following:

Constant specific heat (CSH) model.   The air and conbustion gases at inlet and exit of each component are modeled as perfect gases with constant specific heats (calorically perfect gases). The values of the specific heats are allowed to change from inlet to exit of combustion processes (main burner and afterburner) and the mixing of two air streams. Representative values of the specific heats must be judiciously chosen for the engine inlet, main burner exit, and afterburner exit. The mixer exit specific heat properties are calculated from basic thermodynamics. This is the basic model used in the first edition of this textbook and the equations are included on the accompanying CD-ROM.

Modified specific heat (MSH) model.   This model uses the constant specific heat (CSH) model to calculate all engine properties except the fuel used. Using input exit total temperatures (T_{t4} and T_{t7}) and the total temperatures obtained from the CSH model for the inlet to the main burner (T_{t3}) and afterburner (T_{t6A}), the amounts of fuel burned are calculated using Eqs. (4.10a) and (4.10b), where the total enthalpies (h_t) come directly from the variable specific heat (VSH) model and h_{PR} is given. For the purpose of these estimates, $C_{12}H_{23}$ is used as the representative fuel. This improvement over the CSH model gives better estimates of the fuel used with few additional calculations.

Variable specific heat (VSH) model.   The air and combustion gases at inlet and exit of each component are modeled as perfect gases in thermodynamic equilibrium and their properties are based on the NASA Glenn thermochemical data and the Gordon–McBride equilibrium algorithm. For the purpose of these estimates, $C_{12}H_{23}$ is used as the representative fuel. This is the most complex model and requires considerable computing power. It is possible that performance calculations may not converge with a preset number of iterations due to the iterative nature of some solution schemes.

To strengthen your confidence in and deepen your understanding of the parametric analysis, we strongly encourage you to do one reference point calculation completely by hand, and demonstrate to yourself that the algebraic equations reduce to those given in Ref. 2 for a more restrictive case, such as the afterburning turbojet or the nonafterburning mixed flow turbofan.

Inputs

Flight parameters:	M_0, T_0, P_0
Aircraft system parameters:	β, C_{TOL}, C_{TOH}
Design limitations:	
Fuel heating value:	h_{PR}
Component figures of merit:	$\varepsilon_1, \varepsilon_2$
	$\pi_b, \pi_{d\,max}, \pi_{M\,max}, \pi_{AB}, \pi_n$
	$e_f, e_{cL}, e_{cH}, e_{tH}, e_{tL}$
	$\eta_b, \eta_{AB}, \eta_{mL}, \eta_{mH}, \eta_{mPL}, \eta_{mPH}$
Design choices:	$\pi_f, \pi_{cL}, \pi_{cH}, \alpha, T_{t4}, T_{t7}, M_6, P_0/P_9$

The *inputs* have been arranged in the order of increasing designer control but greater possible range of variation. The search boils down to finding the best combination of the 8 design choices on the bottom line while making sure that the other 25 parameters are realistic. One of the strengths of this approach that should be used is to perform a sensitivity study (see Sec. 4.4.5) in order to determine which of the 25 parameters must be accurately known. You may wonder why theta break/throttle ratio and the T_{t3max} limit (see Appendix D) are missing from this set of inputs. This happens because the *TR* and θ_{0break} are relevant to performance away from the reference point and because T_{t3} is a simple function of M_0, T_0, and π_c that can be separately tested against T_{t3max}.

Considering all of the intermediate and supporting parameters, there is a vast array of possible *outputs*, and a judicious selection must be made. The basis of their selection is primarily, of course, to reveal overall engine parametric performance, but a variety of internal quantities are provided in order to check for consistency and permit easy hand calculation of those quantities not presented.

Outputs

Overall performance: $F/\dot{m}_0$, S, f_o
η_P, η_{TH}, V_9/V_0, P_{t9}/P_9, T_9/T_0

Component behavior: π_{tH}, π_{tL}
τ_f, τ_{cL}, τ_{cH}, τ_{tH}, τ_{tL}, τ_λ, $\tau_{\lambda AB}$
f, f_{AB}
M_{16}, M_{6A}, M_9

There follows next a sample case of input and output for a typical mixed flow afterburning turbofan engine cycle. This calculation was performed for the modified specific heat (MSH) model described above where the specific heats are constant through all components except the combustor and afterburner. The first step in becoming familiar with the use of the ONX computer program should be to reproduce these results.

Before closing this section, we need to bring to your attention the fact that you are now in a position to generate an almost uncontrollable amount of information about parametric engine performance. It is therefore essential that you henceforth maintain clear and consistent records of your computations. To help you achieve this goal, we have provided both the means to insert individual file names and an automatic date/time mark for each computation. You will find it valuable to prepare a separate document summarizing the purpose of each computation.

4.3 Finding Promising Solutions

The parametric calculations described in detail in the preceding section and embodied in the accompanying ONX computer program must be used repeatedly in order to find the best combinations of design parameters for an engine. Basically, a search must be conducted to find the influence of each of the design parameters and from that to find the combinations that work well at each of the important flight conditions. Selecting the flight conditions for study of a complex mission requires some judgment. As a minimum, one should examine engine behavior at the extreme conditions as well as at those conditions that play the greatest role in the constraint analysis or the mission analysis.

As each mission phase is studied, for each combination of input design parameters the primary result will be the variation of uninstalled thrust specific fuel consumption (S) with uninstalled specific thrust ($F/\dot{m}_0$) as π_c is varied, as shown in the carpet plots of Figs. 4.3 and 4.4. In this representation, the most desirable direction to move is always down and to the right. Unfortunately the laws of nature

Sample ONX Computer Output

On-Design Calcs (ONX V5.00)　　　　　　Date: X/XX/XX X:XX:XX PM
File: E1ON.onx

Turbofan Engine with Afterburning
using Variable Specific Heat (VSH) Model

******************** Input Data ************************

Mach No	=	1.600	Alpha	=	0.400
Alt (ft)	=	35000	Pi f / Pi cL	=	3.800/3.800
T0 (R)	=	394.10	Pi d (max)	=	0.960
P0 (psia)	=	3.467	Pi b	=	0.950
Density	=	.0007352	Pi n	=	0.970
(Slug/ft^3)			Efficiency		
			Burner	=	0.999
			Mech Hi Pr	=	0.995
			Mech Lo Pr	=	0.995
			Fan/LP Comp	=	0.890/0.890 (ef/ecL)
Tt4 max	=	3200.0 R	HP Comp	=	0.900 (ecH)
h - fuel	=	18400 Btu/lbm	HP Turbine	=	0.890 (etH)
CTO Low	=	0.0000	LP Turbine	=	0.900 (etL)
CTO High	=	0.0150	Pwr Mech Eff L	=	1.000
Cooling Air #1	=	5.000 %	Pwr Mech Eff H	=	0.990
Cooling Air #2	=	5.000 %	Bleed Air	=	1.000 %
P0/P9	=	1.0000			

** Afterburner **

Tt7 max	=	3600.0 R	Pi AB	=	0.950
			Eta A/B	=	0.990
*** Mixer ***			Pi Mixer max	=	0.970

********************* RESULTS ************************

Tau r	=	1.510	a0 (ft/sec)	=	974.7
Pi r	=	4.237	V0 (ft/sec)	=	1559.4
Pi d	=	0.924	Mass Flow	=	200.0 lbm/sec
Tt4/T0	=	8.120	Area Zero	=	5.422 sqft
PTO Low	=	0.00 KW	Area Zero*	=	4.336 sqft
PTO High	=	301.34 KW			
Pt16/P0	=	14.876	Tt16/T0	=	2.3124
Pt6/P0	=	13.792	Tt6/T0	=	5.7702
Pi c	=	16.000	Tau m1	=	0.9684
Pi f	=	3.8000	Tau m2	=	0.9742
Tau f	=	1.5372	Tau M	=	0.8206
Eta f	=	0.8681	Pi M	=	0.9771
Pi cL	=	3.800	Tau cL	=	1.5372
Eta cL	=	0.8681			
Pi cH	=	4.2105	M6	=	0.4000
Tau cH	=	1.5734	M16	=	0.5159
Eta cH	=	0.8795	M6A	=	0.4331
Pi tH	=	0.4693	A16/A6	=	0.1844
Tau tH	=	0.8457	Gamma M	=	1.3165
Eta tH	=	0.8980	CP M	=	0.2849
Pi tL	=	0.4939	Eta tL	=	0.9070
Tau tL	=	0.8504			

Without AB			With AB		
Pt9/P9	=	12.745	Pt9/P9	=	12.418
f	=	0.03127	f	=	0.03127
			f AB	=	0.03222
F/mdot	=	62.859 lbf/(lbm/s)	F/mdot	=	110.634 lbf/(lbm/s)
S	=	1.1386 (lbm/hr)/lbf	S	=	1.6878 (lbm/hr)/lbf
T9/T0	=	2.5428	T9/T0	=	5.3364
V9/V0	=	2.268	V9/V0	=	3.142
M9/M0	=	1.439	M9/M0	=	1.416
A9/A0	=	1.136	A9/A0	=	1.775
A9/A8	=	2.372	A9/A8	=	2.489
Thrust	=	12572 lbf	Thrust	=	22127 lbf
Thermal Eff	= 55.89 %		Thermal Eff	=	47.40 %
Propulsive Eff	= 61.62 %		Propulsive Eff	=	49.01 %

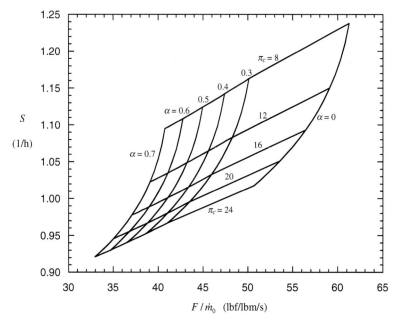

Fig. 4.3   Parametric performance of mixed flow turbofans (no AB).

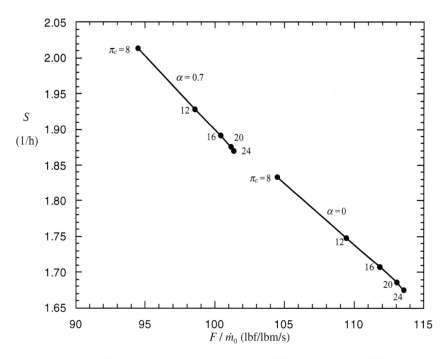

Fig. 4.4   Parametric performance of mixed flow turbofans (w/AB).

do not always fully cooperate, and there is usually a tradeoff between S and $F/\dot{m}_0$, where one can be improved only at the expense of the other. Be prepared for intuition to go wrong at this point because increases in cycle temperatures (e.g., τ_λ) and component pressure ratios (e.g., π_c) do not always lead to improved performance. You may find recourse to propulsive, thermal, and overall efficiency and Eq. (4.32) to be helpful in discovering the root cause of parametric performance trends. This explains why they are always included in the output quantities. To make use of the computed results, initial goals must be established for S and $F/\dot{m}_0$, as described next.

4.3.1 Uninstalled Specific Fuel Consumption (S)

Clear targets can be set for S because of the initial expectations already established by mission analysis. The main caution to be raised is that the mission analysis is based on *installed* specific fuel consumption (TSFC), while the cycle analysis yields *uninstalled* specific fuel consumption (S). A good rule of thumb is that installed exceeds uninstalled by 0 to 10%, depending on the situation (see Chapter 6), or a conservative average value of about 5%. Hence, the most revealing way to display the parametric analysis results is to plot the target or goal value of S on the carpet plot of S vs $F/\dot{m}_0$.

The totality of results must be used with care. On the one hand, reference point values of S may be different than the corresponding off-design values that will be computed later. Also, installation effects will vary with distance from the final reference point. On the other hand, it is needlessly restrictive to require that the specific fuel consumption be less than or equal to the target value at *every* flight condition. It is necessary only that the total fuel consumption, integrated over the entire mission, meets its goal. Therefore, a higher fuel consumption on one leg may be traded for a lower fuel consumption on another, provided that the integrated gains equal or outweigh the losses. A good general rule is to concentrate on reducing S for those legs using the most fuel (i.e., smallest Π) in the mission analysis.

4.3.2 Uninstalled Specific Thrust (F/$\dot{m}_0$)

Because the physical size of the engine (i.e., $\dot{m}_0$ design) is not known at this point, no stated target for $F/\dot{m}_0$ exists. Although the size of the engine can always be increased to provide the needed total thrust, it is always desirable to achieve large values of $F/\dot{m}_0$ in order to decrease the size (as well as the initial and maintenance cost, volume, and weight) of the engine. Once again, it should be noted that a constraint analysis is based on *installed* thrust (T), while the cycle analysis yields *uninstalled* thrust (F), with F exceeding T by 0 to 10% depending on the situation and distance from the final design point.

A good general rule here is to concentrate on increasing $F/\dot{m}_0$ for those legs that formed the boundary of the solution space in the constraint analysis. The lower thrust required for flight conditions away from that boundary will be attained by reducing T_{t7} and/or T_{t4}. In fact, for flight conditions that require considerably less than the available thrust, it is more realistic to run these parametric computations at less than the maximum values of T_{t7} and/or T_{t4}.

Even though no precise goal for $F/\dot{m}_0$ is available, ballpark figures can be easily generated using ONX, a representative sample of which is given in Table 4.1.

These numbers will also be useful in the initial estimation of

$$C_{TO} = \frac{P_{TO}}{\dot{m}_0 h_0} = \frac{P_{TO}}{F h_0} \frac{F}{\dot{m}_0} \qquad (4.33)$$

4.3.3 Parametric vs Performance Behavior

During this process of selecting a set of reference point parameters for each critical flight condition, it is important to remember that the final engine will always be running off-design and will therefore behave differently at each operating point. Thus, it makes little sense to try to find an engine, for example, of *fixed* π_c, π_f, α, and T_{t4} that works reasonably well at every operating point. It is, however, desirable to have the selected sets of reference point parameters generally follow the natural path of a single engine running off-design. Applying this logic will increase the probability of success of a design.

But how is this natural path established in advance? There is no simple answer to this question, but some good approximations are available. The best would be to run several off-design computations (see Chapter 5) for promising designs in order to generate directly applicable guidance. This would be equivalent to coupling parametric and performance computations in an iterative manner and, time permitting, offers a rich design experience. A simple and direct, but less reliable, method is to use the typical off-design parameter behavior information of Figs. 4.5–4.11, which are generated by the performance computer program portion

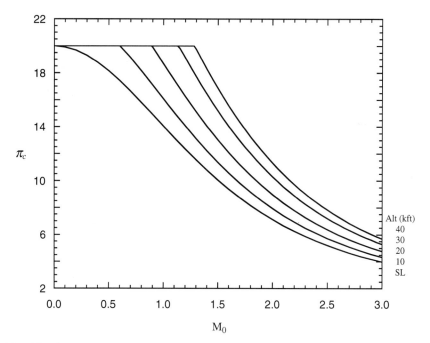

Fig. 4.5   Compressor pressure ratio (π_c) performance characteristics for a turbojet with *TR* = 1.0.

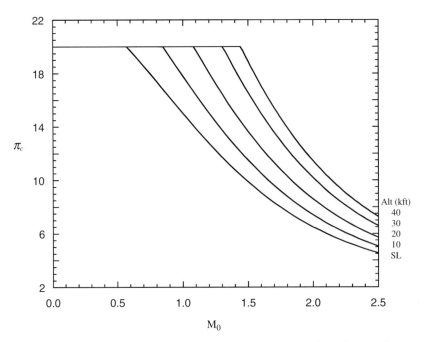

Fig. 4.6   Compressor pressure ratio (π_c) performance characteristics for a low bypass ratio mixed flow turbofan with $TR = 1.065$.

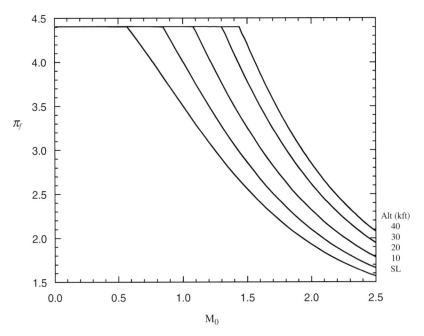

Fig. 4.7   Fan pressure ratio (π_f) performance characteristics for a low bypass ratio mixed flow turbofan with $TR = 1.065$.

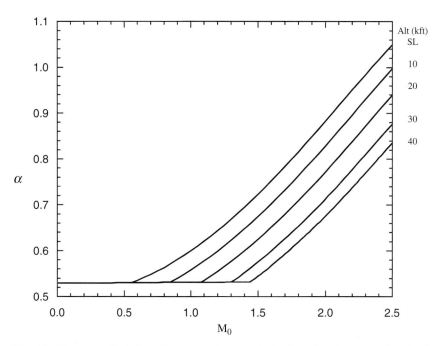

Fig. 4.8 Bypass ratio (α) performance characteristics for a low bypass ratio mixed flow turbofan with $TR = 1.065$.

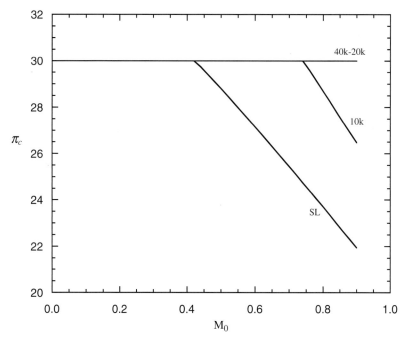

Fig. 4.9 Compressor pressure ratio (π_c) performance characteristics for a high bypass ratio turbofan with $TR = 1.035$.

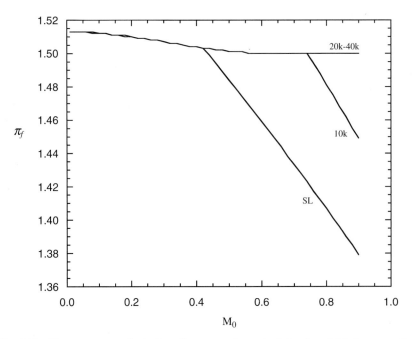

Fig. 4.10   Fan pressure ratio (π_f) performance characteristics for a high bypass ratio turbofan with $TR = 1.035$.

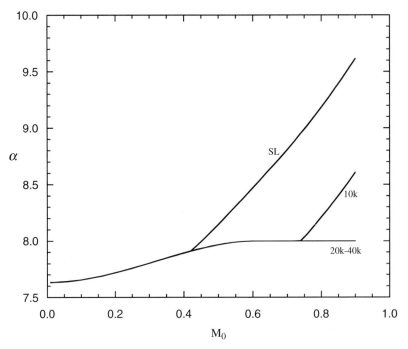

Fig. 4.11   Bypass ratio (α) performance characteristics for a high bypass ratio turbofan with $TR = 1.035$.

of the AEDsys program developed in Chapter 5. Please note that the high- and low-pressure turbine total temperature and total pressure ratios are almost constant [see Eqs. (4.21c) and (4.22c) and Appendix D] and that afterburner operation has no effect on these results because it is assumed (and almost universally true) that the nozzle throat area (A_8) is controlled to make the mixer and all upstream components oblivious to the afterburner conditions by maintaining a constant value of the pressure at the mixer exit. Also, the results shown for 40 kft represent those for all altitudes above the tropopause. Another means to understand and predict off-design behavior is to employ the algebraic methods found in Appendix D.

Figures 4.5–4.11 all display the unmistakable signature of performance analysis, namely the theta break imposed by the control system at $\theta_0 = \theta_{0break} = TR$ (see Appendix D). We will explain in much greater detail how to integrate performance analysis computations into the search for promising reference points in Sec. 4.4.4.

4.3.4 Influence of the Mixer

One of the things about to be encountered is the remarkable impact of the seemingly innocuous mixer on the range of acceptable design parameters for mixed exhaust flow engines. The main reason for this influence is that the fan and core streams are not separately exhausting to atmosphere, where their behavior would be uncoupled and the only physical constraint would be $P_t > P_0$, but they are brought together in pressure contact within confined quarters. For this situation, the operating parameters are much more restricted because neither M_6 nor M_{16} can be less than zero (reverse flow) or greater than one (choked). In fact, it is desirable that neither M_6 nor M_{16} even begin to approach zero because the corresponding flow area would increase the engine cross-sectional (or frontal) area beyond reason. Finally, common sense would encourage keeping design point values of M_6 and M_{16} in the range of 0.4–0.6 because they are certain to migrate away during off-design operation and therefore should start off with some cushion.

It is challenging to balance π_c, π_f, α, and T_{t4} in order to make M_6 and M_{16} behave properly. One available life preserver is to recognize that this desired behavior requires P_{t6} approximately equal to P_{t16}, or

$$\frac{P_{t6}}{P_{t16}} = \frac{P_0 \pi_r \pi_d \pi_{cL} \pi_{cH} \pi_b \pi_{tH} \pi_{tL}}{P_0 \pi_r \pi_d \pi_f} \approx 1$$

which reduces to

$$\pi_{cL} \pi_{cH} \pi_{tH} \pi_{tL} / \pi_f \approx \frac{1}{\pi_b} \approx 1 \qquad (4.34)$$

and then to use Eqs. (4.21c) and (4.22c) to reveal how to make π_{cH}, π_{tH}, and π_{tL} bring P_{t6} and P_{t16} together. For example, if π_{cH}, π_{tH}, and π_{tL} are too large, Eq. (4.22c) clearly shows that τ_{tL}, and therefore π_{tL}, can be reduced by increasing α or π_f and by decreasing τ_λ. The physical interpretation of this is that the low pressure turbine drives the increase of fan airflow and pressure ratio. Also, as τ_λ and the capacity for each pound of air to do work in the low pressure turbine decrease, π_{tL} must decrease in order to maintain the same power output. A valuable feature of the ONX computer program is its ability to calculate the fan pressure ratio (π_f) for a given bypass ratio (α), or vice versa, that automatically matches the total pressures at stations 6 and 16 using the complete Eqs. (4.21a) and (4.22a). This feature is activated by following the directions at the bottom of the ONX input data window for the mixed flow turbofan engine.

The final safety net is that the ONX computer program has been arranged to override the input of M_6 if M_{16} is out of limits in order to obtain a legitimate solution. Even if the solution is not a useful one (i.e., $M_{16} \simeq 0$), the results will indicate the right direction. If no solution is possible, the printout will tell which of the two mixer entry total pressures was too high.

4.3.5 The Good News

Applying the ONX parametric engine cycle computer program to a new set of requirements is an exhilarating experience. The tedious work is done so swiftly and the results are so comprehensive that natural curiosity simply takes over. Almost any search procedure from almost any starting point quickly leads to the region of most promising results. The influence of any single input parameter on all of the output quantities can be immediately determined by changing its value only slightly. This is the basis of sensitivity analysis (see Sec. 4.4.5). The behavior of each component can also be clearly traced and the possibility of exceeding some design limitation (e.g., compression ratio or temperature) easily avoided.

In addition to fun, there is also learning. Armed with computational power and an open mind, the best solutions made possible by natural laws literally make themselves known. Simultaneously, the payoff made possible by various technological improvements or changes in the ground rules is determined. For the moment, each participant really is like an engine company preliminary design group, with similar capabilities and limitations. No wonder it is exhilarating.

4.4 Example Engine Selection: Parametric Cycle Analysis

Using the methods of the preceding sections, the search begins for the best combinations of engine design parameters for the Air-to-Air Fighter (AAF) described in the Request for Proposal (RFP) of Chapter 1. Of the three thermodynamic models available with the ONX program, we have chosen to use for this exercise the modified specific heat model MSH (constant specific heats through all components except the combustor and afterburner where variable specific heats give a more accurate estimate of the fuel consumption). This engine model gives the best of both worlds—quick and accurate estimates of engine parametric behavior. Possible combinations of engine design points at selected critical flight conditions will be investigated in order to narrow the ranges of key engine design parameters. Once the most promising ranges of these parameters have been found, off-design or performance analysis (Chapter 5) can proceed and the selected engine sized (Chapter 6) to produce the installed thrust required.

4.4.1 Selection of Suitable Ranges of Design Point Parameters

In the constraint analysis of Chapter 2, a preliminary choice was made of the engine's throttle ratio (*TR*), and a value of 1.07 was selected. The AAF constraint and mission flight conditions are plotted vs theta zero (θ_0) in Fig. 4.E1. Note that the corresponding flight conditions bracket the 1.07 value of θ_0. The engine is T_{t4} limited to the right of $\theta_0 = 1.07$ and π_c limited to the left (see Appendix D).

To shrink the bewilderingly large number of promising reference point choices to a manageable size, it is not necessary to conduct an exhaustive investigation of

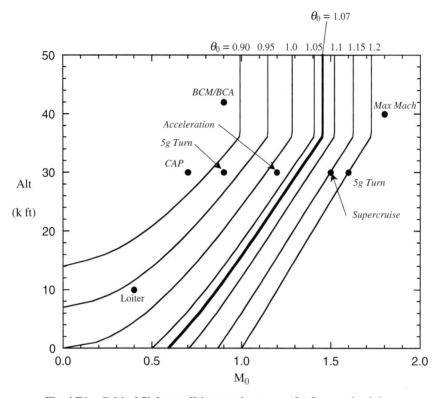

Fig. 4.E1 Critical flight conditions vs theta zero (θ_0) for standard day.

all possible combinations of aircraft flight conditions and engine design points. Instead, a few critical flight conditions having significantly different characteristics and/or large fuel usage (small Π) may be used to establish important trends. For the AAF of the RFP, the following represent such a sample:

1) Takeoff, 100°F at 2,000 ft—High thrust is required at a flight condition ($\theta_0 > 1.07$) where the engine operation is T_{t4} limited. This is not plotted in Fig. 4.E1 because the flight condition does not occur on a standard day.

2) Subsonic Cruise Climb (BCM/BCA), 0.9M/42 kft—Low fuel consumption is required in phases 3–4 ($\Pi = 0.9736$) and 10–11 ($\Pi = 0.9698$).

3) Supersonic Penetration and Escape Dash, 1.5M/30 kft—High thrust is required to permit low fuel consumption without afterburning (supercruise) in phases 6–7 segment G ($\Pi = 0.9382$) and 8–9 ($\Pi = 0.9795$).

4) Supersonic Acceleration, 1.2M/30 kft—Both high thrust and low fuel consumption with afterburning are required in phases 6–7 segment F ($\Pi = 0.9837$) and 7–8 segment K ($\Pi = 0.9828$).

4.4.2 Component Design Performance Parameters

Referring to the data of Table 4.4, and recognizing that the AAF engine will use the most advanced engine technology available, the design will be based on the following component performance parameters and information:

Description	Input value
Polytropic efficiency	
Fan (e_f)	0.89
Low-pressure compressor (e_{cL})	0.89
High-pressure compressor (e_{cH})	0.90
High-pressure turbine (e_{tH})	0.89
Low-pressure turbine (e_{tL})	0.91
Total pressure ratio	
Inlet ($\pi_{d\,max}$)	0.97
Burner (π_b)	0.96
Mixer ($\pi_{M\,max}$)	0.97
Afterburner (π_{AB})	0.95
Nozzle (π_n)	0.98
Component efficiency	
Burner (η_b)	0.995
Afterburner (η_{AB})	0.97
Mechanical	
Low-pressure spool (η_{mL})	0.995
High-pressure spool (η_{mH})	0.995
Power takeoff—LP spool (η_{mPL})	0.995
Power takeoff—HP spool (η_{mPH})	0.995
Fuel (JP-8) heating value (h_{PR})	18,400 Btu/lbm
Main burner exit ($T_{t4\,max}$)	$\leq 3400°$R
Afterburner (T_{t7})	$3600°$R
Turbine cooling air	
$T_{t4\,max} > 2400°$R	$\varepsilon_1 = \varepsilon_2 = (T_{t4\,max} - 2400)/16{,}000$
$T_{t4\,max} \leq 2400°$R	$\varepsilon_1 = \varepsilon_2 = 0$

4.4.3 Analysis of Results

The ONX parametric computer program accompanying this textbook was used to study 60 different design point combinations of the design parameters π_c, π_f, α, T_{t4}, and T_{t7} for the three flight conditions selected as critical for fuel consumption in Sec. 4.4.1. The carpet plots in Figs. 4.E2–4.E6 are the results of this study for the most promising combinations of design choices. The results are plotted as uninstalled specific fuel consumption vs uninstalled specific thrust. The required uninstalled specific fuel consumption (S) is plotted in order to allow for convenient comparison with the estimated value of the uninstalled fuel consumption. Please note that $\alpha = 0$ corresponds to a zero bypass turbofan, normally known as a turbojet. Incorporation of the engine control into the parametric analysis requires that T_{t4} be limited to values less than T_{t4max} for flight conditions where θ_0 is less than the throttle ratio (TR). The value of T_{t4} for these flight conditions can be calculated using (see Appendix D)

$$T_{t4} = \frac{\theta_0}{TR} T_{t4max} \tag{4.35}$$

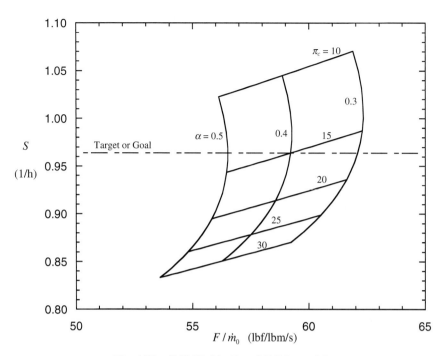

Fig. 4.E2   BCM/BCA, T_{t4} = 2613°R, no AB.

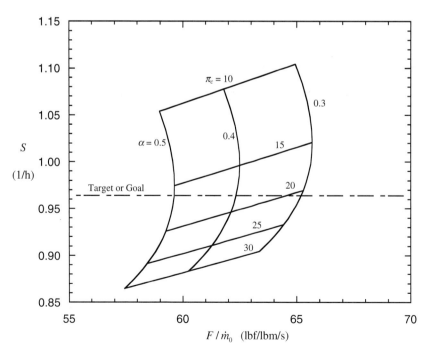

Fig. 4.E3   BCM/BCA, T_{t4} = 2776°R, no AB.

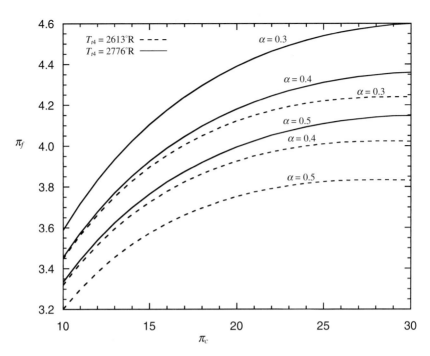

Fig. 4.E4   BCM/BCA, fan pressure ratio vs compressor pressure ratio, $T_{t4} = 2613$ **and 2776°R.**

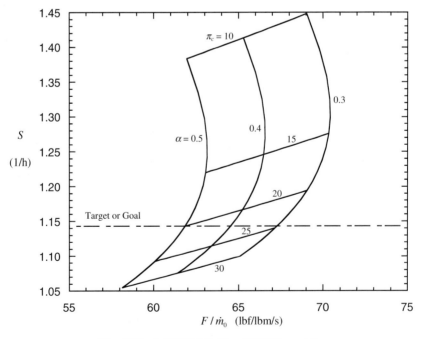

Fig. 4.E5   1.5M/30 kft, $T_{t4} = 3200°R$, **no AB.**

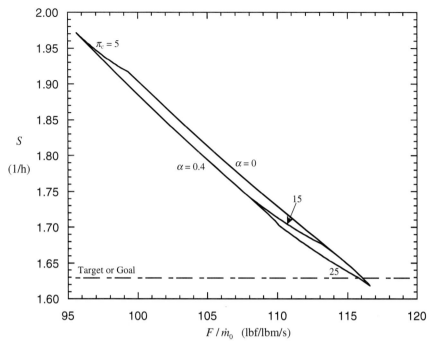

Fig. 4.E6   1.2M/30 kft, T_{t4} = 3059°R, T_{t7} = 3600°R.

The design T_{t4} and the target or goal S values are presented in Table 4.E1 for the three flight conditions of interest.

Subsonic cruise climb BCM/BCA, 0.9M/42 kft.   Examination of the carpet plots of the computed results in Figs. 4.E2 and 4.E3 reveals that the uninstalled specific fuel consumption (S) and specific thrust ($F/\dot{m}_0$) depend strongly upon bypass ratio (α) and compressor pressure ratio (π_c). Comparison of Figs. 4.E2 and 4.E3 shows the familiar result that both S and $F/\dot{m}_0$ increase along with peak cycle temperature (T_{t4}). On the other hand, Fig. 4.E4 shows that fan pressure ratio (π_f) increases with π_c and T_{t4} and decreases with α. Consequently, the focus here

Table 4.E1   Combustor temperatures and fuel consumption goals

Flight condition	Mach	Altitude, kft	θ_0	T_{t4max}	T_{t4}	TSFC	Target or goal S[a]
BCM/BCA	0.9	42	0.8737	3200	2613	1.015	0.964
				3400	2776		
Supercruise	1.5	30	1.151	3200	3200	1.203	1.143
Acceleration	1.2	30	1.023	3200	3059	1.714	1.629

[a]Based on data in Sec. 3.4.1 and a 5% installation loss.

will be upon the selection of useful ranges of α and π_c, and consideration of π_f and T_{t4} will be delayed pending later results.

Increasing α alone causes both $F/\dot{m}_0$ and S to decrease, in accordance with normal expectations for subsonic turbofan engines, as the available exhaust kinetic energy is spread over more incoming air. Because the slope of the line of constant π_c shows that $F/\dot{m}_0$ is decreasing percentage-wise roughly twice as fast as S, it does not seem advisable to choose an α greater than 0.5. Conversely, because S meets the target or goal for moderate to high pressure ratios, no α less than 0.3 should be considered. Thus, the best α for this flight condition is probably in the range of 0.3–0.5.

Increasing π_c alone produces a more complex behavior of $F/\dot{m}_0$ and S because a maximum of $F/\dot{m}_0$ occurs while S continuously decreases. This behavior is typical of turbine engines, as demonstrated in Refs. 1 and 2. The maximum value of $F/\dot{m}_0$ is due to the simple fact that increasing values of π_c (and thus T_{t3}) eventually limit the amount of fuel than can be added before the allowable T_{t4} is reached. One should logically select values of π_c that are located below the knee of the curve, but not so far below that $F/\dot{m}_0$ is falling rapidly for slight reductions in S. Moreover, no π_c should be chosen that exceeds reasonable expectations, with that value today being in the range of 35–40. Computations reveal, however, that π_c cannot reach that limit at high Mach flight conditions before T_{t3} exceed s current capabilities ($T_{t3\max} > 1700°R$). Taken together, these reasons indicate that π_c should be held in the range of 20–30 for this flight condition.

Supersonic penetration and escape dash, 1.5M/30 kft. Very similar remarks to those just stated, both qualitative and quantitative, can be made about the influence of π_c, π_f, α, and T_{t4} on S and $F/\dot{m}_0$ at this flight condition. The main differences, as illustrated by the carpet plot of Fig. 4.E5, are that $F/\dot{m}_0$ decreases more rapidly with π_c as well as less rapidly with α in the critical area below the knee and that there is no sign of choking of the core flow at the highest allowable values of π_c. Taking these factors into account, including the special need for high thrust at this flight condition, the useful ranges of parameters are $15 < \pi_c < 25$ and $0.3 < \alpha < 0.4$.

Supersonic acceleration, 1.2M/30 kft. The carpet plot of the computed results in Fig. 4.E6 reveal that both S can be reduced and $F/\dot{m}_0$ increased by increasing π_c and reducing α. Again, changing either T_{t4} or T_{t7} would have the usual effect of increasing both S and $F/\dot{m}_0$.

By this time it has become clear that the desired fuel consumption goals can be achieved at some flight conditions, but not all. Consequently, the focus of our search must continue to be on reduced fuel consumption over the entire mission. Otherwise, the takeoff weight (W_{TO}) of the AAF will certainly grow beyond the initial estimate of Chapter 3 and, because Eq. (3.49), which determines W_{TO}, is extremely nonlinear, W_{TO} could become unacceptably large. While it is still possible that S will be reduced when the engine is throttled back to the required thrust, or the installation penalties will be less than estimated, or the TSFC models of Table 4.E1 are conservative, nothing may yet be taken for granted.

Consequently, the engine performance information generated at this flight condition shows that $20 < \pi_c < 30$ and $0 < \alpha < 0.4$. The results obtained so far suggest that T_{t4} and T_{t7} must be limited in order to achieve acceptable fuel consumption, even though increasing them will increase specific thrust and thereby reduce the size of the required engine. Their limits will be arbitrarily selected as $T_{t4} = 3200°R$ and $T_{t7} = 3600°R$ because even these values will push the material and cooling capabilities expected to be available for the AAF (see Table 4.4). These assumptions, as well as any others, can be changed if later calculations indicate a positive benefit.

4.4.4 Integrated Results: Range of Design Choices

Before the final ranges of interest for key engine reference point parameters are selected, two facts must be recognized. First, it makes sense to state them only in conjunction with a specific flight condition (i.e., P_0, T_0, and M_0), preferably one that will be near the final reference point. Because the AAF must operate well over the $0.9 < M_0 < 1.8/30–45$ kft range, it is reasonable to conclude that the reference point will be in the vicinity of 1.5M/35 kft. Second, any selection must take into account the normal behavior of parameters when the engine is operating off-design. A sensible goal is for the key engine parameters to be in their best ranges at all critical operating points. Thus, the engine will appear to be properly designed for each.

The three critical operating points were therefore added to scaled Figs. 4.6 and 4.8, which are representative of the type of engine emerging for the AAF application, and the results reproduced here as Figs. 4.E7 and 4.E8.

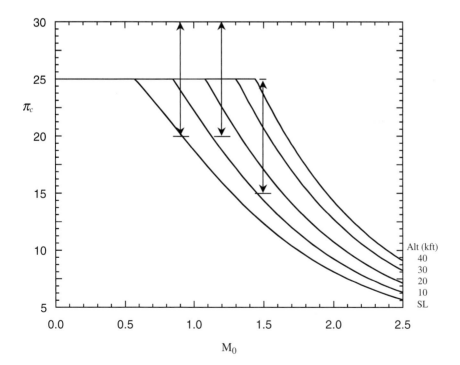

Fig. 4.E7   Compressor integrated results.

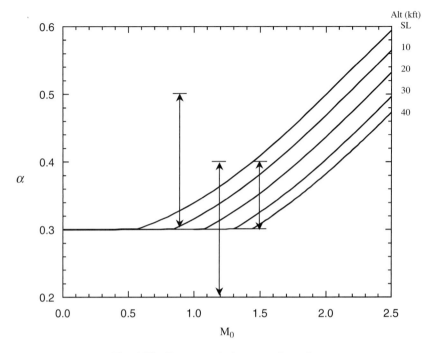

Fig. 4.E8   Bypass ratio integrated results.

Referring to Fig. 4.E7, it can be seen that both the desired and available π_c decrease with M_0, so that selecting the range $15 < \pi_c < 25$ at 1.5M/35 kft will provide the desired π_c at other flight conditions. In other words, using the trends of Fig. 4.E7 and imagining that the reference point is moved through the range $15 < \pi_c < 25$ at 1.5M/35 kft, one sees that the desirable π_c at other flight conditions will be included.

Referring to Fig. 4.E8, it can be seen that the situation is different, and that only the relatively small range of $0.3 < \alpha < 0.4$ at the reference point of 1.5M/35 kft will provide desirable α at the other critical flight conditions.

The foregoing reasoning leads to the final choices for the most promising ranges of key engine design parameters:

$$1.2 \leq M_0 \leq 1.6$$

$$30 \leq h \leq 45\,\text{kft}$$

$$15 \leq \pi_c \leq 25$$

$$0.3 \leq \alpha \leq 0.4$$

$$3 \leq \pi_f \leq 5$$

$$T_{t4} \leq 3200°\text{R}$$

$$T_{t7} \leq 3600°\text{R}$$

$$0.35 \leq M_6 \leq 0.45$$

A good first design should have both the compressor pressure ratio and the combustor exit temperature at their maximum values at a theta break θ_0 equal to the *TR* (see Appendix D). In this case the *TR* has initially been chosen to be 1.07, which would correspond, for example, to 1.318 Mach at 30 kft or 1.454 Mach at any altitude above the tropopause. Consequently, the selection of h depends on the choice of M_0 and vice versa.

4.4.5 Sensitivity Analysis

The power of the parametric engine cycle performance calculations can be better understood and appreciated by means of this final investigation known as a sensitivity analysis. This is a process in which the percentage change of all output quantities with respect to the percentage change of each independent input quantity is determined by varying the input parameters only slightly and one at a time. For example, if one is interested in how sensitive the specific fuel consumption (S) is to the cycle bypass ratio (α) alone, one would form the quantity

$$\frac{(S_2 - S_1)/S_1}{(\alpha_2 - \alpha_1)/\alpha_1} = \frac{\delta S}{\delta \alpha}$$

from two successive reference point calculations that differ only in $\delta\alpha \ll \alpha$. Such ratios, in the limit, represent the mathematical slopes or derivatives that are generally too difficult to obtain in closed form for such a complex set of equations.

The qualitative meaning of these ratios is easy to grasp. When they are very small compared to one, the input variable has little influence on the output variable. If the entire array were very small compared to one, the design point would be located on some type of a plateau, perhaps near to an optimum. Those ratios of the order of one offer the opportunity for improvement and point out the desired direction of change.

Consider the sensitivity of specific thrust and thrust specific fuel consumption to changes in flight conditions and engine design choices for a mixed flow turbofan engine having the component performance design values corresponding to those of the printout reproduced in Sec. 4.2.7, which has the engine reference point

$$M_0 = 1.6 \qquad \alpha = 0.4$$
$$\text{Alt} = 35 \text{ kft} \qquad T_{t4} = 3200^\circ\text{R}$$
$$\pi_c = 16 \qquad T_{t7} = 3600^\circ\text{R}$$
$$\pi_f = 3.8 \qquad P_0/P_9 = 1$$

Table 4.E2 presents the computed sensitivity of $F/\dot{m}_0$ and S to changes in the design choices at the engine reference point. These data were obtained from a fractional change of $+0.05$ in each design choice given. Because S and $F/\dot{m}_0$ are at a minimum and maximum respectively for $P_0/P_9 = 1.0$, the sensitivities are shown for a ($+$) and ($-$) variation in P_0/P_9. From the table, the sensitivity of thrust specific fuel consumption to a change in bypass ratio, for example, is seen to be

$$\frac{\delta S}{\delta \alpha} = -0.0723 \text{ mil power}$$

$$= +0.0341 \text{ max power}$$

Table 4.E2   Sensitivity analysis

Fractional Variation of/with	Military power		Maximum power	
	$F/\dot{m}_0$	S	$F/\dot{m}_0$	S
T_{t4}	+1.0526	+0.5872	+0.2165	−0.0976
T_{t7}	——	——	+0.8437	+0.8411
π_c	−0.0914	−0.1464	+0.0301	−0.0375
π_f	−0.0091	+0.0069	−0.0063	+0.0068
α	−0.2098	−0.0723	−0.0369	+0.0341
M_6	−0.0026	+0.0034	−0.0022	+0.0023
P_0/P_9	−0.0039	+0.0034	−0.0033	+0.0034
	+0.0042	−0.0052	+0.0035	−0.0045
M_0	−0.5956	+0.0706	−0.1965	+0.0613
Alt	+0.1900	−0.0362	+0.1109	−0.0715

neither of which shows a significant sensitivity of S to α. Fortunately, this insensitivity is not typical of all of the results of the analysis.

Referring to Table 4.E2, and recalling that everything possible must be done to reduce S, particularly at military power, there seem to be several useful indications, namely:

1) An overall mission improvement in fuel consumption can be achieved by reducing both T_{t4} and T_{t7}, but only at the expense of a considerably larger reduction in $F/\dot{m}_0$, and hence an increase in the size of the engine(s). The message here confirms earlier conclusions regarding the necessity to put upper limits on T_{t4} and T_{t7} in order to achieve fuel consumption goals. In that sense no real benefits result from making the engine "hotter."

2) Relatively large changes of π_c, π_f, and α are required to measurably impact $F/\dot{m}_0$ and S, particularly in maximum power. The most promising possibility is to increase π_c, which improves both $F/\dot{m}_0$ and S with and without afterburning. Next in line for consideration is an increase of π_f, provided that the decrease of military power $F/\dot{m}_0$ is tolerable. Because changing α has such conflicting effects, no clear advice for its final selection is yet available.

3) Changing M_6 has no performance consequences. Performance cannot be improved by changing P_9/P_0 and, as expected, it will suffer if P_9 is taken far from P_0 and the exhaust nozzle is incorrectly expanded.

4) For completeness, the sensitivity of engine performance to reference point Mach number and altitude has also been included. The large apparent benefits of reducing Mach number and increasing altitude are illusory, because the flight conditions are specified by the RFP and the gains would be lost when the engine is returned to the present reference point (i.e., 1.5M/35 kft). Nevertheless, in order to understand engine behavior more fully, recall that for any single exhaust stream jet engine

$$\frac{F}{\dot{m}_0} = \frac{\eta_o f h_{PR}}{a_0 M_0}$$

and

$$S = \frac{\dot{m}_f}{F} = \frac{a_0 M_0}{\eta_o h_{PR}}$$

where η_o is the overall cycle energy conversion efficiency from fuel energy to thrust work (see Appendix E). Because η_o varies relatively slowly with flight conditions, the overwhelming effect of decreasing M_0 or decreasing a_0 (i.e., increasing altitude) is to improve both $F/\dot{m}_0$ and S. Thus, the ranges of M_0 and h are retained in the parameters only to allow the effects of different mission balance points to be examined.

These sensitivity analysis results lead to the conclusions that π_f and π_c should be selected from the high ends of their respective ranges, while T_{t4} and/or T_{t7} should be allowed to drift down from their limiting values. Meanwhile, changes of α and M_{16} will not have a significant impact on the leading propulsion performance parameters.

References

[1]Oates, G. C., *The Aerothermodynamics of Gas Turbine and Rocket Propulsion*, 3rd ed., AIAA Education Series, AIAA, Reston, VA, 1997.

[2]Mattingly, J. D., *Elements of Gas Turbine Propulsion*, McGraw–Hill, New York, 1996.

[3]"Gas Turbine Engine Performance Station Identification and Nomenclature." Society of Automotive Engineers, Aerospace Recommended Practice (ARP) 755A, Warrendale, PA, 1974.

[4]Reynolds, W. C., and Perkins, H. C., *Engineering thermodynamics*, 2nd ed., McGraw–Hill, New York, 1977.

[5]U.S. Dept. of Defense, "Model Specification for Engines, Aircraft, Turbojet," Military Specification MIL-E-5008B, Washington, DC, Jan. 1959.

[6]Oates, G. C., "Performance Estimation for Turbofans with and Without Mixers," *Journal of Propulsion and Power*, Vol. 1, No. 3, 1985, pp. 252–256.

[7]Gordon, S., and McBride, B., "Computer Program for Calculation of Complex Chemical Equilibrium Compositions," NASA SP-273, 1971.

5
Engine Selection: Performance Cycle Analysis

5.1 Concept

The parametric cycle analysis of Chapter 4 showed how reference point (design point or on-design) engine performance was determined by design choices. This made it possible to examine trends in engine specific performance (specific thrust and thrust specific fuel consumption) with changes in design variables and to begin to narrow the desirable range for each design parameter. Now that the first steps have been taken toward finding an optimum engine for a particular application, it is time to determine an engine's steady state operating performance.

The object of performance cycle analysis is to determine the engine's performance over its operating envelope. The performance of several different engines can then be compared to reveal trends in engine performance with design choices. Thus, it is possible to focus in on the most promising designs and to ultimately find the engine reference point that has the best balanced performance over the whole mission spectrum. Once an engine cycle and its design choices are made, the results of the performance cycle analysis are used to size the engine by the methods presented in Chapter 6. The performance of a selected engine can also serve to determine how well the thrust lapse model and the fuel consumption estimates, used in the constraint and mission analyses of Chapters 2 and 3, are met by the engine.

Performance analysis differs significantly from parametric analysis. In parametric (reference or design point) cycle analysis all of the design choices (including the flight conditions) are free to be selected by the designer, and the engine performance characteristics per unit mass flow are determined for each selected set of choices. In contrast, in performance cycle analysis the design choices have been made, and the performance of this specific reference point engine is needed at all possible operating conditions. The independent variables in performance analysis are flight conditions, throttle settings, and nozzle settings. Once the engine is sized and the mass flow rate specified, performance analysis is employed to determine how a selected engine performs at all operating conditions within its flight envelope.

The mental image usually attached to this stage of development is that of an engine of fixed configuration that we have manufactured for testing in a facility that can simulate the desired flight conditions (see Appendix E). Although the absolute size of the engine may be arbitrary during performance analysis, and we may lack most of the details of the geometry of the individual components, it is still best to think of it as a piece of hardware that we have built in order to explore the behavior of this reference point engine.

For performance analysis, individual component performance can be modeled as a function of operating conditions or actual component characteristics can be obtained from component hardware performance data. These two approaches

A)

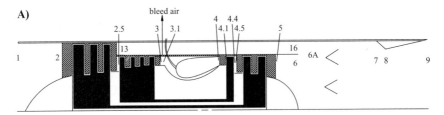

Fig. 5.1a   Reference stations—mixed stream turbofan engine.

correspond to varying degrees of accuracy. In the absence of actual component hardware in a preliminary engine design, simple models of component performance are used to give preliminary estimates of engine performance.

In the following section, relationships are developed for determining the engine performance of the engine cycle whose parametric (reference point) performance was covered in Chapter 4. The analysis is an extension of that presented in Refs. 1 and 2. The task now is to develop design tools in the form of equations and their solution procedures that will permit determination of the component and hence engine performance at any condition.

5.2   Design Tools

5.2.1   The Performance Problem

The performance of a selected design point mixed flow turbofan engine of the type shown in Figs. 5.1a and 5.1b is desired at any flight conditions, throttle settings, and nozzle settings. It is assumed that a parametric (design point) cycle analysis has been performed for the reference point engine using the methods of Chapter 4 to give so-called reference conditions (subscript R) for the engine (S_R, $[F/\dot{m}_0]_R$, etc.), for each engine component (π_{fR}, τ_{fR}, etc.), and for the flight conditions (M_{0R}, P_{0R}, and T_{0R}).

To better understand the performance problem, it is instructive to review how the parametric analysis proceeds. In the *parametric* cycle analysis, Eqs. (H.1–H.16) of Appendix H constitute 16 independent equations for directly finding values of the

B)   power extraction

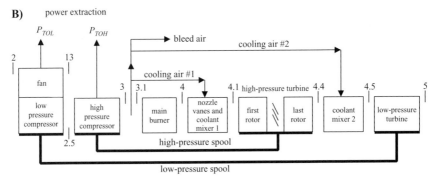

Fig. 5.1b   Reference stations—bleed and turbine cooling air flows.

Table 5.1 Engine performance variables

Component	Independent variable	Constant or known quantity	Dependent variable
Engine	M_0, T_0, P_0	β	$\dot{m}_0, \alpha$
Diffuser	——	$\pi_d = f(M_0)$	——
Fan	——	η_f	π_f, τ_f
Low-pressure compressor	——	η_{cL}	π_{cL}, τ_{cL}
High-pressure compressor	——	η_{cH}	π_{cH}, τ_{cH}
Burner	T_{t4}	π_b	f
Coolant mixer 1	——	ε_1	τ_{m1}
High-pressure turbine	——	η_{tH}, M_4	π_{tH}, τ_{tH}
Coolant mixer 2	——	ε_2	τ_{m2}
Low-pressure turbine	——	$\eta_{tL}, M_{4.5}$	π_{tL}, τ_{tL}
Mixer	——	$\pi_{M\,max}, A_6,$	$\pi_M, \tau_M, \alpha',$
		A_{16}, A_{6A}	M_6, M_{16}, M_{6A}
Afterburner	T_{t7}	π_{ABdry}, π_{AB}	f_{AB}
Exhaust nozzle	P_0/P_9	$\pi_n, A_{8\,dry}$	M_8, M_9
Total number	6	——	24

16 dependent component performance variables in the order $\tau_f, \tau_{cL}, \tau_{cH}, f, \tau_{m1}$, $\tau_{tH}, \pi_{tH}, \tau_{m2}, \tau_{tL}, \pi_{tL}, \alpha', \tau_M, M_{16}, M_{6A}, \pi_M$, and f_{AB} for given values of the independent quantities consisting of flight conditions, aircraft system parameters, and design choices. With values of these 16 component variables in hand, the engine reference point performance in terms of $F/\dot{m}_0, S, \eta_P$, and η_{TH} is readily found.

Similarly, to find the engine performance, the operational performance values of the 24 dependent variables listed in Table 5.1 must be determined and then, in turn, related by 24 independent equations to obtain a solution for each component performance variable. Because performance analysis is an indirect problem as opposed to the direct problem of parametric analysis, the solution of the 24 performance equations is not as straightforward as in the parametric case. Regardless of the difficulty in solving the equations, once the values of the 24 dependent variables in Table 5.1 are known, the engine performance in terms of $f, f_{AB}, F/\dot{m}_0, S, \eta_P$, and η_{TH} follows immediately from Eqs. (4.18), (4.19), (4.14), (4.31), (4.32a), and (4.32b), respectively.

Please notice in the "Constant or known variable" column of Table 5.1 that π_b, π_{AB}, and π_n are assumed to remain constant, that τ_d, τ_{m2}, and τ_n are assumed equal to one, and that π_{m1} is contained in π_{tH}. Also please be aware that, because power extraction is considered in the analysis, a preliminary estimate of $\dot{m}_0$ {Eq. (4.33) and Table 4.1} is required to proceed with the performance analyses. The correct value of $\dot{m}_0$ is finally determined when the engine is sized (see Chapter 6).

5.2.2 Assumptions

The engine of interest is shown in Figs. 5.1a and 5.1b, where the notation of Chapter 4 has been retained. *In addition to the assumptions summarized in Sec. 4.2.6*, the following assumptions are employed in performance analysis:

1) The flow areas are constant at stations 4, 4.5, 6, 16, 6A, and 8 dry (afterburner off).

2) The flow is choked at the high-pressure turbine entrance nozzles (choking area 4), at the low-pressure turbine entrance nozzles (choking area 4.5), and at the exhaust nozzle (station 8). Because the exhaust nozzle may unchoke at low throttle settings and affect the fan operating line (see Fig. 7.E10), the case of the unchoked exhaust nozzle (station 8) is also included in this analysis.

3) The component efficiencies (η_f, η_{cL}, η_{cH}, η_b, η_{tH}, η_{tL}, η_{AB}, η_{mL}, η_{mH}, η_{mPL}, and η_{mPH}) and total pressure ratios (π_b, $\pi_{M\,max}$, π_{ABdry}, and π_n) do not change from their design values.

4) Bleed air and cooling air fractions are constant. Power takeoffs are constant.

5) The air and combustion gases are modeled as perfect gases in thermodynamic equilibrium, and their properties are based on the NASA Glenn thermochemical data and the Gordon–McBride equilibrium algorithm reference.[8]

6) The simplifying gas model of a calorically perfect gas is included in the analysis. It assumes that the gases are calorically perfect upstream and downstream of the burner and afterburner and values of γ_t, c_{pt}, γ_{AB}, and c_{pAB} do not vary with throttle setting, but included is the variation of γ and c_p due to mixing with bypass ratio. For this model, fuel-air ratios f and f_{AB} are ignored when compared with unity.

7) The exit area A_9 of the exhaust nozzle is adjustable so that the pressure ratio P_0/P_9 can be set to a predetermined value.

8) The area at each engine station is constant. However the area of station 8 changes with the afterburner setting to maintain constant pressure at the mixer exit or nozzle entrance.

9) The diffuser total pressure ratio, π_d, is given by Eqs. (4.12a–4.12d).

5.2.3   Referencing and the Mass Flow Parameter (MFP)

Two techniques are worthy of discussion at this point to prepare the path for their efficient and frequent use in the analysis to follow. The first is called referencing and involves the use of reference point conditions to evaluate constants appearing in equations for the dependent performance variables. The second exploits the mass flow parameter, introduced in Sec. 1.9.3, to capitalize on the law of conservation of mass.

Referencing.   The functional relations for engine cycle analysis are based on the application of mass, energy, momentum, and entropy considerations to the one-dimensional steady flow of a perfect gas at an engine reference or off-design steady state operating point. Thus, if at any off-design point

$$f(\tau, \pi) = \text{constant}$$

represents a relationship between the two performance variables τ and π at a steady state operating point, then the constant can be evaluated at the reference point, so that

$$f(\tau, \pi) = f(\tau_R, \pi_R) = \text{constant}$$

because $f(\tau, \pi)$ applies to both on-design and off-design points. This technique for replacing constants with reference point values is used frequently in the performance analysis to follow.

Mass flow parameter.   The mass flow parameter (*MFP*) is defined as the grouping $\dot{m}\sqrt{T_t}/P_t A$ that can be written as

$$MFP = \frac{\dot{m}\sqrt{T_t}}{P_t A} = M\sqrt{\frac{\gamma g_c}{R}} \frac{P}{P_t}\sqrt{\frac{T_t}{T}}$$

The static to total pressure and temperature ratios (P/P_t, T/T_t) are functions of the total temperature of gas, chemical equilibrium properties, and the Mach number. Thus the mass flow parameter can be written in the following functional form:

$$MFP = \frac{\dot{m}\sqrt{T_t}}{P_t A} = M\sqrt{\frac{\gamma g_c}{R}} \frac{P}{P_t}\sqrt{\frac{T_t}{T}} = MFP(M, T_t, f) \qquad (4.24)$$

The subroutine RGCOMP that is used to calculate the compressible flow functions (P/P_t, T/T_t, and MFP) is given in Appendix F. For the simplifying case of the calorically perfect gas, the properties P/P_t, T/T_t, and MFP are given by

$$\frac{T}{T_t} = \left(1 + \frac{\gamma - 1}{2}M^2\right)^{-1} \qquad (1.1)$$

$$\frac{P}{P_t} = \left(1 + \frac{\gamma - 1}{2}M^2\right)^{-\frac{\gamma}{\gamma-1}} \qquad (1.2)$$

$$MFP = \frac{\dot{m}\sqrt{T_t}}{P_t A} = M\sqrt{\frac{\gamma g_c}{R}}\left(1 + \frac{\gamma - 1}{2}M^2\right)^{\frac{\gamma+1}{2(1-\gamma)}} \qquad (1.3)$$

5.2.4   Performance of Turbines with/without Coolant Mixers

The first step in determining the performance of the entire engine at conditions away from the reference point is to analyze the behavior of the high- and low-pressure turbines. This is greatly expedited by the fact that they are both deliberately designed to be choked in their entrance stator airfoil or vane passages, and that the static pressure downstream of the low-pressure turbine is tied to the mixer entrance conditions. As you will see in the development that follows, this both restricts turbines to a very narrow range of operation and furnishes us with a straightforward method of solution. The remainder of the engine performance analysis flows directly from this step because the turbines, in conjunction with the throttle setting (i.e., T_{t4}), provide the power for the fan and compressors and control the fan and compressor mass flows (see Sec. 5.2.5).

The performance (π_t and τ_t) of a turbine at off-design is primarily determined by the efficiency and mass conservation relationships. It is shown in Ref. 1 that π_{tH} and τ_{tH} remain constant for an uncooled turbine with constant specific heats (calorically perfect gas). Similarly, as shown below, these ratios can be considered constant for a cooled turbine with constant specific heats (calorically perfect gas).

When a cooled turbine with variable specific heats is modeled, it is found that π_{tH} and τ_{tH} vary only slightly with engine operating condition.

It is also shown in Ref. 1 that π_{tL} and τ_{tL} are constant in an uncooled low-pressure turbine with calorically perfect gas for a turbofan engine having choked separate (unmixed) fan and core streams. For a mixed flow turbofan, on the other hand, these ratios cannot be considered constant because π_{tL} (and hence τ_{tL}) must modulate at off-design conditions to maintain $P_6 = P_{16}$, the Kutta condition, at the mixer entrance.

Variable specific heats. Consider a high-pressure turbine with cooling air fractions ε_1 and ε_2 modeled as in Fig. 5.1b. Let the nozzle throat stations just downstream of stations 4 and 4.5 be denoted by $4'$ and $4.5'$. With choked flow at stations $4'$ and $4.5'$, Eq. (4.24) yields, assuming $P_{t4} = P_{t4'}$ and $P_{t4.5} = P_{t4.5'}$

$$\frac{\dot{m}_{4'}}{\dot{m}_{4.5'}} \frac{P_{t4.5}/P_{t4}}{\sqrt{T_{t4.5}/T_{t4}}} \frac{A_{4.5'}}{A_{4'}} = \frac{MFP(M_{4'}, T_{t4}, f)}{MFP(M_{4.5'}, T_{t4.5}, f_{4.5})}$$

or, since $\pi_{m2} = 1$, $\pi_{tH} = P_{t4.4}/P_{t4}$ and

$$\frac{\dot{m}_{4.5'}}{\dot{m}_4} = \frac{\dot{m}_4 + \dot{m}_C(\varepsilon_1 + \varepsilon_2)}{\dot{m}_4} = 1 + \frac{(\varepsilon_1 + \varepsilon_2)}{(1 - \beta - \varepsilon_1 - \varepsilon_2)(1 + f)}$$

then

$$\frac{\pi_{tH}}{\sqrt{T_{t4.5}/T_{t4}}} = \left\{ 1 + \frac{(\varepsilon_1 + \varepsilon_2)}{(1 - \beta - \varepsilon_1 - \varepsilon_2)(1 + f)} \right\} \frac{A_{4'}}{A_{4.5'}} \frac{MFP(M_{4'}, T_{t4}, f)}{MFP(M_{4.5'}, T_{t4.5}, f_{4.5})}$$

$$(5.1)$$

where the right-hand side of the equation is essentially constant for the assumptions of this analysis, namely $A_{4'}/A_{4.5'} = $ constant, $M_{4'} = 1$, $M_{4.5'} = 1$, and constant bleed and cooling airflow fractions. Since

$$f_{4.5} = \frac{f}{1 + f + (\varepsilon_1 + \varepsilon_2)/(1 - \beta - \varepsilon_1 - \varepsilon_2)} \qquad (4.8j)$$

then for a specific value of T_{t4} and f, Eq. (5.1) can be used to calculate π_{tH} for an assumed value of $T_{t4.5}$.

Likewise, for given values of T_{t4}, f, π_{tH}, and η_{tH}, the resultant turbine exit temperature ($T_{t4.5}$) can be determined as follows:

1) The total enthalpy at state $t4.1(h_{t4.1})$ follows from that at state $t4(h_{t4})$ and the total enthalpy ratio of coolant mixer 1 (τ_{m1}).

$$h_{t4.1} = h_{t4} \frac{h_{t4.1}}{h_{t4}} = h_{t4}\tau_{m1} \qquad (5.2a)$$

where τ_{m1} is given by

$$\tau_{m1} = \frac{(1 - \beta - \varepsilon_1 - \varepsilon_2)(1 + f) + \varepsilon_1 \tau_r \tau_{cL} \tau_{cH}/\tau_\lambda}{(1 - \beta - \varepsilon_1 - \varepsilon_2)(1 + f) + \varepsilon_1} \qquad (4.20a)$$

and

$$f_{4.1} = \frac{f}{1 + f + \varepsilon_1/(1 - \beta - \varepsilon_1 - \varepsilon_2)} \qquad (4.8i)$$

2) With state $t4.1$ known and using Eq. (4.9d), the reduced pressure at the ideal exit state $t4.4i$ ($P_{r\,t4.4i}$) follows from its value at state $t4.1$ ($P_{r\,t4.1}$) and the turbine total pressure ratio (π_{tH}).

$$P_{r\,t4.4i} = \pi_{tH} P_{r\,t4.1} \tag{4.9d}$$

3) With $P_{r\,t4.4i}$ known and noting that $f_{4.4} = f_{4.1}$, then $h_{t4.4i}$ is known using the subroutine FAIR. The total enthalpy ratio of the ideal turbine (τ_{tHi}) follows directly using its definition

$$\tau_{tHi} = h_{t4.4i}/h_{t4.1} \tag{4.9d}$$

4) By the assumption of constant efficiency of the high-pressure turbine, Eq. (4.9d) can be solved for the high-pressure turbine enthalpy ratio (τ_{tH})

$$\tau_{tH} = 1 - \eta_{tH}(1 - \tau_{tHi}) \tag{5.2b}$$

5) With the total enthalpy ratio of coolant mixer 2 (τ_{m2}) given by

$$\tau_{m2} = \frac{(1 - \beta - \varepsilon_1 - \varepsilon_2)(1 + f) + \varepsilon_1 + \varepsilon_2\{\tau_r \tau_{cH} \tau_{cL}/(\tau_\lambda \tau_{m1} \tau_{tH})\}}{(1 - \beta - \varepsilon_1 - \varepsilon_2)(1 + f) + \varepsilon_1 + \varepsilon_2} \tag{4.20b}$$

and $f_{4.5}$ given by Eq. (4.8j), the total enthalpy at station 4.5 ($h_{t4.5}$) can be calculated using

$$h_{t4.5} = h_{t4}\frac{h_{t4.1}}{h_{t4}}\frac{h_{t4.4}}{h_{t4.1}}\frac{h_{t4.5}}{h_{t4.4}} = h_{t4}\tau_{m1}\tau_{tH}\tau_{m2} \tag{5.2c}$$

6) With $h_{t4.5}$ and $f_{4.5}$ known, $T_{t4.5}$ follows directly using the subroutine FAIR. We will refer to this system of equations used to determine $T_{t4.5}$ as Eq. (5.2).

Equations (5.1) and (5.2) give us a system of equations to satisfy that determine the high-pressure turbine performance τ_{tH} and π_{tH}. This system of equations is programmed into the cooled turbine subroutine TURBC outlined in Appendix F. Subroutine TURBC solves this system by first assuming an initial value of $T_{t4.5}$ and using Eq. (5.1) to find π_{tH}. Using this value of π_{tH}, Eq. (5.2) gives a new value of total temperature at station 4.5 called $T_{t4.5n}$. This new value is input into Eq. (5.1) and calculations are repeated until successive values are within 0.01. Figure 5.2 shows the variation of π_{tH} with throttle setting (T_{t4}) for a typical mixed flow turbofan engine. Note that π_{tH} only varies 0.9%, which shows the common assumption used in the constant specific heat analysis that $\pi_{tH} = $ constant is a very good approximation.

A similar, but simpler, set of equations can be solved for the uncooled low pressure turbine. Writing Eq. (5.1) for the low-pressure turbine gives

$$\frac{\pi_{tL}}{\sqrt{T_{t5}/T_{t4.5}}} = \frac{A_{4.5'}}{A_5}\frac{MFP(M_{4.5'}, T_{t4.5}, f_{4.5})}{MFP(M_5, T_{t5}, f_{4.5})}$$

Because the flow is assumed to be isentropic from engine station 5 to station 6 and we know the area at station 6, we use the Mach number and area at engine station 6 for the low-pressure turbine exit and write

$$\frac{\pi_{tL}}{\sqrt{T_{t5}/T_{t4.5}}} = \frac{A_{4.5'}}{A_6}\frac{MFP(M_{4.5'}, T_{t4.5}, f_{4.5})}{MFP(M_6, T_{t5}, f_{4.5})} \tag{5.3}$$

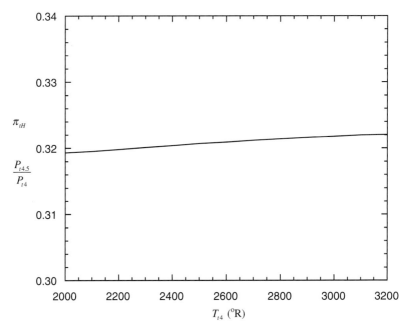

Fig. 5.2 **Variation of high pressure turbine pressure ratio with throttle setting (T_{t4}) for a typical mixed flow turbofan engine.**

where $A_{4.5'}/A_6 = $ constant and $M_{4.5'} = 1$. Then for a specific value of $T_{t4.5}$, $f_{4.5}$, and M_6, Eq. (5.3) can be used to calculate π_{tL} for an assumed value of T_{t5}.

Likewise, for given values of $T_{t4.5}$, $f_{4.5}$, π_{tL}, η_{tL}, and M_6, the resultant turbine exit temperature (T_{t5}) can be determined as follows:

1) Using Eq. (4.9e), the reduced pressure at the ideal exit state $t5i$ ($P_{r\,t5i}$) follows from its value at state $t4.5$ ($P_{r\,t4.5}$) and the turbine total pressure ratio (π_{tL}).

$$P_{r\,t5i} = \pi_{tL} P_{r\,t4.5} \tag{4.9e}$$

2) With $P_{r\,t5i}$ known, then h_{t5i} is known using the subroutine FAIR. The total enthalpy ratio of the ideal turbine (τ_{tLi}) follows directly using its definition:

$$\tau_{tLi} = h_{t5i}/h_{t4.5} \tag{4.9e}$$

3) By the assumption of constant efficiency of the low-pressure turbine, Eq. (4.9e) can be solved for the low-pressure turbine enthalpy ratio (τ_{tL})

$$\tau_{tL} = 1 - \eta_{tL}(1 - \tau_{tLi}) \tag{5.4}$$

4) T_{t5} follows directly using the subroutine FAIR.

We will refer to this system of equations used to determine T_{t5} as Eq. (5.4).

Equations (5.3) and (5.4) give us a system of equations to satisfy that determine the low-pressure turbine performance π_{tL} and τ_{tL}. This system of equations is programmed into the uncooled turbine subroutine TURB outlined in Appendix F. Subroutine TURB solves this system by first assuming an initial value of T_{t5} and using Eq. (5.3) to find π_{tL}. Using this value of π_{tL}, Eq. (5.4) gives a new value of total temperature at station 5 called T_{t5n}. This new value is input into Eq. (5.3), and calculations are repeated until successive values are within 0.01.

Constant specific heats.   In the case of a perfect gas with constant specific heats [calorically perfect gas (CPG)], the equations that model the performance of the high-pressure and low-pressure turbines are simplified. The mass flow parameter for a CPG is given by Eq. (1.3). Since the *MFP* is the same at stations 4' and 4.5' when $M_{4'} = M_{4.5'} = 1$, $\gamma_{4'} = \gamma_{4.5'} = \gamma_t$, and $R_{4'} = R_{4.5'} = R_t$, then Eq. (5.1) becomes

$$\frac{\pi_{tH}}{\sqrt{\tau_{tH}}} = \left\{1 + \frac{(\varepsilon_1 + \varepsilon_2)}{(1 - \beta - \varepsilon_1 - \varepsilon_2)(1 + f)}\right\} \frac{A_{4'}}{A_{4.5'}} \sqrt{\tau_{m1} \tau_{m2}} \quad \text{(5.1a-CPG)}$$

where

$$\frac{A_{4'}}{A_{4.5'}} = \text{constant}$$

and where, by the assumptions of Sec. 5.2.2,

$$1 + \frac{(\varepsilon_1 + \varepsilon_2)}{(1 - \beta - \varepsilon_1 - \varepsilon_2)(1 + f)} = \text{constant}$$

and where, combining Eqs. (4.20a) and (4.20b),

$$\tau_{m1} \tau_{m2} = \left[1 + \frac{(\varepsilon_1 + \varepsilon_2/\tau_{tH})\tau_r \tau_{cL} \tau_{cH}/\tau_\lambda}{(1 - \beta - \varepsilon_1 - \varepsilon_2)(1 + f)}\right] \Big/ \left[1 + \frac{\varepsilon_1 + \varepsilon_2}{(1 - \beta - \varepsilon_1 - \varepsilon_2)(1 + f)}\right]$$

$$\text{(5.1b-CPG)}$$

Consider the order of magnitude of the second term in the numerator of Eq. (5.1b-CPG) compared with unity. Noting that, for the performance operation of interest, $\tau_{tH} \approx 0.85$ and

$$\frac{\tau_\lambda}{\tau_r \tau_{cL} \tau_{cH}} = \frac{c_{pt} T_{t4}}{c_{pc} T_{t3}} \approx 2 \rightarrow 4$$

the second term in the numerator of Eq. (5.1b-CPG) will be of the order of ε or less and its variation at engine off-design can be considered small in comparison with unity. The denominator is constant, whence the product $\tau_{m1} \tau_{m2}$ can be considered constant and Eq. (5.1a-CPG) becomes

$$\frac{\pi_{tH}}{\sqrt{\tau_{tH}}} = \text{constant} \quad \text{(5.1c-CPG)}$$

when ε is an order of magnitude less than unity.

For a calorically perfect gas, Eq. (5.2b) can be written as

$$\tau_{tH} = 1 - \eta_{tH}\left\{1 - \pi_{tH}^{(\gamma_t - 1)/\gamma_t}\right\}$$

and, by the assumption of constant efficiency of the high-pressure turbine, can be rewritten as

$$\frac{1 - \tau_{tH}}{1 - \pi_{tH}^{(\gamma_t - 1)/\gamma_t}} = \eta_{tH} = \text{constant} \quad \text{(5.2b-CPG)}$$

To satisfy both Eqs. (5.1c-CPG) and (5.2b-CPG), the total pressure ratio and the total temperature ratio of the high-pressure turbine must be constant, or

$$\pi_{tH} = \text{constant}$$
$$\tau_{tH} = \text{constant}$$

When the same order of magnitude analysis used with Eq. (5.1b-CPG) is applied to Eqs. (4.20a) and (4.20b) separately for τ_{m1} and τ_{m2}, the coolant mixer total temperature ratios are found to be approximately constant, or

$$\tau_{m1} = \text{constant}$$
$$\tau_{m2} = \text{constant}$$

For the low-pressure turbine with a CPG and $M_{4.5} = 1$, Eq. (5.3) can be written as

$$\frac{\pi_{tL}}{\sqrt{\tau_{tL}}} = \frac{A_{4.5'}}{A_6} \frac{1}{M_6} \left\{ \frac{2}{\gamma_t + 1} \left(1 + \frac{\gamma_t - 1}{2} M_6^2 \right) \right\}^{\frac{\gamma_t + 1}{2(\gamma_t - 1)}} \qquad \text{(5.3-CPG)}$$

where

$$A_{4.5'}/A_6 = \text{constant}$$

Likewise, Eq. (5.4) can be written as

$$\tau_{tL} = 1 - \eta_{tL} \left\{ 1 - \pi_{tL}^{(\gamma_t - 1)/\gamma_t} \right\}$$

and, by the assumption of constant efficiency of the low-pressure turbine, can be rewritten as

$$\frac{1 - \tau_{tL}}{1 - \pi_{tL}^{(\gamma_t - 1)/\gamma_t}} = \eta_{tL} = \text{constant} \qquad \text{(5.4-CPG)}$$

For a given value of the Mach number at station 6 (M_6) and the constant values of the area ratio ($A_{4.5'}/A_6$) and the turbine efficiency (η_{tL}), there is only one set of low-pressure turbine total properties (τ_{tL}, π_{tL}) that satisfies both Eqs. (5.3-CPG) and (5.4-CPG).

5.2.5 Component Performance Analysis

The performance of the mixed flow turbofan engine in Figs. 5.1a and 5.1b can now be analyzed using the assumptions of Sec. 5.2.2 and the techniques of Secs. 5.2.3 and 5.2.4. The goal is to obtain the 24 independent equations required to determine the dependent performance variables of Table 5.1. To underscore the logic of the iteration solution sequence that follows in Sec. 5.2.6, the required equations will be developed in the order that each arises in the solution flowcharts of Figs. 5.3a and 5.3b. The equations to be developed next are represented in turn by the following 24 functional relationships between the 24 dependent performance

A)

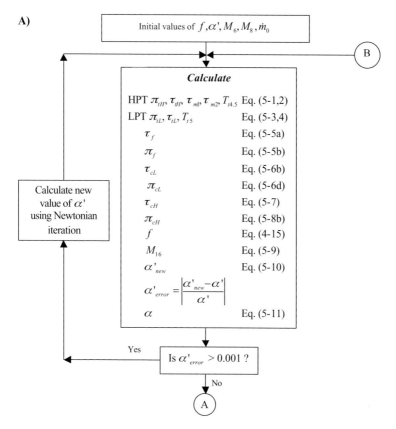

Fig. 5.3a Flowchart of iterative solution scheme (Part I).

variables of interest:

$$\pi_{tH} = f_1(\tau_{m1}, \tau_{tH}, \tau_{m2}, f)$$
$$\tau_{tH} = f_2(\pi_{tH}, f)$$
$$\tau_{m1} = f_3(\tau_{cL}, \tau_{cH}, f)$$
$$\tau_{m2} = f_4(\tau_{cL}, \tau_{cH}, \tau_{m1}, \tau_{tH}, f)$$
$$\pi_{tL} = f_5(\tau_{tL}, f)$$
$$\tau_{tL} = f_6(\pi_{tL}, f)$$
$$\tau_f = f_7(\tau_{tH}, \tau_{tL}, \tau_{cL}, \tau_{cH}, \alpha, f, \dot{m}_0)$$
$$\pi_f = f_8(\tau_f)$$
$$\tau_{cL} = f_9(\tau_f)$$
$$\pi_{cL} = f_{10}(\tau_{cL})$$
$$\tau_{cH} = f_{11}(\tau_{tH}, \tau_{cL}, \tau_{cH}, \alpha, f, \dot{m}_0)$$
$$\pi_{cH} = f_{12}(\tau_{cH})$$
$$f = f_{13}(\tau_{cL}, \tau_{cH})$$
$$M_{16} = f_{14}(\pi_f, \pi_{cL}, \pi_{cH}, \pi_b, \pi_{tH}, \pi_{tL}, M_6)$$
$$\alpha' = f_{15}(P_{t6}/P_{t16}, T_{t6}/T_{t16}, M_6, M_{16})$$
$$\alpha = f_{16}(\alpha')$$
$$\tau_M = f_{17}(\tau_f, \tau_{m1}, \tau_{tH}, \tau_{m2}, \tau_{tL}, \alpha')$$
$$M_{6A} = f_{18}(M_6, M_{16}, \alpha')$$
$$\pi_M = f_{19}(\tau_M, M_6, M_{6A}, \alpha')$$
$$M_8 = f_{20}(\pi_{cL}, \pi_{cH}, \pi_b, \pi_{tH}, \pi_{tL}, \pi_M, f)$$
$$M_6 = f_{21}(\tau_M, \pi_M, M_8, \alpha')$$
$$\dot{m}_0 = f_{22}(\pi_{cL}, \pi_{cH}, \alpha)$$
$$f_{AB} = f_{23}(\tau_{m1}, \tau_{tH}, \tau_{m2}, \tau_{tL}, \tau_M, f)$$
$$M_9 = f_{24}(\pi_{cL}, \pi_{cH}, \pi_b, \pi_{tH}, \pi_{tL}, \pi_M, f)$$

B)

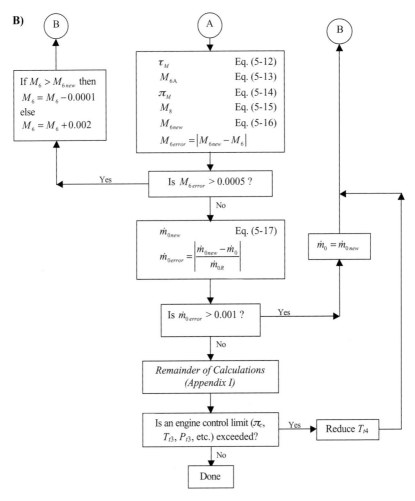

Fig. 5.3b   Flowchart of iterative solution scheme (Part II).

Please notice that each equation can be solved, in principle, in the order listed for given initial estimates of the three component performance variables α', M_6, and $\dot{m}_0$ (see Sec. 5.2.6). As the solution progresses, these estimates are compared with their newly computed values and iterated if necessary until satisfactory convergence is obtained.

It is very important to recognize that the first six quantities of the solution sequence (i.e., π_{tH}, τ_{tH}, τ_{m1}, τ_{m2}, π_{tL}, and τ_{tH}) can be determined by the methods presented in Sec. 5.2.4. The fuel/air ratios f and f_{AB} are found using Eqs. (4.18) and (4.19), respectively. Additionally, the fuel/air ratios $f_{4.1}$, $f_{4.5}$, and f_{6A} at stations 4.1, 4.5, and 6A, respectively, are required to solve the system of equations for variable specific heats. Equations (4.8i), (4.8j), and (4.8k) give the needed relationships for $f_{4.1}$, $f_{4.5}$, and f_{6A} in terms of f, f_{AB}, α, and β.

Fan temperature ratio (τ_f) and low-pressure compressor temperature ratio (τ_{cL}). From the low-pressure spool power balance, we have

$$\tau_{tL} = 1 - \frac{\tau_r\{(\tau_{cL} - 1) + \alpha(\tau_f - 1)\} + (1 + \alpha)C_{TOL}/\eta_{mPL}}{\eta_{mH}\tau_\lambda\tau_{tH}\{(1 - \beta - \varepsilon_1 - \varepsilon_2)(1 + f) + (\varepsilon_1 + \varepsilon_2/\tau_{tH})\tau_r\tau_{cL}\tau_{cH}/\tau_\lambda\}}$$

(4.22a)

which can be rearranged to yield

$$\tau_f = 1 + \frac{(1 - \tau_{tL})\eta_{mL}\left\{\dfrac{\dot{m}_4}{\dot{m}_C}\dfrac{\tau_\lambda\tau_{tH}}{\tau_r} + (\varepsilon_1\tau_{tH} + \varepsilon_2)\tau_{cL}\tau_{cH}\right\} - \dfrac{(1 + \alpha)}{\tau_r\eta_{mPL}}\dfrac{P_{TOL}}{\dot{m}_0 h_0}}{\{(\tau_{cL} - 1)/(\tau_f - 1) + \alpha\}}$$

where, from Fig. 4.2, $\dot{m}_4/\dot{m}_C = (1 - \beta - \varepsilon_1 - \varepsilon_2)(1 + f)$

Because the low-pressure compressor and the fan are on the same shaft, it is reasonable to assume that the ratio of the enthalpy rise across the fan to the enthalpy rise across the low-pressure compressor is constant. Using referencing, we can therefore write

$$\frac{h_{t13} - h_{t2}}{h_{t2.5} - h_{t2}} = \frac{\tau_f - 1}{\tau_{cL} - 1} = \frac{(\tau_f - 1)_R}{(\tau_{cL} - 1)_R}$$

Thus the fan enthalpy ratio can be written as

$$\tau_f = 1 + \frac{(1 - \tau_{tL})\eta_{mL}\left\{\dfrac{\dot{m}_4}{\dot{m}_C}\dfrac{\tau_\lambda\tau_{tH}}{\tau_r} + (\varepsilon_1\tau_{tH} + \varepsilon_2)\tau_{cL}\tau_{cH}\right\} - \dfrac{(1 + \alpha)}{\tau_r\eta_{mPL}}\dfrac{P_{TOL}}{\dot{m}_0 h_0}}{\{(\tau_{cL} - 1)_R/(\tau_f - 1)_R + \alpha\}}$$

(5.5a)

and the low-pressure compressor enthalpy ratio can be written as

$$\tau_{cL} = 1 + (\tau_f - 1)[(\tau_{cL} - 1)_R/(\tau_f - 1)_R]$$

(5.5b)

For a calorically perfect gas, $h_0 = c_{pc}T_0$ in Eq. (5.5a) and Eq. (5.5b) is unchanged.

Fan pressure ratio (π_f) and low-pressure compressor pressure ratio (π_{cL}). From the definition of fan efficiency, Eq. (4.9a),

$$h_{t13i} = h_{t2}\{1 + \eta_f(\tau_f - 1)\}$$

(5.6a)

Given h_{t13i}, the subroutine FAIR will give the reduced pressure $P_{r\,t13i}$. Thus the fan pressure ratio is calculated using Eq. (4.9a) written as

$$\pi_f = \frac{P_{r\,t13i}}{P_{r\,t2}}$$

(5.6b)

Likewise, from the definition of low-pressure compressor efficiency, Eq. (4.9b),

$$h_{t2.5i} = h_{t2}\{1 + \eta_{cL}(\tau_{cL} - 1)\}$$

(5.6c)

Given $h_{t2.5i}$, the subroutine FAIR will give the reduced pressure $P_{r\,t2.5i}$. Thus the low-pressure compressor pressure ratio is calculated using Eq. (4.9b) written as

$$\pi_{cL} = \frac{P_{r\,t2.5i}}{P_{r\,t2}} \qquad (5.6d)$$

For a calorically perfect gas, Eqs. (5.6a) and (5.6b) become

$$\pi_f = \{1 + \eta_f(\tau_f - 1)\}^{\frac{\gamma_c}{\gamma_c - 1}} \qquad (5.6b\text{-CPG})$$

and Eqs. (5.6c) and (5.6d) become

$$\pi_{cL} = \{1 + \eta_{cL}(\tau_{cL} - 1)\}^{\frac{\gamma_c}{\gamma_c - 1}} \qquad (5.6d\text{-CPG})$$

High-pressure compressor temperature ratio (τ_{cH}).   The high-pressure spool power balance of Eq. (4.21a) can be rearranged to yield

$$\tau_{cH} = \frac{1 + (1 - \tau_{tH})\eta_{mH}\left\{(1 - \beta - \varepsilon_1 - \varepsilon_2)(1 + f)\left(\dfrac{\tau_\lambda}{\tau_r \tau_{cL}}\right)\right\} - \left[\dfrac{(1 + \alpha)}{\tau_r \tau_{cL}\eta_{mPH}}\right]\dfrac{P_{TOL}}{\dot{m}_0 h_0}}{1 - \varepsilon_1(1 - \tau_{tH})\eta_{mH}}$$

$$(5.7)$$

For a calorically perfect gas, $h_0 = c_{pc}T_0$ in Eq. (5.7).

High-pressure compressor pressure ratio (π_{cH}).   From the definition of high-pressure compressor efficiency, Eq. (4.9c),

$$h_{t3i} = h_{t2.5}\{1 + \eta_{cH}(\tau_{cH} - 1)\} \qquad (5.8a)$$

Given h_{t3i}, the subroutine FAIR will give the reduced pressure $P_{r\,t3i}$. Thus the low-pressure compressor pressure ratio is calculated using Eq. (4.9c) written as

$$\pi_{cH} = \frac{P_{r\,t3i}}{P_{r\,t2.5}} \qquad (5.8b)$$

For a calorically perfect gas, Eqs. (5.8a) and (5.8b) become

$$\pi_{cH} = \{1 + \eta_{cH}(\tau_{cH} - 1)\}^{\frac{\gamma_c}{\gamma_c - 1}} \qquad (5.8b\text{-CPG})$$

Mach number at station 16 (M_{16}).   The definition of total pressure yields M_{16} once P_{t16}/P_{16} is evaluated. Since $P_{16} = P_6$, then

$$\frac{P_{t16}}{P_{16}} = \frac{P_{t16}}{P_{t6}}\frac{P_{t6}}{P_6}$$

where

$$\frac{P_{t16}}{P_{t6}} = \frac{P_{t2}\pi_f}{P_{t2}\pi_{cL}\pi_{cH}\pi_b\pi_{tH}\pi_{tL}} = \frac{\pi_f}{\pi_{cL}\pi_{cH}\pi_b\pi_{tH}\pi_{tL}}$$

so that

$$\frac{P_{t16}}{P_{16}} = \frac{\pi_f}{\pi_{cL}\pi_{cH}\pi_b\pi_{tH}\pi_{tL}}\frac{P_{t6}}{P_6} \qquad (5.9)$$

For the flow to be in the proper direction, $P_{t16} > P_{16}$. With P_{t16}/P_{16} and T_{t16} known, then the compressible flow subroutine RGCOMP yields M_{16}. For the flow to be subsonic, $M_{16} < 1.0$.

For a calorically perfect gas, Eq. (5.9) becomes

$$\frac{P_{t16}}{P_{16}} = \frac{\pi_f}{\pi_{cL}\pi_{cH}\pi_b\pi_{tH}\pi_{tL}} \frac{P_{t6}}{P_6} = \frac{\pi_f}{\pi_{cL}\pi_{cH}\pi_b\pi_{tH}\pi_{tL}} \left(1 + \frac{\gamma_t - 1}{2} M_6^2\right)^{\frac{\gamma_t}{\gamma_t - 1}}$$

$$(5.9\text{a-CPG})$$

and the Mach number at station 16 is given by

$$M_{16} = \sqrt{\frac{2}{\gamma_c - 1}\left\{\left(\frac{P_{t16}}{P_{t6}}\right)^{\frac{\gamma_c - 1}{\gamma_c}} - 1\right\}}$$

$$(5.9\text{b-CPG})$$

Mixer bypass ratio (α').   From the definition of the mixer bypass ratio and the mass flow parameter,

$$\alpha' = \frac{\dot{m}_{16}}{\dot{m}_6} = \frac{P_{t16}}{P_{t6}} \frac{A_{16}}{A_6} \frac{MFP_{16}}{MFP_6} \sqrt{\frac{T_{t6}}{T_{t16}}}$$

$$(4.8\text{f})$$

or

$$\alpha' = \frac{\pi_f}{\pi_{cL}\pi_{cH}\pi_b\pi_{tH}\pi_{tL}} \frac{A_{16}}{A_6} \frac{MFP_{16}}{MFP_6} \sqrt{\frac{T_{t6}}{T_{t16}}}$$

$$(5.10)$$

For a calorically perfect gas, Eq. (5.10) is unchanged. The mixer bypass ratio is iterated, as shown in Fig. 5.3a, until successive values are within 0.001.

Engine bypass ratio (α).   From the definitions of the engine and mixer bypass ratios,

$$\alpha = \frac{\dot{m}_F}{\dot{m}_C} = \frac{\dot{m}_{16}}{\dot{m}_6} \frac{\dot{m}_6}{\dot{m}_C} = \alpha'\{(1 - \beta - \varepsilon_1 - \varepsilon_2)(1 + f) + \varepsilon_1 + \varepsilon_2\}$$

$$(4.8\text{a})$$

or

$$\alpha = \alpha'\{(1 - \beta - \varepsilon_1 - \varepsilon_2)(1 + f) + \varepsilon_1 + \varepsilon_2\}$$

$$(5.11)$$

Equation (5.11) is unchanged for a calorically perfect gas.

Mixer enthalpy ratio (τ_M).   Equations (G.3) and (G.4) yield

$$\tau_M = \frac{1 + \alpha'(\tau_r\tau_f/\tau_\lambda\tau_{m1}\tau_{tH}\tau_{m2}\tau_{tL})}{1 + \alpha'}$$

$$(5.12)$$

For a calorically perfect gas, Eq. (5.12) becomes

$$\tau_M = \frac{1 + \alpha'(\tau_r\tau_f/\tau_\lambda\tau_{m1}\tau_{tH}\tau_{m2}\tau_{tL})}{1 + \alpha' c_{pc}/c_{pt}}$$

$$(5.12\text{-CPG})$$

Mach number at station 6A (M_{6A}). From the momentum equation applied to the ideal mixer, we have

$$\sqrt{\frac{R_{6A}T_{6A}}{\gamma_{6A}}}\frac{1+\gamma_{6A}M_{6A}^2}{M_{6A}} = \sqrt{\frac{R_6 T_6}{\gamma_6}}\frac{\left(1+\gamma_6 M_6^2\right)+A_{16}/A_6\left(1+\gamma_{16}M_{16}^2\right)}{M_6(1+\alpha')}$$

(4.29)

rearranged into

$$M_{6A} = \sqrt{\frac{R_{6A}T_{6A}}{\gamma_{6A}}}\frac{1+\gamma_{6A}M_{6A}^2}{\text{Constant}}$$

(5.13)

where

$$\text{Constant} = \sqrt{\frac{R_6 T_6}{\gamma_6}}\frac{\left(1+\gamma_6 M_6^2\right)+A_{16}/A_6\left(1+\gamma_{16}M_{16}^2\right)}{M_6(1+\alpha')}$$

For a given value of the total temperature and fuel/air ratio at station 6A, Eq. (5.13) is solved by functional iteration in combination with the isentropic temperature ratio (T_{t6A}/T_{6A}).

For a calorically perfect gas, the Mach number at station 6A (M_{6A}) can be solved for directly using the following system of equations:

$$\phi(M_6, \gamma_6) = \frac{M_6^2\left[1+(\gamma_6-1)M_6^2/2\right]}{\left(1+\gamma_6 M_6^2\right)^2};$$

$$\phi(M_{16}, \gamma_{16}) = \frac{M_{16}^2\left[1+(\gamma_{16}-1)M_{16}^2/2\right]}{\left(1+\gamma_{16}M_{16}^2\right)^2}$$

(5.13a-CPG)

$$R_{6A} = \frac{R_6+\alpha' R_{16}}{1+\alpha'}; \quad \gamma_{6A} = \frac{c_{p6A}}{c_{p6A}-R_{6A}}$$

(5.13b-CPG)

$$\Phi = \left\{(1+\alpha')\bigg/\left[\frac{1}{\sqrt{\phi(M_6,\gamma_6)}}+\alpha'\sqrt{\frac{\gamma_6 R_{16}}{\gamma_{16}R_6}}\sqrt{\frac{T_{t16}/T_{t6}}{\phi(M_{16},\gamma_{16})}}\right]\right\}^2\frac{\gamma_6 R_{6A}}{\gamma_{6A}R_6}\tau_M$$

(5.13c-CPG)

$$M_{6A} = \left\{\frac{2\Phi}{(1-2\gamma_{6A})+\sqrt{1-2(\gamma_{6A}+1)\Phi}}\right\}^{\frac{1}{2}}$$

(5.13d-CPG)

Mixer total pressure ratio (π_M). Equation (G.6) gives

$$\pi_{M\,ideal} = (1+\alpha')\sqrt{\frac{T_{t6A}}{T_{t6}}}\frac{A_6}{A_{6A}}\frac{MFP(M_6, T_{t6}, f_6)}{MFP(M_{6A}, T_{t6A}, f_{6A})}$$

(5.14a)

The mixer total pressure ratio is the product of the frictional loss ($\pi_{M\,max}$) and the mixing loss ($\pi_{M\,ideal}$) or

$$\pi_M = \pi_{M\,max}\pi_{M\,ideal} \qquad (5.14b)$$

For a calorically perfect gas, Eq. (1.3) is used to calculate the mass flow parameters in Eq. (5.14a), and Eq. (5.14b) is unchanged.

Mach number at station 8 (M_8).   The Mach number at station 8 depends on the pressure ratio P_{t9}/P_0 with the afterburner off (dry). This ratio must be equal to or greater than that corresponding to Mach one for the flow to be choked at station 8. We write

$$\left[\frac{P_{t9}}{P_0}\right]_{dry} = \pi_r\pi_d\pi_{cL}\pi_{cH}\pi_b\pi_{tH}\pi_{tL}\pi_M\pi_{AB\,dry}\pi_n \qquad (5.15)$$

The compressible flow subroutine RGCOMP is input this total to static pressure ratio in combination with the fuel/air ratio (f_{6A}) and the Mach number at station 9 (M_9) is output for matched static pressures ($P_9 = P_0$) and afterburner off. If $M_9 \geq 1$, then $M_8 = 1$ else $M_8 = M_9$.

For a calorically perfect gas, Eq. (5.15) is unchanged, and the Mach number at station 9 (M_9) is solved directly from Eq. (1.2) or

$$M_9 = \sqrt{\frac{2}{\gamma_{6A} - 1}\left(\left[\frac{P_{t9}}{P_0}\right]_{dry}^{\frac{\gamma_{6A}-1}{\gamma_{6A}}} - 1\right)}$$

If $M_9 \geq 1$, then $M_8 = 1$ else $M_8 = M_9$.

Mach number at station 6 (M_6). M_6 can be obtained from the mass flow parameter (MFP_6) once the latter is determined. Writing the ratio of mass flow rates at station 8 to station 6 for nonafterburning operation gives

$$\frac{\dot{m}_8}{\dot{m}_6} = \frac{P_{t8dry}}{P_{t6}}\frac{A_{8dry}}{A_6}\frac{MFP_8}{MFP_6}\sqrt{\frac{T_{t6}}{T_{t8}}} = 1 + \alpha'$$

Solving for the mass flow parameter at station 6 yields

$$MFP_6 = \pi_M\pi_{AB\,dry}\frac{A_{8dry}}{A_6}\frac{MFP_8}{1+\alpha'}\sqrt{\frac{T_{t6}}{T_{t6A}}} \qquad (5.16)$$

With MFP_6 known, the compressible flow subroutine RGCOMP yields $M_6 < 1$. The Mach number at station 6 is iterated, as shown in Fig. 5.3b, until successive values are within 0.0005.

For a calorically perfect gas, Eq. (5.16) is unchanged, and the Mach number at station 6 (M_6) is solved for using Eq. (1.3).

Engine mass flow rate ($\dot{m}_0$).   Conservation of mass and the definition of the bypass ratio (α) yield

$$\dot{m}_0 = (1 + \alpha)\dot{m}_C = (1 + \alpha)\frac{\dot{m}_{4'}}{(1 - \beta - \varepsilon_1 - \varepsilon_2)(1 + f)}$$

From Eq. (1.3)

$$\dot{m}_{4'} = \frac{P_{t4'} A_{4'} MFP_{4'}}{\sqrt{T_{t4'}}} = \frac{P_{t4} A_{4'} MFP_{4'}}{\sqrt{T_{t4}}}$$

where, by assumption, $P_{t4} = P_{t4'}$ and $T_{t4} = T_{t4'}$. Combining the preceding two equations and denoting station 4' as 4 gives

$$\dot{m}_0 = \frac{(1+\alpha)P_0\pi_r\pi_d\pi_{cL}\pi_{cH}\pi_b}{(1-\beta-\varepsilon_1-\varepsilon_2)(1+f)} \frac{A_4}{\sqrt{T_{t4}}} MFP_4 \qquad (5.17)$$

For a calorically perfect gas, Eq. (5.17) is unchanged.

Mach number at station 9 (M_9). The Mach number at station 9 depends on the pressure ratio P_{t9}/P_9. We write

$$\frac{P_{t9}}{P_9} = \frac{P_0}{P_9}\pi_r\pi_d\pi_{cL}\pi_{cH}\pi_b\pi_{tH}\pi_{tL}\pi_M\pi_{AB}\pi_n \qquad (5.18)$$

The compressible flow subroutine RGCOMP is input this total to static pressure ratio in combination with the fuel/air ratio at the afterburner exit (f_7) and the Mach number at station 9 (M_9) is output.

For a calorically perfect gas, Eq. (5.18) is unchanged, and the Mach number at station 9 (M_9) is solved directly from Eq. (1.2), or

$$M_9 = \sqrt{\frac{2}{\gamma_{AB}-1}\left\{\left(\frac{P_{t9}}{P_9}\right)^{\frac{\gamma_{AB}-1}{\gamma_{AB}}} - 1\right\}}$$

5.2.6 Iterative Solution Scheme

Because there are 24 dependent variables and 24 equations, there are many different ways that the off-design cycle analysis equations can be ordered to obtain a solution. Our experience convinced us that the mixer bypass ratio (α'), the core entrance Mach number to the mixer (M_6), and the engine mass flow rate ($\dot{m}_0$) are the preferred iteration variables. The iterative solution scheme shown in Figs. 5.2 and 5.3 has been custom tailored to this application so that it will converge on a solution for a wide range of input values. Note that M_6 is the second dependent variable that is iterated and successful solution of the off-design performance depends on its convergence. Referring to the functional relationships listed in Sec. 5.2.5, note that values of α', M_6, and $\dot{m}_0$ are estimated to begin a solution of the off-design equations. Making reasonable initial estimates can significantly reduce the number of iterations required for a solution. Conversely, sufficiently inaccurate initial estimates can prevent convergence altogether. Because M_6 varies only slightly over the off-design range of the engine and $\dot{m}_0$ has a small influence in the calculation of τ_{cL} in Eq. (5.5b), each has a secondary influence on the iteration scheme. The reference point values of M_6 and $\dot{m}_0$ can therefore serve as satisfactory initial estimates for these two terms, or

$$M_6 = M_{6R} \tag{5.19a}$$

$$\dot{m}_0 = \dot{m}_{0R} \tag{5.19b}$$

However, the mixer bypass ratio

$$\alpha' = \frac{\alpha}{(1 - \beta - \varepsilon_1 - \varepsilon_2)(1 + f) + \varepsilon_1 + \varepsilon_2} \tag{5.19c}$$

varies considerably over the expected flight envelope because it is proportional to the engine bypass ratio α (see Figs. 4.8 and 4.11). We have found that a reasonable initial estimate of α' can be obtained using Eq. (5.19c) with α estimated by

$$\alpha \approx \alpha_R \frac{T_0}{T_{0R}} \frac{\tau_r}{\tau_{rR}} \tag{5.19d}$$

where the altitude and Mach number effects on α are accounted for by T_0 and τ_r, respectively. When using the AEDsys software for repeating calculations where only one off-design independent variable is changed, the initial values of α', M_6, and $\dot{m}_0$ for each subsequent calculation are taken from the solution already converged.

Certain features of the programmed iteration methods used in the AEDsys performance computations deserve highlighting, as follows:

1) If either the pressure ratio at the splitter plate (P_{t16}/P_{16}) or the Mach number in the fan stream (M_{16}) is out of limits, the core entrance Mach number to the mixer (M_6) is incremented by 0.01. If M_{16} is too low, M_6 is increased.

2) If the new value of the mixer bypass ratio (α') calculated by Eq. (5.10) is not within 0.001 of the preceding value, then Newtonian iteration is used to converge to a solution.

3) Functional iteration is used for both core entrance Mach number to the mixer (M_6) and the mass flow rate $(\dot{m}_0)$.

5.2.7 Variation in Engine Speed

As is shown in Sec. 8.2.1, the change in total enthalpy across a fan or compressor is proportional to the shaft rotational speed (N) squared. For the low-pressure compressor, we can therefore write

$$h_{t2.5} - h_{t2} = K_1 N_L^2$$

which can be rewritten, using referencing, as

$$\frac{N_L}{N_{LR}} = \sqrt{\frac{h_{t2.5} - h_{t2}}{h_{t2.5R} - h_{t2R}}} = \sqrt{\frac{h_{t2}}{h_{t2R}} \frac{\tau_{cL} - 1}{\tau_{cLR} - 1}}$$

$$= \sqrt{\frac{h_{t0}}{h_{t0R}} \frac{\tau_{cL} - 1}{\tau_{cLR} - 1}} \cong \sqrt{\frac{\theta_0}{\theta_{0R}} \frac{\tau_{cL} - 1}{\tau_{cLR} - 1}} \tag{5.20a}$$

Likewise, for the high-pressure compressor, we have

$$\frac{N_H}{N_{HR}} = \sqrt{\frac{h_{t3} - h_{t2.5}}{h_{t3R} - h_{t2.5R}}} = \sqrt{\frac{h_{t2.5}}{h_{t2.5R}} \frac{\tau_{cH} - 1}{\tau_{cHR} - 1}}$$

$$= \sqrt{\frac{h_{t0}}{h_{t0R}} \frac{\tau_{cL}}{\tau_{cLR}} \frac{\tau_{cH} - 1}{\tau_{cHR} - 1}} \cong \sqrt{\frac{\theta_0}{\theta_{0R}} \frac{\tau_{cL}}{\tau_{cLR}} \frac{\tau_{cH} - 1}{\tau_{cHR} - 1}} \qquad (5.20b)$$

For a calorically perfect gas, Eqs. (5.20a) and (5.20b) are unchanged.

5.2.8   Software Implementation of Performance Calculations

The performance computer program embedded in the Engine Test portion of the AEDsys program uses the system of equations listed in Appendix I, which is based on the solution technique outlined in Secs. 5.2.4–5.2.6 and portrayed in Figs. 5.3a and 5.3b. The performance program is intended to be used in conjunction with the reference point program ONX discussed in Chapter 4.

The reference point of the engine whose performance behavior at off-design is to be investigated is initially obtained using the computer program ONX. The inputs and outputs of the reference point analysis are the source of the reference values (subscript R) used in the performance computer program. The inputs listed next for the performance analysis, therefore, include those required for the reference point analysis as well as those that specify and are unique to the performance point being analyzed (e.g., flight conditions and limits).

Sample printouts of the reference point (ONX) and off-design calculations (Engine Test portion of AEDsys) for a typical performance analysis with and without afterburning are given in printout samples A, B, and C. AEDsys will automatically transfer all input values (reference values) from ONX for performance computations other than the Performance Choices and Engine Control Limits. The output consists of overall engine performance parameters, component behavior information, and a large selection of internal variables of interest. In fact, sufficient output data are provided to allow the hand calculation of any desired quantity not included in the printout.

The Engine Test portion of the AEDsys program is a powerful learning and design tool. The AEDsys program will automatically scale the thrust and mass flow of the input reference engine when required to match the thrust loading set in the Mission Analysis portion. The program uses the thrust scale factor (TSF) to represent this scaling. TSF is calculated by determining the input engine's thrust at sea level, static conditions (F_{SL}), and dividing this by the required sea level, static thrust ($T_{SL\,req}$) or $TSF = F_{SL}/T_{SL\,req}$. Note that a thrust scale factor (TSF) of 0.9372 is printed on printout samples B and C, and the reference mass flow rate has been reduced to 187.45 lbm/s from the 200 lbm/s (Design Point of sample printout A).

As shown in Fig. 5.3b, the software checks to see if a control limit has been exceeded. It uses an iterative procedure to reduce the throttle (T_{t4}) until the most constraining limit is just met.

Inputs

Performance choices:

Flight parameters:	M_0, T_0, P_0
Throttle setting:	T_{t4}, T_{t7}
Exhaust nozzle setting:	P_0/P_9

Design constants:

π:	$\pi_{d\,max}$, π_b, $\pi_{M\,max}$, π_{ABR}, π_n
η:	η_f, η_{cL}, η_{cH}, η_{tH}, η_{tL}, η_b, η_{mL}, η_{mH}, η_{mPL}, η_{mPH}
A:	A_4, $A_{4.5}$, A_6, A_{16}, A_{6A}, $A_{8wo/AB}$
Others:	β, ε_1, ε_2, h_{PR}, P_{TOL}, P_{TOH}

Reference condition:

Flight parameters:	M_{0R}, T_{0R}, P_{0R}
Component behavior:	π_{fR}, π_{cLR}, π_{cHR}, π_{tHR}, π_{tLR}
	τ_{fR}, τ_{cLR}, τ_{cHR}, τ_{tHR}, τ_{tLR}
	M_{6R}, M_{16R}, M_{6AR}, M_{8R}
Others:	τ_{m1R}, τ_{m2R}, f_R, f_{ABR}, M_{9R}, M_{19R}, α_R, α'_R
	F_R, $\dot{m}_{0R}$, S_R
Engine control limits:	$\pi_{c\,max}$, $T_{t3\,max}$, $P_{t3\,max}$, $\%N_L$, $\%N_H$

Outputs

Overall performance:	F, $\dot{m}_0$, S, f_o, η_P, η_{TH}, η_O, V_9/α_0, α
	P_{t9}/P_9, P_9/P_0, T_9/T_0
Component behavior:	π_f, π_{cL}, π_{cH}, π_{tH}, π_{tL}
	τ_f, τ_{cL}, τ_{cH}, τ_{tH}, τ_{tL}, τ_λ
	τ_{m1}, τ_{m2}, f, f_{AB}
	M_6, M_{16}, M_{6A}, M_8, M_9

Sample Printout A

On-Design Calcs (ONX V5.00)   Date: 10/01/2002 6:00:00 AM
File: C:\Program Files\AEDsys\AAF Base Line Engine.ref
Turbofan Engine with Afterburning
using Modified Specific Heat (MSH) Model

************************   Input Data   ************************

Mach No	= 1.451		Alpha	= −001.000
Alt (ft)	= 36000		Pi f/Pi cL	= 3.900/3.900
T0 (R)	= 390.50		Pi d (max)	= 0.960
P0 (psia)	= 3.306		Pi b	= 0.950
Density	= .0007102		Pi n	= 0.970
(Slug/ft^3)			Efficiency	
Cp c	= 0.2400 Btu/lbm-R		Burner	= 0.999
Cp t	= 0.2950 Btu/lbm-R		Mech Hi Pr	= 0.995
Gamma c	= 1.4000		Mech Lo Pr	= 0.995
Gamma t	= 1.3000		Fan/LP Comp	= 0.890/0.890
				(ef/ecL)
Tt4 max	= 3200.0 R		HP Comp	= 0.900 (ecH)

h—fuel	= 18400 Btu/lbm		HP Turbine	= 0.890 (etH)
CTO Low	= 0.0000		LP Turbine	= 0.900 (etL)
CTO High	= 0.0152		Pwr Mech Eff L	= 1.000
Cooling Air #1	= 5.000%		Pwr Mech Eff H	= 1.000
Cooling Air #2	= 5.000%		Bleed Air	= 1.000%
P0/P9	= 1.0000			

** Afterburner **

Tt7 max	= 3600.0 R		Pi AB	= 0.950
Cp AB	= 0.2950 Btu/lbm-R		Eta A/B	= 0.990
Gamma AB	= 1.3000			

*** Mixer *** Pi Mixer max = 0.970

*************************** RESULTS ***************************

Tau r	= 1.421	a0 (ft/sec)	= 968.8
Pi r	= 3.421	V0 (ft/sec)	= 1405.7
Pi d	= 0.935	Mass Flow	= 200.0 lbm/sec
TauL	= 10.073	Area Zero	= 6.227 sqft
PTO Low	= 0.00 KW	Area Zero*	= 5.440 sqft
PTO High	= 300.61 KW		
Pt16/P0	= 12.481	Tt16/T0	= 2.1997
Pt6/P0	= 12.428	Tt6/T0	= 5.5576
Alpha	= 0.4487		
Pi c	= 20.000	Tau m1	= 0.9673
Pi f	= 3.9000	Tau m2	= 0.9731
Tau f	= 1.5479	Tau M	= 0.8404
Eta f	= 0.8674	Pi M	= 0.9637
Pi cL	= 3.900	Tau cL	= 1.5479
Eta cL	= 0.8674		
Pi cH	= 5.1282	M6	= 0.4000
Tau cH	= 1.6803	M16	= 0.3940
Eta cH	= 0.8751	M6A	= 0.4188
Pi tH	= 0.4231	A16/A6	= 0.2715
Tau tH	= 0.8381	Gamma M	= 1.3250
Eta tH	= 0.8995	CP M	= 0.2782
Pi tL	= 0.4831	Eta tL	= 0.9074
Tau tL	= 0.8598		

Without AB		With AB	
Pt9/P9	= 11.327	Pt9/P9	= 11.036
f	= 0.03069	f	= 0.03069
		f AB	= 0.03352
F/mdot	= 62.493 lbf/(lbm/s)	F/mdot	= 110.829 lbf/(lbm/s)
S	= 1.0862 (lbm/hr)/lbf	S	= 1.6938 (lbm/hr)/lbf
T9/T0	= 2.5755	T9/T0	= 5.2970
V9/V0	= 2.402	V9/V0	= 3.384
M9/M0	= 1.542	M9/M0	= 1.531
A9/A0	= 1.080	A9/A0	= 1.625
A9/A8	= 2.261	A9/A8	= 2.272
Thrust	= 12499 lbf	Thrust	= 22166 lbf
Thermal Eff	= 55.43%	Thermal Eff	= 45.25%
Propulsive Eff	= 59.14%	Propulsive Eff	= 46.26%

Sample Printout B

AEDsys (Ver. 3.00)   Turbofan with AB—Dual Spool   Date: 10/01/2002 6:00:00 AM
Engine File: C:\Program Files\AEDsys\AAF Base Line Engine.ref

Input Constants

Pidmax = 0.9600	Pi b = 0.9500	Eta b = 0.9990	Pi n = 0.9700
cp c = 0.2400	cp t = 0.2950	Gam c = 1.4000	Gam t = 1.3000
Pi AB = 0.9500	Eta AB = 0.9900	cp AB = 0.2950	Gam AB = 1.3000
Eta cL = 0.8674	Eta cH = 0.8751	Eta tH = 0.8995	Eta tL = 0.9074
Eta mL = 0.9950	Eta mH = 0.9950	Eta PL = 1.0000	Eta PH = 1.0000
Eta f = 0.8674	PTO L = 0.0KW	PTO H = 281.9KW	hPR = 18400
Bleed = 1.00%	Cool 1 = 5.00%	Cool 2 = 5.00%	
Control Limits:	Tt4 = 3200.0	Pi c = 20.00	

** Thrust Scale Factor = 0.9372

Parameter	Reference**	Test**
Mach Number @ 0	1.4510	1.8000
Temperature @ 0	390.50	390.00
Pressure @ 0	3.3063	2.7299
Altitude @ 0	36000	40000
Total Temp @ 4	3200.00	3200.00
Total Temp @ 7	3600.00	3600.00
Pi r/Tau r	3.4211/1.4211	5.7458/1.6480
Pi d	0.9354	0.9067
Pi f/Tau f	3.9000/1.5479	3.0054/1.4259
Pi cL/Tau cL	3.9000/1.5479	3.0054/1.4259
Pi cH/Tau cH	5.1282/1.6803	4.7208/1.6377
Tau m1	0.9673	0.9673
Pi tH/Tau tH	0.4231/0.8381	0.4231/0.8381
Tau m2	0.9731	0.9731
Pi tL/Tau tL	0.4831/0.8598	0.5023/0.8667
Control Limit		Tt4
LP Spool RPM (% of Reference Pt)	100.00	94.88
HP Spool RPM (% of Reference Pt)	100.00	100.00
Mach Number @ 6	0.4000	0.3835
Mach Number @ 16	0.3940	0.4559
Mach Number @ 6A	0.4188	0.4187
Gamma @ 6A	1.3250	1.3282
cp @ 6A	0.2782	0.2762
Pt16/Pt6	1.0042	1.0492
Pi M/Tau M	0.9637/0.8404	0.9735/0.8268
Alpha	0.449	0.530
Pt9/P9	11.0362	13.3874
P0/P9	1.0000	1.0000
Mach Number @ 9	2.2217	2.3377
Mass Flow Rate @ 0	187.45	188.72
Corr Mass Flow @ 0	251.91	196.83
Flow Area @ 0	5.836	5.734
Flow Area* @ 0	5.099	3.985
Flow Area @ 9	9.481	10.736
MB—Fuel/Air Ratio (f)	0.03070	0.02975
AB—Fuel/Air Ratio (fAB)	0.03353	0.03371
Overall Fuel/Air Ratio (fo)	0.05216	0.05080
Specific Thrust (F/m0)	110.83	104.69
Thrust Spec Fuel Consumption (S)	1.6941	1.7468
Thrust (F)	20775	19757
Fuel Flow Rate	35195	34513
Propulsive Efficiency (%)	46.26	53.42
Thermal Efficiency (%)	45.25	47.10
Overall Efficiency (%)	20.93	25.16

Sample Printout C

AEDsys (Ver. 3.00)   Turbofan with AB—Dual Spool   Date: 10/01/2002 6:00:00 AM
Engine File: C:\Program Files\AEDsys\AAF Base Line Engine.ref

Input Constants

Pidmax = 0.9600	Pi b = 0.9500	Eta b = 0.9990	Pi n = 0.9700
cp c = 0.2400	cp t = 0.2950	Gam c = 1.4000	Gam t = 1.3000
Pi AB = 0.9500	Eta AB = 0.9900	cp AB = 0.2950	Gam AB = 1.3000
Eta cL = 0.8674	Eta cH = 0.8751	Eta tH = 0.8995	Eta tL = 0.9074
Eta mL = 0.9950	Eta mH = 0.9950	Eta PL = 1.0000	Eta PH = 1.0000
Eta f = 0.8674	PTO L = 0.0KW	PTO H = 281.9KW	hPR = 18400
Bleed = 1.00%	Cool 1 = 5.00%	Cool 2 = 5.00%	
Control Limits:	Tt4 = 3200.0	Pi c = 20.00	

** Thrust Scale Factor = 0.9372

Parameter	Reference**	Test**
Mach Number @ 0	1.4510	1.9000
Temperature @ 0	390.50	390.00
Pressure @ 0	3.3063	2.4806
Altitude @ 0	36000	42000
Total Temp @ 4	3200.00	2277.00
Total Temp @ 7	3600.00	1269.42
Pi r/Tau r	3.4211/1.4211	1.6913/1.1620
Pi d	0.9354	0.9600
Pi f/Tau f	3.9000/1.5479	2.8692/1.4051
Pi cL/Tau cL	3.9000/1.5479	2.8692/1.4051
Pi cH/Tau cH	5.1282/1.6803	4.5285/1.9197
Tau m1	0.9673	0.9673
Pi tH/Tau tH	0.4231/0.8381	0.4231/0.8381
Tau m2	0.9731	0.9731
Pi tL/Tau tL	0.4831/0.8598	0.5023/0.8705
Control Limit		Tt4 Set
LP Spool RPM (% of Reference Pt)	100.00	77.70
HP Spool RPM (% of Reference Pt)	100.00	81.97
Mach Number @ 6	0.4000	0.3748
Mach Number @ 16	0.3940	0.4814
Mach Number @ 6A	0.4188	0.4185
Gamma @ 6A	1.3250	1.3302
cp @ 6A	0.2782	0.2750
Pt16/Pt6	1.0042	1.0706
Pi M/Tau M	0.9637/0.8404	0.9779/0.8119
Alpha	0.449	0.576
Pt9/P9	11.0362	4.0243
P0/P9	1.0000	1.0000
Mach Number @ 9	2.2217	1.5814
Mass Flow Rate @ 0	187.45	59.80
Corr Mass Flow @ 0	251.91	195.80
Flow Area @ 0	5.836	3.999
Flow Area* @ 0	5.099	3.964
Flow Area @ 9	9.481	3.553
MB—Fuel/Air Ratio (f)	0.03070	0.01975
AB—Fuel/Air Ratio (fAB)	0.03353	0.00000
Overall Fuel/Air Ratio (fo)	0.05216	0.01115
Specific Thrust (F/m0)	110.83	43.50
Thrust Spec Fuel Consumption (S)	1.6941	0.9228
Thrust (F)	20775	2601
Fuel Flow Rate	35195	2400
Propulsive Efficiency (%)	46.26	55.78
Thermal Efficiency (%)	45.25	43.25
Overall Efficiency (%)	20.93	24.12

5.3 Component Behavior

Off-design cycle analysis requires a model for the behavior of each engine component over its actual range of operation. The more accurately and completely this is done, the more reliable the computed results. Even though the approach (constant efficiency of rotating components and constant total pressure ratio of the other components) used in this textbook gives answers that are perfectly adequate for this type of preliminary design, it is important to know that the usual industrial practice is to use data or correlations having more accuracy and definition in the form of component "maps." The material in this section will explain the role and usefulness of these maps and will demonstrate that the approach of this textbook is essentially correct. Indeed, the principal values of the maps are to improve the understanding of component behavior and to slightly increase the accuracy of the results.

5.3.1 Dimensionless and Corrected Performance Parameters

The first step is to use dimensional analysis to identify correlating parameters that allow data taken under one set of conditions to be extended to other conditions. This is necessary because it is always impractical to accumulate experimental data for the bewildering number of possible operating conditions and because it is often impossible to reach many of them in a single, affordable facility.

The quantities of pressure and temperature are normally made dimensionless by dividing each by their respective standard sea level static value. The dimensionless pressure and temperature are represented by δ and θ, respectively. When total (stagnation) properties are nondimensionalized, a subscript is used to indicate the station number of that property. The only static properties made dimensionless are freestream, the symbols for which carry no subscripts. Thus,

$$\delta_i \doteq P_{ti}/P_{std} \tag{5.21}$$

and

$$\theta_i \doteq T_{ti}/T_{std} \tag{5.22}$$

where $P_{std} = 2116.2 \ \text{lb/ft}^2$ and $T_{std} = 518.69°\text{R}$.

Dimensional analysis of engine components yields many useful dimensionless and/or modified component performance parameters. Some examples of these are the compressor pressure ratio, adiabatic efficiency, Mach number at the engine face, ratio of the blade (tip) speed to the speed of sound, and the Reynolds number.[2]

The "corrected mass flow rate" at engine station i used in this analysis is defined as

$$\dot{m}_{ci} \doteq \dot{m}_i \sqrt{\theta_i}/\delta_i \tag{5.23}$$

and is related to the engine face Mach number. The "corrected engine speed" is defined as

$$N_{ci} \doteq N/\sqrt{\theta_i} \tag{5.24}$$

and is related to the Mach number of the rotating airfoils.

There is another interpretation of the corrected mass flow rate that you may find intuitively appealing. Starting from the definition of the mass flow parameter, substituting Eqs. (5.21–5.23), and rearranging, you will find that

$$\dot{m}_{ci} = \frac{P_{std} A_i}{\sqrt{T_{std}}} MFP_i$$

Thus, $\dot{m}_{ci}$ is the amount of mass that would flow under standard conditions if A_i and MFP_i (i.e., γ and M_i) were fixed. In other words, it is the mass flow that would be measured if a given machine were tested at standard conditions with the critical similarity parameter M_i kept equal to the desired operating value.

It must be understood that this selection of parameters represents a first approximation to the complete set necessary to reproduce nature. This collection would not reflect, for example, the effects of viscosity (Reynolds number), humidity, or gas composition. Nevertheless, it is extremely useful and has become the propulsion community standard. When required, the effects of the mission parameters are supplied by "adjustment factors" also based upon experience. Please note also the appearance, for the first time, of rotational speed (N), a quantity of obvious significance to the structural designer.

5.3.2 Fan and Compressor Performance Maps

The performance map of a compressor or fan is normally presented using the following performance parameters: total pressure ratio, corrected mass flow rate, corrected engine speed, and adiabatic efficiency.

The performance of two modern high-performance fan stages is shown in this format in Fig. 5.4. They have no inlet guide vanes. One has a low tangential Mach number (0.96) to minimize noise. The other has supersonic tip speed and a considerably larger pressure ratio. Both have high axial Mach numbers.

Variations in the axial flow velocity in response to changes in pressure cause the multistage compressor to have quite different mass flow vs pressure ratio characteristics than one of its stages. The performance map of a typical high-pressure ratio compressor is shown in Fig. 5.5.

A limitation on fan and compressor performance of special concern is the stall or surge line. Steady operation above the line is impossible and entering the region even momentarily is dangerous to the engine and aircraft.

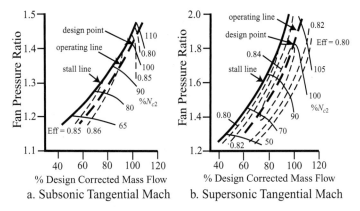

a. Subsonic Tangential Mach b. Supersonic Tangential Mach

Fig. 5.4 Typical fan stage maps.[3]

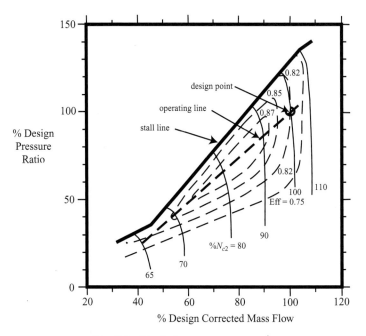

Fig. 5.5   Typical compressor map.[4]

5.3.3 Combustor Maps

The combustor performance parameters that are most important to overall engine performance are the pressure loss through the combustor and combustion efficiency. The pressure loss performance of a combustor (π_b) is normally plotted vs the corrected mass flow rate through the combustor ($\dot{m}_3\sqrt{\theta_3}/\delta_3$) for different fuel-air ratios as shown in Fig. 5.6a. The efficiency of the combustor (η_b) can be presented as a plot vs the temperature rise in the combustor or fuel-air ratio for various values of inlet pressure as shown in Fig. 5.6b.

5.3.4 Turbine Maps

In a turbine, the entry stationary airfoils, often called inlet guide vanes or nozzles, expand the entering flow and discharge it into rotating airfoils, known as rotors or blades. The flow of gas through the turbine nozzles has much in common with the flow of a compressible fluid through an exhaust nozzle, including choking at the minimum area when the backpressure is below the critical value. Therefore, the flow through the turbine nozzles is a function of the turbine pressure ratio (π_t), the turbine inlet total pressure (P_{t4}), and the turbine inlet total temperature (T_{t4}) when the nozzles are operating at a subcritical pressure ratio and are not choked. Conversely, the flow through the turbine nozzles depends only upon the inlet total pressure (P_{t4}) and the inlet total temperature (T_{t4}), once choking occurs.

The work extraction of modern gas turbines is usually so large, and π_t so small, that the nozzles are usually choked for the design point and the surrounding region. If not, the throat Mach number is sufficiently close to one that the mass flow

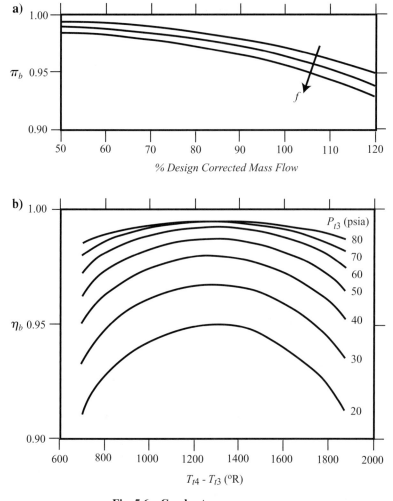

Fig. 5.6   Combustor maps.

parameter approximates that of choking (Ref. 1). The analytical convenience this makes possible has already been capitalized upon in Chapters 4 and 5.

The parameters that are normally used to express the performance of a turbine are total pressure ratio, corrected mass flow rate, corrected engine speed, and adiabatic efficiency.

Figure 5.7 shows the reciprocal turbine total pressure ratio $(1/\pi_t)$, also known as the expansion ratio, plotted as a function of the corrected mass flow rate $(\dot{m}_4\sqrt{\theta_4}/\delta_4)$ and corrected mechanical speed $(N/\sqrt{\theta_4})$. The maximum flow of gas that can be accommodated by the nozzles when choked is clearly evident.

For reasons of size, it is desirable that the turbine mass flow rate per annulus area be as large as possible, which also points to choking and a high reciprocal total pressure ratio $(1/\pi_t)$. Because the mass flow rate is nearly independent of

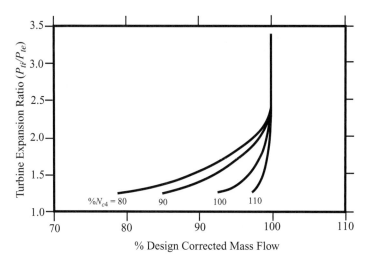

Fig. 5.7   Turbine map.

speed for the pressure ratios of interest, all speed characteristics collapse onto a single line when plotted vs the turbine expansion ratio $(1/\pi_t)$ and the turbine has the mass flow characteristics of a choked nozzle. So that only one map is required to show the performance of a turbine, the abscissa can be taken as the corrected mass flow rate multiplied by the corrected engine speed; thus, a separate plot for the turbine adiabatic efficiency is not required. A map for a typical 50% reaction (at mean radius) single-stage turbine is shown in this format in Fig. 5.8.

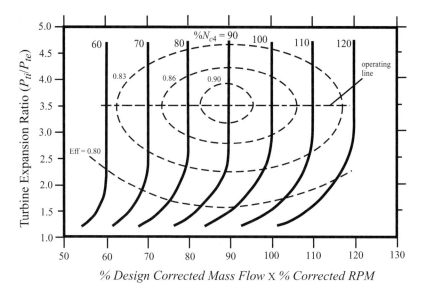

Fig. 5.8   Typical turbine map.

Because the turbine adiabatic efficiency does not vary as rapidly with off-design variations as in a compressor, the turbine characteristic can be approximated for preliminary design calculations by a constant adiabatic turbine efficiency (η_t) and a choked mass flow characteristic. These are the characteristics that were used in performance analysis.

5.3.5 Component Matching

This is the time to clarify what appears to be a shortcoming or internal inconsistency in the off-design calculation procedure. The heart of the matter is this: the off-design equations are silent with regard to the rotational speeds of the rotating machines, despite the obvious fact that each compressor is mechanically connected via a permanent shaft to a turbine, whence they must always share the same rotational speed. The rotational speed will, in general, be different from the design point speed and, for this purpose, dimensionless compressor and turbine performance maps (e.g., Figs. 5.4 and 5.8) also contain data pertaining to rotational speed. It would seem, then, that the off-design equation set lacks some true physical constraints (i.e., $N_c = N_t$) and must therefore produce erroneous results. The following discussion will demonstrate that this appearance is, fortunately, misleading.

The business of ensuring that all of the relationships that join a compressor and turbine are obeyed, including mass flow, power, total pressure, and rotational speed, is known as "component matching." The off-design calculation procedure of this textbook correctly maintains all known relationships except rotational speed.

The simplest and most frequently cited example of component matching found in the open literature is that of developing the "pumping characteristics" for the "gas generator" (i.e., compressor, burner, and turbine) of a nonafterburning, single-spool turbojet (e.g., Refs. 1, 2, 5–7). Careful scrutiny of this component matching process reveals that the compressor performance map is used to update the estimate of compressor efficiency and to determine the shaft rotational speed; the turbine performance map and shaft rotational speed are then used only to update the estimate of turbine efficiency. In other words, the main use of enforcing $N_c = N_t$ is to provide accurate values of compressor and turbine efficiency.

If suitable compressor and turbine performance maps were available, they could, of course, be built into the off-design calculation procedure, and the iteration just described would automatically be executed internally. When such performance maps are not available, as is often the case early in a design study, the best approach is to supply input values of η_c and η_t based on experience. This "open-loop" method can also be employed later when satisfactory performance maps become available.

The principal conclusion is that accurate estimation of η_c and η_t at the off-design conditions has the *same* result as using performance maps and setting $N_c = N_t$. Consequently, the off-design calculation procedure of this textbook is both correct and complete. An important corollary to this conclusion is that the "operating line" (i.e., π or τ vs $\dot{m}\sqrt{\theta}/\delta$) of every component in the engine is a "free" byproduct of the off-design calculations, even when the engine cycle is arbitrarily complex.

To make these conclusions even more concrete, it is useful to look more closely at the turbine. According to the typical turbine performance map of Fig. 5.8, this machine can provide the same work (i.e., $1 - \tau_t$) for a wide range of $N_c = N_t$, while η_t varies only slightly. Please recall that as long as the flow in the turbine

Station:

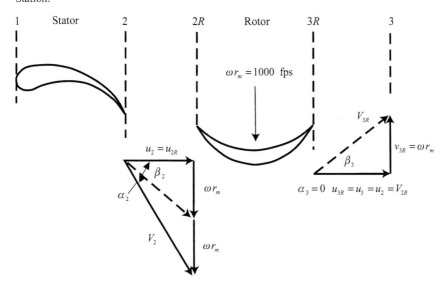

Fig. 5.9   Single stage impulse turbine.

inlet guide vane and some downstream flow area remains choked and η_t does not vary significantly, then Eq. (5.2) has demonstrated that π_t and τ_t must be essentially constant. The question, then, is how the turbine flow conditions can adjust themselves in order to provide the *same* τ_t at *different* values of ωr. If the mechanics of adjustment are straightforward, then the entire process of component matching should be more easily comprehended.

Consider the single-stage, impulse, maximum work (i.e., no exit swirl), isentropic, constant height turbine of Fig. 5.9 (see Ref. 2). At its design point, this turbine has a choked inlet guide vane and an entirely subsonic flow relative to the rotor. The flow angles are all representative of good practice. In short, this is a rather standard design.

Isentropic calculations have been performed at rotational speeds $\pm10\%$ from design, which would encompass the entire operating range for most compressors. The necessary condition for a solution was that τ_t have a design point value of 0.896. The results are displayed in Table 5.2.

These results confirm the message of the Euler turbine equation. Since $(1 - \tau_t)$ is proportional to $\omega r_m (v_{2R} - v_{3R})$, then M_2, M_{2R}, and M_{3R} must increase in order to compensate for reductions in ωr_m, and vice versa. Nevertheless, even for such large differences in ωr_m, the aerodynamic results are far from disastrous. For one thing, the inlet guide vanes remain choked ($M_2 > 1$) and the rotor airfoils remain subsonic ($M_{2R} < 1$ and $M_{3R} < 1$) at all times. For another, the rotor airfoil relative inlet flow angle (β_2) and the inlet flow angle to the downstream stator airfoils (α_3) are well within the low loss operating range for typical turbine cascades. Finally, one might expect the frictional losses to increase and the efficiency to decrease as ωr_m decreases and the blade scrubbing velocity increases, but only gradually.

Table 5.2   Turbine off-design performance

Quantity	-10%	Design	+10%
ωr_m, ft/s	900	1000	1100
M_2	1.22	1.10	1.02
α_2, deg	50.6	52.0	52.4
β_2, deg	35.2	32.6	28.4
M_{2R}	0.947	0.804	0.708
M_{3R}	0.820	0.804	0.790
α_3, deg	-4.2	0	3.5
τ_t	0.899	0.896	0.898

$T_{t2} = 2800°\mathrm{R}$; $\gamma = 1.33$; $g_c R = 1716$ ft^2/(s^2 − °R).

This turbine therefore performs gracefully as expected, providing the same τ_t with slight changes in η_t for a wide range of $N_c = N_t$, all of the while remaining choked.

5.3.6   Engine Performance Program Predictions

The engine performance portion (referred to as Engine Test) of the AEDsys program, based on the equations developed in this chapter, can determine the performance of many types of engines at different altitudes, Mach numbers, and throttle settings. The accuracy of the resulting computer output depends on the validity of the assumptions specified in Sec. 5.2.2. The engine speed (N) is not incorporated in the off-design equations and is needed only when the efficiency of the rotating components (fan, compressor, or turbine) vary significantly over the operating speed (N) of the engine. Thus, the assumption of constant component efficiency (η_f, η_{cL}, η_{cH}, η_{tH}, and η_{tL}) removes the engine speed from the system of equations for prediction of off-design performance. This absence of engine speed from the off-design equations allows the determination of engine performance without the prior knowledge of each component's design point (knowledge of each component's design point and off-design performance by way of a map is required to include engine speed in the off-design performance). As shown in the maps of Figs. 5.4, 5.5, and 5.8, the efficiency of a rotating component remains essentially constant along the operating line in the 70–100% engine speed range of design $N/\sqrt{\theta}$. However, a significant reduction in component efficiency occurs when the engine speed exceeds 110% or drops below 60% of design $N/\sqrt{\theta}$.

The component maps of Figs. 5.4, 5.5, and 5.8 give considerable insight into the variation of engine speed with changes in flight conditions. High values of fan or compressor pressure ratio correspond to high engine speed and low values of pressure ratio correspond to low engine speed. Figures 4.5, 4.6, 4.7, 4.9, and 4.10 show that pressure ratio increases with altitude and decreases with Mach number with T_{t4} held constant. Thus, engine speed increases with altitude and decreases with Mach number with T_{t4} held constant. The operating regimes where the assumption of constant component efficiency may not apply then correspond to the regions of high-altitude/low Mach number and low-altitude/high Mach number flight. Some of the high-altitude/low Mach number region is excluded from the operational envelope of many aircraft because of its low dynamic pressure and the high coefficient of lift (C_L) required to sustain flight. Some of the low-altitude/high Mach number region is excluded from the operational envelope of many aircraft because of the structural limits of the airframe and the presence of very high dynamic pressure in this flight region.

The effect of decreasing component efficiency is to reduce the pressure ratio, engine air mass flow rate, and thrust and increase the thrust specific fuel consumption from that predicted by the off-design computer program. The magnitude and range of this effect depends on each component's design and design point, which are not known at this point in the analysis.

The predicted performance of the engine over the aircraft mission is used to select the best engine cycle, size the selected engine, and select component design points. Output of the performance portion (Engine Test) of the AEDsys computer program can be used to create plots of the compressor operating line at full throttle, as shown in Fig. 5.10, and the variation of the compressor pressure ratio at full throttle with changes in the flight condition, as shown in Fig. 5.11. However when the maximum compressor pressure ratio that the engine control system will allow is equal to the sea-level static value, the control system limits the fuel flow and the compressor pressure ratio is limited as shown at low Mach/high altitude in Fig. 5.11.

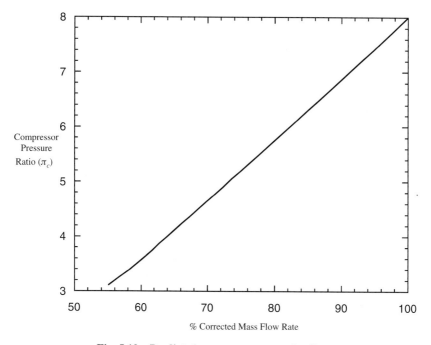

Fig. 5.10   Predicted compressor operating line.

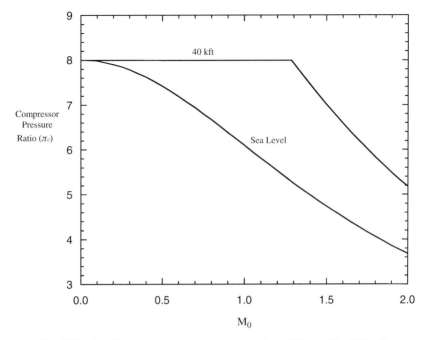

Fig. 5.11   Predicted compressor pressure ratio at full throttle ($TR = 1$).

5.4   Example Engine Selection: Performance Cycle Analysis

In the example of Chapter 2, the takeoff wing and installed thrust loadings of $W_{TO}/S = 64$ lbf/ft^2 and $T_{SL}/W_{TO} = 1.25$ were selected for the Air-to-Air Fighter (AAF) of the Request for Proposal (RFP) of Chapter 1 in order to ensure that all of the AAF flight constraints of the RFP are met. The mission analysis in Sec. 3.4 produced the AAF takeoff weight of $W_{TO} = 24,000$ lbf, which established the required AAF wing area and sea level installed thrust to be $S = 375$ ft^2 and $T_{SL} = 30,000$ lbf.

The parametric cycle analysis example of Chapter 4 narrowed the seemingly unlimited range of engine design choices for the AAF to reasonable and manageable ranges and found that the search for a design point engine for the AAF must focus on reduced fuel consumption. In addition, the Chapter 4 parametric sensitivity analysis led to the conclusions that the selection of the engine design point fan and compressor pressure ratios should be from the high sides of their respective ranges and that the design point combustor and afterburner temperatures should be allowed to drift down from their limiting values. Moreover, the high altitude and high Mach number operational requirements of the AAF require an engine with a high specific thrust to obtain a low frontal area for reduced drag. This drives the engine selection to that of an afterburning, low bypass, mixed flow turbofan engine.

Because the engine design point choice is based on thrust specific fuel consumption and specific thrust, the design point selection is independent of the engine thrust. Thus, whether the AAF is a single- or two-engine fighter need not be known until the engine is sized. When the engine is sized, however, in Chapter 6, the number of engines must be specified by the airframe and propulsion design teams.

With the detailed results of the preceding examples and the parametric (on-design) and performance (off-design tools) embedded in the textbook's computer programs ONX and AEDsys, the systematic search begun in Chapter 4 for an optimum combination of engine design choices that satisfy the AAF mission requirements will now be extended. In the search here, the influence of each of the design parameters on the engine performance at the off-design critical flight conditions of the mission is determined. The goal is to find the best combination of design choices for the AAF engine. The search is well on its way as a result of the extensive work accomplished in Sec. 4.4.

5.4.1 Critical Flight Conditions

The first engine to be selected in the search for the optimum AAF design point engine will serve as the baseline engine. The performance of this engine over the critical legs of the mission forms a basis for comparison of other engine candidates. It is necessary at the outset, therefore, to establish which mission legs are to be judged as critical for the search. Any leg that 1) has a high fuel consumption (low $\prod$) as determined from Table 3.E3 and Sec. 3.4.4; 2) represents a boundary of the solution space in the revised constraint diagram of Fig 3.E5; or 3) is an extreme operating condition should be considered critical. Based on these criteria, the flight conditions listed in Table 5.E1 are considered critical for this study. The power setting or, if the leg is at constant speed, the required uninstalled thrust [$F_{req} = D/0.95$, allowing in Eq. (6.1) for 5% installation losses] is given in the table for each mission leg listed. The required thrust can be used in the AEDsys performance analysis to find the requisite throttle setting (i.e., T_{t4} and T_{t7}) for type B, $P_s = 0$ legs. The weight fraction and the estimated installed thrust specific fuel consumption (TSFC) obtained in Sec. 3.3 are also listed for those legs considered fuel critical. The last four legs given in the table represent the takeoff constraint boundary limit, Combat Turn 2 constraint (0.9/30 kft, 5g), and the maximum Mach number extreme operating condition.

5.4.2 Mission Fuel Consumption

Mission fuel usage plays a dominant role in the selection of the AAF engine design. There are two methods for calculating the fuel used: 1) the mission analysis portion of the AEDsys computer program, or 2) an estimate based on the algebraic analysis of Sec. 3.4.2.

Computer calculated mission analysis.   Based on an input takeoff weight, the mission analysis portion of the AEDsys computer program flies the aircraft and reference point engine through the mission and determines the fuel used for each leg and the overall fuel used. This powerful tool includes the engine performance engine model described in this chapter. All you need to do to begin is design an engine using the ONX computer program's "single point" calculation capability and save the resulting reference engine as a reference data file (*.REF). The reference data file is then input into the AEDsys program by selecting "Cycle Deck" from the Engine pull-down menu (or opening the "Engine Data" window),

Table 5.E1   AAF critical mission legs

Mission phases and segments		M_0	Alt, kft	F_{req}, lbf	Table 3.E3	
					Π	TSFC, 1/h
1–2:	A—Warm-up	0.00	2^a	Mil	0.9895	0.9352
2–3:	E—Climb/acceleration	0.875	23	Mil	0.9806	1.067
3–4:	Subsonic cruise climb	0.9	42	2,600	0.9736	1.015
5–6:	Combat air patrol	0.697	30	2,366	0.9675	0.9883
6–7:	F—Acceleration	1.09	30	Max	0.9837	1.688
6–7:	G—Supersonic penetration	1.5	30	11,305	0.9382	1.203
7–8:	I—1.6M/5g turn	1.6	30	19,170	0.9753	1.509
7–8:	J—0.9M/5g turns	0.9	30	14,840	0.9774	1.544
7–8:	K—Acceleration	1.2	30	Max	0.9828	1.713
8–9:	Escape dash	1.5	30	11,190	0.9795	1.203
10–11:	Subsonic cruise climb	0.9	48	1,926	0.9698	1.015
12–13:	Loiter	0.394	10	1,747	0.9677	0.9825
1–2:	B—Takeoff acceleration	0.1	2^a	Max	——	——
1–2:	C—Takeoff rotation	0.182	2^a	Max	——	——
	0.9M/5g turns at Maneuver weight	0.9	30	16,030	——	——
	Maximum Mach	1.8	40	10,210	——	——

^{a}At 100°F.

selecting the "input reference data file" function, and entering the file name. Then the maximum compressor pressure ratio (and other operational limits) must be entered into the engine controls input data. The constant installation loss model is selected until better installation loss models become available (see Chapter 6) and the appropriate estimate of the loss entered into the input field. Then the "Engine Data" window is closed and the "Mission" window opened. Each leg of the mission is reviewed and the appropriate throttle limits set for T_{t4}. Refer to the *AEDsys Users Manual* on the accompanying CD-ROM for detailed instructions.

Algebraic mission analysis estimate.   The mission fuel fraction, from Sec. 3.4.2, is

$$\frac{W_F}{W_{TO}} = \left(1 - \prod_{1\,n}\right) + \frac{W_{PE_1}}{W_{TO}}\left(1 - \prod_{j\,n}\right) + \frac{W_{PE_2}}{W_{TO}}\left(1 - \prod_{k\,n}\right) \quad (5.E1)$$

Because this expression is a function of the weight fractions $\prod_{1n}$, $\prod_{jn}$, and $\prod_{kn}$, the most important need is for a simple method for finding the weight fraction ($\prod_{ij}$) of each critical mission leg for a 2given engine design. As a critical mission leg is flown with different reference point engines, only the value of the TSFC term of Table 5.E1 will change in the weight fraction equation for the leg. Therefore, from either Eq. (3.14) when $P_s > 0$ or Eq. (3.16) when $P_s = 0$, for any given leg flown with a different engine,

$$\prod_{i\,j} = \exp\{-TSFC \times \text{constant}\} \tag{5.E2}$$

and for the special case of warm-up with a different engine, Eq. (3.42) yields, assuming the same thrust lapse for all engines,

$$\prod_{i\,j} = 1 - TSFC \times \text{constant} \tag{5.E3}$$

Therefore, in order to find $\prod_{i\,j}$ for a candidate engine in the search for an optimum engine, it is necessary only to adjust the Table 5.E1 value of $\prod_{i\,j}$ to reflect the new $TSFC$ as found from the engine cycle analysis. It is important to recall at this point that the $TSFC$ values of Table 5.E1 are based on the highly generalized models found in Sec. 3.3.2. You should therefore expect to find differences, some significant, between the universal models and the AEDsys cycle computations. The goal of the search remains, in fact, to find reference point engines that, on balance, are clearly superior.

Because the AEDsys engine performance analysis gives S, the uninstalled thrust specific fuel consumption, the mission analysis $TSFC$ is estimated as $S/0.95$, which allows 5% for installation losses. Therefore, the adjusted mission leg fraction $\{(\prod_{i\,j})_N\}$ can be found from Table 5.E1 data and the AEDsys engine performance analysis data by the equations

$$\left(\prod_{i\,j}\right)_N = \left(\prod_{i\,j}\right)^{(S/0.95)/TSFC} \tag{5.E4}$$

in general, and

$$\left(\prod_{i\,j}\right)_N = 1 - \frac{S/0.95}{TSFC}\left(1 - \prod_{i\,j}\right) \tag{5.E5}$$

for warm-up. These equations follow directly from Eqs. (5.E2) and (5.E3).

5.4.3 Getting Started

The search for the AAF engine begins with a baseline reference point engine and its off-design performance over the critical mission legs given in Table 5.E1. But how are the design choices (M_0, h, π_c, π_f, α, T_{t4}, T_{t7}, and M_6) for the first engine to be chosen? A great wealth of guidance is available to help with this selection. In the first place, the reference point study of Sec. 4.4 reduced the design choices to the following manageable ranges:

$$1.2 \leq M_0 \leq 1.6$$
$$30 \leq h \leq 45\,\text{kft}$$
$$15 \leq \pi_c \leq 25$$
$$0.3 \leq \alpha \leq 0.4$$

$$3 \leq \pi_f \leq 5$$
$$T_{t4} \leq 3200°R$$
$$T_{t7} \leq 3600°R$$
$$0.35 \leq M_6 \leq 0.45$$

In addition, the conclusions of the sensitivity study of Sec. 4.4.5 indicated that π_f and π_c should be selected from the high ends of their respective ranges, while, T_{t4} and/or T_{t7} should be allowed to drift down from their limiting values in order to reduce fuel consumption. Moreover, as shown in Sec. 4.3.4, the selections of π_c and π_f are interdependent. Because we will select cycles for which

$$\pi_f \cong \pi_{cL} \qquad (5.E6)$$

then, from Eq. (4.34)

$$\pi_{cH} \approx \frac{1}{\pi_{tH}\pi_{tL}} \qquad (5.E7)$$

Finally, because π_{tH} and π_{tL} must be less than about 0.5 in order to ensure that the turbine entrance nozzles are choked, we conclude that

$$\pi_{cH} > 4 \qquad (5.E8)$$

Simultaneously, note that the requirement that π_{tH} and π_{tL} be less than 0.5 requires τ_{tH} and τ_{tL} to be less than about 0.87 [see Eqs. (4.9d) and (4.9e)]. This impacts on the selection of π_f and α because π_f, α, τ_{tH}, and τ_{tL} are related through the low pressure spool power balance. As an approximation for the purposes here, consider the low spool power balance for a turbofan with no bleed air, no turbine cooling, and no power takeoff. Solving the low-pressure spool power balance equation [Eq. (4.22a)] for π_f yields

$$\pi_f = \left\{ 1 + \frac{\eta_{mL}\tau_\lambda\tau_{m1}\tau_{tH}\tau_{m2}(1-\tau_{tL})}{(1+\alpha)\tau_r} \frac{\dot{m}_{4.5}}{\dot{m}_C} \right\}^{\gamma_c e_f/(\gamma_c - 1)} \qquad (5.E9)$$

where, from Fig. 4.2

$$\frac{\dot{m}_{4.5}}{\dot{m}_C} = (1 - \beta - \varepsilon_1 - \varepsilon_2)(1 + f) + \varepsilon_1 + \varepsilon_2 \cong 1$$

Thus, Eq. (5.E9) provides a relationship between π_f and α for the given flight conditions and design constants and for the approximate value of 0.87 for τ_{tH} and τ_{tL}.

Finally, as mentioned in Sec. 4.3.4, common sense would encourage keeping the design choice of M_6 in the range 0.35–0.45 because it is certain to migrate away during off-design operation.

5.4.4 The Baseline Engine

The search is begun by selecting the reference point for a baseline engine, verifying its operating envelope, performing a sensitivity analysis at its design point, and determining its off-design performance. The sensitivity analysis provides guidance in selecting subsequent engines to be studied, while the detailed off-design performance of the baseline engine will illustrate the off-design analysis to be followed for other candidate engines in the search. As noted in Sec. 4.2.8, the MSH (Modified Specific Heat) model is used in all of the ensuing AAF engine performance calculations.

Selection: baseline engine. Referring to the discussion of Sec. 4.4.4, the reference point flight conditions for the baseline engine are selected to be $M_0 = 1.451$ and 36,000 ft ($\theta_0 = 1.07$). The design values of T_{t4} and T_{t7} are selected to be $3200°R$ and $3600°R$. These choices fix τ_r and τ_λ at 1.421 and 10.07, respectively.

Now Eq. (5.E9) is used to relate the selection of π_f and α. Using $\gamma_c = 1.4$, $\tau_{tH} = \tau_{tL} = 0.87$, $\tau_{m1} = \tau_{m2} = 0.97$, $\eta_{mL} = 0.995$, $e_f = 0.89$, and $\dot{m}_{4.5}/\dot{m}_C = 1.02$ along with the design point values of τ_r and τ_λ, Eq. (5.E9a) yields

$$\pi_f = \left\{ 1 + \frac{0.765}{1 + \alpha} \right\}^{3.12}$$

Selecting a midrange bypass ratio of 0.4 for α, the reference point choice of π_f from this equation is about 3.9. As suggested by the sensitivity study and in order to make $\pi_{cH} > 4.0$ [Eq. (5.E8)], a high range value of 20 is selected for π_c, which from Eq. (5.E7) gives a reference point value of 5.13 for π_{cH}. Finally, the Mach number at station 6 is chosen to be 0.4 at the reference point.

Before the performance of any engine with power takeoff can be calculated, an estimate of the nondimensional power takeoff (C_{TO}) is required. We elect to have the 300 kW of external power driven by the high-pressure spool to minimize the impact on the mixer. Because the power takeoff, P_{TO}, is a small fraction of the overall power produced by the high-pressure turbine, a rough estimate of the nondimensional power takeoff will suffice at this point. With

$$C_{TO} = \frac{P_{TO}}{\dot{m}_0 h_0} = \left\{ \frac{P_{TO}}{F h_0} \right\} \frac{F}{\dot{m}_0}$$

then values of F and $F/\dot{m}_0$ need be determined only to obtain the desired estimate because P_{TO}/h_0 is known. From Table 4.1, $F/\dot{m}_0$ is estimated to be 110 lbf/(lbm/s). Thus, with $F = T_{SL} = 30,000$ lbf, we find the mass flow at the sea level static to be

$$\dot{m}_0 = F/(F/\dot{m}_0) \approx 270 \text{ lbm/s}$$

which is also the corrected mass flow rate at sea level static. Like the maximum compressor pressure ratio, the corrected mass flow rate is limited to its sea level static value for flight conditions where $\theta_0 \leq TR$ (see Appendix D). Because this point corresponds to $\theta_0 \approx TR$, the mass flow rate at the reference point can be calculated from the corrected mass flow rate using Eq. (5.23) rewritten as

$$\dot{m}_0 = \dot{m}_2 = \dot{m}_{c2} \delta_2 / \sqrt{\theta_2}$$

With $\dot{m}_{c2} = 270$ lbm/s, $\theta_2 = \theta_0 = TR = 1.07$, and $\delta_2 = \pi_d \delta_0 = \pi_r \pi_d \delta = (3.421)$ (0.9354)(0.2250) = 0.7200, then

$$\dot{m}_0 = 270 \times 0.720 / \sqrt{1.07} \approx 200 \text{ lbm/s}$$

Hence, the nondimensional power takeoff, with $P_{TO} = 300$ kW and $h_0 = 93.72$ Btu/lbm $[c_{pc} = 0.24$ Btu/(lbm-°R), $T_0 = 390.5$°R, and $h_0 = c_{pc}T_0]$, is estimated to be 0.01517 or in round figures, say, 0.0152, which makes $P_{TO} = 300.6$ kW ≈ 300 kW.

All engines to be examined in the search will use this design point value of 0.0152 for C_{TO}. In addition, the mixer inlet design point Mach number (M_6) will be 0.4 for all engines to be studied.

Please bear in mind the fact that the size or scale of the engine, as represented here by $\dot{m}_0$, can and will be easily changed within AEDsys to match the precise requirements of the aircraft system over the entire mission. Moreover, the scale of the engine has no effect on any specific performance properties, which includes the vast majority of the engine cycle quantities of interest.

In summary, the reference point parameters for the baseline engine are as follows:

$$M_0 = 1.451 \quad \pi_f = 3.9 \quad T_{t4} = 3200°R \quad C_{TOH} = 0.0152$$

$$h = 36 \text{ kft} \quad \alpha = 0.4487 \quad T_{t7} = 3600°R$$

$$\pi_c = 20 \quad M_6 = 0.4 \quad \dot{m}_0 = 200 \text{ lbm/s}$$

Note that the bypass ratio has increased from its initial assumed value of 0.4 to 0.4487. This is mainly caused by the decreases in τ_{tH} and τ_{tL} from their assumed values of 0.87 (see the following).

The reference point performance of this engine at military power is summarized next. Performance results of particular interest are $F/\dot{m}_0$ and S. These and other data, which are of interest because they are the cumulative result of many approximations and arguments (Sec. 5.4.3) used as guidance in the selection of the design choices, are as follows:

$$F/\dot{m}_0 = 62.49 \text{ lbf/(lbm/s)} \quad S = 1.0863 \text{ (lbm/h)/lbf}$$

$$\pi_{tH} = 0.4231 < 0.5 \quad \tau_{tL} = 0.8598 < 0.87$$

$$\pi_{tL} = 0.4831 < 0.5 \quad P_{t6}/P_{t16} = 1.0$$

$$\tau_{tH} = 0.8381 < 0.87 \quad M_{16} = 0.394 \approx M_6 = 0.4$$

Operating envelope: baseline engine. Before examining the performance of the baseline engine, it is important to first ascertain the Mach number and altitude ranges over which the engine can operate at full throttle ($T_{t4\,max}$ with or without afterburning), i.e., its full throttle operating envelope. It may come as a surprise at first that an engine might not be able to operate at certain combinations of Mach number and altitude. The full throttle Mach number and altitude operational limits of a mixed flow turbofan engine are caused by the requirement that both the Kutta condition ($P_6 = P_{16}$) in the fixed area mixer and the power balance between the fan plus low-pressure compressor and the low-pressure turbine (which fixes P_6) must be satisfied simultaneously. There are Mach number/altitude combinations where both of these conditions cannot be met simultaneously, as indicated by the inability of the Engine Test feature of the AEDsys computer program to converge on a solution for M_{16} and/or τ_{tL}.

To find these boundaries for the baseline engine, a performance analysis is performed using the Engine Test feature of the AEDsys program with full throttle

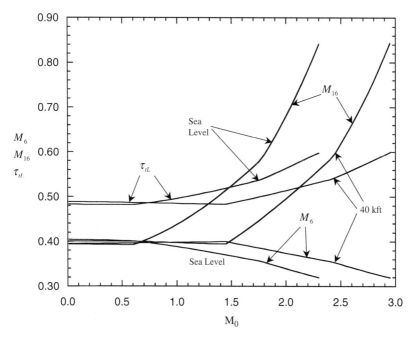

Fig. 5.E1   Variation of M_6, M_{16}, and τ_{tL} for baseline engine at full throttle.

(with imposed limits of $T_{t4\,\max} = 3200°R$, $\pi_{c\,\max} = 20$, and $T_{t3\,\max} = 1660°R$) over the expected Mach number/altitude envelope of the AAF. The results are shown in Fig. 5.E1 as the variations of M_6, M_{16}, and τ_{tL} with Mach number at constant values of altitude. The right endpoints in the plots are limiting operating points for the engine. The values of Mach number and altitude at these points determine an engine's operational envelope (e.g., see Fig. 5.E4) in a Mach number/altitude coordinate system.

The results show that the baseline engine cannot operate in the high Mach/low-altitude regime. Fortunately, this region of inoperability is outside of the AAF flight envelope. Having established that the baseline engine is acceptable, its performance over the critical mission legs will be examined next.

The performance of the engine at partial throttle ($T_{t4} < T_{t4\,\max}$) is also important to understand because M_6, M_{16}, and τ_{tL} can vary far from their design values. Figure 5.E2 shows the variation of M_6, M_{16}, and τ_{tL} of the baseline engine with reduced throttle (T_{t4}) at 1.451M/36 kft. Note that M_{16} increases with reduced throttle while M_6 decreases. Thus, it is possible that as these Mach numbers diverge, the engine cycle deck may have trouble converging on a solution at reduced throttle.

Mission performance: baseline engine.   The baseline engine is now flown through the AAF mission using the Mission Analysis portion of AEDsys. The results of these computations are presented in Table 5.E2. The bottom line result is an increase in fuel consumption of 130 lbf from the initial estimate of Table 3.E3,

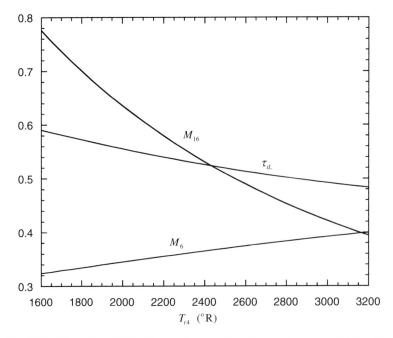

Fig. 5.E2   Variation of M_6, M_{16}, and τ_{tL} for baseline engine at partial throttle.

Table 5.E2   AAF mission—baseline engine

Mission phases and segments		Table 3.E3 $\prod$	W_F, lbf	Baseline engine $\prod$	W_F, lbf	% change
1–2:	A—Warm-up	0.9895	252	0.9892	258	2.4
1–2:	B—Takeoff acceleration	0.9958	100	0.9954	108	4.0
1–2:	C—Takeoff rotation	0.9984	39	0.9985	36	−7.7
2–3:	D—Horizontal acceleration	0.9935	155	0.9935	153	−1.3
2–3:	E—Climb/acceleration	0.9806	453	0.9796	479	5.7
3–4:	Subsonic cruise climb	0.9736	607	0.9760	552	−9.1
5–6:	Combat air patrol	0.9675	729	0.9685	705	−3.3
6–7:	F—Acceleration	0.9837	354	0.9813	406	14.7
6–7:	G—Supersonic penetration	0.9382	1317	0.9410	1256	−4.6
7–8:	I—1.6M/5g turn	0.9753	478	0.9752	481	0.6
7–8:	J—0.9M/5g turns[a]	0.9774	427	0.9727	516	20.8
7–8:	K—Acceleration	0.9828	317	0.9806	357	12.6
8–9:	Escape dash	0.9795	358	0.9801	346	−3.4
9–10:	Zoom climb	0.9970	51	0.9972	50	−2.0
10–11:	Subsonic cruise climb	0.9698	516	0.9704	500	−2.7
12–13:	Loiter	0.9677	535	0.9626	616	15.1
	Total	—	6688	—	6818	2.0

[a]9.68% increase required from $T_{SL}/W_{TO} = 1.25$ to meet thrust required for 0.9M/30 kft, 5g turns at maneuver weight.

and 128 lbf more than the initial goal of 6690 lbf. The relative fuel savings in phases 3–4, 5–6, and 6–7 G are more than offset by the increased fuel consumed in phases 2–3 E, 6–7 F, 7–8 J, 7–8 K, and 12–13. A worthwhile investment of your time would be to calculate the fuel consumption results using the algebraic mission analysis estimation method just described and compare it with the precise values of Table 5.E2.

Although the AEDsys computations reveal that the baseline engine is 9.68% too small for the 0.9M/30 kft, 5g turn, at maneuver weight, the engine will not be resized until we have a better estimate of the installation losses. The maximum Mach flight condition of 1.8M/40 kft requires 10,210 lbf of uninstalled thrust. As shown in sample printout B, given earlier, the baseline engine can produce 19,770 lbf, which is more than enough.

With the baseline engine performance in hand, the design choices of the engine are now varied systematically to obtain the performance of other reference point engines. The fuel consumption of these candidate engines is compared with that of the baseline engine to find the engine with the lowest fuel consumption. Hereafter, the baseline engine is called Engine 1.

5.4.5 The Search

The search methodology is straightforward. The Engine 1 (baseline engine) design choices (π_c, π_f, h, and M_0) are varied one at a time. Each candidate engine is flown in the AAF through the mission using the AEDsys software and the mission fuel usage determined. Each engine is also tested at the maximum Mach condition of 1.8M/40 kft to ensure its operation. The mission fuel used (W_F) and the specific thrust ($F/\dot{m}_0$) are the initial figures of merit.

We have carried out that search and the reference points of the most promising engines and the performance of those engines that would operate at all critical mission legs are shown in Table 5.E3. The engine performance is given in terms of fuel saved (referenced to the 6690 lbf of fuel used that was estimated in Sec. 3.4) and the specific thrust and mass flow rate at takeoff.

The search progression followed the sequence evident in Table. 5.E3. The cycle pressure ratio (π_c) was the first design choice varied. As it was changed from 20 to 22, 24, 26, and 28, increasing amounts of fuel were saved. At a pressure ratio of 24 (Engine 3), the fuel used becomes less than the initial estimate of 6690 lbf determined in Chapter 3. The fan pressure ratio (π_f) was the next design choice varied. As it was changed from 3.9 to 3.7, 3.5, and 3.3, increasing amounts of fuel were saved. Once again, the bypass ratio α is no longer an independent variable when the designer chooses to match total pressures at the mixer entrance. Note that the total temperature leaving the engine during dry operation (T_{t6A}) at the supercruise flight condition (1.5M/30 kft) decreases with increasing compressor pressure ratio and decreasing fan pressure ratio. A low value of T_{t6A} is desirable to reduce the infrared signature of the aircraft.

An overarching conclusion is that fuel consumption is reduced by increasing π_c (thus improving thermal efficiency) and/or α (thus improving propulsive efficiency). This can be readily confirmed by reviewing the complete engine

Table 5.E3 Summary of AAF engine search

	Engine design point								Engine performance on mission				
Engine number	π_c	π_f	α	M_0	h, kft	θ_0	%T/W, increase required[a]	$F/\dot{m}_0$, lbf/lbm/s @SLS	$\dot{m}_0$, lbm/s @SLS	P_{TO}, kW	Fuel saved, lbf	T_{t6A}, °R @1.5M/30 kft
1	20	3.9	0.4487	1.451	36	1.07	9.68	116.0	258.6	281.9	−128	1817
2	22	—	0.4734	—	—	—	9.66	—	—	—	−29	1775
3	24	—	0.4890	—	—	—	9.65	—	—	—	51	1741
4	26	—	0.4975	—	—	—	9.65	—	—	—	118	1715
5	28	—	0.5003	—	—	—	9.65	—	—	—	175	1693
6	20	3.7	0.5715	1.451	36	1.07	9.23	113.7	263.8	287.6	−63	1732
7	22	—	0.5955	—	—	—	9.21	—	—	—	31	1694
8	24	—	0.6102	—	—	—	9.20	—	—	—	108	1664
9	26	—	0.6176	—	—	—	9.20	—	—	—	172	1640
10	28	—	0.6192	—	—	—	9.20	—	—	—	226	1620
11	20	3.5	0.7132	1.451	36	1.07	8.70	111.2	269.7	294.0	−1	1647
12	22	—	0.7384	—	—	—	8.70	—	—	—	88	1613
13	24	—	0.7501	—	—	—	8.69	—	—	—	161	1587
14	26	—	0.7562	—	—	—	8.69	—	—	—	222	1565
15	28	—	0.7563	—	—	—	8.69	—	—	—	273	1528
16	20	3.3	0.8785	1.451	36	1.07	8.10	108.5	275.7	301.5	56	1563
17	22	—	0.9008	—	—	—	8.09	—	—	—	140	1533
18	24	—	0.9132	—	—	—	8.08	—	—	—	206	1509
19	26	—	0.9178	—	—	—	8.08	—	—	—	253	1490
20	28	—	0.9162	—	—	—	8.09	—	—	—	292	1475
21	28	3.5	0.7138	1.451	35	1.08	8.69	111.3	269.7	309.7	267	1567
22	—	—	0.7622	—	37	1.07	8.69	111.2	—	280.1	281	1545
23	28	3.5	0.7997	1.428	36	1.06	8.67	111.2	269.7	286.4	258	1528
24	—	—	0.7129	1.474	36	1.08	8.69	—	—	300.6	272	1568

[a]Increase required from $T_{SL}/W_{TO} = 1.25$ to meet thrust required for 0.9M/30 kft, 5g turn at maneuver weight.

182

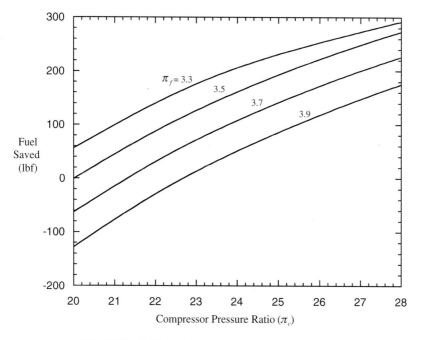

Fig. 5.E3   Fuel saved referenced to W_F = 6690 lbf.

performance results. Unfortunately, as we have come to expect, the reverse is true for the specific thrust.

The fuel saved for these engines is plotted in Fig. 5.E3. Engine 15 is selected for further investigation (even though Engine 20 saves 19 lbf more fuel) because it saves significant fuel while keeping the engine specific thrust above 110 lbf/(lbm/s). Compressor pressure ratios above 28 are not shown because they result in temperatures leaving the compressor greater than 1660°R at the maximum Mach flight condition of 1.8M/40 kft.

When the reference point altitude of Engine 15 is changed to 35 kft (Engine 21), less fuel is saved. And when it is changed to 37 kft (Engine 22), more fuel is saved. However these savings are exaggerated when compared with Engine 15 because the difference in power takeoff (P_{TO}) accounts for about 8 lbf of fuel (assuming a thermal efficiency of 45%, 300kW of P_{TO} for the 1.5 hr AAF mission consumes 185 lbf of fuel). Thus the savings caused by altitude changes are negligible. Likewise the changes in fuel saved for the changes in design Mach number (Engines 23 and 24) are caused mainly by the changes in power takeoff (P_{TO}).

Note that the specific thrust ($F/\dot{m}_0$) does not appear to change with compressor pressure ratio (π_c) for a given fan pressure ratio (π_f). This is because the exit total pressure is determined by the fan pressure ratio (π_f) and the exit total temperature (T_{t7}) is fixed. The increases in compressor pressure (π_c) permit larger engine bypass ratios (α) with corresponding lower fuel consumption.

The Engine 15 design parameters are as follows:

$$M_0 = 1.451 \quad \pi_f = 3.5 \quad T_{t4} = 3200°R \quad C_{TOH} = 0.0152$$

$$h = 36 \text{ kft} \quad \alpha = 0.7563 \quad T_{t7} = 3600°R$$

$$\pi_c = 28 \quad M_6 = 0.4 \quad \dot{m}_0 = 200 \text{ lbm/s}$$

The results of the reference point calculations for the Engine 15 engine were given earlier in sample printout A. Sample printout B and sample printout C give the performance of this engine at one full throttle and partial throttle operating condition, respectively.

5.4.6 AAF Engine: Operational Envelope and Mission Performance

Having selected a promising engine for the AAF, its capability to operate over the aircraft's flight regime must be confirmed and its performance for all mission legs determined. The operational envelope is confirmed, as with the baseline engine, by flying the engine at military power over the expected Mach number/altitude flight envelope of the AAF. The engine operational envelope thus obtained is shown in Fig. 5.E4. The flight regime of the AAF is well within the engine operational envelope.

Table 5.E4 contains a summary of the mission performance of the AAF engine in terms of $\prod_{ij}$ and W_F. When the values of the AAF weight fractions with Engine 15 are compared with the estimated values from Chapter 3, it is found that the Engine

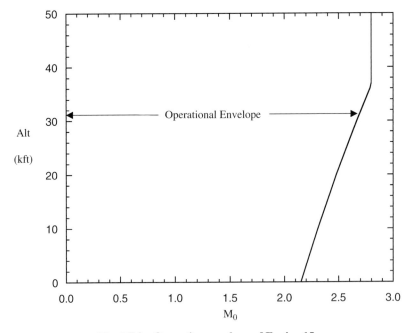

Fig. 5.E4   Operation envelope of Engine 15.

Table 5.E4   AAF mission—Engine 15

Mission phases and segments	Table 3.E3 $\prod\limits_{i\ f}$	W_F, lbf	Engine 15 $\prod\limits_{i\ f}$	W_F, lbf	% change
1–2: A—Warm-up	0.9895	252	0.9916	202	−19.4
1–2: B—Takeoff acceleration	0.9958	100	0.9952	113	13.0
1–2: C—Takeoff rotation	0.9984	39	0.9984	38	−2.6
2–3: D—Horizontal acceleration	0.9935	155	0.9942	138	−11.0
2–3: E—Climb/acceleration	0.9806	453	0.9804	461	1.8
3–4: Subsonic cruise climb	0.9736	607	0.9796	471	−22.4
5–6: Combat air patrol	0.9675	729	0.9719	634	−13.0
6–7: F—Acceleration	0.9837	354	0.9809	420	18.6
6–7: G—Supersonic penetration	0.9382	1317	0.9460	1161	−11.8
7–8: I—1.6M/5g turn	0.9753	478	0.9748	497	4.0
7–8: J—0.9M/5g turns[a]	0.9774	427	0.9716	546	27.9
7–8: K—Acceleration	0.9828	317	0.9803	369	16.4
8–9: Escape dash	0.9795	358	0.9819	319	−10.9
9–10: Zoom climb	0.9970	51	0.9975	46	−9.8
10–11: Subsonic cruise climb	0.9698	516	0.9734	457	−11.4
12–13: Loiter	0.9677	535	0.9674	547	2.2
Total	——	6688	——	6417	−4.2

[a]Increase required from $T_{SL}/W_{TO} = 1.25$ to meet thrust required for 0.9 M/30 kft, 5g turn at maneuver weight.

15 uses significantly less fuel in the Warm-up 1–2 A, Horizontal Acceleration 2–3, Subsonic Cruise Climb 3–4, and Supercruise 6–7 phases. For all other mission phases, the Engine 15 consumes about the same or more fuel, with the net result that Engine 15 consumes 4% less fuel for the complete mission giving a cushion of 271 lbf vs the total fuel consumption of 6690 lbf of Chapter 3.

5.4.7   Second Reprise

Now that the performance of the selected AAF engine is known in terms of the fuel used, the effect of these changes in aircraft weight on aircraft performance can be updated from the First Reprise of Sec. 3.4.3. Table 5.E5 summarizes current estimates of the aircraft weight fractions and the preceding estimates of Table 3.E3. These results highlight another interesting and inevitable conflict for the designer. Although low fuel consumption is essential to achieving low W_{TO}, it also results in increased values of the instantaneous weight fraction β, which increases the required values of thrust loading T_{SL}/W_{TO}. In the case of the AAF, the most notable are the 0.9/30 kft 5g Turns 7–8 J phase and the Descend and Land 13–14 phase.

For the 0.9M/30 kft 5g Turns phase, the decrease in engine thrust lapse (α) of the AAF engine (0.4670 vs 0.5033 in Chapter 2) and the increase in weight fraction at maneuver (0.8221 vs 0.78 in Chapter 2) result in a 8.69% increase of the required

Table 5.E5   Summary of results—mission analysis—24,000 lbf W_{TO}

Mission phases and segments		Table 3.E3		Table 5.E4	
		β at end of leg	$\prod_{i\,f}$	β at end of leg	$\prod_{i\,f}$
1–2 A:	Warm-up	0.9895	0.9895	0.9916	0.9916
1–2 B:	Takeoff acceleration	0.9853	0.9958	0.9868	0.9952
1–2 C:	Takeoff rotation	0.9837	0.9984	0.9853	0.9984
2–3 D:	Acceleration	0.9773	0.9935	0.9795	0.9942
2–3 E:	Climb/acceleration	0.9584	0.9806	0.9603	0.9804
3–4:	Subsonic cruise climb	0.9331	0.9736	0.9407	0.9796
4–5:	Descend	0.9331	1.0000	0.9407	1.0000
5–6:	Combat air patrol	0.9027	0.9675	0.9143	0.9719
6–7 F:	Acceleration	0.8880	0.9837	0.8968	0.9809
6–7 G:	Supersonic penetration	0.8331	0.9382	0.8485	0.9461
7–8 H:	Fire ARAAMs	0.8060	——	0.8213	——
7–8 I:	1.6M/5g turn	0.7860	0.9753	0.8006	0.9748
7–8 J:	0.9M/5g turns	0.7682	0.9774	0.7778	0.9716
7–8 K:	Acceleration	0.7550	0.9828	0.7625	0.9803
7–8 L:	Fire AIM-9Ls and $\frac{1}{2}$ ammo	0.7276	——	0.7351	——
8–9:	Escape dash	0.7127	0.9795	0.7218	0.9819
9–10:	Minimum time climb	0.7106	0.9970	0.7199	0.9974
10–11:	Subsonic cruise climb	0.6891	0.9698	0.7009	0.9735
11–12:	Descend	0.6891	1.0000	0.7009	1.0000
12–13:	Loiter	0.6668	0.9677	0.6781	0.9674
13–14:	Descend and land	0.6668	1.0000	0.6781	1.0000
End	Remove permanent payload	0.6106	——	0.6219	——

thrust loading from 1.25 to 1.36. Because this is based on a installation loss of 5% for this full throttle flight condition where the engine is limited by the compressor pressure ratio, this estimate is most likely conservative, and the thrust loading will not be changed until a better estimate of the installation loss is obtained in the next chapter.

Constraint analysis shows that the increase in landing weight fraction requires either a decrease in the wing loading from 64 to 62.7 lbf/ft² or an increase in the maximum lift coefficient for landing from 2.0 to 2.05. The increase in maximum lift coefficient is preferred to keep the wing area down and its resultant fuel consumption at cruise. Consequently, Engine 15 meets all the known constraints and promises satisfactory fuel consumption for the AAF mission, and provides a satisfactory starting point for the remaining studies.

We would do well to pause at this point to take stock of our situation. We have come far in short order because of the powerful conceptual and computational tools at our disposal. Several promising reference point engines have been discovered that can apparently make possible an aircraft that can meet all of the requirements of the AAF RFP. One of those engines, designated Engine 15, has been selected for further investigation, although we are free to return to this step to choose others if the studies ahead make reconsideration desirable or necessary. The remaining task is to develop tools that characterize the installation losses more realistically, accounting in particular for the effects of flight conditions and throttle position. Once these are in hand, we can fly our aircraft over the entire AAF flight envelope in general, and the AAF mission in particular.

References

[1]Oates, G. C., *The Aerothermodynamics of Gas Turbine and Rocket Propulsion*, 3rd ed., AIAA Education Series, AIAA, Reston, VA, 1997.

[2]Mattingly, J. D., *Elements of Gas Turbine Propulsion*, McGraw–Hill, New York, 1996.

[3]Nikkanen, J. P., and Brooky, J. D., "Single Stage Evaluation of Highly Loaded High Mach Number Compressor Stages V," NASA CR 120887 (PWA-431 2).

[4]Oates, G. C. (ed.), *Aerothermodynamics of Aircraft Engine Components*, AIAA Education Series, AIAA, New York, 1985.

[5]Hill, P. G., and Peterson, C. R., *Mechanics and Thermodynamics of Propulsion*, 2nd ed., Addison Wesley Longman, Reading, MA, 1992.

[6]Kerrebrock, J. L., *Aircraft Engines and Gas Turbines*, 2nd ed., Massachusetts Inst. of Technology Press, Cambridge, MA, 1992.

[7]Bathie, W. W., *Fundamentals of Gas Turbines*, 2nd ed., Wiley, New York, 1995.

[8]Gordon, S., and McBride, B., "Computer Program for Calculation of Complex Chemical Equilibrium Compositions," NASA SP-273, 1971.

6
Sizing the Engine: Installed Performance

6.1 Concept

At some point in the design process, the absolute size of the engine, in terms of some reference thrust or airflow, must be determined. Until now, a careful distinction has been made between the installed thrust (T) required by the aircraft and the uninstalled thrust (F) that would be produced by the isolated engine. The difference between T and F is neither academic nor insignificant.

The uninstalled thrust represents only the ideal performance of the engine, in the sense that it corresponds to an installation without external drag (see Appendix E). Unfortunately, placing the engine within an airframe inevitably induces forces on the external surfaces that increase the total drag. One might call the additional forces the "self-drag" of the engine, but, whatever their name, they must also be overcome by the available thrust of the engine. The uninstalled thrust must therefore be the sum of the installed thrust and the self-drag; the latter must be accounted for before the size, or uninstalled thrust, can be known.

This reasoning is quite logical and correct, but its practical application is not trivial. Because the presence of the engine and its inlet, nozzle, and exhaust stream actually influence the flow and pressure distribution over the *entire* aircraft, where does the propulsion "system" begin and end? Defining the physical boundaries of the propulsion system has been one of the greatest challenges of the aeronautics industry, and enormous amounts of time and energy have been invested in locating the proper "interface" between the airframe and the propulsion system.

It was not always thus. In the early days of jet-propelled aircraft, when only relatively small turbojet engines (high $F/\dot{m}_0$) were available, the unfavorable interactions between the engine and airframe were not significant. During that period of time, it was conventional to confine the engine to its "flange-to-flange" domain, which meant from the bolt circle at the compressor entry to the bolt circle at the nozzle entry. When the turbofan arrived in the mid-1960s, with its larger diameter (lower $F/\dot{m}_0$) and more sensitive and complex compression systems, installation effects could no longer be ignored. An exciting and painful period of adjustment then took place wherein the narrow engine boundaries were expanded in order to improve the integrated performance of the aircraft and engine, as well as to give engine manufacturers more control over the internal performance and operability of their products. A clear example of this trend is evident in the case of the nacelle mounted, high bypass ratio engines introduced around 1970 in order to dramatically reduce fuel consumption. On the one hand, internal performance calculations favor much higher bypass ratios, but the larger diameters and resulting installation penalties prevent the benefits from being fully realized. On the other, transport engine manufacturers have moved far from their flange-to-flange world and now supply the entire nacelle/engine package in order to achieve the best-integrated or installed performance.

For such high performance aircraft as the Air-to-Air Fighter (AAF) of this textbook, the engine is likely to be "buried" within the fuselage, and the division of territorial jurisdiction becomes difficult. The engine designer would like to have control over those external surfaces that directly interact with the engine, but cannot possibly be responsible for the entire envelope that surrounds the engine. In the end, the engine designer will be allowed to influence those parts that are believed to generate the bulk of the installation penalties and are affected by the inlet and exhaust flows. This will generally include the inlet and the nozzle, the exact boundaries being decided by negotiation in each case. As you will see, the external drag on the inlet and nozzle is strongly affected by the throttle setting, and it is therefore referred to as "throttle dependent drag."

The foregoing should persuade you that engine integration has itself become a major technology in modern aircraft design and development. Aircraft and engine companies alike have invested heavily in this area and now have expert organizations available to deal with its problems; the government and industry have acted collectively to produce clarifying standards.[1] Today it is known that engine integration can have beneficial and satisfying results when considered from the outset and done properly. When done poorly (or not at all), development crises are invited that, in the past, have led to dramatic examples of reduced aircraft performance and engine operability, increased program time and cost, and/or bitter recriminations.

The purpose of this chapter is to provide some preliminary tools for estimating the installation penalties that must be compensated for by added uninstalled thrust. Only inlet and nozzle external losses will be considered, and they will be expressed in their most convenient form, namely as a fraction of the uninstalled thrust, so that

$$T = F - \phi_{inlet} F - \phi_{nozzle} F$$

or

$$F = \frac{T}{1 - \phi_{inlet} - \phi_{nozzle}} > T \qquad (6.1)$$

where

$$\phi_{inlet} = D_{inlet} / F \qquad (6.2a)$$

and

$$\phi_{nozzle} = D_{nozzle} / F \qquad (6.2b)$$

Please note that ϕ_{inlet} and ϕ_{nozzle} will vary with flight condition and throttle setting for any given engine.

In addition to entering a territory rich in history and jurisprudence, this is the first encounter in this textbook with individual engine components: inlets and nozzles. In later chapters, the focus will be on their internal behavior in order to ensure that they will deliver the performance assumed in the cycle calculations, but now only their external behavior will be considered. Despite their outward appearance of simplicity, inlets and nozzles are actually very complex devices because they must meet many simultaneous requirements and they can have a very detrimental effect on system performance if they do not function properly. Much good technical work on engine/aircraft integration has been accomplished and reported over the past 30 years, so that many references are now available. The basics can be found in Refs. 2 and 3, and an excellent survey is located in Chapter 4 of Ref. 4. The contents of Ref. 4 also have been updated and have been published in three textbooks as part of the AIAA Education Series; see Refs. 2, 5, and 6. From such writings it is possible to construct a partial list of the requirements to be met by inlets and nozzles that emphasizes the many roles they play, as follows:

Both inlets and nozzles:

1) Minimize installation drag on their own and adjacent aircraft surfaces (over wide ranges of angles of attack and throttle settings).

2) Maximize internal total pressure recovery (π_d, π_n).

3) Provide controllable flow matching for all operating conditions. (Remember, the engine knows how much flow it wants.)

4) Minimize weight and cost while meeting life and reliability goals.

5) Suppress acoustic and radar signatures.

Inlets:

6) Control inlet spatial and temporal distortion.

7) Provide good starting and stability characteristics.

Nozzles:

8) Suppress infrared (IR) signatures.

9) Provide thrust reversing and vectoring.

Merely skimming Ref. 5 will reveal that many types of inlets and nozzles have been developed to meet these requirements, depending upon the specific operating conditions. It will also become clear that the analysis and testing of these devices have become very sophisticated. Nevertheless, it is not the purpose of this textbook to provide comprehensive design methods for every conceivable inlet and nozzle configuration. Instead, some typical preliminary design estimation tools for ϕ_{inlet} and ϕ_{nozzle} will be developed. If more accuracy is required, the open literature is recommended.

What really matters here is that some account must be made at this point in the design cycle for installation penalties. The sooner the problems are identified, the sooner the engine and aircraft designers can start working to solve them.

Once an agreement is reached on the means for computing ϕ_{inlet} and ϕ_{nozzle} as a function of flight conditions (altitude, Mach number, and angle of attack) and throttle setting (T_{t4} and T_{t7}), the engine performance models of Chapter 5 contained within the AEDsys program may be used to size the engine. Starting from the design point engine and mass flow selected by the methods of Chapter 5, the engine is "tested" at each critical flight condition at either military power or maximum power in accordance with the Request for Proposal (RFP) requirement and then the engine is "flown" through the mission. Next, either the engine mass flow (size) is adjusted until the required and available thrust are equal at the flight condition requiring the largest engine by the method of Fig. 6.E2 or the required size may be found in the following manner. From Eqs. (2.2a) and (6.1) it follows for each flight condition that

$$\dot{m}_0 = \frac{F}{F/\dot{m}_0} = \frac{T}{(F/\dot{m}_0)(1 - \phi_{inlet} - \phi_{nozzle})}$$

$$= \frac{W[(D+R)/W + P_s/V]}{(F/\dot{m}_0)(1 - \phi_{inlet} - \phi_{nozzle})} \tag{6.3}$$

To find which of the flight conditions is most "demanding" (that is, requires the largest engine), each $\dot{m}_0$ is merely multiplied by the relevant, $(\dot{m}_{0\,req}/\dot{m}_{0\,avail})$ evaluated at sea level static as obtained from the performance computations. The procedure for determining these quantities will be described in detail in Sec. 6.4.3. You will be pleased to discover that this sizing process has been automated in AEDsys via the Thrust Scale Factor. The largest resulting product corresponds to what would be the largest design point engine and, therefore, the required size. This engine will, naturally, be too large for all except the most demanding flight condition, and actual performance at the others must be obtained later by throttling down T_{t4} and/or T_{t7} until

$$F = W \left\{ \frac{D + R}{W} + \frac{P_s}{V} \right\} \Big/ (1 - \phi_{inlet} - \phi_{nozzle}) \qquad (6.4)$$

for an engine of the chosen size. Not until this is done will the true behavior of the engine, and especially its fuel consumption, be known.

6.2 Design Tools

6.2.1 Subsonic Inlet Drag

The systematic bookkeeping method for determining uninstalled thrust has been developed in Appendix E, where it is shown that the inlet drag is given by the expression

$$D_{inlet} = \int_0^m (P - P_0)\, dA \geq 0 \qquad (E.15)$$

Referring to Fig. 6.1, it can be shown that this pressure integral between station 0 and station 1 is always positive (Refs. 1 and 2). This force is known as the

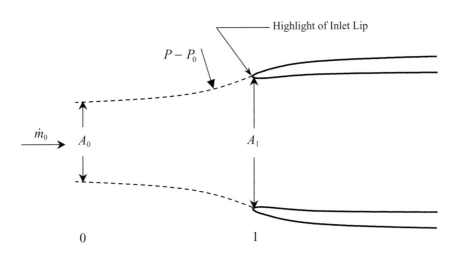

Fig. 6.1   Subsonic inlet flow.

"additive drag"

$$D_{add} = \int_0^1 (P - P_0)\, dA$$

Applying stream thrust analysis to the stream tube control volume between station 0 and station 1, we find that

$$D_{add} = P_1 A_1 (1 + \gamma M_1^2) - P_0 A_0 \left(\frac{A_1}{A_0} + \gamma M_0^2 \right) \tag{6.5}$$

A good inlet would, of course, recover most of this force through suction on the external surface, or "lip," of the inlet, but the accompanying adverse pressure gradients make boundary-layer separation a constant danger, in which case the additive drag will not be regained. An unfortunate fact is that larger additive drags are harder to regain because they are associated with more severe adverse pressure gradients along the cowl. Please note that external friction is not included in this analysis because external viscous forces are included in airplane drag as far as "accounting" goes.

Therefore, a reasonable "worst case," or upper limit, for subsonic inlet drag would be to assume massive separation and no recovery of additive drag. For this situation, Eqs. (6.2a) and (6.5), conservation of mass, and the usual perfect gas relationships can be combined to show that

$$\phi_{inlet} = \frac{D_{add}}{\dot{m}_0 (F/\dot{m}_0)} = \frac{\frac{M_0}{M_1}\sqrt{T_1/T_0}(1 + \gamma M_1^2) - (A_1/A_0 + \gamma M_0^2)}{\{F g_c/(\dot{m}_0 a_0)\}(\gamma M_0)} \tag{6.6a}$$

which can easily be evaluated assuming adiabatic, isentropic flow for any set of values of M_0, M_1, a_0, and $F/\dot{m}_0$. The static inlet drag may be estimated from the reduced form of Eq. (6.6a), as follows:

$$\phi_{inlet/static} = \frac{(1 + \gamma M_1^2)/\sqrt{1 + (\gamma - 1)M_1^2/2} - [1 + (\gamma - 1)M_1^2/2]^{\frac{(\gamma+1)}{2(\gamma-1)}}}{\{F g_c/(\dot{m}_0 a_0)\}(\gamma M_1)} \tag{6.6b}$$

Figure 6.2a shows the results of calculations for a variety of M_0 and M_1 combinations and $F g_c/(\dot{m}_0 a_0) = 4$. Figure 6.2b shows the static inlet drag for several $F g_c/(\dot{m}_0 a_0)$ values ranging from a high of 4 (afterburning fighter engines) to a low of 0.5 (high bypass transport engines). The information contained there leads to the following conclusions:

1) ϕ_{inlet} is not large if M_0 is near M_1. This is the natural result of D_{add} being exactly zero when $M_0 = M_1$ and the entering stream tube experiences neither a change in flow area nor streamwise pressure forces on the surface. In this region, lip separation can *still* occur, especially during vigorous maneuvers, and the drag estimate of Eq. (6.6) may be low.

2) For the usual range of subsonic flight ($0.2 < M_0 < 0.9$), it is desirable to keep M_1 in the vicinity of 0.4–0.6.

3) Unacceptably high values of ϕ_{inlet} occur at $M_0 = 0$, the beginning of every flight, reaching at least 0.05–0.10, but as much as 0.40–0.50. This explains the

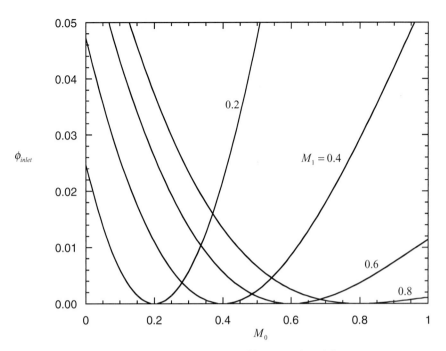

Fig. 6.2a   Subsonic inlet additive drag ($\gamma = 1.4$).

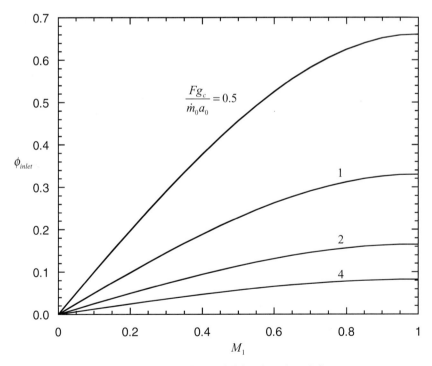

Fig. 6.2b   Static inlet additive drag ($\gamma = 1.4$)

special doors found on most cowls and nacelles, which open only during takeoff to allow for both the effective reduction of M_1 and better prevention of boundary layer separation. High bypass turbofan engines are also throttled up in a systematic manner to limit losses.

The sharp leading edges of supersonic inlets, such as those of the AAF, prevent the suction and additive drag recovery from occurring except when M_0 is quite near M_1, in which case ϕ_{inlet} is quite near zero anyway. Equation (6.6a) therefore can be used to provide a useful preliminary (and conservative) estimate of ϕ_{inlet} for the example aircraft. The information necessary to apply Eq. (6.6a) comes directly from the flight condition (i.e., M_0 and T_0) and the engine power setting (i.e., A_0 and $Fg_c/\dot{m}_0$) once the design point value of A_1 has been fixed. The subsonic inlet additive drag of Eq. (6.6a) is included in the AEDsys Mission Analysis, Constraint, and Contour Plot computations.

6.2.2 Supersonic Inlet Drag

Internal inlet drag.   Because signals of the presence of the inlet cannot propagate upstream to warn the oncoming flow and because the flow near the inlet is dominated by oblique and normal shock waves as well as boundary layer separation, supersonic inlets must be analyzed differently from subsonic inlets. For the same reasons, there are many generic types of supersonic inlet configurations, including fixed and variable geometry versions of internal, external, and mixed compression inlets,[5] as illustrated in Fig. 6.3. As a result of this variety, there are a proportionately large number of methods for predicting the upper and lower limits and the actual values of ϕ_{inlet} for each condition.

The method employed in this textbook is based upon Fig. 6.4, which corresponds to the inlet "swallowing" its projected image (i.e., $A_1 \geq A_0$) and, therefore, involves no additive drag in the strictest sense on the stream tube. Swallowing the flow at each flight condition will require a variable geometry inlet, which positions the shock system properly. We will assume that A_1 *is fixed at its largest required value.* Thus this inlet will have more airflow than the engine requires at all other

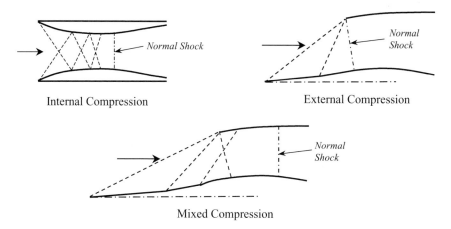

Internal Compression   External Compression

Mixed Compression

Fig. 6.3   Types of supersonic inlets.

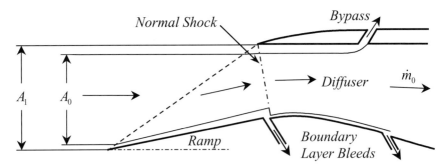

Fig. 6.4   Supersonic inlet model.

flight conditions. The excess inlet airflow must then be dumped overboard upstream of the engine face, but at a lower velocity than it had in the freestream. The loss of momentum of this "bypass" air results in a drag on the inlet.

Before proceeding with the analysis, a few related points will be considered. First, the information presented in Ref. 4 makes it clear that this is not usually the minimum drag condition. By moving the shock system forward so that some air "spills" outside the inlet lip, a favorable trade between spillage drag and bypass drag can be made, which results in a lower total inlet drag. The calculations done here will therefore be slightly conservative, but they avoid much greater complexity. Second, even when no bypass air is present, the inlet is usually designed to accept slightly more airflow than the engine requires in order to prevent internal boundary layer separation. The extra air flow that is "bled off" the internal surfaces and its loss of momentum are also chargeable to the inlet system as drag. The inlet area (A_1) must be initially sized to provide the necessary boundary layer bleed air at its design condition. Third, it will be assumed that the bypass and bleed flows are returned to the freestream with velocities that are sonic and aligned with the freestream velocity. This greatly simplifies the analysis and rests upon the observation that, even after passing through a normal shock, supersonic airflows recover sufficient total pressure to isentropically reaccelerate beyond sonic velocity if returned to their original static pressure. This can be demonstrated very quickly with the help of the isentropic compressible flow and normal shock portions of the GASTAB computer program. Finally, this approach does not account for internal friction, the disturbed external pressure field on the (essentially straight) cowl, or the shock overpressure available for lift. With this as background, the supersonic inlet drag is estimated to equal the momentum change of the bypass and bleed flows or

$$\phi_{inlet} = \frac{\rho_0 V_0 (A_1 - A_0)(V_0 - V_e)}{F g_c} = \frac{(A_1/A_0 - 1)(1 - V_e/V_0)}{F g_c/(\dot{m}_0 V_0)} \tag{6.7}$$

where V_e is the velocity with which the bypass and bleed flows leave the inlet. Since $T_{te} = T_{t0}$, it follows that

$$\frac{V_e}{V_0} = \frac{a_e M_e}{a_0 M_0} = \frac{M_e}{M_0}\sqrt{T_e/T_0} = \frac{M_e}{M_0}\left\{\frac{1 + (\gamma - 1/2)M_0^2}{1 + (\gamma - 1/2)M_e^2}\right\}^{1/2}$$

or, because $M_e = 1$

$$\frac{V_e}{V_0} = \frac{1}{M_0}\left\{\frac{2}{\gamma+1} + \frac{\gamma-1}{\gamma+1}M_0^2\right\}^{1/2}$$

so that

$$\phi_{inlet} = \left(\frac{A_1}{A_0} - 1\right)\left\{M_0 - \left(\frac{2}{\gamma+1} + \frac{\gamma-1}{\gamma+1}M_0^2\right)^{1/2}\right\}\bigg/\{Fg_c/(\dot{m}_0 a_0)\} \quad (6.8)$$

For typical values [e.g., $A_1/A_0 = 1.2$, $M_0 = 1.5$, and $Fg_c/(\dot{m}_0 a_0) = 4$], Eq. (6.8) yields $\phi_{inlet} \cong 0.02$, which, again, is not large. Note also that ϕ_{inlet} approaches zero both when M_0 approaches unity and when A_0 approaches A_1 (the sizing condition), so that ϕ_{inlet} can matter only when M_0 is far from both conditions.

Once A_1 has been selected, this equation can be directly evaluated at any given flight condition (i.e., a_0 and M_0) and engine power setting (i.e., A_0 and $Fg_c/\dot{m}_0$). The supersonic internal inlet drag of Eq. (6.8) is included in the AEDsys Mission Analysis, Constraint, and Contour Plot computations.

External inlet drag.   You may have noticed that the external surfaces of the nacelles of supersonic engines are often closely aligned with the direction of the freestream flow. This is because there is an additional drag due to the pressures exerted on any external surfaces exposed to the oncoming flow that would contribute to the inlet drag of Eq. (E.15). The most obvious example of this phenomenon is the overpressure caused by oblique shock waves on the forward facing portion of the inlet that is inclined to the flow, as in the simple case illustrated in Fig. 6.5.

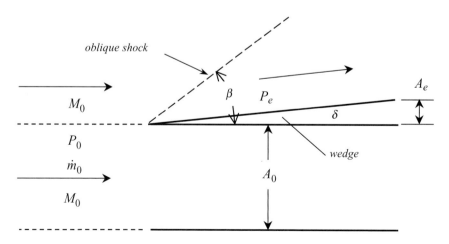

Fig. 6.5   Flow in the region of a wedge shaped two-dimensional inlet.

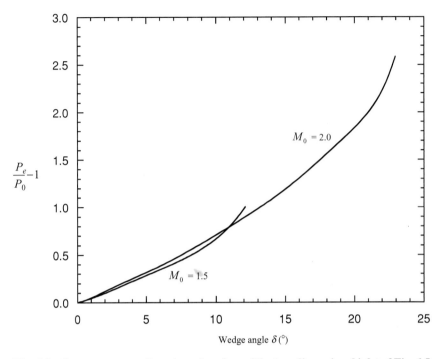

Fig. 6.6   Overpressure on the external surface of the two-dimensional inlet of Fig. 6.5 as a function of δ and M_0, from the GASTAB computer program.

The contribution of the axial projection of the external portion of the inlet to the drag is given by the expression

$$\phi_{inlet} = \frac{(P_e - P_0)A_e}{F}$$ (6.9)

which, by means of the usual substitutions, becomes

$$\phi_{inlet} = \frac{(P_e/P_0 - 1)(A_e/A_0)}{(Fg_c/\dot{m}_0a_0)(\gamma M_0)}$$ (6.10)

The term $(P_e/P_0 - 1)$ appearing in Eq. (6.10) is a function of the wedge angle δ and the freestream Mach number that can be computed using the two-dimensional oblique shock portion of the GASTAB computer program. The results of such computations for representative values of δ and M_0 are shown in Fig. 6.6. It can be seen that $(P_e/P_0 - 1)$ is insensitive to M_0 but increases rapidly with δ, encouraging designers to avoid large wedge angles.

For the same typical values used in the preceding examples, and for $\delta = 10$ deg and $A_e/A_0 = 0.2$, $\phi_{inlet} \cong 0.02$, which is not large but worth avoiding. The interested reader can easily repeat these computations for the analogous case of axisymmetric inlets using the conical oblique shock portion of the GASTAB computer program. Would you expect the drag to increase or decrease for the axisymmetric case?

A similar analysis could be carried out for the drag caused by the oblique expansion waves that reduce the pressure on rearward facing portions of the nacelle. In this case, however, the absolute magnitude of $(P_e/P_0 - 1)$ can never exceed one because P_e must exceed zero. The supersonic external drag of Eq. (6.10) is not included in the AEDsys Mission Analysis, Constraint Analysis, or Contour Plot computations because the shape of the cowl is not generally known in sufficient detail at this stage of design.

6.2.3 Exhaust Nozzle Drag

As in the case of inlets, it is assumed that the exhaust nozzle external viscous forces are accounted for in the airplane drag. Referring to Fig. 6.7, which contains a drawing of the type of nozzle to be used as a basis for drag estimation, it can be seen that there is always a region of separated flow surrounding the point s, which would otherwise be a stagnation point for the external flow. The external boundary layer separation causes a pressure or "base" drag to occur, and this constitutes the preponderance of the nozzle drag. The nozzle drag situation is completely analogous to the inlet, in that the separation prevents attainment of the high pressures near s that would compensate for the suction on the remainder of the surface and result in zero pressure drag.

An interesting and useful correlation method presented in Ref. 7 has been developed for predicting the exhaust nozzle pressure drag

$$D_{nozzle} \doteq \int_m^9 (P - P_0)\, dA \geq 0 \qquad (E.16)$$

in subsonic and supersonic flows, based on the "integral mean slope" (IMS) as defined by the equation

$$IMS = \frac{1}{(1 - A_9/A_{10})} \int_1^{A_9/A_{10}} \frac{d(A/A_{10})}{d[x/(R_{10} - R_9)]} d\left(\frac{A}{A_{10}}\right) \qquad (6.11)$$

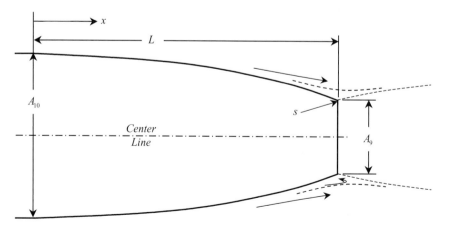

Fig. 6.7   Axisymmetric exhaust nozzle model.

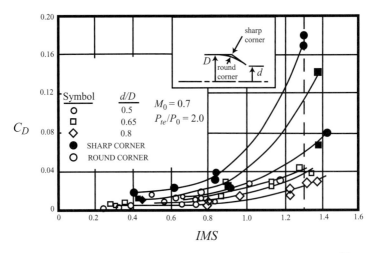

Fig. 6.8 Convergent nozzle boattail pressure drag coefficients.[4,7]

where the geometrical dimensions are the same as those of Fig. 6.7. This equation by itself underscores the complex nature of engine/airframe integration because the location of the "end" of the airframe and the "beginning" of the nozzle (i.e., A_{10}) is a judgmental decision.

Once the *IMS* is computed from the nozzle geometry, the corresponding drag coefficient can be obtained from Fig. 6.8 when $0 < M_0 < 0.8$ and from Fig. 6.9 plus the empirical relationship

$$\frac{C_D(M_0)}{C_D(1.2)} = \frac{1 - 1.4\exp\left(-M_0^2\right)}{\sqrt{M_0^2 - 1}} \tag{6.12}$$

when $1.2 < M_0 < 2.2$. When $0.8 \leq M_0 \leq 1.2$, the drag coefficient is given in Fig. 6.10 as a function of M_0 and L/D_{10}.

Lacking actual nozzle contours (i.e., D vs x), it is impossible to precisely evaluate the *IMS* using Eq. (6.11). Real progress can be made, nevertheless, by evaluating the *IMS* for the general family of nozzle contours described by

$$\frac{D}{D_{10}} = 1 - \left(1 - \frac{D_9}{D_{10}}\right)\left(\frac{x}{L}\right)^n$$

or

$$\frac{A}{A_{10}} = \left\{1 - \left(1 - \frac{D_9}{D_{10}}\right)\left(\frac{x}{L}\right)^n\right\}^2 \tag{6.13}$$

The shape of these "boattails" for $D_9/D_{10} = \frac{1}{2}$ and a range of n is shown in Fig. 6.11. Note that for all $n > 1$ they have a smooth transition to the fuselage and avoid sharp corners, which often cause large drag. Because of the need to store supporting structure, actuators, and coolant passages, as well as to avoid sharp, hard-to-cool trailing edges, practical nozzles have $1 < n < 3$.

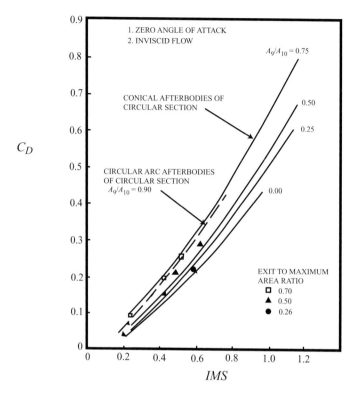

C_D

1. ZERO ANGLE OF ATTACK
2. INVISCID FLOW

$A_9/A_{10} = 0.75$

CONICAL AFTERBODIES OF
CIRCULAR SECTION

0.50

0.25

CIRCULAR ARC AFTERBODIES
OF CIRCULAR SECTION
$A_9/A_{10} = 0.90$

0.00

EXIT TO MAXIMUM
AREA RATIO
□ 0.70
▲ 0.50
● 0.26

IMS

Fig. 6.9 Comparison of IMS correlation and theoretical wave drag for isolated axisymmetric afterbodies—Mach 1.2.[4,7]

Substituting Eq. (6.13) in Eq. (6.11) and integrating leads to the result that

$$\frac{IMS}{(D_{10} - D_9/L)(1 - D_9/D_{10})}$$

$$= \frac{4n^2}{(1 + D_9/D_{10})} \left\{ \frac{1}{2n - 1} - \frac{2(1 - D_9/D_{10})}{3n - 1} + \frac{(1 - D_9/D_{10})^2}{4n - 1} \right\} \qquad (6.14)$$

The behavior of Eq. (6.14) with n and D_9/D_{10} is shown on Fig. 6.12. The inescapable conclusion is that one must hardly be concerned with the exact shape of the nozzle at this point in the design and that

$$IMS \approx 1.8 \left(\frac{D_{10} - D_9}{L} \right) \left(1 - \frac{D_9}{D_{10}} \right) \qquad (6.15)$$

This result is intuitively appealing because the adverse effects of separation should increase both with the slope of the external nozzle contour and the amount of area change.

This enormously simplifying step makes it possible to estimate the *IMS* from gross nozzle design parameters, obtain the drag coefficient from either

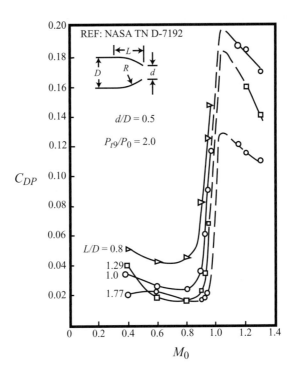

Fig. 6.10   Experimental pressure drag coefficients of some circular—arc boattails.[7]

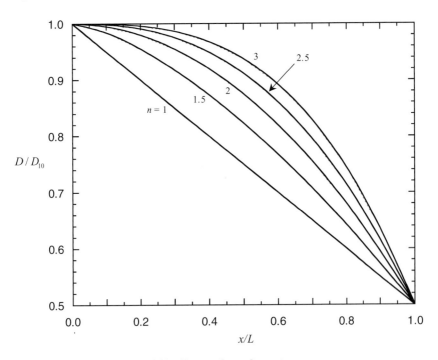

Fig. 6.11   External nozzle contours.

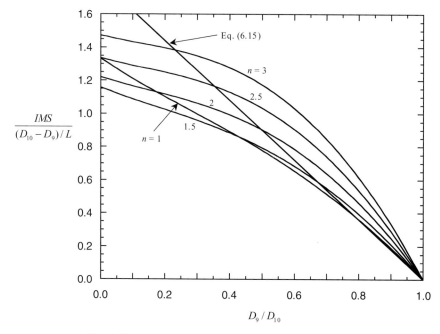

Fig. 6.12   Influence of external nozzle contour on *IMS*.

Figs. 6.8 or 6.9 and Eq. (6.12), depending upon M_0, and compute the nozzle installation penalty from

$$\phi_{nozzle} = \frac{D_{nozzle}}{F} = \frac{qC_D(A_{10} - A_9)}{\dot{m}_0(F/\dot{m}_0)} = \frac{M_0\dfrac{C_D}{2}(A_{10} - A_9)/A_0}{Fg_c/(\dot{m}_0 a_0)} \qquad (6.16)$$

The nozzle installation penalty when $0.8 \leq M_0 \leq 1.2$ uses Fig. 6.8 and

$$\phi_{nozzle} = \frac{M_0(C_{DP}/2)(A_{10}/A_0)}{Fg_c/(\dot{m}_0 a_0)} \qquad (6.17)$$

For a typical supercruise case [e.g., $C_D = 0.10$, $(A_{10} - A_9)/A_0 = 0.8$, $Fg_c/(\dot{m}_0 a_0) = 2.0$ and $M_0 = 1.5$], $\phi_{nozzle} = 0.03$.

The nozzle external drag of Eqs. (6.16) and (6.17) is included in the AEDsys Mission Analysis, Constraint, and Contour Plot computations.

6.2.4 Sizing the Inlet Area (A_1)

The size of the inlet area A_1 is required by Eqs. (6.6a) and (6.8) to estimate the inlet loss ϕ_{inlet} for subsonic and supersonic inlets, respectively. The assumption of a constant inlet area simplifies the problem to finding the flight condition(s) that requires the largest inlet area, thus sizing A_1. Because the engine size is not fixed at this point in the design process, the required inlet area A_1 can be conveniently referenced to the freestream area of choked flow A_0^* of the engine at sea level, static conditions (designated as A_{0ref}), and stating the required values in terms of

A_1/A_{0ref}. When the engine is resized to a new value of A_{0ref}, then the new required inlet capture area A_1 can be determined directly because both the sizing flight condition and the ratio A_1/A_{0ref} are constant.

During *subsonic flight*, the engine airflow is usually accelerated from the freestream Mach number M_0 to the inlet Mach number M_1. To prevent choking of the inlet, M_1 must be less than unity (usually 0.8 or less to allow for inlet boundary layer displacement or blockage); in other words, the inlet physical area A_1 must be slightly larger than the area that would be required to choke the engine flow, A_0^*. For subsonic flight, the flight condition with the largest A_0^* therefore determines the inlet physical area. In addition to sizing the inlet for $M_1 = 0.8$ or less to allow for boundary layer displacement, a safety margin of 4% is provided to account for any aerodynamic or mechanical effects that may further restrict the flow. As an example, an A_1 is to be selected for the typical high bypass turbofan engine running at maximum throttle setting (max π_c or T_{t4}) as shown in Fig. 6.13. From Fig. 6.13, the largest required A_0^* occurs at the flight condition of $M_0 = 0.9$ and altitudes greater than 20 kft where $A_0^* = 1.055A_{0ref}$. Therefore, sizing A_1 for $M_1 = 0.8$ plus a 1.04 safety factor gives

$$A_1 = 1.04(A_1/A_1^*)_{M_1=0.8}A_0^* = (1.04)(1.038)(1.055A_{0ref}) = 1.139A_{0ref}$$

During *supersonic flight*, no freestream deceleration or stream-tube contraction is expected, so the inlet area A_1 must simply exceed the largest required A_0 by the minimum amount needed for boundary layer bleed and margin of safety. The

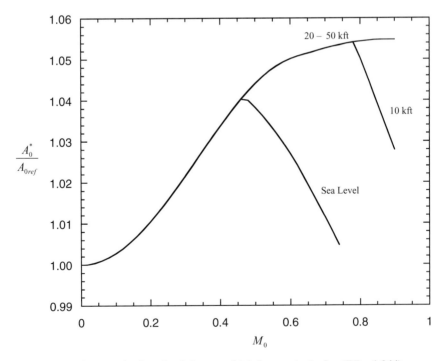

Fig. 6.13   Required engine inlet area, high bypass turbofan (*TR* = 1.044).

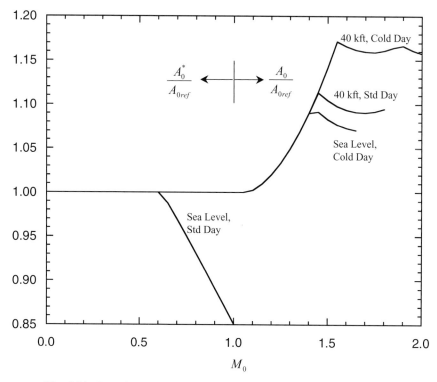

Fig. 6.14   Required engine inlet area, low bypass turbofan ($TR = 1.07$).

amount of boundary layer bleed depends on inlet type and design (see Sec. 10.2.3), and, for example, will be about 4% for a Mach 2 external compression inlet.

Sizing an inlet that is required to operate in *both subsonic and supersonic flight* regimes rests upon an analysis that includes both of the preceding requirements for physical inlet area. Combining the constraints of subsonic and supersonic flight operations on inlet area A_1 for a specific engine size A_{0ref} gives a family of curves of A_0^*/A_{0ref} (for $M_0 \leq 1$) and A_0/A_{0ref} (for $M_0 \geq 1$) as shown in Fig. 6.14 for a typical low bypass, turbofan engine running at maximum throttle setting (max π_c or T_{t4}). In this figure, each line represents the required inlet area at one altitude. The lines are continuous at $M_0 = 1$ because $A_0 = A_0^*$ there. From Fig. 6.14, the maximum inlet area occurs at the flight condition of Mach 1.55 at 40 kft altitude on a cold day, where the required $A_0 = 1.17A_{0ref}$. Sizing A_1 for a 1.04 safety factor gives

$$A_1 = 1.04(1.17A_{0ref}) = 1.217A_{0ref}$$

6.2.5   Sizing the Exhaust Nozzle (A_9)

To evaluate the exhaust nozzle loss ϕ_{nozzle}, Eqs. (6.15–6.17) require the values of A_9, A_{10}, and L. The nozzle exit area A_9 for any flight condition is obtained directly from the Engine Test portion (or the second summary page of the Mission

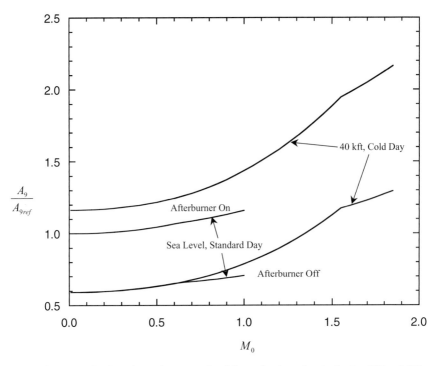

Fig. 6.15   Required engine exit area, mixed flow afterburning turbofan ($TR = 1.07$).

Analysis portion) of the AEDsys program. Figure 6.15 shows the variation of the A_9 required for a mixed flow afterburning turbofan engine to match the exit pressure P_9 to the ambient pressure P_0. In this figure, A_9 is referenced to its sea level, standard day value with full afterburning, known as A_{9ref}. Good judgement is used to size A_{10} and L with the data for A_9 available. To ensure that A_{10} is not smaller than A_9 for any flight condition, it should be made somewhat larger than the greater of the largest A_9 required in the flight mission or the A_9 required for the maximum Mach number flight requirement of the aircraft. With A_9 and A_{10} fixed, the choice of the nozzle length (L) can be based on their values, a reasonable estimate being 1–2 times D_9.

6.3   AEDsys Software Implementation of Installation Losses

The AEDsys software incorporates the installation loss models of this chapter as well as the constant loss model used in the preceding chapter. When either of these installation loss models is selected, all of the computations in Mission Analysis, Constraint Analysis, and Contour Plots use that loss model. The sizing of the engine and determining its installed performance is straightforward using this software.

The user enters the inlet area A_1, afterbody area A_{10}, and nozzle length L into the data fields on the Engine Data window. To reduce the inlet additive drag during takeoff (see Fig. 6.2), the program includes an auxiliary inlet area (A_{1aux}) that will be open from static conditions through the input cutoff Mach number (M_{aux}).

The preliminary inlet and afterbody dimensions are obtained by operating the aircraft over its mission and performance requirements using an initial estimate of the constant installation loss over the flight envelope. With this loss estimate, the Mission Analysis gives the required area of the engine mass flow at inlet (A_0^* or A_0) and the nozzle exit area (A_9) for each leg. These data are used to select the inlet area A_1, afterbody area A_{10}, and nozzle length L as described in Secs. 6.2.4 and 6.2.5. The Engine Test window allows the user to determine the required engine inlet end exit areas over the entire range of operation for the required uninstalled engine thrust $F_{req} = (T_{SL}/W_{TO})_{req}W_{TO}$.

Once the inlet area A_1, afterbody area A_{10}, and nozzle length L are determined and entered into the Engine Data window of AEDsys, the installation losses are computed using Eqs. (6.6), (6.8), (6.16), and (6.17). These models are also used in the Mission Analysis, Constraint Analysis, and Contour Plots. As was shown in Chapter 5, the improvements in the engine model between those of Chapter 2 and Chapter 5 resulted in better estimates of fuel usage and thrust loading for the AAF. The improved installation loss models further refine these estimates and allow the final determination of the engine size.

When the available thrust loading $(T_{SL}/W_{TO})_{avail}$ or the number of engines is changed in the AEDsys program, the Thrust Scale Factor (TSF) is updated and the user is asked if they want to automatically scale the inlet area (A_1), afterbody area (A_{10}), and nozzle length (L). Because the preceding design values are based on the preceding thrust loading or number of engines, responding "yes" saves the user these calculations.

The external drag for the supersonic inlet of Eq. (6.10) is not included in the AEDsys software because the shape of the cowl is not yet known and because the internal drag estimate of Eqs. (6.6a) and (6.8) is deliberately conservative.

Finally, the iteration process ends when the selected engine size meets all of the thrust requirements of the aircraft as verified by Constraint Analysis and Mission Analysis computations including the final inlet and nozzle installation losses.

6.4 Example Installed Performance and Final Engine Sizing

This phase of engine design has two objectives. First, to use the installation loss models presented in this chapter to determine a better estimate of the installed engine performance and its impact on the engine design choices made in Chapter 5. It is possible that the installation effects could even change the cycle design choices. Second, to use the installation loss models to determine the engine size that will meet all the AAF RFP performance and mission requirements.

As noted in Secs. 4.2.8 and 5.4.4, the MSH (modified specific heat) performance model is used in all of the ensuing AAF engine computations.

6.4.1 Critical Constraint/Mission Legs for Sizing

The process begins by selecting the legs that are most likely to require the largest values of T_{SL}/W_{TO}, A_9, or A_1. If they are not evident by this point, a wide search must be executed. In the case of the AAF, the critical constraint/mission points, as explained next, are 1) takeoff constraint; 2) supercruise constraint; 3) 1.6M/30 kft, 5g turn constraint; 4) 1.6M/30 kft, 5g turn constraint; 5) acceleration constraint; and 6) maximum Mach number constraint.

In Fig. 3.E5 the constraint boundaries of legs 1, 2, 4, and 5 are all close to the available thrust loading $\{(T_{SL}/W_{TO})_{avail}\}$ of 1.25 selected for the AAF. At these flight conditions, the engine can be expected to be running near its full thrust and to have therefore the larger values of $(T_{SL}/W_{TO})_{req}/(T_{SL}/W_{TO})_{avail}$. Flight conditions 1, 3, 4, 5, and 6 are afterburner operating points that require the larger exhaust nozzle settings and areas (A_9). From Fig. 6.14, it is evident that the high Mach number, high-altitude flight conditions on a cold day are the most demanding for the inlet area requirement (A_1) for this type of aircraft.

6.4.2 AAF Engine Search Including Installed Performance

Incorporating the Chapter 5 engine performance models into the Constraint, Mission Analysis, and Contour Plot portions of the AEDsys software makes this search effortless. The search begins with the calculation of the Constraint and Mission Analysis for all candidate engines with constant 5% installation loss, as was done in Chapter 5 to obtain the results of Table 5.E3. When Mission Analysis is based on a candidate engine, the second summary page provides the area of the engine mass flow at inlet (A_0^* or A_0) and the nozzle exit area (A_9) for each mission leg. These data are used to select the inlet area A_1, afterbody area A_{10}, and nozzle length L.

As just noted, the most demanding flight condition for sizing the inlet of the AAF occurs at 1.6M/40 kft on a cold day (similar to Fig. 6.14). To obtain this information for any candidate engine, the Engine Test portion of AEDsys program is used to calculate the uninstalled performance on a cold day at 40 kft over a range of Mach numbers. The printed and plotted results give the variation of engine mass flow inlet area (A_0^* or A_0) and nozzle exit area (A_9) with flight Mach number.

We found that the largest nozzle exit area corresponds to the AAF Mission Segment 6–7 F acceleration with full afterburner at 1.465M/30 kft. Although a larger nozzle exit area is predicted for the maximum Mach flight constraint (1.8M/40 kft) with full afterburner and $P_0/P_9 = 1$, this large an engine or nozzle is not needed to meet this flight condition [uninstalled engine thrust of 10,750 lb ($=10,210/0.95$)]. You can verify this conclusion by testing the engine at 1.8M/40 kft over a range of T_{t7} and noting the required nozzle exit area corresponding to the required uninstalled thrust or testing the engine at the required uninstalled thrust and noting the exit area listed on the Summary of Test Results output of the Engine Test window.

Table 6.E1 shows the maximum engine areas (A_0^* or A_0 and A_9) for Engines 1–20 of Table 5.E3. The selected values of the inlet area A_1, afterbody area A_{10}, and nozzle length L are also listed. These are entered into the Chapter 6 installation loss model data of the Engine Data window. To reduce installation loss at takeoff, an auxiliary air intake area A_{1aux} equal to the inlet area A_1 was selected for the AAF up to $M_0 = 0.3$.

The installed performance was calculated for the 20 candidate engines at an available thrust loading $[(T_{SL}/W_{TO})_{avail}]$ of 1.25. The mission fuel usage results are given in Table 6.E1 and plotted in Fig. 6.E1. Comparison with Table 5.E3 and Fig. 5E.3 shows that the overall fuel saved is now 20 to 70 lbf less than predicted earlier. An improved estimate of the required engine thrust loading $[(T_{SL}/W_{TO})_{req}]$ was obtained using Constraint Analysis with the aircraft weight fraction (β) set to 0.8221 (see Sec. 3.4.3) for maneuver weight and calculations performed for wing

Table 6.E1 Summary of search for final AAF engine for $(T_{SL}/W_{TO})_{avail} = 1.25$

Engine	π_c	π_f	α	Max A_0^a ft²	Max A_0^{*a} ft²	Max A_9^b ft²	A_1^c ft²	A_{10} ft²	L^d ft	Fuel saved, lbf[e]	$(T_{SL}/W_{TO})_{req}^f$
1	20	3.9	0.4487	6.130	5.217	8.944	6.38	8.95	6.08	−202	1.322
2	22	—	0.4734	—	—	8.938	—	—	—	−98	1.322
3	24	—	0.4890	—	—	8.932	—	—	—	−12	1.322
4	26	—	0.4975	—	—	8.926	—	—	—	59	1.322
5	28	—	0.5003	—	—	8.921	—	—	—	119	1.322
6	20	3.7	0.5715	6.254	5.323	9.337	6.51	9.34	6.21	−121	1.316
7	22	—	0.5955	—	—	9.331	—	—	—	−22	1.316
8	24	—	0.6102	—	—	9.325	—	—	—	59	1.316
9	26	—	0.6176	—	—	9.318	—	—	—	126	1.316
10	28	—	0.6192	—	—	9.312	—	—	—	183	1.316
11	20	3.5	0.7132	6.395	5.444	9.786	6.65	9.79	6.34	−43	1.312
12	22	—	0.7384	—	—	9.780	—	—	—	50	1.312
13	24	—	0.7501	—	—	9.773	—	—	—	127	1.311
14	26	—	0.7562	—	—	9.766	—	—	—	191	1.311
15	28	—	0.7563	—	—	9.759	—	—	—	245	1.310
16	20	3.3	0.8785	6.557	5.581	10.30	6.82	10.3	6.52	31	1.303
17	22	—	0.9008	—	—	10.30	—	—	—	119	1.303
18	24	—	0.9132	—	—	10.29	—	—	—	186	1.304
19	26	—	0.9178	—	—	10.28	—	—	—	232	1.305
20	28	—	0.9162	—	—	10.28	—	—	—	271	1.305

[a] Cold day @ 40 kft.

[b] 1.465M/30 kft with full afterburner.

[c] $A_1 = 1.04\, A_{0max}$.

[d] $L = 1.8 \times D_{10}$.

[e] Referenced to the fuel usage of 6690 lbf made in Chapter 3.

[f] Subsonic turn (0.9M/30 kft, 5g) at a weight fraction (β) of 0.8221.

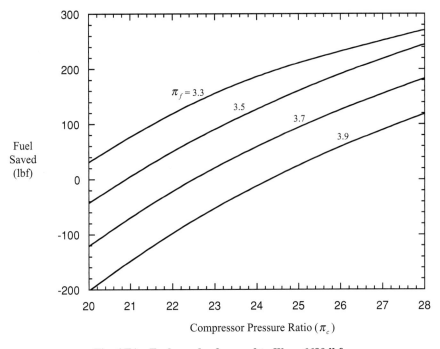

Fig. 6.E1 Fuel saved referenced to $W_F = 6690$ lbf.

loading of 64 lbf/ft^2. On balance, Engine 15 remains the preferred choice for the AAF. It consumes 245 lbf of fuel less than the Chapter 3 estimate of 6690 lbf and the required thrust loading $\{(T_{SL}/W_{TO})_{req}\}$ is one of the lowest available (see Sec. 5.4.5).

The Engine 15 thrust loading required for aircraft performance at both the 5% constant installation loss and the loss model of this chapter are presented in Table 6.E2. The large changes in required thrust loading $(T_{SL}/W_{TO})_{req}$ between the estimates of Chapters 5 and 6 are as a result of the improved installation loss model. Nevertheless, the RFP performance requirement of the subsonic 5g turn at 0.9M/30 kft continues to size the AAF engine. The increase in fuel consumption (decrease in fuel saved from Table 5.E3) is caused by the increase of the installation losses in the Combat Air Patrol 5–6, Supersonic Penetration 6–7G, and Loiter 12–13 legs of the AAF mission (see Table 6.E9 for final details of the sized AAF Engine).

6.4.3 AAF Engine Sizing Procedure

The design tools developed in this chapter and incorporated into the AEDsys software are used to estimate the installed thrust loading (T_{SL}/W_{TO}) necessary to meet the AAF RFP requirements. The minimum engine size necessary is that for which the design engine mass flow gives the available installed thrust (T_{avail}) equal to the required installed thrust (T_{req}) for the flight condition that is the most demanding as measured by the ratio of required-to-available thrust loading $[(T_{SL}/W_{TO})_{req}/(T_{SL}/W_{TO})_{avail}]$.

Table 6.E2   Required thrust loading for Engine 15[a]

Performance requirement	M_0	Alt, kft	Chapter 5 $(T_{SL}/W_{TO})_{req}$	Chapter 6			
				$(T_{SL}/W_{TO})_{req}$	α[b]	T_{req},[c] lbf	$\phi_{inlet} + \phi_{nozzle}$[b]
Takeoff (100°F)	0.1	2	1.223	1.179	0.8461	23,940	0.0135
Supercruise	1.5	30	1.231	1.235	0.3610	10,700	0.0520
Supersonic 5g turn	1.6	30	0.9436	0.9235	0.8334	18,470	0.0288
Subsonic 5g turn	0.9	30	1.359	1.310	0.4842	15,220	0.0152
Horizontal acceleration	1.2	30	1.091	1.047	0.6678	16,780	0.0093
Maximum Mach	1.8	40	0.6367	0.6181	0.6564	9,740	0.0209

[a] $\beta = 1.0$ at takeoff and 0.8221 at all other flight conditions.
[b] Based on data in Table 6.E1.
[c] $T_{req} = \alpha(T_{SL}/W_{TO})_{req} W_{TO}$.

To find this minimum engine size for the AAF, the procedure diagrammed in Fig. 6.E2 and listed next will be followed:

1) Select as critical RFP mission points those flight conditions having the potential to require a) the largest fraction of available thrust $\{(T_{SL}/W_{TO})_{req}/(T_{SL}/W_{TO})_{avail}\}$, b) the largest exhaust nozzle exit area (A_9), or c) the largest inlet area (A_1) at engine station 1 (Figs. 4.1a and 6.4).

2) Assuming a constant installation loss of 5% and available thrust loading $(T_{SL}/W_{TO})_{avail}$ of 1.25, determine $(T_{SL}/W_{TO})_{req}$ for the selected engine (Engine 15) at the critical mission points and required performance constraints. The resultant thrust loadings $\{(T_{SL}/W_{TO})_{req}\}$ for critical aircraft performance are summarized in Table 6.E2 under the Chapter 5 column. This was done for each engine of Chapter 5 and summarized in Table 5.E3 as percent increase in thrust loading.

3) Based on the largest $(T_{SL}/W_{TO})_{req}$ and estimated W_{TO} from Chapter 3, find the tentative engine size $(T_{SL})_{req}$. Separately examine the feasibility of a single- or multiengine installation and select the number of engines to be used in the AAF (see Sec. 6.4.4 for guidance). Simply entering the selected number into its input field on the Engine Data window of AEDsys changes the number of engines. When the number of engines is changed, the TSF is updated and the user is asked if he or she wants to automatically scale the inlet area (A_1), afterbody area (A_{10}), and nozzle length (L). Because the preceding design values are based on the preceding thrust loading or number of engines, responding "yes" saves the user these calculations.

4) Determine the required A_1, A_{10}, and L for the engine with available thrust loading $(T_{SL}/W_{TO})_{avail}$ of 1.25. This was done in Sec. 6.4.1 for the 20 engines under consideration and summarized in Table 6.E1 for a single-engine installation. Select "Installation Loss Model of Chapter 6" in the Engine Data window of AEDsys and input the data for A_1, A_{10}, and L. Note that area can be input for an auxiliary air intake to be used at low Mach number to reduce installation loss. An auxiliary

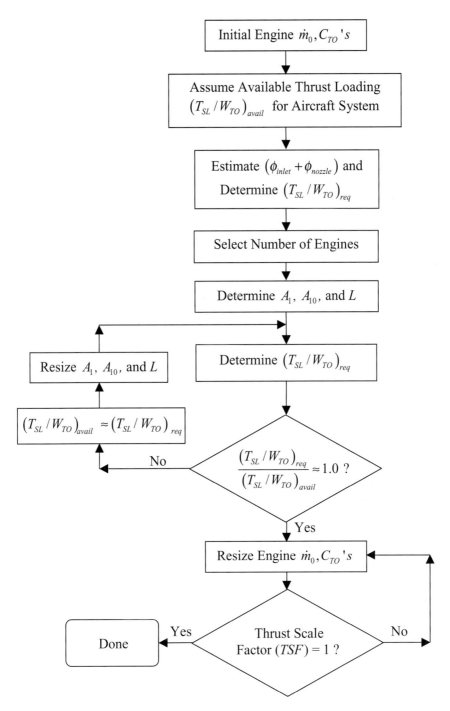

Fig. 6.E2   Flowchart for engine sizing.

air intake area A_{1aux} equal to the inlet area A_1 is selected for the AAF for M_0 up to 0.3. (See data used in revised engine search of Table 6.E1.)

5) Determine the required thrust loading $(T_{SL}/W_{TO})_{req}$ for the revised mission and constraint performance with this improved installation loss model. This was done for the 20 engines under consideration and summarized in Table 6.E1 under required thrust loading.

6) Change the available thrust loading $(T_{SL}/W_{TO})_{avail}$ in the Mission Analysis window of AEDsys to a value slightly larger than the required value $(T_{SL}/W_{TO})_{req}$ in order to resize the engine and have the program automatically scale the inlet and afterbody data.

7) Based on the Thrust Scale Factor (TSF), resize engine mass flow rate $(\dot{m}_0)$ in the parametric program for the engine design. Check that the engine(s) produce the required power $(P_{TOL}$ and/or $P_{TOH})$. If not, adjust the respective design values of power takeoff coefficient $(C_{TOL}$ and/or $C_{TOH})$. Generate a new reference engine data file (*.ref) and input it into the AEDsys program. Check that the TSF is one and that the engine(s) meet the required performance.

8) As required, repeat steps 6 and 7 until satisfactory convergence is obtained.

6.4.4 Selecting the Number of Engines

The choice of a one- or two-engine installation for the AAF is a design study all its own and involves many tradeoffs between safety, performance, and cost. The airframe design team is normally responsible for these studies in cooperation with the propulsion design group. For engine designers, the purpose here is only to verify that the engine size for either a single-or a twin-engine fighter is feasible from the point of view of engine manufacturing and testing capabilities.

As was seen in Table 6.E2, the subsonic $5g$ turn sizes the Engine 15 with a required thrust loading of 1.31 based on inlet and nozzle losses for one engine. We therefore proceed with an available thrust loading $(T_{SL}/W_{TO})_{avail}$ of 1.32 for the AAF in order to provide some safety margin. With an available thrust loading $(T_{SL}/W_{TO})_{avail}$ of 1.32, the TSF for one engine is 1.0323. The engine size for a one- or two-engine installation can now be established and the feasibility of each determined. Assuming the approximate installation losses included in Table 6.E2, an engine design mass flow rate of either $200 \times 1.0323 = 206.5$ lbm/s for a single-engine airplane or 103.3 lbm/s for a two-engine airplane is required. The sea level static performance of each of these engines is shown in Table 6.E3.

Table 6.E3   Sea level static performance of four engines

Type of aircraft	Engine design mass flow rate, lbm/s[a]	Sea level static performance	
		$\dot{m}_0$, lbm/s	F, lbf
One engine	206.5	284.8	31,680
Two engine	103.3	142.4	15,840
F100-PW-229 engine[b]	——	248	29,000
F404-GE-400 engine[b]	——	142	16,000

[a] 1.451M/36 kft.
[b] Appendix C.

The engine size for the one-engine installation has a static sea level mass flow rate that is about 15% higher than the F100-PW-229 engine (used in both the Air Force F-15 and F-16) and a considerably higher maximum thrust, whereas the engine for the two-engine installation has about the same mass flow rate as the F404-GE-400 engine (used in the U.S. Navy F-18) and a slightly lower maximum thrust. The size of each engine is therefore within current manufacturing and testing capabilities for afterburning turbofan engines and either a single- or twin-engine AAF is feasible. We have chosen a twin-engine installation for the AAF to provide you with the experience of using this information in the computations. Thus, the Air-to-Air Fighter for the RFP of Chapter 1 is configured to be a *two-engine fighter*.

With the number of engines for the AAF now specified as two, the final sizing of Engine 15 starts with an available system thrust loading $(T_{SL}/W_{TO})_{avail}$ of 1.32 and the Chapter 6 installation loss. The resultant TSF is 0.5161. This corresponds to an engine having sea level static thrust of 15,840 lb and a design mass flow rate of 103.3 lbm/s.

6.4.5   Final Engine Sizing of Engine 15 for $(T_{SL}/W_{TO})_{avail}$ = 1.32

AAF Engine 15 will be sized using these procedures by finding the values of the required-to-available thrust loading $\{(T_{SL}/W_{TO})_{req}/(T_{SL}/W_{TO})_{avail}\}$ at the critical mission points. To determine this ratio, preliminary estimates of the inlet and exhaust nozzle design parameters must first be established. Then, the installation losses are found using the design tools of Sec. 6.2. Next, $(T_{SL}/W_{TO})_{req}/(T_{SL}/W_{TO})_{avail}$ is determined following the procedure diagrammed in Fig. 6.E2. Unless $(T_{SL}/W_{TO})_{req}/(T_{SL}/W_{TO})_{avail} \sim 1.0$, the engine is resized as indicated in Fig. 6.E2.

The following series of calculations is presented here to show the methods and procedures implemented in the AEDsys software. You may either carry out the hand calculations for the installation loss as follows or use the AEDsys software to do these calculations.

Inlet and exhaust nozzle design parameters—$(T_{SL}/W_{TO})_{avail}$ = 1.32

Inlet size.   Based on the discussion in Sec. 6.2.4, the flight conditions requiring the largest inlet area A_1 can be determined by developing a plot of A_0^*/A_{0ref} and A_0/A_{0ref} as in Fig. 6.14 for a low bypass ratio turbofan engine cycle. From this plot, the limiting flight conditions can be identified and the inlet area determined. Figure 6.E3 is such a plot of A_0^*/A_{0ref} (for $M_0 \leq 1$) and A_0/A_{0ref} (for $M_0 \geq 1$) vs flight Mach number and altitude for this engine at full throttle. Note that the high altitude, high Mach number flight conditions on a cold day are the most demanding for the inlet area size. For this engine, the value of A_{0ref} (A_0^* @ SLS) is 2.882 ft². (The required inlet A_0^*/A_0 is listed in Table 6.E5 for the critical mission points.)

The most demanding flight condition for sizing this inlet is at 1.56M/40 kft on a cold day where the A_0/A_{0ref} equals 1.174. Thus, allowing for a 4% margin of safety, the inlet area is selected to be

$$A_1 = 1.04 \times A_0/A_{0ref} \times A_{0ref} = 1.04 \times 1.174 \times 2.882 = 3.519 \, \text{ft}^2.$$

Exhaust nozzle size.   The value of A_{10} is selected to be at least 10% greater than the largest value of A_9 for critical operational mission points. Figure 6.E4 shows the exit area required at maximum and military power. For this engine, the

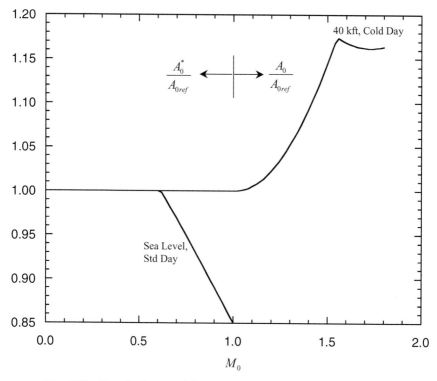

Fig. 6.E3   Required engine inlet area at maximum throttle, Engine 15.

value of $A_{9ref}(=A_9@SLS)$ is 3.047 ft^2. Although the largest A_9 required occurs at 1.8M/40 kft on a cold day with maximum power (see Fig. 6.E4), this condition will not determine the size of A_{10} because maximum power is not required for this performance point.

Table 6.E4 contains the values of A_9 for the critical mission and performance points. The exit area A_9 corresponding to maximum power have been computed for each critical point except Supersonic Turn (1.6M/30 kft, 5g) and Maximum Mach (1.8M/40 kft). The exit areas A_9 computed for these two flight conditions are those corresponding to the engine producing the required thrust because the exit areas corresponding to maximum power are much larger than required at any other flight condition and the required engine performance can be obtained at partial power. As can be seen in Fig. 6.E5 (calculated using AEDsys), the reduction in exit area A_9 decreases P_0/P_9 with a corresponding decrease in uninstalled thrust F. The results pictured here are consistent with our basic understanding that ideal expansion produces the maximum uninstalled thrust, but that performance does not change rapidly in the neighborhood of perfect expansion (Refs. 2, 3, and 5). For the Supersonic Turn with maximum power, an exit area of 5.150 ft^2 is obtained at P_0/P_9 of 0.927 with a reduction in thrust less than 0.04%. Similar results are obtained for the Maximum Mach flight condition.

Based on the data of Table 6.E4, A_{10} is selected to be 5.153 ft^2. Thus D_{10} and L for this engine are 2.561 ft and, choosing $L = 1.8 \times D_{10}$, 4.611 ft, respectively.

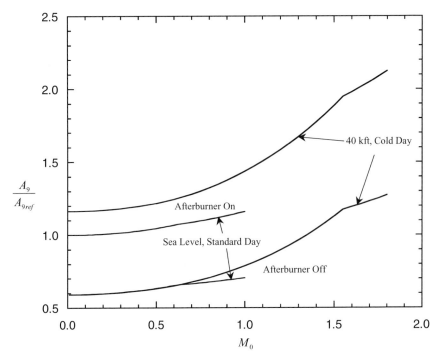

Fig. 6.E4   Required engine exit area at maximum throttle, Engine 15.

Table 6.E4   Engine 15 exhaust nozzle A_9 and *IMS* for $(T_{SL}/W_{TO})_{avail} = 1.32$

Performance requirement	M_0/Alt, kft	T_{req}, lbf[a]	F_{req}, lbf[b]	% F_{avail}	A_9, ft²	*IMS*[c]
Takeoff (100°F)	0.1/2	23,940	Max	100.0	2.930[d]	0.0604
Supercruise	1.5/30	10,700	5,640	43.24	3.065	0.0479
Supersonic 5g turn	1.6/30	18,470	9,510	70.00	4.203	0.0054
Subsonic 5g turn	0.9/30	15,220	7,740	99.38	4.003[d]	——
Acceleration	1.2/30	16,780	8,470	79.33	4.608[d]	——
Maximum Mach	1.8/40	9,740	4,970	46.80	3.854	0.0230
7–8K Part 3 of mission accel	1.465/30	Max	Max	100.0	5.153[d]	0.0000

[a]From Table 6.E2 for single engine.
[b]Two engines (installation loss based on single-engine results in Table 6.E2).
[c]$A10 = 5.153$ ft².
[d]Maximum throttle.

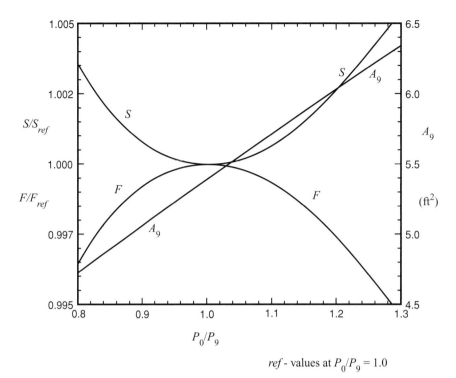

ref - values at $P_0/P_9 = 1.0$

Fig. 6.E5   Effect of exit area (A_9) on Engine 15 performance (supersonic turn).

With these approximate nozzle design parameters determined, the integral mean slope (*IMS*) of the nozzle can be found by using

$$IMS = \{1 - (D_9/D_{10})\}^2 = \{1 - \sqrt{A_9/A_{10}}\}^2$$

which follows from Eq. (6.15) with $L = 1.8 \times D_{10}$. The values of the exhaust nozzle *IMS* are also given in Table 6.E6 for legs with $M_0 > 1.2$ and $M_0 < 0.8$.

Installation losses—$(T_{SL}/W_{TO})_{avail} = 1.32$
Inlet loss coefficient.   The inlet loss coefficients are given in Sec. 6.2 as follows:
Subsonic flight:

$$\phi_{inlet} = \left[\frac{M_0}{M_1} \sqrt{\frac{T_1}{T_0}} (1 + \gamma M_1^2) - \left(\frac{A_1}{A_0} + \gamma M_0^2 \right) \right] \Big/ [(F g_c/\dot{m}_0)(\gamma M_0/a_0)] \quad (6.6)$$

Supersonic flight:

$$\phi_{inlet} = \left(\frac{A_1}{A_0} - 1 \right) \left\{ M_0 - \left(\frac{2}{\gamma + 1} + \frac{\gamma - 1}{\gamma + 1} M_0^2 \right)^{1/2} \right\} \Big/ [F g_c/(\dot{m}_0 a_0)] \quad (6.8)$$

Table 6.E5   Engine 15 inlet loss coefficients for $(T_{SL}/W_{TO})_{avail} = 1.32$

Performance requirement	$M_0/Alt,$ kft	F_{req},[a] lbf	% F_{avail}[a]	A_0^* or A_0, ft^2	$F/\dot{m}_0$, lbf/lbm/s	$\dfrac{Fg_c}{\dot{m}_0 a_0}$	A_1/A_0^* A_1/A_0[b]	M_1	ϕ_{inlet}
Takeoff (100°F)	0.1/2	Max	100.0	2.842	107.5	2.981	2.476	0.242	0.0137
Supercruise	1.5/30	5,640	43.24	3.066	46.10	1.491	1.148	——	0.0384
Supersonic turn	1.6/30	9,510	70.00	2.930	71.21	2.304	1.201	——	0.0386
Subsonic turn	0.9/30	7,740	99.38	2.878	103.9	3.361	1.223	0.572	0.0114
Acceleration	1.2/30	8,470	79.33	2.943	84.17	2.723	1.196	——	0.0184
Maximum Mach	1.8/40	4,970	46.90	3.154	47.88	1.592	1.116	——	0.0420

[a]From Table 6.E4.
[b]$A_1 = 7.038$ ft^2 at takeoff and 3.519 ft^2 elsewhere due to A_{1aux}.

where T_1 is related to T_0 and A_1 is related to A_0 by the usual adiabatic and isentropic flow relationships (see Sec. 1.9).

Once A_1 has been selected, Eqs. (6.6) and (6.8) can be directly evaluated at any given flight condition (M_0 and a_0 or T_0) and engine power setting (A_0^* or A_0 and $Fg_c/\dot{m}_0$). Table 6.E4 gives the flight conditions and T_{req} for each critical mission point. When the engine is operated at the appropriate power setting for each mission leg, the data of Table 6.E5 are obtained.

Exhaust nozzle loss coefficient.   The nozzle coefficients are given in Sec. 6.2.3 as follows:

$M_0 < 0.8$:

$$\phi_{nozzle} = M_0 \frac{C_D}{2} \left(\frac{A_{10} - A_9}{A_0} \right) \Big/ \left(\frac{Fg_c}{\dot{m}_0 a_0} \right) \qquad (6.16)$$

where C_D is a function of *IMS* as given by Fig. 6.8.

$0.8 \leq M_0 \leq 1.2$:

$$\phi_{nozzle} = M_0 \frac{C_{DP}}{2} \left(\frac{A_{10}}{A_0} \right) \Big/ \left(\frac{Fg_c}{\dot{m}_0 a_0} \right) \qquad (6.17)$$

Table 6.E6   Engine 15 exhaust nozzle loss coefficients for $(T_{SL}/W_{TO})_{avail} = 1.32$

Performance requirement	$M_0/Alt,$ kft	F_{req}, lbf[a]	A_0, ft^2	A_9, ft^{2a}	$\dfrac{Fg_c}{\dot{m}_0 a_0}$	*IMS*[a]	C_D	ϕ_{nozzle}[b]
Takeoff (100°F)	0.1/2	Max	16.55	2.930	2.981	0.0604	0.000	0
Supercruise	1.5/30	5,640	3.066	3.065	1.491	0.0479	0.009	0.0031
Supersonic turn	1.6/30	9,510	2.930	4.203	2.304	0.0054	0	0
Subsonic turn	0.9/30	7,740	2.904	4.003	3.361	——	0.017[c]	0.0040
Acceleration	1.2/30	8,470	2.943	4.608	2.723	——	0	0
Maximum Mach	1.8/40	4,970	3.154	3.854	1.592	0.0230	0	0

[a]From Table 6.E3.   [b]$A_{10} = 5.153$ ft^2.   [c]C_{DP}.

Table 6.E7 Engine 15 required thrust loading (T_{SL}/W_{TO}) for $(T_{SL}/W_{TO})_{avail} = 1.32$

Performance requirement	M_0/Alt, kft	F_{avail}, lbf[a]	T_{req}, lbf[a]	$\phi_{inlet} + \phi_{nozzle}$	F_{req}, lbf[b]	$\left(\dfrac{T_{SL}}{W_{TO}}\right)^c_{req}$	$\dfrac{(T_{SL}/W_{TO})_{req}}{(T_{SL}/W_{TO})_{avail}}$
Takeoff (100°F)	0.1/2	13,580	11,970	0.0137	12,140	1.179	0.8932
Supercruise[d]	1.5/30	6,030	5,350	0.0415	5,580	1.236	0.9364
Supersonic turn	1.6/30	13,590	9,240	0.0386	9,610	0.9241	0.7001
Subsonic turn	0.9/30	7,790	7,619	0.0154	7,740	1.311	0.9932
Acceleration	1.2/30	10,680	8,390	0.0184	8,550	1.047	0.7932
Maximum Mach	1.8/40	10,620	4,870	0.0420	5,080	0.6184	0.4685

[a]For each engine. [b]$F_{req} = T_{req}/(1 - \phi_{inlet} - \phi_{nozzle})$.
[c]Constraint analysis of AEDsys for $W_{TO}/S = 64$ lbf/ft^2. [d]Afterburner off.

where C_{DP} is a function of M_0 as given by Fig. 6.10.
$M_0 > 1.2$:
Equation (6.16) applies where C_D at $M_0 = 1.2$ is a function of IMS as shown in Fig. 6.9, and C_D at $M_0 > 1.2$ is found from

$$\frac{C_D(M_0)}{C_D(1.2)} = \frac{1 - 1.4\exp(-M_0^2)}{\sqrt{M_0^2 - 1}} \tag{6.12}$$

Table 6.E6 presents the data for and the results of the nozzle loss coefficient computation for each critical mission point.

Required thrust loading.   The total installation effects on the required uninstalled thrust of this engine and the resulting required-to-available thrust ratio may now be computed, and the results are summarized in Table 6.E7. The 0.9M/30 kft, 5g turn requirement has the highest required-to-available thrust loading and as such determines the engine size. Because $(T_{SL}/W_{TO})_{req}/(T_{SL}/W_{TO})_{avail}$ at that point is 0.9932, $(T_{SL}/W_{TO})_{avail} = 1.32$ will meet all of the AAF RFP requirements within the limits of this analysis, and no further iteration will be necessary. This confirms the earlier assertion that the engine cycle selection process is, fortunately, highly convergent.

6.4.6 Evaluation of AAF Engine 15 for $(T_{SL}/W_{TO})_{avail} = 1.32$

We may safely conclude that an available thrust loading $(T_{SL}/W_{TO})_{avail}$ of 1.320 will permit Engine 15 to meet the AAF RFP requirements. Increasing the thrust loading from 1.25 to 1.32 changes the thrust scale factor, a measure of the engine size, from 0.4888 to 0.5161. The results are tabulated in Table 6.E8.

The new reference point mass flow rate for each of the two engines is simply the original value of 200 lbm/s multiplied by the thrust scale factor (TSF) of 0.5161 or

$$\dot{m}_{0new} = TSF \times \dot{m}_0 = 0.5161 \times 200 = 103.22 \text{ lbm/s}$$

The value of the power takeoff (P_{TO}) produced by the engine must be adjusted from its current value of 155.2 kW to 150 kW (300/2). This is done by adjusting

Table 6.E8 Engine 15 sizing data

Thrust loading $(T_{SL}/W_{TO})_{avail}$	1.25	1.32
Thrust scale factor TSF	0.4888	0.5161
Thrust F_{SL}, lbf	15,000	15,840
Power takeoff P_{TO}, kW	146.9	155.2
Inlet area A_1, ft^2	3.332	3.519
Afterbody area A_{10}, ft^2	4.880	5.153
Afterbody length L, ft	4.487	4.611
Required thrust loading $(T_{SL}/W_{TO})_{req}$	1.311	1.311
$(T_{SL}/W_{TO})_{req}/(T_{SL}/W_{TO})_{avail}$	1.0488	0.9932

the power takeoff coefficient (C_{TO}) as follows:

$$C_{TOH\,new} = \frac{P_{TOH\,new}}{P_{TOH\,ref}}C_{TOH\,ref} = \frac{150.0}{155.2}(0.0152) = 0.0147$$

This change is too minor to warrant further iteration.

The reference point data for the properly scaled Engine 15 are summarized as follows:

Engine 15 Reference Data

$M_0 = 1.451$	$\pi_f = 3.5$	$T_{t4} = 3200°R$	$C_{TOH} = 0.0147$
$h = 36\,\text{kft}$	$\alpha = 0.7571$	$T_{t7} = 3600°R$	$P_0/P_9 = 1$
$\pi_c = 28$	$M_6 = 0.4$	$\dot{m}_0 = 103.22\,\text{lbm/s}$	

Hereinafter, this engine is simply known as the AAF Engine.

6.5 AAF Engine Performance

6.5.1 Installed Performance of the AAF Engine

In the mission analysis of Chapter 5, the installation losses were estimated at about 5%. By flying the AAF Engine, the Mission Analysis portion of the AEDsys software makes the final estimates of installation penalties. For Type A ($P_s > 0$) mission legs, the calculation of the installation losses requires no iteration. For Type B ($P_s = 0$) mission legs, the engine is throttled back in increments and the corresponding installation losses calculated until installed thrust equals drag. The installation losses of the AAF Engine at the start of each mission leg are summarized in Table 6.E9. Note that the installation losses of the Subsonic Cruise Climb 3–4 and Combat Air Patrol 5–6 phases are about 12%; the Supersonic Penetration 6–7, Escape Dash 8–9, and Warm-up 1–2 A phases are about 6%; and the Loiter phase is about 8%. The net change in fuel consumed was small because the remainder of the mission phases and segments has installation penalties less than 5%. The decrease in fuel used W_F for legs where $P_s > 0$ is mainly caused by the increase in thrust loading T_{SL}/W_{TO} from 1.25 to 1.32. The changes in fuel used W_F for legs where $P_s = 0$ are mainly caused by the changes in installation losses from the initial estimate of 5%.

Table 6.E9   AAF Engine performance

Mission phases and segments		P_s	M_0	Alt, kft	$\phi_{inlet} + \phi_{nozzle}$	$\prod_{i\,f}$	W_F, lbf	%W_F change[a]
1–2:	A—Warm-up[b]	=0	0.0	2	0.0556	0.9911	214	5.9
1–2:	B—Takeoff acceleration[b]	>0	0.0	2	0.0134	0.9956	105	−7.1
1–2:	C—Takeoff rotation[b]	=0	0.182	2	0.0023	0.9983	40	5.3
2–3:	D—Horizontal acceleration[b]	>0	0.441	2	0.0026	0.9946	129	−6.5
2–3:	E—Climb/acceleration	>0	0.875	16	0.0295	0.9818	428	−7.2
3–4:	Subsonic cruise climb	=0	0.900	41.6	0.1161	0.9773	524	11.3
5–6:	Combat air patrol	=0	0.700	30	0.1239	0.9697	683	7.7
6–7:	F—Acceleration	>0	1.090	30	0.0408	0.9821	391	−6.9
6–7:	G—Supersonic penetration	=0	1.500	30	0.0622	0.9449	1183	1.9
7–8:	I—1.6M/5g turn	=0	1.600	30	0.0416	0.9761	470	−5.4
7–8:	J—0.9M/5g turns*	=0	0.900	30	0.0164	0.9740	498	−8.8
7–8:	K—Acceleration	>0	1.195	30	0.0446	0.9815	346	−6.2
8–9:	Escape dash	=0	1.500	30	0.0638	0.9818	322	0.9
9–10:	Zoom climb	=0	1.326	30	0.0271	0.9974	44	−4.3
10–11:	Subsonic cruise climb	=0	0.900	47.6	0.1177	0.9716	491	7.4
12–13:	Loiter	=0	0.397	10	0.0844	0.9662	569	4.0
	Total	—	—	—	—	—	6439	0.3

[a]Change from Table 5.E4.   [b]100°F.

It is interesting and important to note that the total fuel consumed changed only by about 0.3% from the estimate at the end of Chapter 5. The AAF engine consumes 251 lbf of fuel less than the 6690 lbf mission fuel estimate of Chapter 3. This process has clearly demonstrated that the general engine performance models of Secs. 2.3.2 and 3.3.2 were more than adequate for their purpose, and that they undoubtedly contributed to the rapid convergence.

6.5.2   Final Reprise

A comparison of the installed thrust lapse α of the AAF Engine to that estimated for this type of engine in Sec. 2.3.2 provides insight into the change in the mission phases restricting the engine size from the combination of Takeoff and Combat Turn 2 to Supercruise and Combat Turn 2. This is best accomplished by comparing the estimated installed thrust lapses found in Fig. 2.E1b for throttle ratio (*TR*) of 1.07 to the computed thrust lapses of the AAF Engine, as shown in Fig. 6.E6 for both military and maximum power settings at sea level and 30 kft on a standard day.

The estimated and computed AAF Engine thrust lapses α agree fairly well over the entire AAF's flight envelope. Both military and maximum predicted thrust lapses at sea level increase more with increasing Mach number than the AAF Engine. The estimated thrust lapse for military power decreases less with increasing altitude than the AAF Engine. The difference in thrust lapses with Mach number is caused mainly by the moderate bypass ratio of the AAF Engine. The estimated and computed AAF Engine maximum thrust lapses at 30 kft have the same trend

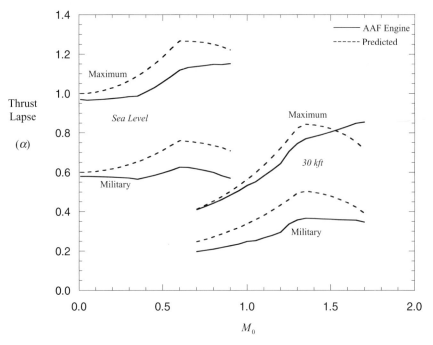

Fig. 6.E6   Comparison of installed thrust lapses α at maximum and military power (standard day).

until $\theta_0 > 1.07$ (TR) where the estimated thrust lapse drops off more rapidly than the AAF Engine.

In preceding chapters, a reprise was performed when better information than the preliminary data used to start the design process became available. The AAF Constraint Analysis of Chapter 2 was based on estimated engine thrust lapse and preliminary aerodynamic data. The constraints were calculated and plotted (see Fig. 2.E3), and a preliminary choice was made of the thrust loading $(T_{SL}/W_{TO} = 1.25)$ and wing loading $(W_{TO}/S = 64\ \text{lbf/ft}^2)$ for the AAF. The engine sizing, performed in Sec. 6.4, results in a static sea level installed thrust for two AAF Engines of 31,680 lbf (vs 30,000 lbf estimated in Chapter 3) that provides a revised thrust loading of 1.32 for the AAF. A reprise of the Constraint Analysis would be most appropriate now that improved thrust lapse data are available. Only through this analysis can the question about the influence of the new thrust lapse and aircraft weight fraction data on wing loading be answered. Table 6.E10 presents new values of the thrust lapse and aircraft weight fraction for each constraint boundary of Chapter 2. Using these new values of α and β, computing and plotting the new constraint boundaries yields Fig. 6.E7. Please note that AEDsys automatically updates the thrust lapse information in Constraint Analysis and Contour Plots, but that you must enter the updated weight fraction manually.

Any specific boundary will shift about the constraint diagram with changes in thrust lapse α and aircraft weight fraction β. Increases in thrust lapse α will reduce the required thrust loading T_{SL}/W_{TO} and decreases in the thrust lapse will increase

Table 6.E10   AAF thrust lapse and weight fraction

		Initial		Revised	
Constraint	Throttle	α	β	α	β
Takeoff, 0.1M/2 kft, 100°F	Max	0.9006	1.0	0.8460	1.0
Supercruise, 1.5M/30 kft	Mil	0.4792	0.78	0.3606	0.8221
Supersonic turn, 1.6M/30 kft, 5g	Max	0.7829	0.78	0.8329	0.8221
Subsonic turn, 0.9M/30 kft, 5g	Max	0.5033	0.78	0.4841	0.8221
Acceleration, 1.2M/30 kft	Max	0.7216	0.78	0.6677	0.8221
Maximum Mach, 1.8M/40 kft	Max	0.5575	0.78	0.6561	0.8221

the required thrust loading. Likewise, increases in the aircraft weight fraction β will reduce the required wing loading W_{TO}/S, and decreases in aircraft weight fraction will increase the required wing loading. As shown in Table 6.E10, both of the values of thrust lapse and aircraft weight fraction have changed for each constraint. Finally, Fig. 6.E7 reveals that the Subsonic 5g Turn and Takeoff no longer constrain the solution as they did in Fig. 2.E3 and the aircraft design point of $T_{SL}/W_{TO} = 1.32$ and $W_{TO}/S = 64$ lbf/ft^2 is at the intersection of the Landing and Subsonic 5g Turn constraints.

It is worthwhile to pause for a moment at this point to contemplate the real world. If, as has happened in the past, negotiations between the participants led

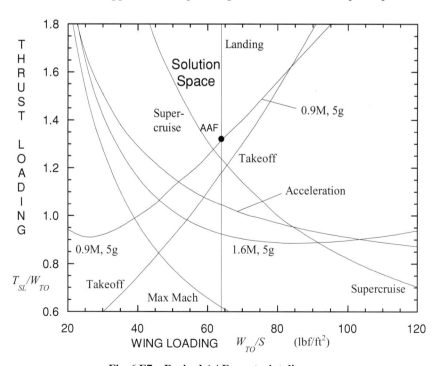

Fig. 6.E7   Revised AAF constraint diagram.

to a reduction of the Subsonic 5g Turn and/or Landing RFP requirements for the purpose of reducing thrust loading and engine size, Supercruise would soon become a barrier. This would, of course, lead to another search for the best AAF engine.

Because the required wing loading is not below our initial estimate of 64 lbf/ft^2, the revised aircraft design points of $T_{SL}/W_{TO} = 1.32$ and $W_{TO}/S = 64$ lbf/ft^2 are reconfirmed, and further revision of the required aircraft size and engine thrust is not necessary at this time. This is a happy moment because engine cycle design can now come to an end and engine component design can begin. The performance of the AAF Engine is summarized in the following section before starting the design of the engine components in Chapter 7.

6.5.3 AAF Engine Uninstalled Performance Summary

Plots of the uninstalled engine thrust, thrust specific fuel consumption, and mass flow rate vs flight Mach number and altitude are the means by which engine performance is traditionally presented for use by engineering staffs. Figures 6.E8–6.E12 present the standard day uninstalled performance of the AAF Engine at military and maximum power settings. They were generated by the Engine Test portion of AEDsys. Figure 6.E13 presents the partial throttle performance at

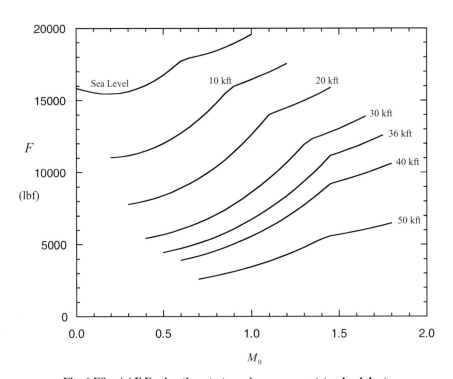

Fig. 6.E8   AAF Engine thrust at maximum power (standard day).

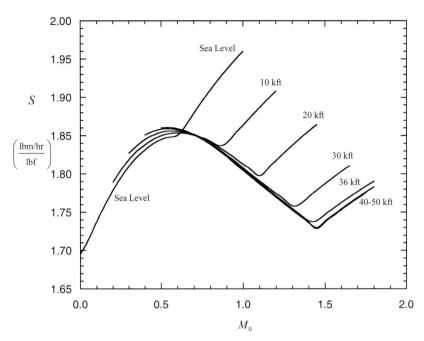

Fig. 6.E9 AAF Engine thrust specific fuel consumption at maximum power (standard day).

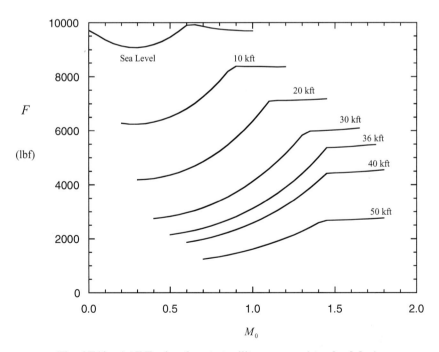

Fig. 6.E10   AAF Engine thrust at military power (standard day).

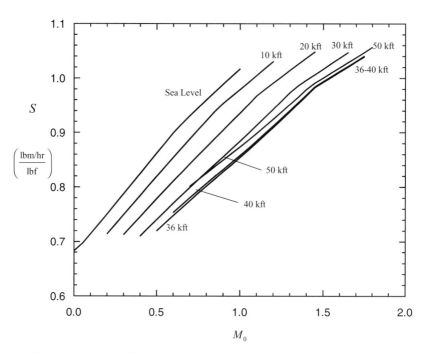

Fig. 6.E11   AAF Engine thrust specific fuel consumption at military power (standard day).

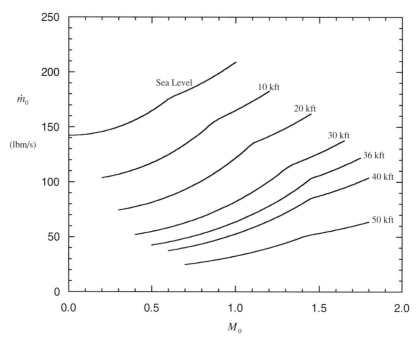

Fig. 6.E12   AAF Engine air mass flow rate at maximum/military power (standard day).

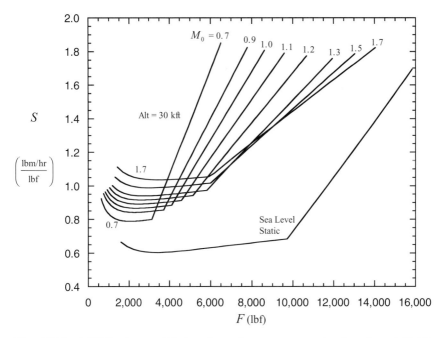

Fig. 6.E13   AAF Engine partial throttle performance at sea level static and 30 kft (standard day).

altitudes of 30 kft and sea level static. These are known in the propulsion community as "power hooks" because of their shape. The kink caused by the control system theta break is evident on every curve of Figs. 6.E8–6.E13. The uninstalled, sea level static AAF Engine performance at military and maximum power settings are as listed in Table 6.E11.

The complete, uninstalled AAF Engine performance, as computed using the MSH model by the AEDsys program at the engine reference point and sea level static, is presented next. As we bring Part I, Engine Cycle Design to a close, it is important to note that this AAF Engine *reference point* will be referred to as the AAF Engine *design point* in Part II, Engine Component Design.

Table 6.E11   Uninstalled AAF Engine performance at sea level static

Thrust (lbf)	15,840/9,713
Thrust specific fuel consumption (1/h)	1.6956/0.6829
Air mass flow rate (lbm/s)	142.35
Compressor pressure ratio	28.0
Fan pressure ratio	3.50
Bypass ratio	0.754
Bleed air flow rate (lbm/s)	0.81
Power takeoff (kW)	150

AEDsys (Ver. 3.00)   Turbofan with AB—Dual spool   Date:10/1/2002 6:00:00 AM
Engine File: C:\Program Files\AEDsys\AAF Data\AAF Final Engine.ref

Input Constants

Pidmax = 0.9600	Pi b	= 0.9500	Eta b	= 0.9990	Pi n	= 0.9700
cp c = 0.2400	cp t	= 0.2950	Gam c	= 1.4000	Gam t	= 1.3000
Pi AB = 0.9500	Eta AB	= 0.9900	cp AB	= 0.2950	Gam AB	= 1.3000
Eta cL = 0.8693	Eta cH	= 0.8678	Eta tH	= 0.9028	Eta tL	= 0.9087
Eta mL = 0.9950	Eta mH	= 0.9950	Eta PL	= 1.0000	Eta PH	= 1.0000
Eta f = 0.8693	PTO L	= 0.0KW	PTO H	= 150.0KW	hPR	= 18400
Bleed = 1.00%	Cool 1	= 5.00%	Cool 2	= 5.00%		

** Thrust Scale Factor = 1.0000

Parameter	Reference**	Test**
Mach Number @ 0	1.4510	0.0100
Temperature @ 0	390.50	518.69
Pressure @ 0	3.3063	14.6960
Altitude @ 0	36000	0
Total Temp @ 4	3200.00	2983.39
Total Temp @ 7	3600.00	3600.00
Pi r/Tau r	3.4211/1.4211	1.0001/1.0000
Pi d	0.9354	0.9600
Pi f/Tau f	3.5000/1.4951	3.4998/1.4950
Pi cL/Tau cL	3.5000/1.4951	3.4998/1.4950
Pi cH/Tau cH	8.0000/1.9351	8.0052/1.9355
Tau m1	0.9693	0.9693
Pi tH/Tau tH	0.3083/0.7853	0.3083/0.7853
Tau m2	0.9772	0.9772
Pi tL/Tau tL	0.4236/0.8366	0.4235/0.8366
Mach Number @ 6	0.4000	0.4001
Mach Number @ 16	0.3998	0.3994
Mach Number @ 6A	0.4242	0.4241
Gamma @ 6A	1.3360	1.3360
cp @ 6A	0.2715	0.2715
Pt16/Pt6	1.0074	1.0071
Pi M/Tau M	0.9635/0.7797	0.9635/0.7805
Alpha	0.757	0.754
Pt9/P9	9.8719	2.9621
P0/P9	1.0000	1.0000
Mach Number @ 9	2.1544	1.3779
Mass Flow Rate @ 0	103.22	142.35
Corr Mass Flow @ 0	138.72	142.34
Flow Area @ 0	3.214	166.743
Flow Area* @ 0	2.808	2.881
Flow Area @ 9	5.459	3.046
MB—Fuel/Air Ratio (f)	0.02803	0.02550
AB—Fuel/Air Ratio (fAB)	0.03800	0.03969
Overall Fuel/Air Ratio (fo)	0.05198	0.05241
Specific Thrust (F/m0)	108.24	111.27
Thrust Spec Fuel Consumption (S)	1.7289	1.6956
Thrust (F)	11172	15840
Fuel Flow Rate	19316	26858
Propulsive Efficiency (%)	46.93	0.65
Thermal Efficiency (%)	43.70	25.71
Overall Efficiency (%)	20.51	0.17

References

[1] *In-Flight Thrust Determination and Uncertainty*, Society of Automotive Engineers Special Publication 674, Society of Automotive Engineers, Warrendale, PA, 1986.

[2] Oates, G. C., *The Aerothermodynamics of Gas Turbine and Rocket Propulsion*, 3rd. ed., AIAA Education Series, AIAA, Reston, VA, 1997.

[3] Mattingly, J. D., *Elements of Gas Turbine Propulsion*, McGraw-Hill, New York, 1996.

[4] Oates, G. C. (ed.), *The Aerothermodynamics of Aircraft Gas Turbine Engines*, AFAPL-TR-78–52, Wright–Patterson AFB, Ohio, July 1978.

[5] Oates, G. C. (ed.), *Aircraft Propulsion Systems Technology and Design*, AIAA Education Series, AIAA, Washington, DC, 1989.

[6] Oates, G. C. (ed.), *Aerothermodynamics of Aircraft Engine Components*, AIAA Education Series, AIAA, New York, 1985.

[7] Swavely, C. E., and Soileau, J. F., "Aircraft Aftbody/Propulsion System Integration for Low Drag," AIAA Paper 72-1101, 1972.

PART II
Engine Component Design

7
Engine Component Design: Global and Interface Quantities

7.1 Concept

This chapter plays a pivotal role because it provides the bridge between treating the propulsion system as a whole and beginning the design of those parts that have traditionally been identified as components and subsystems. No standard or completely comprehensive list of components and subsystems is available because they differ from company to company and engine to engine, but any reasonable collection would include at least the following components:

1) inlet
2) fan and booster
3) propeller and variable pitch control
4) low-pressure compressor (LPC)
5) high-pressure compressor (HPC)
6) main or primary burner
7) high-pressure turbine (HPT)
8) low-pressure turbine (LPT)
9) free or power turbine
10) mixer
11) afterburner or augmentor exhaust nozzle
12) and thrust reverser.

The subsystems would include the following:

1) nacelle
2) fuel delivery system
3) instrumentation and controls
4) starting and ignition system
5) structure
6) shafts, bearings, and seals
7) accessory gearbox and drive
8) propeller gearbox
9) lubrication and cooling systems
10) and fire control.

Within any engine company each of these is represented by a team of experts, many of whom have dedicated their entire careers to success. It is good to remember that, although the propulsion industry has found by experience that this breakup is most effective for management, no one component or subsystem is free from the influence of all of the others. The entire engine is coupled through aerodynamics, thermodynamics, structures, and controls; therefore, integration is a vital activity at all stages of design and development. One should also approach each component and subsystem with a minimum of prejudice about its importance to the whole.

For example, the instrumentation and controls package ordinarily accounts for 20–30% of the total cost and weight of the engine, and a fuel delivery system that allows some trapped fuel to drain into the burner after the engine has stopped running increases the danger of internal fire and explosion.

Component and subsystem design can commence now because there is an abundance of "inside information" about the chosen design point engine (referred to in Part I as the reference point). By running AEDsys Performance computations at the desired flight conditions and throttle settings, the behavior of the flow properties at the interfaces between the flowpath components as well as across these components can be established.

This supplies the quantitative information necessary to allow the separate design of each flowpath component to begin, which, in turn, will generate the requirements and constraints for the supporting subsystems. Equally important to the remainder of the project is the institution of a systematic approach to component and subsystem integration. There must be methods and procedures to ensure that everyone shares the same assumptions and goals. Frequent updating of quantitative information and communication about problems and lines of attack are key ingredients of the process. You would be amazed to discover how easily communication breaks down and how severe are the consequences.

7.2 Design Tools

The emphasis here is on assembling a complete set of flow quantities at each engine station as well as several derived properties of interest. You will find it helpful to recognize the diverse roles played in the following discussions by the engine reference stations (see Sec. 4.2.1). First, each is the interface between two sequential flowpath components. Second, each is the entrance to one component and the exit for another. Third, any two successive engine stations provide the boundary conditions for an individual flowpath component.

Systematic procedures for calculating the most important interface and other derived quantities will now be developed. The source document is a complete set of ONX engine design point (reference point of Part I) computations, such as that of the Air-to-Air Fighter (AAF) Engine presented in Fig. 7.1. Please note for the final time that these computations, as well as all of the ensuing global and interface quantities, are based on the MSH (modified specific heat) model described in Sec. 4.2.7.

7.2.1 Total Pressure, Total Enthalpy, and Total Temperature

Total pressure and total temperature are of special importance to the engine designer because they are the most thermodynamically meaningful and far easier to measure than their corresponding static properties. The total pressure and total enthalpy are found directly from the definitions of Sec. 4.2.3.

For example, the total pressure at the interface between the high-pressure compressor and the burner is given by the expression

$$P_{t3} = P_0 \, \pi_r \, \pi_d \, \pi_{cL} \, \pi_{cH} = P_0 \, \pi_r \, \pi_d \, \pi_c \tag{7.1}$$

```
On-Design Calcs (ONX V5.00)              Date: XX/XX/2002 XX:XX:XX AM
File: C:\Program Files\AEDsys\AAF Data\AAF Engine.ref
                Turbofan Engine with Afterburning
                using Modified Specific Heat (MSH) model
********************    Input Data    ********************
        Mach No   =  1.451          Alpha         =-001.000
        Alt (ft)  =  36000          Pi f / Pi cL  =3.500/3.500
        T0 (R)    =  390.50         Pi d (max)    =  0.960
        P0 (psia) =  3.306          Pi b          =  0.950
        Density   = .0007102        Pi n          =  0.970
         (Slug/ft^3)                Efficiency
        Cp c   = 0.2400 Btu/lbm-R     Burner       =  0.999
        Cp t   = 0.2950 Btu/lbm-R     Mech Hi Pr   =  0.995
        Gamma c = 1.4000             Mech Lo Pr   =  0.995
        Gamma t = 1.3000             Fan/LP Comp  =0.890/0.890 (ef/ecL)
        Tt4 max = 3200.0 R           HP Comp      =  0.900 (ecH)
        h - fuel = 18400 Btu/lbm     HP Turbine   =  0.890 (etH)
        CTO Low  = 0.0000            LP Turbine   =  0.900 (etL)
        CTO High = 0.0147            Pwr Mech Eff L =  1.000
        Cooling Air #1 =  5.000 %    Pwr Mech Eff H =  1.000
        Cooling Air #2 =  5.000 %    Bleed Air    =  1.000 %
        P0/P9    = 1.0000
          ** Afterburner **
        Tt7 max  = 3600.0 R          Pi AB        =  0.950
        Cp AB    = 0.2950 Btu/lbm-R  Eta A/B      =  0.990
        Gamma AB = 1.3000
        *** Mixer ***                Pi Mixer max =  0.970
********************    RESULTS    ********************
        Tau r     =  1.421          a0 (ft/sec)  =  968.8
        Pi r      =  3.421          V0 (ft/sec)  = 1405.7
        Pi d      =  0.935          Mass Flow    = 103.2 lbm/sec
        TauL      = 10.073          Area Zero    = 3.214 sqft
        PTO Low   =   0.00 KW       Area Zero*   = 2.808 sqft
        PTO High  = 150.04 KW
        Pt16/P0   = 11.201          Tt16/T0      = 2.1246
        Pt6/P0    = 11.119          Tt6/T0       = 5.0997
        Alpha     = 0.7571
        Pi c      = 28.000          Tau m1       = 0.9693
        Pi f      = 3.5000          Tau m2       = 0.9772
        Tau f     = 1.4951          Tau M        = 0.7797
        Eta f     = 0.8693          Pi M         = 0.9635
        Pi cL     = 3.500           Tau cL       = 1.4951
        Eta cL    = 0.8693
        Pi cH     = 8.0000          M6           = 0.4000
        Tau cH    = 1.9351          M16          = 0.3998
        Eta cH    = 0.8678          M6A          = 0.4242
        Pi tH     = 0.3083          A16/A6       = 0.4641
        Tau tH    = 0.7853          Gamma M      = 1.3360
        Eta tH    = 0.9028          CP M         = 0.2715
        Pi tL     = 0.4236          Eta tL       = 0.9087
        Tau tL    = 0.8366
Without AB                      With AB
        Pt9/P9    = 10.132          Pt9/P9       =  9.872
        f         = 0.02803         f            = 0.02803
                                    f AB         = 0.03800
        F/mdot    = 51.995 lbf/(lbm/s)  F/mdot   =108.237 lbf/(lbm/s)
        S         = 0.9830 (lbm/hr)/lbf  S        = 1.7289 (lbm/hr)/lbf
        T9/T0     = 2.2208          T9/T0        = 5.4351
        V9/V0     = 2.172           V9/V0        = 3.323
        M9/M0     = 1.495           M9/M0        = 1.485
        A9/A0     = 1.027           A9/A0        = 1.699
        A9/A8     = 2.098           A9/A8        = 2.123
        Thrust    = 5367 lbf        Thrust       = 11172 lbf
        Thermal Eff   = 57.26 %     Thermal Eff  = 43.70 %
        Propulsive Eff = 63.37 %    Propulsive Eff = 46.93 %
        Overall Eff   = 36.29 %     Overall Eff  = 20.51 %
```

Fig. 7.1   AAF Engine design point performance data.

and the total enthalpy at that interface is given by the expression

$$h_{t3} = h_0 \, \tau_r \, \tau_d \, \tau_{cL} \, \tau_{cH} = h_0 \, \tau_r \, \tau_d \, \tau_c \tag{7.2}$$

The total temperature T_t is obtained from the subroutine FAIR of Table 4.2 once the total enthalpy h_t and fuel/air ratio f are known. For the case of a calorically perfect gas, the total temperature at station 3 is given by

$$T_{t3} = T_0 \, \tau_r \, \tau_d \, \tau_{cL} \, \tau_{cH} = T_0 \, \tau_r \, \tau_d \, \tau_c \tag{7.2-CPG}$$

7.2.2 Corrected Mass Flow Rate

The corrected mass flow rate at the entrance of an engine component is a very useful quantity in the characterization and design of that component (see Sec. 5.3.1). Component performance presented in the form of a performance map normally uses corrected mass flow rate as the variable of the abscissa (see Figs. 5.4–5.8).

For example, the corrected mass flow rate at the entrance of the fan is given by the expression

$$\dot{m}_{c2} = \dot{m}_2 \frac{\sqrt{\theta_2}}{\delta_2} = \dot{m}_0 \frac{\sqrt{\theta \tau_r}}{\delta \pi_r \, \pi_d} \tag{7.3}$$

or, when the corrected mass flow rate at station 0 is known, by

$$\dot{m}_{c2} = \dot{m}_0 \frac{\sqrt{\theta \tau_r}}{\delta \pi_r \, \pi_d} = \frac{\dot{m}_{c0}}{\pi_d} \tag{7.4}$$

Similarly, the corrected mass flow rate at the entrance of the combustor is given by the expression

$$
\begin{aligned}
\dot{m}_{c3.1} = \dot{m}_{3.1} \frac{\sqrt{\theta_{3.1}}}{\delta_{3.1}} &= \frac{\dot{m}_0 (1 - \varepsilon_1 - \varepsilon_2 - \beta)}{1 + \alpha} \frac{\sqrt{\theta \tau_r \tau_{cL} \tau_{cH}}}{\delta \pi_r \, \pi_d \, \pi_{cL} \, \pi_{cH}} \\
&= \frac{\dot{m}_{c0} (1 - \varepsilon_1 - \varepsilon_2 - \beta)}{1 + \alpha} \frac{\sqrt{\tau_{cL} \tau_{cH}}}{\pi_d \, \pi_{cL} \, \pi_{cH}}
\end{aligned}
\tag{7.5}
$$

7.2.3 Static Pressure, Static Enthalpy, Static Temperature, and Velocity

With the total pressure and temperature in hand, the static properties can be calculated from the isentropic compressible flow functions, either by using the subroutine RGCOMP of Table 4.3, or, in the case of calorically perfect gases, from Eqs. (1.1) and (1.2) or the Gas Tables portion of AEDsys, provided that the local Mach number M and fuel/air ratio f are given or assumed. Once that is done, the velocity can be calculated from the equation

$$V = Ma = M\sqrt{\gamma g_c RT} \tag{7.6}$$

7.2.4 One-Dimensional Throughflow Area (Annulus Area)

The information available now can be employed to find the *MFP* (M, T_t, f), either by using the subroutine RGCOMP of Table 4.3, or, in the case of calorically perfect gases, from Eq. (1.3) or the Gas Tables portion of AEDsys. The throughflow area is then calculated from Eq. (1.3), rearranged into the form

$$A = \frac{\dot{m}\sqrt{T_t}}{P_t\, MFP} \tag{7.7}$$

where the definitions and equations of Sec. 4.2.4 are used to obtain the value of $\dot{m}$ at any given engine station.

7.2.5 Flowpath Force on Component

The net axial force in the positive x direction exerted on the fluid by each component is given by the streamwise increase from entrance to exit of the interface quantity:

$$I \doteq PA + \rho V^2 A = PA(1 + \gamma M^2) \tag{1.5}$$

which is known as the impulse function in one-dimensional gas dynamics (see Sec. 1.9.5). The net axial force includes all contributions of pressure and viscous stresses on flowpath walls and any bodies immersed in the stream. The net axial force exerted on the component is equal and opposite to the force exerted on the fluid. Thus, a positive axial force on the fluid contributes a force on the component in the desired thrust direction.

The impulse function provides important information to the design engineer because it reveals the distribution of major axial forces throughout the engine. Unfortunately, it does not precisely locate the distribution of forces within the component. In the case of the compressor or turbine, for example, axial force can be easily "moved" from the rotor to the stator by means of static pressure forces applied to their extensions outside the flowpath. These static pressure forces are often applied to circular disks and are therefore known as "balance piston" loads.

One strategy frequently employed is to manage the balance piston loads so that most of the axial force is delivered to the stator assembly, which is firmly attached to the outside case of the engine, leaving only enough net axial force on the shaft, which is attached to the rotor assembly, to ensure that it has the same sign under all operating conditions. This will guarantee that the shaft thrust bearing, which prevents axial motion of the shaft, always feels enough force to avoid skidding and the resulting rapid consumption of its life.

The uninstalled thrust also depends fundamentally on the impulse function, as we can see from the expression derived in Appendix E:

$$F = I_9 - I_0 - P_0(A_9 - A_0) \tag{E.13}$$

The torque exerted by the components provides an interesting contrast to this discussion of forces. To begin with, the net steady-state torque on any rotating component must be zero, or the rotational speed would have to change. Furthermore, because the freestream and exhaust flows usually have no swirl, the net torque exerted on the fluid is zero, and the net torque exerted by the stationary components must therefore also be zero. Finally, if the exhaust flow does contain some swirl the torque must therefore have been exerted by the stationary components.

7.3   Engine Systems Design

Even the most casual glance at a turbine engine reveals that it consists of much more than the flowpath components. The many individual components could not function separately or together if they were not supplied a great deal of support. The art of providing all of the necessary functions and services in an integrated package is called engine systems design. This art can be taught only by experience because it requires knowledge of many different technologies as well as the ability to make judgments when confronted with many diverse demands. It also helps to have previously explored the pros and cons of many alternate systems design options.

A list of the major subsystems was presented at the beginning of this chapter. Their design will ultimately determine the size, weight, cost, reliability, maintainability, and safety of the engine. Consequently, it is important to highlight this area, although it is difficult to duplicate because it involves the simultaneous consideration of so many competing factors. It is possible, nevertheless, to develop an appreciation for the overall scope and significance of engine systems design and an understanding of some of the underlying technologies. Many of the latter, in fact, are adequately described in standard handbooks and company manuals. One readily available reference is *Aircraft Gas Turbine Engine Technology*.[1] The genius of the designer is largely the ability to weave them together.

A great way to start is to examine as many of the AEDsys Engine Pictures digital images of engines as similar to the type being designed as possible. Then these general questions should be studied and discussed until they are understood:

1) What are all of the parts doing there (including those mounted outside the case, known as accessories, externals, or dressings)?

2) How are all of the major functions accomplished?

Once this is done, it is possible to focus on any specific portion of the engine, depending on personal preference, need, interest, and background. The following sections outline some of the considerations involved in each subsystem, which are both informative and essential to good design.

7.3.1   Engine Static Structure

1) How is the engine connected to the airframe? What kinds of load transferring joints are used and why? Does the thrust reaction cause a bending moment to be applied to the engine outer case, and, if so, what are the consequences? Could they cause the case to ovalize?

2) Sketch the load paths for the entire engine. Show, in particular, how the outer case(s) are held together and how the bearings are supported.

3) How large and in what direction are the forces on the inner surfaces of the inlet and nozzle? What types of forces and moments are generated on the inlet during angle of attack operation and what may they cause to happen? How are the

exhaust nozzle throat and exit area variations actuated, and what keeps the nozzle cooled and sealed?

4) How are the compressor variable stators actuated?

5) Does the design include active clearance control for the tips of the rotating airfoils? If not, how could this be accomplished?

6) How is the engine assembled and disassembled?

7.3.2 Shafts and Bearings

1) Locate and describe all of the engine shafts. Why are they not simple cylindrical tubes? How is the torque transmitted to and from the shafts? How is any net axial force transferred from the shafts to the stationary structure?

2) Find how the shafts are supported by the bearings. What is the relationship between bearing axial spacing (or number of bearings) and shaft critical speed? Can a shaft have a critical speed within the engine operating range?

3) Why would we find intershaft bearings in a counter-rotating engine (i.e., the low-pressure spool and high-pressure spool turn in opposite directions)? Would intershaft bearing have special operating conditions? Can you positively identify a counter-rotating engine in the AEDsys Engine Pictures folder?

4) Show how the pressure could be adjusted in the high-pressure compressor and high-pressure turbine cavities adjacent to the combustor in order to transfer axial force from rotating to stationary parts and thereby control the net axial force acting on the thrust bearing. (These are called "balance piston" loads.) What requirements should be put on the net thrust bearing axial force, considering the fact that if it passes through zero at any time, the bearing will skid to destruction and/or the shaft will move freely away from the thrust bearing? How can these balance piston forces be generated for the low-pressure spool?

5) Design the shaft(s) and bearings for the AAF Engine.

6) Locate and describe the accessory gearbox and drive, including the power takeoff shaft.

7.3.3 Lubrication System

1) What are the real functions of the lubricant, and how are they accomplished? What are the main perils faced by the lubricating fluid?

2) Describe how the lubricant is pressurized, filtered, cooled, delivered to the bearings, and then returned to the storage tank without leaking into engine compartments and causing mischief. What is the sump and where is it located? How does the lube system work when the aircraft is flying upside down?

3) What are breather tubes and where can they be found?

4) Select the type, amount, and flow rate of lubricant for the engine of your study.

7.3.4 Fuel System

1) Describe how the fuel is pressurized, filtered, metered, heated, and delivered from the aircraft tanks to the burner and afterburner. What are the main perils faced by the fuel?

2) How does a typical fuel control system work? What instrumentation and actuation are needed to support the fuel control? Appendix O can be helpful here.

3) Select the fuel pressure and temperature and the type of fuel nozzle for the engine of your study. Why do the fuel delivery lines have loops along their length? What happens to the fuel that drains out of the delivery lines after the engine is turned off?

4) Can you locate any mixers upstream of the afterburners in the AEDsys Engine Pictures files? If so, what types of shapes do they have? Can you locate the afterburner spray bars (i.e., fuel injectors) and flame holders? If so, what types of shapes do they have?

7.3.5 Cooling and Bleed Air

1) Describe how the cooling air from the compressor is delivered to the burner and turbine. How are the many separate flow rates controlled? Where does the cooling air for the afterburner and nozzle walls originate?

2) How are the compressor and turbine stationary and rotating airfoil rows sealed at the hubs and tips in order to reduce leakage?

3) Where is the aircraft bleed air removed from the flowpath? How is the flow rate controlled?

4) Where is the anti-icing bleed air for the spinner and inlet guide vanes removed from the flowpath? How does it reach its destination?

5) Are any other functions performed by engine air?

7.3.6 Starting

1) Describe the method of starting the engine. In particular, how are airflow and shaft rotation initiated, and how is ignition of the fuel accomplished? How is afterburner ignition accomplished?

7.3.7 Overall

1) Are all of the engines in the AEDsys Engine Pictures folder purely axial flow machines? If not, find some extreme examples. Through how many degrees is the flow turned during its journey through these engines, and how are the combustors configured and the fuel delivered? Why?

2) Can you find any examples of deliberate acoustic or chemical emissions control for environmental (civilian) or low observability (military) purposes?

After these and any other interesting explorations of your own making are completed, it is possible to put your knowledge to the test by means of questions involving the engine as a whole. For example, it is a challenge to estimate the weight (and cost) of the major components and subsystems and a real accomplishment to sketch a typical engine entirely from memory. Similarly, it is a revealing exercise to imagine what basic mechanical changes would be needed for a completely different cycle.

The real goal of this work, of course, is to finally be able to draw the engine being designed in detail (e.g., for the AAF Engine), making certain that all of the vital parts are not only present, but also fit and function together.

7.4   Example Engine Global and Interface Quantities

7.4.1   AAF Engine Design Point Flow Properties

The flow properties at the identified engine stations for the AAF Engine design point are presented in Table 7.E1. These results were obtained as described in Sec. 7.2. The values of γ found there are typical of MSH performance computations; the flow is presumed to be choked at Stations 4, 4.5, and 8, and arbitrary but reasonable assumptions for M have been made for Stations 2, 3.2, 5, and 7. The calculations required for Table 7.E1 can be generated automatically by selecting Interface Quantities from the AEDsys Engine Test screen after the engine has been scaled at the design point and several requested Mach numbers have been entered. You will find this to be a welcome labor-saving device, but we recommend that you do it once by hand to make certain that you understand the procedures involved. You may also find it rewarding to compare the results of Table 7.E1 to your expectations.

The AAF Engine design point uninstalled thrust is calculated from Eq. (E.13), yielding $F = I_9 - I_0 - P_0(A_9 - A_0) = 18{,}281.1 - 6039.9 - 3.306(144)(5.459 - 3.214) = 11{,}172$ lbf, which agrees with the result of Fig. 7.1.

The impulse function information of Table 7.E1 was used to calculate the net axial force $\Delta I = I_{exit} - I_{entry}$ exerted by the AAF Engine components on the fluid at the design point (see Sec. 1.9.5), and the results catalogued in Table 7.E2. As we have come to expect, they raise many questions, some of which are troublesome

Table 7.E1   AAF Engine design point interface quantities

Station	m_0, lbm/s	γ	P_t, psia	T_t,°R	P, psia	T,°R	M	V, ft/s	A, ft²	A^*, ft²	I, lbf
0	103.22	1.4	11.311	554.93	3.306	390.50	1.4510	1405.5	3.214	2.808	6039.9
1	103.22	1.4	11.021	554.93	3.460	398.54	1.4008	1370.8	3.214	2.881	5999.0
2	103.22	1.4	10.581	554.93	8.920	528.51	0.5	563.46	4.022	3.002	6973.4
13	103.22	1.4	37.032	829.66	33.067	803.24	0.4056	563.46	1.649	1.049	9658.8
Core	58.75	1.4	37.032	829.66	33.067	803.24	0.4056	563.46	0.938	0.597	5497.1
Bypass	44.48	1.4	37.032	829.66	33.067	803.24	0.4056	563.46	0.71	0.452	4161.7
2.5	58.75	1.4	37.032	829.66	33.067	803.24	0.4056	563.46	0.938	0.597	5497.1
3	58.75	1.4	296.26	1605.45	279.54	1579.0	0.2893	563.46	0.218	0.104	9812.5
3.1	52.28	1.4	296.26	1605.45	279.54	1579.0	0.2893	563.46	0.194	0.092	8733.0
3.2	52.28	1.4	293.29	1605.45	291.98	1603.4	0.08	157.03	0.677	0.093	28738
4	53.75	1.3	281.44	3200	153.59	2782.6	1.0	2483.0	0.144	0.144	7338.9
4.1	56.69	1.3	—	3101.87	—	—	—	—	—	—	—
4.4	56.69	1.3	86.773	2435.96	—	—	—	—	—	—	—
4.5	59.62	1.3	86.773	2380.3	47.354	2069.8	1.0	2141.5	0.448	0.448	7021.4
5	59.62	1.3	36.761	1991.42	29.269	1889.4	0.6	1227.6	1.153	0.967	7136.1
6	59.62	1.3	36.761	1991.42	33.17	1944.7	0.4	830.33	1.549	0.967	8936.5
16	44.48	1.4	37.032	829.66	33.17	803.96	0.3998	555.73	0.719	0.452	4201.4
6A	104.1	1.336	35.419	1552.66	31.463	1507.1	0.4242	787.15	2.338	1.534	13138
7	108	1.3	33.648	3600	28.687	3469.9	0.5	1386.4	3.466	2.572	18973
8	108	1.3	33.648	3600	18.363	3130.4	1.0	2633.7	2.572	2.572	15641
9	108	1.3	32.639	3600	3.306	2122.4	2.1544	4671.9	5.459	2.651	18281

$A_{6A} = (A_6 + A_{16})/\pi_{M\,max}$.

Table 7.E2   AAF Engine design point component axial forces

Component	Stations	Axial force ΔI, lbf	Cumulative Stations	Cumulative Axial force $\sum \Delta I$, lbf
Freestream tube	0 to 1	−40.9	0 to 1	−40.9
Inlet	1 to 2	974.4	0 to 2	933.5
Fan	2 to 13/2.5	2685.4	0 to 13/2.5	3618.9
High-pressure compressor	2.5 to 3	4315.4	0 to 3	7934.3
Main burner	3 to 4	−2473.6	0 to 4	5460.7
High-pressure turbine	4 to 4.5	−317.5	0 to 4.5	5143.2
Low-pressure turbine	4.5 to 6	1915.1	0 to 6	7058.3
Bypass duct	1.3 to 16	39.7	0 to 6/16	7098
Mixer	6/16 to 6A	−0.1	0 to 6A	7097.9
Afterburner	6A to 7	5834.9	0 to 7	12932.8
Nozzle	7 to 9	−691.6	0 to 9	12241.2

because they are counterintuitive. Why is there a positive thrust on the inlet? Why not fly the inlet alone? Why is there a negative thrust on the high-pressure turbine? Which has the greater thrust, the high-pressure spool or the low-pressure spool? How is the thrust exerted by the fluid on the main burner, mixer, and afterburner? Why is there a negative thrust on the main burner? Why is there a positive thrust on the afterburner? Why is there a negative thrust on the nozzle? Must this always be true? Why not simply cut the nozzle off?

7.4.2 Predicted AAF Engine Component Performance

We are also now in a position to examine the behavior of the AAF Engine components over their full range of operation. This is easily done by selecting the independent variable; entering the operating (flight) condition and range of calculations (maximum, minimum, and calculation step size); and selecting the Perform Calcs button on the AEDsys Engine Test screen. Similar calculations can be performed at other operating (flight) conditions and the desired results plotted. All of the computations were done for a standard atmosphere and use the MSH gas model.

The computed variation of the fan pressure ratio π_f, high-pressure compressor pressure ratio π_{cH}, low-pressure turbine pressure ratio π_{tL}, and engine bypass ratio α are plotted for full throttle vs flight Mach number and altitude in Figs. 7.E1, 7.E2, 7.E3, and 7.E4, respectively. Table 7.E3 summarizes the pressure ratios and maximum total temperature changes of these rotating components at $\theta_0 = \theta_{0\,break}$, sea level, standard day. (This point also corresponds to the maximum physical speed.) Figures 7.E1–7.E4 and Table 7.E3 will be necessary for the design of the fan, high-pressure compressor, high-pressure turbine, and low-pressure turbine that follows in Chapter 8.

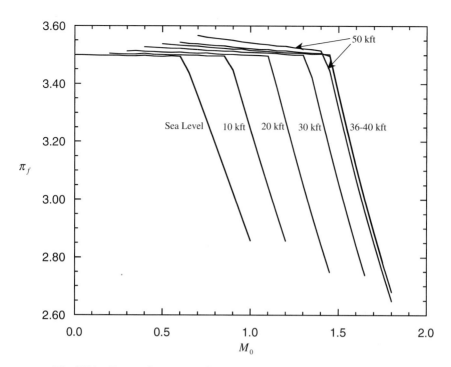

Fig. 7.E1   Fan performance—fan pressure ratio (π_f) (standard day).

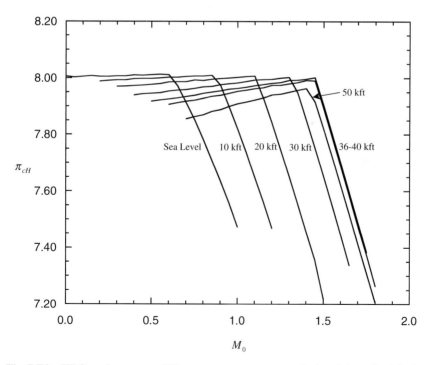

Fig. 7.E2   HPC performance—HP compressor pressure ratio (π_{cH}) (standard day).

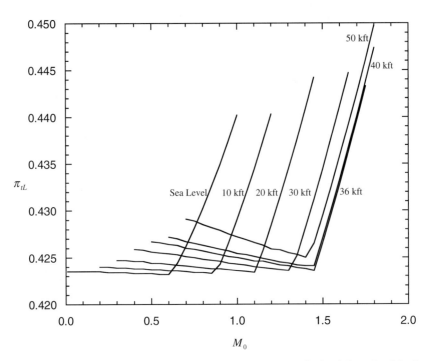

Fig. 7.E3 Low-pressure turbine performance—pressure ratio (π_{tL}) (standard day).

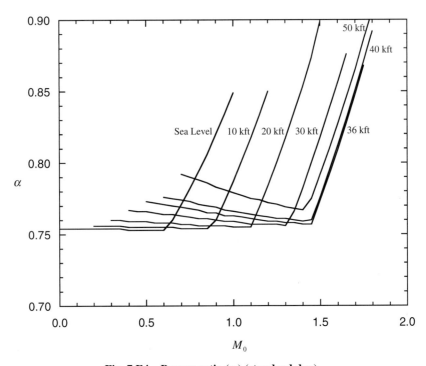

Fig. 7.E4 Bypass ratio (α) (standard day).

244

Table 7.E3   AAF Engine turbomachinery performance at $\theta_0 = \theta_{0\,break}$, sea level, standard day ($M_0 = 0.612$)

Component	Value	ΔT_t, °R	Value	Mass flow rate $\dot{m}$, lbm/s	Inlet P_t, psia	T_t, °R
Fan, π_f	3.50	$T_{t13} - T_{t2}$	275.7	177.0	18.17	557.5
High-pressure compressor, π_{cH}	8.00	$T_{t3} - T_{t2.5}$	780.1	101.0	63.51	833.3
High-pressure turbine, $1/\pi_{tH}$	3.243	$T_{t4.1} - T_{t4.4}$	665.9	97.4	483.6	3101.9
Low-pressure turbine, $1/\pi_{tL}$	2.364	$T_{t4.5} - T_{t5}$	389.4	102.4	149.1	2380.3

As we have frequently observed, these results clearly demonstrate the presence of the control system theta break. However, the value of the $\theta_{0\,break}$ at sea level, standard day has increased from the design-point value (1.451M/36 kft) of 1.070 to 1.075 because of the requirement for constant power takeoff P_{TO}. Also, the M_0 at sea level, standard day increased from 0.591 to 0.612. This happens because, as altitude decreases, the fraction of turbine power required by the power takeoff reduces and more power is available to a higher $\theta_{0\,break}$ before the $T_{t4\,max}$ limit is reached. Figure 7.E5 compares the AAF engine's $\theta_{0\,break}$ to the basic model of Appendix D. Also, the engine throttle ratio (TR) has increased to 1.073 from the design $\theta_{0\,break}$ value of 1.07. If the engine had no power takeoff P_{TO}, then the value of the $\theta_{0\,break}$ would not change with altitude, and the engine throttle ratio (TR) would equal the $\theta_{0\,break}$ as shown in Appendix D. This also explains why component performance continues to vary above the tropopause altitude of approximately 37 kft. Finally, these effects are likely to be exaggerated in many types of future aircraft that require large quantities of electrical power and/or fly at extremely high altitudes where the total power produced by the engine is diminished.

The requirements of the main burner and afterburner for each mission phase or segment are summarized in Tables 7.E4 and 7.E5, respectively. The main burner and afterburner fuel flow rates at maximum power are plotted in Figs. 7.E6 and 7.E7, respectively. Several notable features include the facts that, although f varies by about a factor of 2, it remains in the narrow range of 0.024–0.028 for most of the legs, that f_{AB} is about 0.04 for all legs except one, and that both the main burner and afterburner absolute fuel flow rates increase with flight Mach number and decrease with altitude. Figures 7.E6 and 7.E7 and Table 7.E4 provide the starting point for the main burner and afterburner designs that follow in Chapter 9.

Plots of the required freestream flow area (A_0^* for $M_0 < 1$ and A_0 for $M_0 \geq 1$) and the required exhaust nozzle exit area A_9 (for both maximum power with $P_9 = P_0$ and military power with $P_9 = P_0$) vs flight Mach number and altitude are presented for the AAF Engine in Figs. 7.E8 and 7.E9, respectively. They are close relatives of results seen earlier (e.g., Sec. 6.4.5) and display the aforementioned variation above the tropopause as a result of the fixed value of P_{TO}.

Table 7.E4   AAF Engine main burner operation

Mission phases and segments		M_0	Alt, kft	P_{t3}, psia	T_{t3}, °R	T_{t4}, °R	$\dot{m}_{3.1}$, lbm/s	f	$\dot{m}_f$, lbm/s
1–2:	A—Warm-up[a,c]	0.0	2	360.9	1611	3200	63.70	0.02794	1.7795
1–2:	B—Takeoff acceleration[a,b]	0.1	2	361.6	1612	3200	63.81	0.02792	1.7820
1–2:	C—Takeoff rotation[a,b]	0.182	2	363.2	1613	3200	64.10	0.02790	1.7882
2–3:	D—Horizontal acceleration[a,b]	0.441	2	375.0	1625	3200	66.20	0.02771	1.8343
2–3:	E—Climb/acceleration[b]	0.875	23	263.5	1457	2910	48.76	0.02480	1.2090
3–4:	Subsonic cruise climb	0.900	41.6	82.11	1180	2370	16.84	0.01915	0.3224
5–6:	Combat air patrol	0.700	30	84.61	1065	2065	18.59	0.01556	0.2893
6–7:	F—Acceleration[b]	1.090	30	247.2	1475	2948	45.45	0.02524	1.1472
6–7:	G—Supersonic penetration	1.500	30	350.0	1633	3200	61.76	0.02757	1.7024
8–9:	and escape dash[c]								
7–8:	I—1.6M/5g turn[b]	1.600	30	363.0	1650	3200	64.07	0.02729	1.7487
7–8:	J—0.9M/5g turns[b]	0.900	30	199.0	1385	2780	37.67	0.02348	0.8846
7–8:	K—Acceleration[b]	1.195	30	280.9	1532	3056	50.72	0.02641	1.3394
9–10:	Zoom climb[c]	1.326	39	217.5	1525	3054	39.27	0.02648	1.0401
10–11:	Subsonic cruise climb	0.900	47.6	61.22	1177	2406	12.46	0.01983	0.2471
12–13:	Loiter	0.397	10	89.20	980	1734	21.39	0.01131	0.2420
	Maximum dynamic pressure	1.2	0	585.1	1660	3139	104.24	0.02592	2.7017

[a] 100°F.   [b] Maximum thrust.   [c] Military thrust.

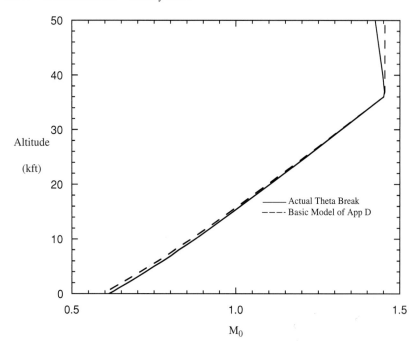

Fig. 7.E5   Comparison of actual theta break of the AAF Engine to the low bypass ratio, mixed flow turbofan engine model of Appendix D (standard day).

Table 7.E5   AAF Engine afterburner operation (maximum power)

Mission phases and segments	M_0	Alt, kft	P_{t6A}, psia	T_{t6A}, °R	T_{t7}, °R	$\dot{m}_{6A}$, lbm/s	f_{AB}	$\dot{m}_{fAB}$, lbm/s
1–2: B—Takeoff acceleration[a]	0.1	2	43.37	1553	3600	127.46	0.03799	4.7752
1–2: C—Takeoff rotation[a]	0.182	2	43.66	1552	3600	128.33	0.03799	4.8078
6–7: F—Acceleration	1.090	30	29.59	1429	3600	90.41	0.04001	3.5715
7–8: I—1.6M/5g turn	1.600	30	45.69	1545	3600	134.64	0.03806	5.0581
7–8: J—0.9M/5g turns	0.900	30	23.84	1346	3600	74.95	0.04135	3.0626
7–8: K—Acceleration	1.195	30	33.60	1483	3600	100.89	0.03915	3.8970
Maximum dynamic pressure	1.2	0	76.86	1514	3600	228.63	0.03852	8.7033

[a] 100°F.

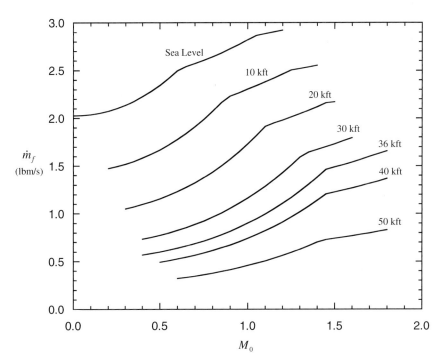

Fig. 7.E6   AAF Engine main burner fuel flow rate at military/maximum power (standard day).

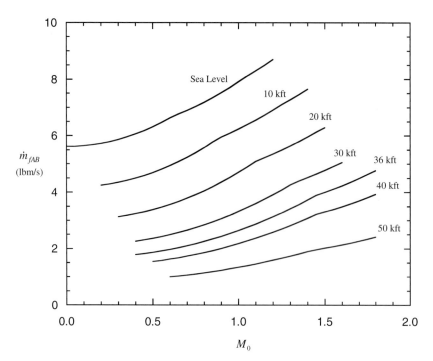

Fig. 7.E7   AAF Engine afterburner fuel flow rate at maximum power (standard day).

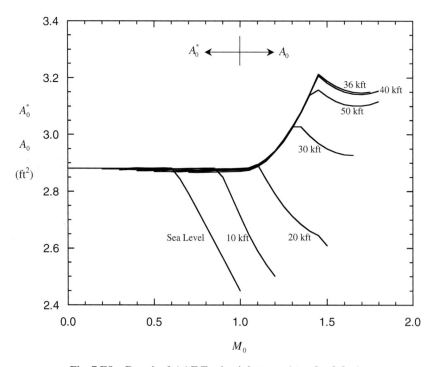

Fig. 7.E8   Required AAF Engine inlet area (standard day).

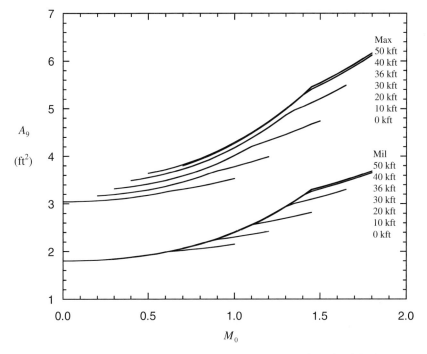

Fig. 7.E9   Required AAF Engine exhaust nozzle area (standard day).

Figures 7.E8 and 7.E9 are the starting points for the inlet and exhaust nozzle designs that follow in Chapter 10.

7.4.3   AAF Engine Component Operating Lines

The computed standard atmosphere full throttle variation of π_f, π_{cH}, π_{tH}, and α with both flight Mach number and altitude were presented in the preceding section. For component design purposes, a more useful presentation of the fan, high-pressure compressor, high-pressure turbine, and low-pressure turbine behavior is in the form of component maps (see Secs. 5.3 and 7.2.2). The computed full throttle operating lines for the fan, high-pressure compressor, and high- and low-pressure turbines are presented in the component map format in Figs. 7.E10, 7.E11, and 7.E12, respectively. It is heartwarming to find that the fan and high-pressure compressor behave as anticipated by the simplified analysis of Appendix D even for this very complex engine configuration. The high-pressure turbine's operating line essentially is a single point because it is designed to be choked both upstream and downstream (see Sec. 5.2.4), and the low-pressure turbine has a vertical operating line because it is designed to be choked at the entrance. Figures 7.E10–7.E12 are used in Chapter 8 as the basis of design for these components.

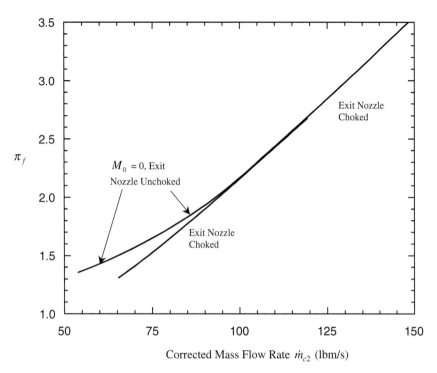

Fig. 7.E10 AAF Engine fan operating line.

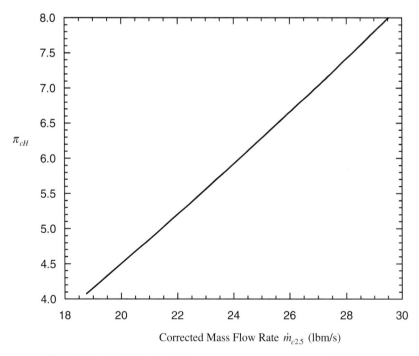

Fig. 7.E11 AAF Engine high-pressure compressor operating line.

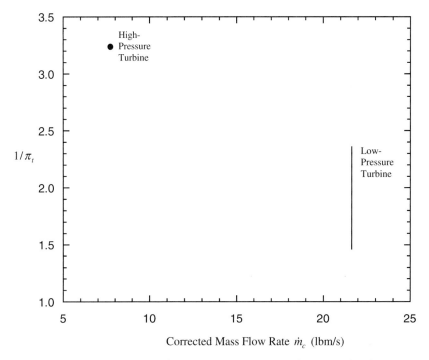

Fig. 7.E12   AAF Engine high- and low-pressure turbine operating lines.

7.4.4   The Road Ahead

The transition process is now complete. All of the information necessary to execute the design of the individual AAF Engine components has either been assembled or is readily available. The remainder of Part II of this textbook is devoted exclusively to this task. Our main goals from this point on will be to design the key AAF Engine components and to identify any issues that might require challenging technological advances, or even necessitate an entirely new design point iteration.

Reference

[1]Treager, I. E., *Aircraft Gas Turbine Engine Technology*, 3rd ed., McGraw–Hill, New York, 1999.

8
Engine Component Design: Rotating Turbomachinery

8.1 Concept

The general purpose of rotating machines is to exchange mechanical energy with a flowing stream of fluid. The turbomachines found in airbreathing engines take many forms, such as fans, compressors, turbines, free or power turbines, and propellers. The design of these devices is one of the most critical and difficult steps in the engine development process, for no progress with real hardware can be made until all of the rotating components are in working order.

Although this chapter begins with the consideration of aerodynamics, durability or life issues are equally important. Because turbomachines are expected to run for thousands of hours without major overhaul, it follows that they cannot be based upon aerodynamic requirements alone. A successful machine results only from a highly iterative series of thoughtful aerodynamic, heat transfer, materials, and structural evaluations. The best solution to each design problem effectively couples respect for the important factors together in the correct proportions. The design tools of this chapter will clearly illustrate the interdependency of aerodynamics and structures. Moreover, the push and pull of the requirements of components attached to the same shaft will also be demonstrated.

This chapter will be flirting with the most impenetrable and "proprietary" domains of the engine companies because of their heavy investment in these technologies, as well as the great competitive advantages that accrue to proven superiority. It is well to take note of the corollary, namely, that the enormous capabilities they possess, including sophisticated computer programs, technical data, and seasoned experience, are virtually impossible to reproduce in the classroom. Indeed, many experts have spent their entire careers learning to deal with one or two facets of the design problems of rotating turbomachinery.

Because there is no single, absolute answer to each question, this is also an area where judgment and personal preferences can strongly influence the outcome. It is therefore true that many decisions are based upon feelings that are not completely articulated.

How can the spirit of this process be captured in a basic design course and still make it possible to create quantitative solutions? Our hopes rest on the design tools that express the primary physical phenomena at work. These tools are simple enough to be rapidly applied, yet they contain enough complexity that final choices must be based on judgment. Those who participate in this process will be impressed with their accomplishments and awed by what must take place in the "real world."

The study of rotating machinery is not new, and many excellent books and reports have been written for the benefit of students and practicing professionals (see Refs. 1–9). Because it is impossible to reproduce even the smallest fraction of that information in one chapter, the readers are urged to use the open literature generously in their work. Special attention is drawn to Refs. 1 and 2, which are textbooks covering turbomachinery and many related propulsion design subjects. They also contain excellent lists of references for those who wish to listen directly to the masters.

To restrain the growth of this textbook, material on such nonaxial turbomachinery components as centrifugal compressors, folded combustors, and radial turbines has not been included. These devices play an important role in propulsion, particularly in small engines, and can be a part of the best design solution. References 2 and 8–11 will provide a starting point for their study.

Finally, when discussing the parts of compressors and turbines, one finds a proliferation of terminology in the open literature. In particular, the stationary airfoils, which are usually suspended from the outer case, are frequently referred to as stators, vanes, or nozzles, whereas the rotating airfoils, which are usually attached to an internal disk, are often called rotors or blades. We have attempted to use uniform, generic terms, but great care is advised as you move through this thicket.

8.2 Design Tools

This material outlines the development and summarizes the results for several key building blocks used in the design of axial flow rotating machines. These tools are consistent with those used throughout this textbook in the sense that they correctly represent the dominant physical phenomena. The results will therefore faithfully reproduce the main trends of the real world, as well as numbers that are in the right ballpark, but without the excessive costs that accompany extreme accuracy. An additional benefit of this approach is an analytical transparency that leads to clearer understanding and sounder reasoning.

These analyses provide all of the procedures required to reach usable results. Their development draws heavily on the material found in Ref. 11. This includes, in particular, the compressor and turbine nomenclature and velocity diagram notation, both of which are consistent with that found in the standard turbomachinery literature, and with the detailed axial flow compressor and turbine design programs of AEDsys designated, respectively, as COMPR and TURBN.

8.2.1 Fan and Compressor Aerodynamics

8.2.1.1 Axial flow, constant axial velocity, repeating stage, repeating row, mean-line design. The primary goal of this section is to describe a method that will allow you to rapidly create advanced fan and compressor stage designs and automatically generate very reliable initial estimates for the truly enormous amounts of technical data required as input for COMPR. This shortcut is the critical ingredient that allows you to make your own design choices, while revealing the essence of how fan and compressor stages behave. If the method strikes you as outrageously effortless, you may find comfort in the fact that similar methods are used as the starting point in industry.

The basic building block of the aerodynamic design of axial flow compressors is the cascade, an endlessly repeating array of airfoils (Fig. 8.1) that results from the conceptual "unwrapping" of the stationary (stator) or rotating (rotor) airfoils. Each

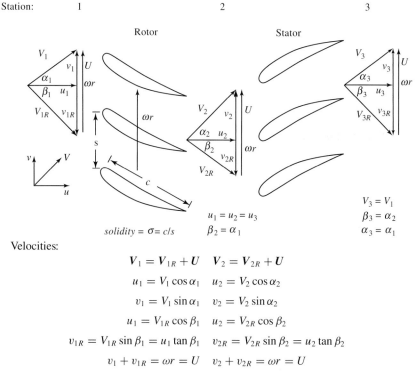

Station: 1   2   3

Fig. 8.1   Repeating row compressor stage nomenclature.

cascade passage acts as a small diffuser and is said to be well designed or behaved when it provides a large static pressure rise without incurring unacceptable total pressure losses and/or flow instabilities caused by shock waves and/or boundary layer separation. The art of compressor design is the ability to find the cascade parameters and airfoil contours that make this happen.

Once a good airfoil cascade has been found, a logical next step would be to place it in series with a rotor that is made up of the same airfoils in mirror image about the axial direction, moving at a speed that maintains the original relative inlet flow angle. In this manner a compressor stage (that is, stator plus rotor) is generated from a cascade, and, likewise, placing similar stages in series may create a multistage compressor. The focus of this section, therefore, is upon the design of well-behaved compressor stages made up of "repeating" (that is, mirror image) rows of airfoils. Finally, the analysis will be based on the behavior of the flow at the average or mean radius. With this introduction in mind, the development of design tools for compressors follows.

Diffusion factor

A commonly employed measure of the degree of difficulty when designing well-behaved compressor cascades or airfoil rows is the "diffusion factor":

$$D \doteq \left(1 - \frac{V_e}{V_i}\right) + \frac{v_i - v_e}{2\sigma V_i} \tag{8.1}$$

where the subscripts i and e correspond to the inlet and exit, respectively. The diffusion factor is an analytical expression directly related to the size of the adverse pressure gradient to be encountered by the boundary layer on the suction surface of the cascade airfoil. It is therefore a measure of the danger of boundary layer separation and unacceptable losses or flow instability. The two terms of Eq. (8.1) clearly embody the physics of the situation, the first representing the average static pressure rise in the airfoil channel and the second the additional static pressure rise along the suction surface due to curvature or lift.

The goal of the designer is to be able to maintain high aerodynamic efficiency at large values of D because that allows the number of stages (that is, lower V_e/V_i) and/or airfoils (that is, lower σ) to be reduced. Thus, the ability to successfully design for large values of D is a sign of technological advancement and the basis for superior compressors. Even in this world of sophisticated computation, fan and compressor designers use the diffusion factor almost universally as the measuring rod of technological capability. Any reasonably competent contemporary organization is able to cope with values of D up to 0.5. Values of D up to 0.6 are possible if you can count on state-of-the-art aerodynamic understanding and design tools, and extensive development testing.

A final note of interest about the diffusion factor is that it is based on the flow geometry alone and is therefore silent about the geometrical details of the airfoil itself. This provides a great convenience that makes much analytical progress possible. In fact, what is unique about the approach employed here is that the diffusion factor equation is used as a constraining relationship from the start, rather than as a feasibility check at the end.

Assumptions

1) Repeating row/repeating airfoil cascade geometry ($\alpha_1 = \beta_2 = \alpha_3, \beta_1 = \alpha_2 = \beta_3$).

2) Two-dimensional flow (that is, no property variation or velocity component normal to the flow).

3) Constant axial velocity ($u_1 = u_2 = u_3$).

4) Stage polytropic efficiency e_c represents stage losses.

5) Constant mean radius.

6) Calorically perfect gas with known γ_c and R_c.

Analysis. Please note that the assumption of constant axial velocity, which is consistent with modern design practice, greatly simplifies the analysis because every velocity triangle in Fig. 8.1 has the same base dimension.

Given: $D, M_1, \gamma, \sigma, e_c$.

1) Conservation of mass:

$$\dot{m} = \rho_1 u_1 A_1 = \rho_2 u_2 A_2 = \rho_3 u_3 A_3$$

or

$$\rho_1 A_1 = \rho_2 A_2 = \rho_3 A_3 \tag{8.2}$$

2) Repeating row constraint:
Since $\beta_2 = \alpha_1$, then

$$v_{2R} = v_1 = \omega r - v_2 \tag{8.3}$$

or

$$v_1 + v_2 = \omega r \tag{8.4}$$

Incidentally, since $\beta_3 = \alpha_2$, then $v_{3R} = v_2$, and

$$v_3 = \omega r - v_{3R} = \omega r - v_2$$

then by Eq. (8.3)

$$v_3 = v_1$$

and the velocity conditions at the stage exit are indeed identical to those at the stage entrance, as shown in Fig. 8.1.

3) Diffusion factor (D):

Since both

$$D = \left(1 - \frac{V_{2R}}{V_{1R}}\right) + \frac{v_{1R} - v_{2R}}{2\sigma V_{1R}} = \left(1 - \frac{V_3}{V_2}\right) + \frac{v_2 - v_3}{2\sigma V_2}$$

and

$$D = \left(1 - \frac{\cos \alpha_2}{\cos \alpha_1}\right) + \left(\frac{\tan \alpha_2 - \tan \alpha_1}{2\sigma}\right) \cos \alpha_2 \tag{8.5}$$

are the same for both the stator and rotor airfoil cascades, they need be evaluated only once for the entire stage. Rearranging Eq. (8.5) to solve for α_2, it is found that

$$\cos \alpha_2 = \frac{2\sigma(1 - D)\Gamma + \sqrt{\Gamma^2 + 1 - 4\sigma^2(1 - D)^2}}{\Gamma^2 + 1} \tag{8.6}$$

where

$$\Gamma \doteq \frac{2\sigma + \sin \alpha_1}{\cos \alpha_1} \tag{8.7}$$

In words, Eq. (8.6–7) shows that there is only *one* value of α_2 that corresponds to the chosen values of D and σ for each α_1. Thus, the entire flowfield geometry is dictated by those choices.

4) Degree of reaction ($^\circ R_c$):

Another common sense measure of good compressor stage design is the degree of reaction

$$^\circ R_c = \frac{\text{rotor static temperature rise}}{\text{stage static temperature rise}} = \frac{T_2 - T_1}{T_3 - T_1} \tag{8.8}$$

For a perfect gas with $\rho \approx constant$,

$$^\circ R_c = \frac{T_2 - T_1}{T_3 - T_1} \approx \left[\frac{P_2 - P_1}{P_3 - P_1}\right]_{\rho \approx const} \tag{8.9}$$

In the general case it is desirable to have $^\circ R_c$ in the vicinity of 0.5 because the stator and rotor rows will then "share the burden" of the stage static temperature rise, and neither will benefit at the expense of the other. This is another way of avoiding excessively large values of D.

A special and valuable characteristic of repeating stage, repeating row compressor stages is that $°R_c$ must be exactly 0.5 because of the forced similarity of the rotor and stator velocity triangles. You can confirm this by inspecting Eq. (8.8) and recognizing that the kinetic energy drop and hence the static temperature rise are the same in the rotor and stator.

5) Stage total temperature increase (ΔT_t) and ratio (T_{t3}/T_{t1}):

From the Euler pump and turbine equation with constant radius

$$h_{t3} - h_{t1} = \frac{\omega r}{g_c}(v_2 - v_1)$$

which, for a calorically perfect gas, becomes

$$c_p(T_{t3} - T_{t1}) = \frac{\omega r}{g_c}(v_2 - v_1) \tag{8.10}$$

whence, using Eq. (8.4)

$$c_p(T_{t3} - T_{t1}) = \frac{1}{g_c}(v_2 + v_1)(v_2 - v_1) = \frac{(v_2^2 - v_1^2)}{g_c} = \frac{(V_2^2 - V_1^2)}{g_c}$$

Thus

$$\Delta T_t = T_{t3} - T_{t1} = \frac{V_2^2 - V_1^2}{c_p g_c} = \frac{V_1^2}{c_p g_c}\left(\frac{\cos^2 \alpha_1}{\cos^2 \alpha_2} - 1\right)$$

or

$$\frac{\Delta T_t}{V_1^2/c_p g_c} = \frac{\cos^2 \alpha_1}{\cos^2 \alpha_2} - 1 \tag{8.11}$$

Since $V^2 = M^2 \gamma R g_c T$ and $T_t = T[1 + (\gamma - 1)M^2/2]$, then the stage temperature ratio is given by

$$\tau_s \doteq \frac{T_{t3}}{T_{t1}} = \frac{(\gamma - 1)M_1^2}{1 + (\gamma - 1)M_1^2/2}\left(\frac{\cos^2 \alpha_1}{\cos^2 \alpha_2} - 1\right) + 1 \tag{8.12}$$

This relationship reveals that, for a given flow geometry, the stage total temperature rise is proportional to T_{t1} and M_1^2.

6) Stage pressure ratio:

From Eq. (4.9b-CPG)

$$\pi_s = \frac{P_{t3}}{P_{t1}} = \left(\frac{T_{t3}}{T_{t1}}\right)^{\gamma e_c/(\gamma - 1)} = (\tau_s)^{\gamma e_c/(\gamma - 1)} \tag{8.13}$$

7) Stage efficiency:

From Eq. (4.9b-CPG)

$$\eta_s = \frac{T_{t3i} - T_{t1}}{T_{t3} - T_{t1}} = \frac{\pi_s^{(\gamma-1)/\gamma} - 1}{\tau_s - 1} = \frac{\tau_s^{e_c} - 1}{\tau_s - 1} \tag{8.14}$$

8) Stage exit Mach number:
Since $V_3 = V_1$ and $V^2 = M^2 \gamma R g_c T$, then

$$\frac{M_3}{M_1} = \sqrt{\frac{T_1}{T_3}} = \sqrt{\frac{1}{\tau_s\left[1 + (\gamma - 1)M_1^2/2\right] - (\gamma - 1)M_1^2/2}} \leq 1 \qquad (8.15)$$

Since $T_3/T_1 > 1$, then $M_3/M_1 < 1$, and the Mach number gradually decreases as the flow progresses through the compressor, causing compressibility effects to become less important.

9) Wheel speed/inlet velocity ratio ($\omega r/V_1$):
One of the most important trigonometric relationships is that between the mean wheel speed (ωr) and the total cascade entrance velocity (V_1) because the latter is usually known and, as you shall find in Sec. 8.2.3, the former places demands upon the materials and structures that can be difficult to meet.
Since

$$V_1 = u_1/\cos\alpha_1 \quad \text{and} \quad \omega r = v_2 + v_1 = u_1(\tan\alpha_1 + \tan\alpha_2)$$

then

$$\omega r/V_1 = \cos\alpha_1 (\tan\alpha_1 + \tan\alpha_2) \qquad (8.16)$$

10) Inlet relative Mach number (M_{1R}):
Since

$$V_1 = M_1 a_1 = u_1/\cos\alpha_1 \quad \text{and} \quad V_{1R} = M_{1R} a_1 = u_1/\cos\alpha_2$$

then

$$\frac{M_{1R}}{M_1} = \frac{\cos\alpha_1}{\cos\alpha_2} \qquad (8.17)$$

Since $\alpha_2 > \alpha_1$, then $M_{1R} > M_1$ and M_1 must be chosen carefully in order to avoid excessively high inlet relative Mach numbers.

General solution. The behavior of every imaginable repeating row compressor stage with given values of D, M_1, γ, σ, and e_c can now be computed. This is done by selecting any initial value for α_1 and using the following sequence of equations expressed as functional relationships:

$$\alpha_2 = f(D, \sigma, \alpha_1) \qquad (8.6)$$

$$\Delta\alpha = \alpha_2 - \alpha_1$$

$$\tau_s = f(M_1, \gamma, \alpha_1, \alpha_2) \qquad (8.12)$$

$$\pi_s = f(\tau_s, \gamma, e_c) \qquad (8.13)$$

$$\omega r/V_1 = f(\alpha_1, \alpha_2) \qquad (8.16)$$

$$M_{1R}/M_1 = f(\alpha_1, \alpha_2) \qquad (8.17)$$

Note that only τ_s and π_s depend upon M_1 and that the process may be repeated to cover the entire range of reasonable values of α_1.

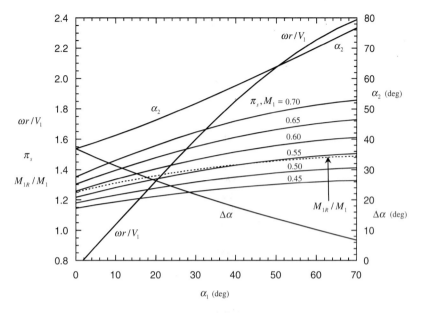

Fig. 8.2a   Repeating row compressor stage ($D = 0.5$, $\sigma = 1$, and $e_c = 0.9$).

These calculations have been carried out for $D = 0.5$; $M_1 = 0.45, 0.5, 0.55$, 0.6, 0.65, and 0.7; $\gamma = 1.4$; $\sigma = 1.0$; $e_c = 0.9$; and $0 < \alpha_1 < 70$ deg, and the results are presented in Fig. 8.2a. The most notable characteristics of these data are that the most direct way to increase π_s is to increase M_1 (or V_1), as indicated by Eqs. (8.12) and (8.13); that in order to operate at higher values of α_1 and π_s higher values of ωr are required; and that the ratio M_{1R}/M_1 is fairly constant at 1.4, so that M_1 must be less than 0.7 in order to avoid supersonic relative flow into the rotor.

Figures 8.2b and 8.2c are intended to demonstrate the influence of the other important design choices, D and σ, upon repeating row compressor stage behavior. Given a constant degree of aerodynamic and mechanical difficulty (that is, M_1, V_1, and ωr or $\omega r/V_1$ fixed), these diagrams show that increasing either D or σ allows a greater π_s and therefore the possibility of fewer stages. This is definitely in accord with intuition, although the improvement from equal percentage increases certainly favors D over σ.

The following two specific numerical examples illustrate the use of this method and are based on the parameters of Fig. 8.2a:

Example 1:
Given: $M_1 = 0.6$, $a_1 = 1200$ ft/s, and $\omega r = 1000$ ft/s.
Then,

$$\frac{\omega r}{V_1} = \frac{\omega r}{a_1 M_1} = 1.39$$

$$\alpha_1 = 22 \text{ deg} \quad \Delta\alpha = 25 \text{ deg}$$

$$\alpha_2 = 47 \text{ deg} \quad \pi_s = 1.42$$

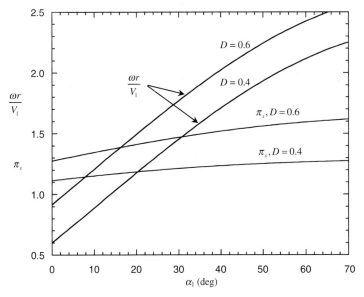

Fig. 8.2b   Repeating row compressor stage—variation with D.

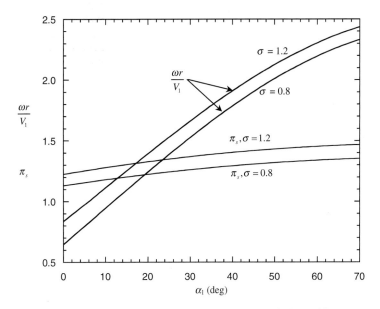

Fig. 8.2c   Repeating row compressor stage—variation with σ.

Example 2:
Given: $M_1/\alpha_1 = 0.5/40$ deg and $0.6/50$ deg, and $a_1 = 1150$ ft/s.
Then,

M_1	α_1, deg	α_2, deg	$\omega r/V_1$	$\omega r/a_1$	π_s
0.5	40	58	1.852	0.926	1.351
0.6	50	64	2.075	1.245	1.558

Because a_1 is fixed, the cost of the higher π_s is greatly increased ωr (that is, $1.245 \div 0.926 = 1.344$).

Because the overall total temperature rise to be supplied by a fan or compressor is an output of the cycle analysis, an initial estimate of the required number of stages could be made by dividing it by the possible total temperature increase per stage. Fortunately, the repeating row compressor stage analysis provides that information. Repetitive application of Eq. (8.11) reveals that the right-hand side is approximately 0.9 for $10 < \alpha_1 < 70$ when $D = 0.5$ and $\sigma = 1$. Because V_1 is of the order of 700 ft/s, then Eq. (8.11) shows that ΔT_t is of the order of $70°$R. You can now use this analysis to estimate the ΔT_t that can be achieved with your choice of cascade design parameters.

8.2.1.2 Recapitulation.
The repeating row, repeating stage compressor design procedure has been integrated into the COMPR program of AEDsys in order to serve as the first step in the design process. You will quickly find that this has several important benefits, including the ability to quickly explore the entire range of design parameters and make promising initial choices, and then to transfer all of the input that the complete COMPR computation requires. The complete COMPR computation detailed in Ref. 11 accurately mimics the mean line compressor design techniques used in the industry and allows every airfoil row to be separately selected. You will be pleasantly surprised, as we were, to discover that the initial repeating row, repeating stage compressor design will require only minor and entirely transparent "tweaking" in order to produce a worthy result that meets all of the imposed constraints.

8.2.1.3 Airfoil geometry.
After the repeating row compressor stage flow field geometry has been selected, it remains to design the physical airfoils that will make it happen. The necessary nomenclature for this step is shown in Fig. 8.3 with the inlet flow angle shown at other than the design point.

A useful method for determining the metal angles γ_1 and γ_2 at the design point is to take $\gamma_1 = \alpha_1$ and use Carter's rule[3,11]

$$\delta_c = \frac{\gamma_1 - \gamma_2}{4\sqrt{\sigma}} \tag{8.18}$$

to compute $\gamma_2 = \alpha_2 - \delta_c$. Thus, for the airfoil cascade of Example 2

$$\gamma_1 = \alpha_1 = 50 \text{ deg} \quad \text{and} \quad \gamma_2 = \alpha_2 - \delta_c = 64 - \frac{50 - \gamma_2}{4\sqrt{1}}$$

whence $\gamma_2 = 68.7$ deg.

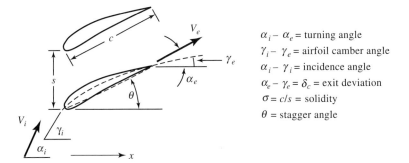

$\alpha_i - \alpha_e$ = turning angle
$\gamma_i - \gamma_e$ = airfoil camber angle
$\alpha_i - \gamma_i$ = incidence angle
$\alpha_e - \gamma_e = \delta_c$ = exit deviation
$\sigma = c/s$ = solidity
θ = stagger angle

Fig. 8.3   Cascade airfoil nomenclature.

8.2.1.4 Flowpath dimensions. Sufficient information is now available to draw a meaningful sketch of the fan or compressor flowpath. The necessary procedures are described next. An entire compressor may now be created by placing a sufficient number n of repeating row stages in succession so that $n[\Delta T_t]_{stage} \geq [\Delta T_t]_{compressor}$. To maintain the consistency of the original design, it is best to retain the same values of V_1 and α_1 (or $u_1 = V_1 \cos\alpha_1$) for every stage at the mean radius.

A realistic estimate of the ratio of the compressor inlet area to exit area A_2/A_3, shown in Fig. 8.4, can be made by first noting that

$$\frac{\rho_3}{\rho_2} \approx \frac{\rho_{t3}}{\rho_{t2}} = \frac{P_{t3}}{P_{t2}}\frac{T_{t2}}{T_{t3}} = \left(\frac{T_{t3}}{T_{t2}}\right)^{\frac{\gamma e_c}{\gamma-1}}\frac{T_{t2}}{T_{t3}} = \left(\frac{T_{t3}}{T_{t2}}\right)^{\frac{1-\gamma(1-e_c)}{\gamma-1}} = \left(\frac{P_{t3}}{P_{t2}}\right)^{\frac{1-\gamma(1-e_c)}{\gamma e_c}}$$

and then, because the mass flow rate and axial velocity are constant, using Eq. (8.2) with $e_c = 0.9$ and $\gamma = 1.4$ to show that

$$\frac{A_2}{A_3} = \frac{\rho_3}{\rho_2} \approx \left(\frac{T_{t3}}{T_{t2}}\right)^{2.15} = \left(1 + \frac{n\Delta T_t}{T_{t2}}\right)^{2.15} = \left(\frac{P_{t3}}{P_{t2}}\right)^{0.68} \tag{8.19}$$

Equation (8.19) reveals that the throughflow area A diminishes continuously and rapidly from the front of the compressor to the back. This is the origin of the characteristically shrinking shape of the compressor annulus, and the sometimes surprisingly small heights of the airfoils in the final stage (see Table 7.E1).

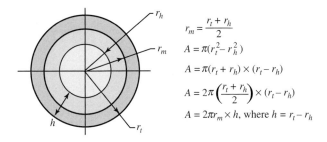

$$r_m = \frac{r_t + r_h}{2}$$

$$A = \pi(r_t^2 - r_h^2)$$

$$A = \pi(r_t + r_h) \times (r_t - r_h)$$

$$A = 2\pi\left(\frac{r_t + r_h}{2}\right) \times (r_t - r_h)$$

$$A = 2\pi r_m \times h, \text{ where } h = r_t - r_h$$

Fig. 8.4   Throughflow annulus dimensions.

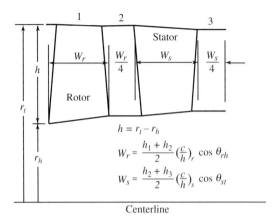

Fig. 8.5   Typical axial dimensions of a compressor stage.

Because the foregoing analysis provides T_{ti}, P_{ti}, and M_i at the mean radius for any station i, the mass flow parameter, as ever, affords the most direct means for determining the throughflow annulus area, namely,

$$A_i = \frac{\dot{m}\sqrt{T_{ti}}}{MFP\, P_{ti} \cos\alpha_i} \tag{8.20}$$

The throughflow area can be calculated using Eq. (8.20), and the mean radius is tied to the required rotor speed at the mean radius ωr_m. The designer can either select ω and calculate the required mean radius r_m, or vice versa. Then the hub radius r_h and tip radius r_t are calculated from the flow area and mean radius. In some calculations, the designer may prefer instead to select the ratio of the hub radius to the tip radius (r_h/r_t) or the blade height $(h = r_t - r_h)$.

Figure 8.5 shows the variation in the throughflow area and the associated dimensions of the flowpath for a typical stage. Blade axial widths (W_r and W_s) of a stage can be calculated for a selected chord-to-height ratio for the rotor and stator blades $[(c/h)_r$ and $(c/h)_s]$ and the blade stagger angle at the rotor hub (θ_{rh}) and the stator tip (θ_{st}) using

$$W_r = \frac{h_1 + h_2}{2}\left(\frac{c}{h}\right)_r \cos\theta_{rh} \tag{8.21a}$$

$$W_s = \frac{h_2 + h_3}{2}\left(\frac{c}{h}\right)_s \cos\theta_{st} \tag{8.21b}$$

As sketched in Fig. 8.5, the spacing between the blade rows can be estimated as one-quarter the width of the preceding blade row. More accurate calculation of this spacing requires analysis beyond the scope of the textbook.

The methods just described have been incorporated into the AEDsys software, and form the basis for the cross-section and blade profile outline drawings within COMPR.

8.2.1.5 Radial variation. One look at the longer fan, compressor, and turbine airfoils in engines reveals that they are not simple radial structures, but they
are "twisted" from hub to tip (that is, the camber and stagger continuously change
with radius). It is natural to inquire whether this is the result of some primary flow
phenomenon or is merely a designer flourish; indeed, it is the former.

The underlying cause is the inevitable fact that the rotating airfoils are subject to solid body motion and therefore have a rotational speed that increases
linearly with radius. If one wishes to do an amount of work on the fluid passing
through a stage that is independent of radius, the Euler pump and turbine equation
[Eq. (8.10)] reveal that less change in tangential velocity or "turning" of the flow
will be required as the radius increases. Moreover, the static pressure must increase
with radius in order to maintain the radial equilibrium because of the tangential
velocity or "swirling" of the flow. All of the airfoil and flow properties must,
therefore, vary with radius.

The main features of the radial variation of the flow in the axial space between
the rows of airfoils are accounted for in the following analysis, which summarizes the original, now classical, approach profitably employed by turbomachinery
designers before computational methods became widely available (see Ref. 3).

Assumptions
1) Constant losses ($s = $ constant with respect to radius).
2) Constant work ($h_t = $ constant).
3) No circumferential variations.
4) No radial velocity.

Analysis. These equations are valid at station 1, 2, or 3 at any radius.
1) Differential enthalpy equation:
From the definition of total (stagnation) enthalpy with no radial velocity, we can
write

$$dh_t = dh + \frac{d(u^2 + v^2)}{2g_c} \tag{i}$$

The Gibbs Equation can be written as $T\,ds = dh - dP/\rho$. With $s = $ constant in
the radial direction, this becomes

$$dh = \frac{dP}{\rho} \tag{ii}$$

Combining Eqs. (i) and (ii) gives

$$dh_t = \frac{dP}{\rho} + \frac{d(u^2 + v^2)}{2g_c}$$

(With h_t and ρ constant this equation becomes the well-known Bernoulli equation.)
Rewriting the preceding equation with respect to the radial variation gives

$$\frac{dh_t}{dr} = \frac{1}{\rho}\frac{dP}{dr} + \frac{1}{g_c}\left(u\frac{du}{dr} + v\frac{dv}{dr}\right) \tag{iii}$$

For radial equilibrium of the fluid element, the pressure gradient in the radial
direction must equal the centrifugal acceleration, or

$$\frac{dP}{dr} = \frac{\rho v^2}{r g_c} \tag{iv}$$

A general form of the enthalpy radial distribution equation is obtained by combining Eqs. (iii) and (iv), giving

$$\frac{dh_t}{dr} = \frac{1}{g_c}\left(u\frac{du}{dr} + v\frac{dv}{dr} + \frac{v^2}{r} \right) \qquad (8.22)$$

This equation prescribes the relationship between the radial variation of the three variables: h_t, u, and v. The designer may specify the radial variation of any two, and Eq. (8.22) allows the radial variation of the third variable to be determined.

For constant work, h_t is constant with respect to radius, and Eq. (8.22) becomes

$$u\frac{du}{dr} + v\frac{dv}{dr} + \frac{v^2}{r} = 0 \qquad (8.23)$$

In this case, if the radial variation of either u or v is prescribed, Eq. (8.23) allows the other to be determined. The traditional approach is to specify the swirl velocity v, as follows.

2) Swirl distributions:

We assume the following general swirl distribution at entry and exit to the rotor

$$v_1 = a\left(\frac{r}{r_m}\right)^n - b\frac{r_m}{r} \quad \text{and} \quad v_2 = a\left(\frac{r}{r_m}\right)^n + b\frac{r_m}{r} \qquad (8.24)$$

where a and b are constants. From the Euler pump equation [Eq. (8.10)], the work per unit mass flow is

$$\Delta h_t = \frac{\omega r(v_2 - v_1)}{g_c} = \frac{2b\omega r_m}{g_c} \qquad (8.25)$$

which is independent of radius. The constant b in Eq. (8.24) is determined from the enthalpy rise across the rotor using Eq. (8.25) and, as will be shown next, the constant a in Eq. (8.24) is related to the degree of reaction at the mean radius r_m. Three cases of the swirl distribution as considered next correspond to $n = -1$, $n = 0$, and $n = 1$.

Free vortex swirl distribution ($n = -1$).   Equation (8.24) becomes

$$v_1 = (a - b)\frac{r_m}{r} \quad \text{and} \quad v_2 = (a + b)\frac{r_m}{r}. \qquad (8.26)$$

Because v varies inversely with radius, this is known as "free-vortex" flow. Thus, if the stator airfoils preceding station 1 produce the flow $v_1 r = v_{1m} r_m$ and the rotor airfoils modify the flow to $v_2 r = v_{2m} r_m$ at station 2, then the Euler equation confirms that this is a constant work. Furthermore, substitution of the free vortex swirl distribution into Eq. (8.23) gives

$$\frac{du}{dr} = 0$$

which requires that the axial velocity u not vary with radius. Equation (8.26) also shows that, as long as r does not vary substantially from r_m (say $\pm 10\%$), the airfoil and flow properties will not vary much from the original mean-line design. Using Eq. (8.8) for a repeating stage ($v_3 = v_1$), the degree of reaction is given by

$$^\circ R_c = 1 - \frac{a}{\omega r_m} \left(\frac{r_m}{r}\right)^2 \tag{8.27}$$

where the constant a in Eq. (8.26) is obtained by evaluating the preceding expression at the mean radius. Thus

$$a = \omega r_m \left(1 - {}^\circ R_{cm}\right) \tag{8.28}$$

where $^\circ R_{cm}$ is the degree of reaction at the mean radius.

Free vortex aerodynamics played a prominent role in the history of turbomachinery. Before high-speed computation became commonplace, this approach enabled designers to understand and cope with the most prominent features of radial variation (see Refs. 3, 7, and 10).

Exponential swirl distribution ($n = 0$).   Equation (8.24) becomes

$$v_1 = a - b\frac{r_m}{r} \quad \text{and} \quad v_2 = a + b\frac{r_m}{r} \tag{8.29}$$

Substitution of the exponential swirl distribution into Eq. (8.23) and integration gives (Ref. 11)

$$u_1^2 = u_{1m}^2 - 2\left(a^2 \ln \frac{r}{r_m} + \frac{ab}{r/r_m} - ab\right) \tag{8.30a}$$

$$u_2^2 = u_{2m}^2 - 2\left(a^2 \ln \frac{r}{r_m} - \frac{ab}{r/r_m} + ab\right) \tag{8.30b}$$

For the case where $u_{1m} = u_{2m}$, the degree of reaction for a repeating stage ($V_3 = V_1$) is given by (see Ref. 11)

$$^\circ R_c = 1 + \frac{a}{\omega r_m} \left\{1 - 2\left(\frac{r_m}{r}\right)\right\} \tag{8.31}$$

First-power swirl distribution ($n = 1$).   Equation (8.24) becomes

$$v_1 = a\frac{r}{r_m} - b\frac{r_m}{r} \quad \text{and} \quad v_2 = a\frac{r}{r_m} + b\frac{r_m}{r} \tag{8.32}$$

Substitution of the exponential swirl distribution into Eq. (8.23) and integration gives (Ref. 11)

$$u_1^2 = u_{1m}^2 - 2\left\{a^2 \left(\frac{r}{r_m}\right)^2 + ab \ln \frac{r}{r_m} - a^2\right\} \tag{8.33a}$$

$$u_2^2 = u_{2m}^2 - 2\left\{a^2 \left(\frac{r}{r_m}\right)^2 - ab \ln \frac{r}{r_m} - a^2\right\} \tag{8.33b}$$

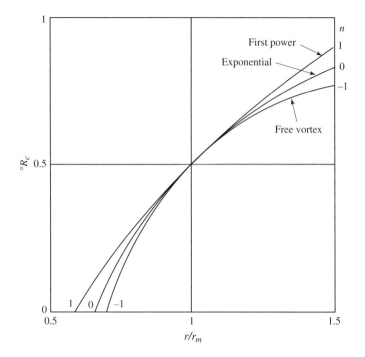

Fig. 8.6   Radial variation of the degree of reaction.[11]

For the case where $u_{1m} = u_{2m}$, the degree of reaction for a repeating stage $(V_3 = V_1)$ is given by (see Ref. 11)

$$^\circ R_c = 1 + \frac{a}{\omega r_m} \left\{ 2 \ln \left(\frac{r}{r_m} \right) - 1 \right\} \tag{8.34}$$

Equations (8.27), (8.31), and (8.34) give the radial variation of the degree of reaction for the free-vortex, exponential, and first power swirl distributions, respectively, for repeating stages $(V_3 = V_1)$ with $u_{1m} = u_{2m}$. The value of the constant a is evaluated at the mean radius and is given by Eq. (8.28) for all three cases.

Consider the case where the degree of reaction at the mean radius is 0.5 ($a = \omega r_m / 2$). Results for this case from Eq. (8.27), (8.31), and (8.34) are plotted in Fig. 8.6 for the range $0.5 < r/r_m < 1.5$. These results show that it is more difficult to design rotor airfoils at $r < r_m$ and stator airfoils at $r > r_m$. In fact, because $^\circ R_c = 0$ at $r/r_m = 0.707$ for the free-vortex and at $r/r_m = 0.6065$ for the first-power swirl distributions, the rotor will actually experience accelerating flow for smaller radii, whereas this is never the case for the stator. For these reasons, modern compressor design has looked to non-free-vortex (nonconstant work) machines, but these are absolutely dependent upon large computers for their definition.

Table 8.1   Range of axial flow compressor design parameters

Parameter	Design range
Fan or low-pressure compressor	
ΔT_t per stage	60–100°F(35–55 K)
Pressure ratio for one stage	1.5–2.0
Pressure ratio for two stages	2.0–3.5
Pressure ratio for three stages	3.5–4.5
Inlet corrected mass flow rate	40–42 lbm/(s-ft^2)
	[195–205 kg/(s-m^2)]
Maximum tip speed	1400–1500 ft/s
	[427–457 m/s]
Diffusion factor	0.50–0.55
High-pressure compressor	
ΔT_t per stage	60–90°F (35–50 K)
Inlet corrected mass flow rate	36–38 lbm/(s-ft^2)
	[175–185 kg/(s-m^2)]
Hub/tip ratio at exit	0.90–0.92
Maximum rim speed at exit	1300–1500 ft/s
	[396–457 m/s]
Diffusion factor	0.50–0.55
Maximum exit temperature	1700–1800°R (945–1000 K)

The three swirl distributions have been incorporated into COMPR to allow you to explore this method for improving the degree of reaction of your designs at small radii. However, we recommend that you begin with the free-vortex distribution because that is most frequently referred to in the open literature.

8.2.1.6   Range of compressor design parameters.   Table 8.1 contains ranges of design parameters that can be used as guides in the preliminary design of axial flow compressors. Additional information about the shape and construction of axial flow compressors can be found by examining the AEDsys Engine Pictures files.

8.2.2   Turbine Aerodynamics

8.2.2.1   Constant axial velocity, adiabatic, selected Mach number, mean-line stage design.   The primary goal of this section is to develop a realistic turbine stage performance model that will reveal the behavior of the important aerodynamic and thermodynamic quantities and serve as an initial input to the complete numerical calculations of TURBN. This is in the same spirit as Sec. 8.2.1, but the design of turbines is different from that of compressors for a number of reasons, including the following:

1) The engine cycle performance models of this textbook require that the turbine stage entrance stator (a.k.a. inlet guide vane or nozzle) be choked and all other stator and rotor airfoil rows be unchoked.

2) The density of the working fluid changes dramatically, so that compressibility or Mach number effects must be included.

3) The turbine generates rather than absorbs power.

4) High inlet temperatures require that heat transfer and cooling be considered.

5) There are no wide-ranging rules for choosing turbine flow and airfoil geometries, such as the compressor diffusion factor.

It is not possible, therefore, to provide quite such comprehensive and general methods for turbine stages as has been done for compressor stages in Sec. 8.2.1. Nevertheless, it is possible to analyze, explore, and understand the behavior of a truly representative class of turbine stages, subject only to the assumption of constant axial velocity and enforcement of the stator and rotor airfoil relative exit Mach number constraints stated above. Because both of these conditions faithfully reflect the engine cycle assumptions of Chapters 4 and 5 and current design practice, the resulting solutions will closely resemble real designs.

A typical turbine stage and its velocity diagrams are shown in Fig. 8.7. The Euler turbine equation [Eq. (8.10)] gives the energy per unit mass flow exchanged between the rotor and the fluid for constant radius as

$$h_{t2} - h_{t3} = c_{pt}(T_{t2} - T_{t3}) = \frac{\omega r}{g_c}(v_2 + v_3) \qquad (8.35)$$

One can see from the velocity triangles of Fig. 8.7 that because of the large angle α_2 at the stator (nozzle) exit and the large turning possible in the rotor, the value of v_3 is often positive (positive α_3). As a result, the two swirl velocity terms on the right side of Eq. (8.35) add, giving larger power output.

Because of compressibility effects, the rotor degree of reaction $°R_t$ has a definition that is more suitable to turbines, namely, the rotor static enthalpy drop divided by the stage total enthalpy drop. For calorically perfect gases this becomes, in the

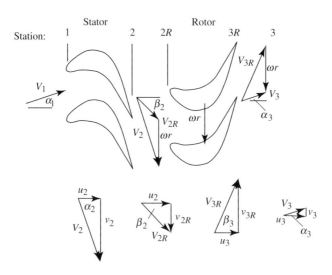

Fig. 8.7   Typical turbine stage and velocity diagrams.

turbine stage nomenclature of Fig. 8.6,

$$^{\circ}R_t = \frac{h_2 - h_3}{h_{t1} - h_{t3}} = \frac{T_2 - T_3}{T_{t1} - T_{t3}} \tag{8.36}$$

This definition retains the same physical insight as the equivalent compressor definition, while allowing the compressible flow turbine analysis to proceed smoothly despite large density changes. Please note that the static pressure drop is roughly proportional to the static temperature drop, and that the stator degree of reaction is approximately the difference between the rotor degree of reaction and one.

Assumptions
1) M_2 and M_{3R} are given.
2) Two-dimensional flow (that is, no property variation or velocity component normal to the flow).
3) Constant axial velocity ($u_1 = u_2 = u_3$).
4) Constant mean radius.
5) Adiabatic flow in the stator and rotor.
6) Calorically perfect gas with known γ_t and R_t.

The derivations that follow reduce the full turbine stage analysis of Sec. 9.5 in Ref. 11 by incorporating the preceding assumptions. Please note that making all velocities dimensionless by dividing them by the velocity $\sqrt{g_c c_{pt} T_{t1}}$ denoted as V' (a known quantity at the entrance of the stage that corresponds to the kinetic energy the fluid would reach if expanded to a vacuum, also referred to as the maximum or vacuum velocity) makes the equations more compact and the results more universal. We use the symbol Ω for the dimensionless rotor speed ωr. Thus,

$$V' = \sqrt{g_c c_{pt} T_{t1}} \tag{8.37}$$

$$\Omega = \frac{\omega r}{V'} \tag{8.38}$$

This approach cannot be used to design a series of stages as it was for compressors because the effect of steadily decreasing static temperatures, when combined with constant velocities, would eventually lead to supersonic velocities everywhere, contradicting one of the central design constraints. Thus, this method is primarily used to reveal the capabilities of individual turbine stages.

Analysis
1) Total velocity at station 2

$$\frac{V_2}{V'} = \sqrt{\frac{(\gamma_t - 1)M_2^2}{1 + (\gamma_t - 1)M_2^2/2}} \tag{8.39}$$

2) Stage axial velocity

$$\frac{u}{V'} = \frac{V_2}{V'} \cos \alpha_2 \tag{8.40}$$

3) Tangential velocity at station 2

$$\frac{v_2}{V'} = \frac{V_2}{V'} \sin \alpha_2 \tag{8.41}$$

4) Rotor relative tangential velocity at station 2

$$\frac{v_{2R}}{V'} = \frac{v_2}{V'} - \Omega \tag{8.42}$$

5) Rotor relative flow angle at station 2

$$\tan \beta_2 = \frac{v_{2R}/V'}{u/V'} \tag{8.43}$$

6) Rotor relative total temperature

$$\frac{T_{t2R}}{T_{t1}} = 1 + \Omega^2 \left(\frac{1}{2} - \frac{v_2/V'}{\Omega} \right) \tag{8.44}$$

7) Rotor relative flow angle at station 3

$$\tan \beta_3 = \sqrt{\frac{T_{t2R}/T_{t1}}{u^2/V'^2} \frac{(\gamma_t - 1)M_{3R}^2}{1 + (\gamma_t - 1)M_{3R}^2/2} - 1} \tag{8.45}$$

8) Rotor flow turning angle $= \beta_2 + \beta_3$ \hfill (8.46)

9) Tangential velocity at station 3

$$\frac{v_3}{V'} = \frac{u}{V'} \tan \beta_3 - \Omega \tag{8.47}$$

10) Stage exit flow angle

$$\tan \alpha_3 = \frac{v_3/V'}{u/V'} \tag{8.48}$$

11) Static temperature at station 3

$$\frac{T_3}{T_{t1}} = \frac{T_{t2R}/T_{t1}}{1 + (\gamma_t - 1)M_{3R}^2/2} \tag{8.49}$$

12) Stage temperature ratio

$$\tau_{ts} = \frac{T_{t3}}{T_{t1}} = \frac{T_3}{T_{t1}} + \frac{u^2}{V'^2} \frac{1 + \tan^2 \alpha_3}{2} \tag{8.50}$$

13) Rotor degree of reaction

$$^\circ R_t = \frac{v_{3R}^2 - v_{2R}^2}{2(1 - \tau_{ts})V'^2} \tag{8.51}$$

14) Rotor solidity based on axial chord c_x

$$\sigma_{xr} = \frac{c_x}{s} = \frac{2 \cos^2 \beta_3 (\tan \beta_2 + \tan \beta_3)}{Z} \tag{8.52}$$

General solution. We may now use this analysis to explore the behavior of turbine stages. The results will be more easily understood if, before proceeding, we circumscribe the results by means of three useful generalizations.

First, we must consider two different types of stages, namely those having either choked or unchoked stators. The former are required as the entrance stages for every turbine and will be represented in our computations by an M_2 of 1.1. The latter are required for all other turbine stages and will be represented in our computations by an M_2 of 0.9. Other supersonic or subsonic stator Mach numbers should be selected and evaluated by the reader.

Second, higher values of M_{3R} always improve stage performance, provided that some margin to avoid rotor choking is provided. The reader should also independently confirm this assertion. Consequently, M_{3R} is set equal to the highest practical value of 0.9 in our computations.

Third, the analysis lends itself well to the intuitively appealing examination of the variation of turbine stage properties for the expected ranges of α_2 and Ω. The open literature strongly suggests that the best performance is obtained when 60 deg $< \alpha_2 < 75$ deg (for example, Ref. 11, Sec. 9.5). The open literature also concludes that larger values of Ω are better, the upper limit being presently in the range $0.2 < \Omega < 0.3$. The ensuing computations will justify these observations. The computations use $\gamma_t = 1.30$ and $g_c c_{pt} = 7378$ ft^2/(s^2-°R), although the equations are formulated to allow you to choose any desired values.

General results. The results of the computations are presented in Figs. 8.8– 8.13. Their contents, and the corresponding consequences, will now be described in turn. To avoid unnecessary repetition and give the primary conclusion the emphasis it deserves, we begin by noting that *every* measure of aerodynamic and

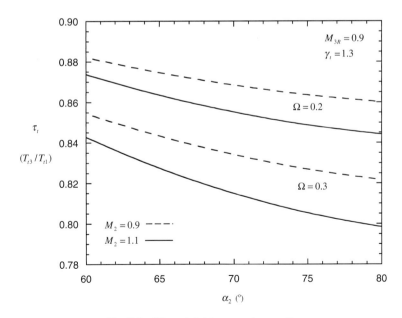

Fig. 8.8   Stage total temperature ratio.

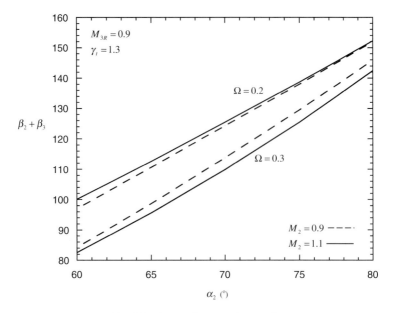

Fig. 8.9 Rotor flow turning angle.

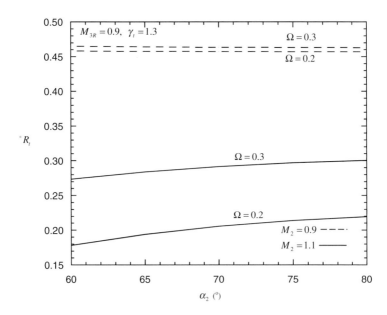

Fig. 8.10 Rotor degree of reaction.

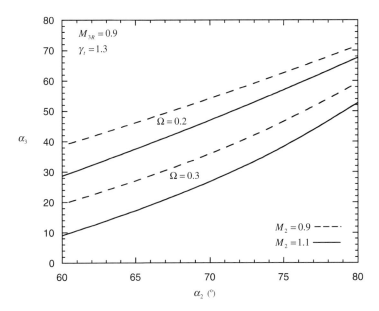

Fig. 8.11   Stage exit flow angle.

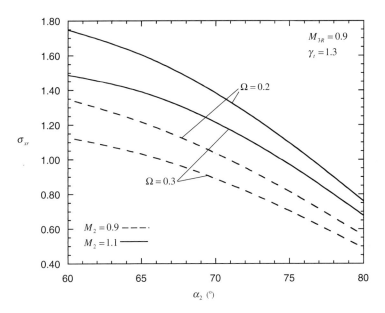

Fig. 8.12   Rotor solidity based on Z = 1.

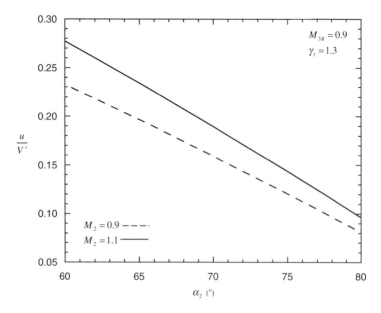

Fig. 8.13   Stage axial velocity.

thermodynamic performance for choked and unchoked stages is improved by increasing Ω. This agrees with the conventional wisdom of the open literature and explains the natural desire of the designer to increase wheel speed to the limit allowed by materials and structural technology. The remainder of the discussion therefore centers on the selection of α_2.

Figure 8.8. The preceding engine cycle selection process has already determined the required turbine temperature ratio. The goal of the designer is to accomplish the desired work extraction with the minimum number of stages, which is equivalent to finding the minimum practical value of τ_{ts}. The results presented in this figure demonstrate that τ_{ts} diminishes as α_2 increases over its expected range for both choked and unchoked stages. Furthermore, the results suggest that τ_{ts} values of less than 0.85 are attainable. If higher values of τ_{ts} are required, they can easily be provided by reducing α_2 and/or Ω. However, they also reveal that it is difficult to reach τ_{ts} values much higher than about 0.88 unless the Mach number assumptions are relaxed. This often motivates designers to shift the work split between the low- and high-pressure compressors so that each turbine stage is working hard and the total number of low- and high-pressure turbine stages is minimized.

Figures 8.9 and 8.10. Creating sound aerodynamics for the turbine airfoils is the heart of the matter for successful turbine design, just as it was for compressors. The fundamental issue is that of avoiding boundary layer separation along the rear portion of the rotor airfoil suction (convex) surface, where local Mach numbers and adverse pressure gradients are the greatest. The smallest amount of separation, even if reattachment follows, is disastrous for turbines because the large local Mach numbers and dynamic pressures cause unacceptable aerodynamic (drag) losses.

Unfortunately, as the results presented in Fig. 8.9 reveal, the tendency to increase stage work extraction by increasing α_2 is accompanied by a surprisingly rapid increase in the rotor flow turning angle. The streamline curvature effects within the passage between adjacent rotor airfoils caused by this flow turning are the principal contributor to the low suction surface static pressures and therefore to the potential for boundary layer separation, especially when the average Mach number is near sonic and shock waves can arise. Carefully tailoring the pressure distribution around the complete airfoil profile by means of sophisticated computational fluid dynamics (CFD) in order to resist separation despite very large rotor flow turning angles is one of the major achievements of modern turbine technology (see Ref. 1). However, because the CFD must account for such exquisite effects as the state of the boundary layer (for example, laminar, turbulent, or transitional), freestream turbulence levels, airfoil roughness, airfoil heat transfer, and locally transonic flow, the application of these methods is beyond the scope of this textbook.

Instead, we will capitalize on our general observation that skillful designers are able to define rotor airfoil profiles that do not separate for flow turning angles $(\beta_2 + \beta_3)$ up to 120–130 deg provided that the rotor degree of reaction is at least 0.20. That is, the average static temperature and pressure drop significantly across the rotor in order to partially counteract the adverse pressure gradient due to streamline curvature. Combining the results of Figs. 8.9 and 8.10, we see that these criteria are met as long as α_2 does not exceed approximately 70 deg, depending on the exact value of Ω. If some margin of safety is required, the selected value of α_2 should be further reduced.

It is worthwhile to pause at this point to consider the relationship between compressor and turbine airfoil design. In the compressor case, the adverse pressure gradient caused by streamline curvature on the rear portion of the suction surface is increased by the average static pressure increase across the row. Thus, the compressor diffusion factor D, which is based on a simple estimate of their sum, is a useful device. In the turbine case, it is reduced by the average static pressure drop across the row. The flow turning angles of compressor airfoils are therefore much smaller than turbine airfoils. Nevertheless, the streamline curvature effects exceed the average static pressure drops in modern turbine stages, and, contrary to the popular but naive notion, the flow runs "uphill" (pressure increasing) rather than "downhill" where it matters most. Turbine and compressor airfoil designers therefore actually share the adventure of working at the same limits allowed by nature.

Figure 8.11. The stage exit flow angle or swirl, which should be kept small whether or not another stage follows. In the former case, a small α_3 reduces the total flow turning for the succeeding inlet stator. In the latter case, the need for turbine exit guide vanes and their accompanying diffusion losses is reduced or avoided.

The consensus of the turbine design community is that α_3 should not exceed about 40 deg. The results presented in this figure show that meeting this criterion depends strongly on both α_2 and Ω, as well as whether the stage is choked or unchoked. In some cases, this criterion could restrict α_3 to values less than 70 deg.

A somewhat subtle but important point is that designing the low-pressure turbine to rotate in the opposite direction can accommodate large amounts of exit swirl from the high-pressure turbine. The so-called counter-rotating, low-pressure turbine will thus require an inlet guide vane with little turning, or perhaps no inlet guide vane at all. This complicates the bearing and support system because the shafts must also counter-rotate, but the overall result must be beneficial because many modern engines apply this approach.

The computations also show that the stator degree of reaction exceeds that of the rotor, and that the stator flow turning ($\alpha_1 + \alpha_2$) is less than that of the rotor (especially for inlet guide vanes where α_1 is zero). Consequently, the aerodynamic design of rotor airfoil profiles is usually more difficult than that of stator airfoils, justifying our focus on rotor airfoil design.

Figure 8.12. Because the individual turbine stator and rotor airfoils are heavy and expensive, especially cooled airfoils that employ exotic materials, elaborate manufacturing processes, and intricate internal flow passages, it is important to reduce their number to the extent possible. The Zweifel coefficient (Ref. 12) provides a reliable and straightforward method for making an initial estimate of the minimum solidity and number of required airfoils (see Ref. 11, Sec. 9.5).

Put simply, the Zweifel coefficient Z is a measure of how closely the turbine designer can tailor the pressure distribution around the airfoil profile to conform to the ideal of static pressure equal to stagnation pressure along the entire pressure (concave) surface and exit static pressure along the entire suction (convex) surface. This rectangular pressure distribution has no adverse pressure gradients and thus is free of boundary layer separation. This ideal pressure distribution has $Z = 1$ according to the mathematical definition of the Zweifel coefficient (see Ref. 11, Sec. 9.5). Most importantly, the CFD procedures that have enabled airfoil designers to increase the flow turning angles for modest degrees of reaction have simultaneously enabled them to achieve Zweifel coefficients one or more for stators and rotors. Thus, Eq. (8.52) can be used to estimate the minimum rotor solidity based on a maximum assumed value of Z.

This figure reveals that the minimum rotor solidity is of the order of one for $Z = 1$, and that it decreases rapidly as α_2 increases for both choked and unchocked stages. The designer is therefore encouraged to select higher values of α_2 in order to reduce the number of rotor airfoils.

Figure 8.13. The dimensionless stage axial velocity is an indicator of the throughflow area that will be required by the stage and hence of the height of the airfoils and the rotor centrifugal stress (see Sec. 8.2.3). The results presented in this figure show that u diminishes rapidly as α_2 increases for both choked and unchoked stages and is independent of Ω. The designer is therefore encouraged to choose values of α_2 less than 70 deg in order to increase u and thus obtain shorter, lighter airfoils, and rotor blades that have lower centrifugal stresses. This evidently creates another conflict between stage performance and airfoil life.

General conclusions. These results are clearly in agreement with the conventional wisdom of turbine stage design. In particular, they support the universal drive for increasing Ω to the limit allowed by materials and structures. Furthermore, they support the contention that the best choice of α_2 is in the range of 60–75 deg. Finally, they provide a sound basis for initial estimates for the detailed TURBN computations that must be carried out for your specific turbine stage designs. Four sets of representative initial design choices that meet all of the design

Table 8.2   Summary of representative initial turbine stage design choices for $M_{3R} = 0.9$, $\gamma_t = 1.30$, $g_c c_{pt} = 7378\,\text{ft}^2/(\text{s}^2\text{-}°\text{R})$, and $Z = 1$

M_2		1.1	0.9
$\Omega = 0.2$	α_2	67 deg	61 deg
	τ_{ts}	0.860	0.880
	$\beta_2 + \beta_3$	116 deg	103 deg
	$°R_t$	0.199	0.458
	α_3	41.2 deg	40.2 deg
	σ_{xr}	1.25	1.09
	u/V'	0.217	0.226
$\Omega = 0.3$	α_2	72 deg	72 deg
	τ_{ts}	0.811	0.831
	$\beta_2 + \beta_3$	120 deg	116 deg
	$°R_t$	0.294	0.463
	α_3	31.1 deg	40.0 deg
	σ_{xr}	0.92	0.67
	u/V'	0.171	0.144

criteria with $M_{3R} = 0.9$, $\gamma_t = 1.30$, $g_c c_{pt} = 7378\,\text{ft}^2/(\text{s}^2\text{-}°\text{R})$, and $Z = 1$ are presented in Table 8.2 for your reference. This compilation indicates that, for a given Ω, increasing M_2 can decrease τ_{ts}, but the airfoil aerodynamics are nearer to the edge.

8.2.2.2 *Stage pressure ratio* (π_{ts}).   Once the turbine stage temperature ratio τ_{ts} and the flowfield and airfoil characteristics are established, several avenues are open for calculating the stage pressure ratio. The most simple and direct method is to apply Eq. (4.9d-CPG), so that

$$\pi_{ts} = \tau_{ts}^{\gamma_t/(\gamma_t-1)e_s} \tag{8.53}$$

and

$$\eta_{ts} = \frac{1 - \tau_{ts}}{1 - \pi_{ts}^{(\gamma_t-1)/\gamma_t}} \tag{8.54}$$

This method will provide a useful and adequate starting point for turbine design. If necessary or desired, it may be refined using the standard design tools detailed in Ref. 11 and contained in the AEDsys TURBN subroutine.

Example case: An uncooled, single-stage turbine is to be designed with the following conditions:

$$M_2 = 1.1 \qquad\qquad M_{3R} = 0.9$$

$$T_{t2} = T_{t1} = 3200°\text{R} \qquad g_c c_{pt} = 7378\,\text{ft}^2/(\text{s}^2\text{-}°\text{R})$$

$$\alpha_2 = 70\ \text{deg} \qquad\qquad \gamma_t = 1.3$$

$$\omega r = 1200\ \text{ft/s} \qquad\qquad Z = 1$$

Then

$$V' = 4859 \text{ ft/s} \qquad \text{Eq. (8.37)}$$

$$\Omega = 0.2470 \qquad \text{Eq. (8.38)}$$

$$V_2 = 2693 \text{ ft/s} \qquad \text{Eq. (8.39)}$$

$$u = 921 \text{ ft/s} \qquad \text{Eq. (8.40)}$$

$$v_2 = 2531 \text{ ft/s} \qquad \text{Eq. (8.41)}$$

$$v_{2R} = 1331 \text{ ft/s} \qquad \text{Eq. (8.42)}$$

$$\beta_2 = 55.31 \text{ deg} \qquad \text{Eq. (8.43)}$$

$$T_{t2R} = T_{t3R} = 2886°\text{R} \qquad \text{Eq. (8.44)}$$

$$\beta_3 = 64.60 \text{ deg} \qquad \text{Eq. (8.45)}$$

$$\beta_2 + \beta_3 = 119.9 \text{ deg} \qquad \text{Eq. (8.46)}$$

$$v_3 = 740 \text{ ft/s} \qquad \text{Eq. (8.47)}$$

$$\alpha_3 = 38.79 \text{ deg} \qquad \text{Eq. (8.48)}$$

$$T_3 = 2573°\text{R} \qquad \text{Eq. (8.49)}$$

$$\tau_s = 0.8337 \qquad \text{Eq. (8.50)}$$

$$°R_t = 0.2540 \qquad \text{Eq. (8.51)}$$

$$\sigma_{xr} = 1.307 \qquad \text{Eq. (8.52)}$$

If one chooses to assume $e_t = e_{ts} = 0.90$, then $\pi_{ts} = 0.4166$ [Eq. (8.53)] and $\eta_{ts} = 90.88\%$ [Eq. (8.54)]. The results for this stage are summarized in Table 8.3.

8.2.2.3 Recapitulation. The turbine stage design procedure of Sec. 8.2.2 and the method of computing the stage pressure ratio have been integrated into the TURBN program of AEDsys in order to serve as the first step in the design process. You will quickly find that this has several important benefits, including the ability to quickly explore the entire range of design parameters and make promising initial choices, and then to transfer all of the input that the complete TURBN computation requires. The complete TURBN computation is very similar to that used in industry,[7,8,11] and the initial Sec. 8.2.2 design will require only minor and entirely transparent tweaking in order to produce a worthy result that meets all of the imposed constraints.

8.2.2.4 Airfoil geometry. The situation in unchoked turbines is similar to that in compressors except that the deviations are markedly smaller owing to the thinner boundary layers. Hence, using the nomenclature of Fig. 8.3,

$$\delta_t = \frac{\gamma_1 - \gamma_2}{8\sqrt{\sigma}} \qquad (8.55)$$

Table 8.3 Summary of example case stage properties ($e_t = 0.90$)

Property/station	2	2R	3R	3
T_t, °R	3200	2886	2886	2668
P_t/P_{t1}	——	——	——	0.4166
P/P_{t1}	——	——	——	0.3563
V, ft/s	2693	1618	2148	1182
u, ft/s	921	921	921	921
v, ft/s	2531	1331	1940	740
α, deg	70.0	——	——	38.79
β, deg	——	55.31	64.60	——

is a good estimate.[7,11] More importantly, however, when the turbine airfoil cascade exit Mach number is near one, the deviation is usually negligible because the cascade passage is similar to a nozzle. In fact, the suction (or convex) surface of the airfoils often has a flat stretch between the throat and the trailing edge, which evokes the name "straight-backed," or may even be slightly concave. Finally, the simple concept of deviation loses all meaning at large supersonic exit Mach numbers because expansion or compression waves emanating from the trailing edge can dramatically alter the final flow direction. This is a truly fascinating field of aerodynamics, but one that requires study beyond the scope of this textbook.[7]

8.2.2.5 Radial variations.
The compressor radial variation material of Sec. 8.2.1 is also generally applicable to turbines. However, because the mass flow rate per unit annulus area (that is, $\dot{m}/A = P_t/MFP\sqrt{T_t}$) is higher in turbines than compressors, turbine airfoils are correspondingly shorter. The result is little radial variation of aerodynamic properties from hub to tip except possibly in the last few stages of the low-pressure turbine. If the aerodynamic design of these stages began as free vortex, the rotor degree of reaction would be the same as for compressors [Fig. 8.6 and Eq. (8.27)], other than the sign of the pressure change across the stage. Consequently, the most difficult airfoil contours to design would be at the hub of the rotating airfoils and the tips of the stationary airfoils. It is therefore possible to find portions of some airfoils near the rear of highly loaded (that is, high work per stage) low-pressure turbines where the static pressure actually rises and boundary layer separation is hard to avoid. In these cases, contemporary turbine designers employ CFD to develop non-free or controlled vortex machines that minimize these troublesome effects and maintain high efficiency at high loading by requiring less work to be produced at the hub and tip.[13]

8.2.2.6 Turbine cooling.
The gas temperatures in modern turbines are high enough to destroy any available materials in short order unless they are protected by cooling air. The unwanted or nuisance heat may be carried or convected away by air flowing within the airfoils or prevented from reaching the airfoils by means of an unbroken external blanket of air. The amount of air required to accomplish the necessary cooling depends entirely upon the cooling configuration, the perversity of nature causing simpler configurations to require more cooling air.[1]

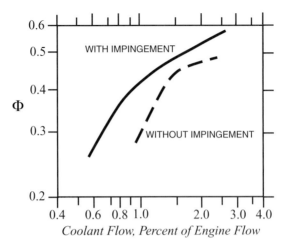

Fig. 8.14   Leading edge turbine cooling effectiveness.[14]

The cooling effectiveness is usually defined as

$$\Phi = \frac{T_g - T_m}{T_g - T_c} \tag{8.56}$$

where T_g, T_m, and T_c are the mainstream gas, average metal, and cooling air temperatures, respectively. Please note that the cooling air temperature T_c can be less than the compressor discharge temperature T_{t3} if the fluid is taken from an earlier compressor stage or, in future designs, if the fluid is cooled by exchanging heat with fan discharge air or fuel. An attractive property of Φ is that it must lie between zero and one—the higher the better. Figure 8.14 provides some typical leading edge cooling effectiveness design data. If, for example, impingement (created by a cooling flow insert that directs the flow against the inside wall) is considered and $T_g = 2400°F$, $T_c = 1200°F$, and $T_m = 2000°F$, then Φ must be at least 0.333, and the coolant flow must be 0.70% of engine flow or more. An unfortunate property of Φ is that it must be determined experimentally in all but the simplest cases.

The sensitivity of cooling flow requirements to Φ and T_m should not be underestimated. If the preceding example were repeated without impingement, the coolant flow would jump to almost 1.1%, a factor of 1.6. If the example were repeated with an advanced material allowing T_m to increase to 2100°F, the coolant flow would drop to 0.55%.

This exercise pertains only to the leading edge cooling of one airfoil row, the job being complete only when all parts of all airfoils are safe from the heat. This leads to two important conclusions. First, the turbine cooling designer must have data available to ensure that all surfaces, including the endwalls, can be protected and how much cooling air is needed. Second, the seemingly small amounts in the preceding example really do add up when all of the threatened surfaces are accounted for, the total cooling flow of modern machines being in the range of 15–25%. These engines therefore take onboard an enormous amount of air that is compressed, led through wondrously complex labyrinths, and expanded with no other purpose than

Table 8.4a   Range of axial flow turbine design parameters

Parameter	Design range
High-pressure turbine	
Maximum AN^2	$4\text{--}5 \times 10^{10}$ in$^2 \cdot$ rpm^2
Stage loading coefficient ψ	1.4--2.0
Exit Mach number	0.4--0.5
Exit swirl angle	0--40 deg
Low-pressure turbine	
Inlet corrected mass flow rate	40--44 lbm/(sec-ft^2)
Hub/tip ratio at inlet	0.35--0.50
Maximum stage loading at hub	2.4
Exit Mach number	0.4--0.5
Exit swirl angle	0--40 deg

helping the turbine survive. Such air does not pass through the burner and, unless afterburning is present, does not contribute to the thrust of the engine.

8.2.2.7 Range of turbine design parameters.   Table 8.4a gives the range of some typical turbine design parameters that can be used for guidance. The stage loading coefficient ψ is a parameter frequently used in the turbine literature as a rough measure of how hard each turbine stage is working and is defined as

$$\psi = \frac{g_c c_{pt} \Delta T_t}{(\omega r)^2} \tag{8.57}$$

You will find it interesting to calculate the stage loading coefficients of the turbines designed by the method of Sec. 8.2.2.

The comparison of the Pratt and Whitney JT3D and JT9D engines of Table 8.4b reveals typical design values and the leading trends in turbine technology. Note especially the increase of high-pressure turbine inlet temperature and cooling airflow and the low-pressure turbine stage loading coefficient. These were all necessary to make it possible to greatly increase the overall pressure ratio (that is, the thermal efficiency) and the bypass ratio (that is, the propulsive efficiency), and thus dramatically reduce the specific fuel consumption (that is, the overall efficiency). These changes combined with the absolute size of the engines, as indicated by the core engine flow, to increase the total power required from the turbines at takeoff to more than 130,000 hp.

8.2.3 Engine Life

8.2.3.1 Background.   Every part of the engine must be certain to last its intended design lifetime. The fundamental truth, therefore, is that a successful engine design must simultaneously meet its aerodynamic, thermodynamic, and structural requirements. Because one of the structural requirements is to reduce the weight, cost, and complexity of the parts, their durability margins must be minimized. The primary concern is for the heavy rotating and highly pressurized parts that can harm or destroy the parent aircraft if large pieces of them are inadvertently set free.

Table 8.4b   Comparison of Pratt and Whitney engines

Parameter	JT3D	JT9D
Year of introduction	1961	1970
Engine bypass ratio	1.45	4.86
Engine overall pressure ratio	13.6	24.5
Core engine flow, lbm/s	187.7	272.0
High-pressure turbine		
Inlet temperature, °F	1745	2500
Power output, hp	24,100	71,700
Number of stages	1	2
Average stage loading coefficient	1.72	1.76
Coolant plus leakage flow, %	2.5	16.1
Low-pressure turbine		
Inlet temperature, °F	1410	1600
Power output, hp	31,800	61,050
Number of stages	3	4
Average stage loading coefficient	1.44	2.47
Coolant plus leakage flow, %	0.7	1.4

These are exemplified by long first-stage fan blades, blades and disks of cooled high-pressure turbines, and outer cases of main combustors. Because engine life is so critical, engine structural design has become an extremely sophisticated science and art. Proving that the engine meets its life requirements is one of the major steps in the development process.

It will become clear in what follows that there is a strong interaction between aerodynamic, thermodynamic, and structural design decisions. The obvious implication is that everyone involved will make better decisions if they are aware of all of the possible consequences in advance. At least the participants will be less likely to be unpleasantly surprised.

The lives that the engine parts must endure can be remarkably strenuous, and they are highly dependent upon the mission of the parent aircraft. To appreciate this point, one need only recognize the difference between the operation or "usage" of fighter and transport engines. Fighter engines experience far more throttle movements or maneuver transients per flight hour and are therefore more susceptible to fatigue-type failures. Transport engines run for long times at elevated temperatures and have greater design lifetimes and are therefore more susceptible to creep-type failures. Both are exposed to considerably more severe duty during pilot training than during normal operations or even combat.

There is a special message for both the engine builder and user here, namely, that the initial "mission usage" specification plays a pivotal role in determining the eventual success of the aircraft. Once agreed to by contract, the engine builder will deliver an engine that will run soundly for the desired time under the specified operating conditions. However, to the extent that the actual mission usage of the engine departs from the original specifications the risk of unanticipated or "show-stopping" failures increases. It is therefore to everyone's advantage to specify the mission usage correctly at the outset. Furthermore, it is essential that the parts be realistically exposed to the life-consuming portions of the engine usage spectrum early and repeatedly in the development process. This is done best with the safety and control made possible by simulated altitude testing in ground test facilities and must be continued until the required engine durability has been confidently demonstrated.

This foreword is meant to underscore the overwhelming importance of structural design for modern aircraft engines. What follows next is an abbreviated, qualitative introduction to the design process. The reader should be aware that much has been written on this subject, and that adequate reference material exists to satisfy almost any curiosity. We are indeed fortunate to be able to include an excellent review of Turbine Engine Life Management, authored by Dr. William Cowie, a pioneer and foremost expert in the field, as Appendix N. You will find this to supply a unique and invaluable background for the engine design process.

The first step in the iterative structural design process is to estimate the stresses that will be experienced by each part. The stresses stem from the environment to which the parts are exposed and can, in turn, be regarded as the forcing functions that consume available life. The second step is to evaluate the response of the parts in terms of their life expectancy. Both steps require intimate knowledge of many properties of the materials involved. If the life of any given part is inadequate (or excessive), its design is changed, and the process is repeated until a satisfactory solution is found.

We are about to embark on the development of several structural design tools consistent with the philosophy of this textbook. Their focus will be on the main source of stresses in rotating parts—the centrifugal force. For the sake of perspective, it is well to bear in mind the fact that the centrifugal force experienced by an element of material rotating at 10,000 rpm and a radius of 1 ft is equivalent to 34,000 g!

Nevertheless, there are many other forces at work that can consume the life (or destroy) stationary or rotating parts, all of which must eventually be accounted for in the design and test process. Some of the most important, not necessarily in order of importance, include the following:

1) Airfoil bending moments are caused by the pressure differences across the stationary and rotating airfoils (or their lift) and are greatest where they are fastened. The centrifugal force can also cause airfoils with complex three-dimensional shapes to twist and bend.

2) Flutter (self-induced vibration) is an unsteady aerodynamic phenomenon that airfoils and/or disks can spontaneously experience, in which they vibrate at a system natural frequency and for which the driving energy is extracted from the flowing gas. This is most commonly found in fan and compressor airfoil rows and comes in many varieties (for example, supersonic flutter, stall flutter, and choke flutter). Once flutter begins, the life of the parts is measured in minutes because of the large stresses and high frequency vibrations (>1000 Hz) that result. Flutter must be avoided at any cost, but the analysis tools are beyond the scope of this textbook.

3) Airfoils, disks, and other flowpath parts are exposed to unsteady aerodynamic forces, such as buffeting (forced vibration) and high cycle fatigue (HCF) that result from temporally and/or spatially nonuniform flows. Care must be taken to avoid

the especially devastating situation where resonance occurs because the upstream or downstream disturbance has an organized pattern (caused, for example, by the pressure fields and/or wakes of support struts, airfoil rows, or fuel injectors) whose apparent or "blade passing" frequency coincides with one of the lower natural frequencies of some airfoil. This condition can only be endured for very short periods of time.[15]

Buffeting can lead to an enormous accumulation of stress cycles during the life of the engine because the natural frequency of parts is of the order of 1–10 kHz. Thus, a single hour of excitation adds approximately 10 million cycles, and only 100 h adds about one billion cycles. HCF has become the leading cause of failures in fighter engines and is presently the subject of intense investigation.

4) Thermal differential stress and low cycle fatigue (LCF) are important. Temperature gradients, particularly in cooled turbine airfoils, disks, and burner liners, can give rise to surprisingly high stresses as the material counteracts uneven local expansion and contraction. These can be amplified during transients as the engine is moving from one power setting or turbine inlet temperature to another. These transient thermal differential stresses are the primary cause of thermal fatigue or LCF, which, for obvious reasons, can rapidly consume the life of hot parts in high temperature fighter engines. Recognition of the importance of the LCF during the 1970s changed the entire approach of the engine community to design and acceptance or qualification testing.[15]

Thermal differential stress is one example of the larger classes of strain-induced stresses. Note should be taken of the fact that many engine parts can be geometrically constrained by their neighbors, and that their stress analysis must take this into account.

5) There are many sources of local stress concentrations, which can much more than double the elastic stress level or even cause plastic flow and permanent deformation to take place. These include holes, slots, inside and outside corners, machine marks, and, the most feared of all, cracks. Crack initiation and growth or propagation is a leading determinant of engine life, and the recent development and application of practical fracture mechanics design tools and test procedures is one of the outstanding accomplishments of the aircraft engine community.[16]

6) Foreign object damage (FOD) and domestic object damage (DOD) must be guarded against if the probability of occurrence is deemed sufficiently high and the consequences sufficiently severe.

There is an insidious, often disastrous, interaction between FOD and HCF. Cracks initiated by FOD are then propagated by HCF with the result that life is significantly reduced. For this reason, FOD is known as the "finger of death." A modern remedy for this problem is to apply surface treatments that reduce or eliminate these interactions by preventing the defects from growing (see Appendix N).

7) The first stage fan blades must withstand a variety of bird strikes, which may be considered a soft-body relative of FOD. This has prevented the use of lightweight, nonmetallic materials for this application for more than three decades. Bird strike testing is a staple of the engine qualification process and is one of the most exciting parts because it is dramatic and the cost of failure is great.

8) During strenuous maneuvers and hard landings, other forces and moments, both inertial and gyroscopic, are generated within the engine. These can damage

the tips of rotating blades, their outer air seals, and any rotating seals, especially when clearances are small, because they are asymmetric.

9) Torsional stresses are inevitable when power is transferred by shaft torque from turbines to compressors. Although the magnitudes of these stresses are not large, they cannot be ignored.

10) There are a number of material composition or chemistry effects that also consume engine life, the most notable being erosion, corrosion, and creep. These are likely to be important in applications where the engine remains at high temperature and pressure for extended periods of time, such as supersonic cruise vehicles.

Each of these technical areas must be tended by true experts if surprises are to be avoided. One must respect the organizations that are able to weld these talents together and produce durable engines. No textbook could hope to capture the total engine life design process, and so we must settle for less. In what follows, these many phenomena shall be accounted for by using an "allowable working stress," which is the amount remaining for the principal tensile stresses alone.

Determining this remaining amount is itself no easy matter and is usually accomplished in engineering practice through the use of company materials specifications that have been proven through time and are thoroughly documented. When such resources are not available, the best approach is to use open literature references, the *Aerospace Structural Metals Handbook*[17] being a good example for general engine design. A cursory review of Ref. 17 will quickly reveal both the amazing amount of information already in hand for construction metals and the many factors that must be considered before the design is final. To provide you with more specific examples and guidance, the data for several materials typically found in the failure critical parts of gas turbine engines are synopsized from Ref. 17 in Appendix M. Failure critical parts, as defined in Appendix N, are those whose failure would threaten the integrity of the engine and/or aircraft and always include the large rotating parts (for example, fan and cooled turbine rotor airfoils, and cooled turbine rotor disks) and highly pressurized parts (for example, the burner outer case).

The creep rupture strength of a material is the maximum tensile stress it can withstand without failing during a specified period of time at a given temperature. As explained in Appendix M, a sensible approach for the designer is to limit stresses to the appropriate creep rupture strength, or some fraction of that for safety. Thus, for the purposes of exploration and the examples that follow, we will use typical engine materials properties as summarized in Table 8.5 and Figs. 8.15 and 8.16

Table 8.5   Material types

Material no.	Type	Density	
		slug/ft^3	kg/m^3
1	Aluminum alloy	5.29	2726
2	Titanium alloy	9.08	4680
3	Wrought nickel alloy	16.0	8246
4	High-strength nickel alloy	17.0	8760
5	Single-crystal superalloy	17.0	8760

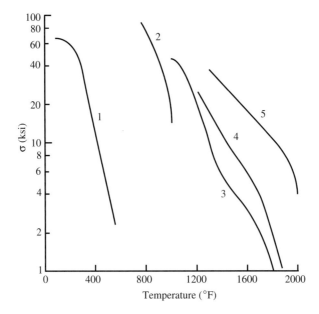

Fig. 8.15 Allowable stress vs temperature for typical engine materials.

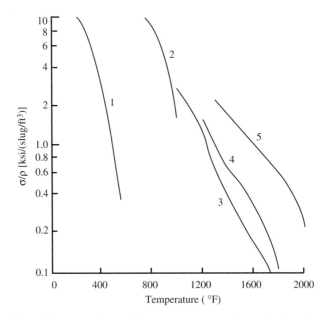

Fig. 8.16 Allowable strength-to-weight vs temperature for typical engine materials.

(Ref. 11). These were derived by taking 80% of the allowable 0.2% creep, 1000-h tensile stress for aluminum alloy and 50% of the allowable 1% creep, 1000-h tensile stress for the other alloys. Please note that, as the ensuing derivations will demonstrate, strength-to-weight or specific strength is the most important property for rotating parts. The typical properties also show that there is a temperature beyond which every class of material rapidly loses capability.

It is therefore fortunate that the Larson–Miller parameter provides a convenient, reliable procedure for extending the data for materials that have been only partially characterized. According to this method, which is based on the assumption that creep is thermally activated, the rupture life of a material at a given stress level will vary with temperature in such a way that the Larson–Miller parameter

$$T(C + \log t) \tag{8.58}$$

remains constant, where the material property C is a dimensionless constant. The value of the material constant may be determined from data acquired at two test conditions by applying Eq. (8.58) twice to obtain

$$C = (T_2 \log t_2 - T_1 \log t_1)/(T_1 - T_2)$$

For example, for the Aluminum 2124 of Fig. M.2 (where rupture at 20 ksi occurs at both 500°F/15 h and 400°F/950 h), $C = 14.3$. Also, for the Rene 80 of Fig. M.13 (where rupture at 60 ksi occurs at both 1600°F/25 h and 1400°F/8000 h), $C = 21.9$. You should try different combinations for these materials and for other materials of Appendix M to increase your familiarity with and confidence for this procedure. Representative values of C are also found in Table 8.6.

Equation (8.58) can also be used to demonstrate the surprising influence of temperature on creep life. For example, a part having $C = 20$ that is designed to fail after 2000 h at a temperature of 1400°F will last only 1130 h if the temperature is raised merely 20°F. This gives rise to the rule of thumb that the creep life of a hot part is halved each time its temperature increases 20°F. Fortunately, it is doubled when the temperature decreases an equal amount. However, because creep

Table 8.6   Larson–Miller constants for selected
materials (Ref. 15)

Material	Constant
Alloy	C
Low carbon steel	18
Carbon moly steel	19
18-8 stainless steel	18
8-8 Mo stainless steel	17
2-1/4 Cr − 1 Mo steel	23
S-590 alloy	20
Haynes Stelite No. 34	20
Titanium D9	20
Cr-Mo-Ti-B steel	22

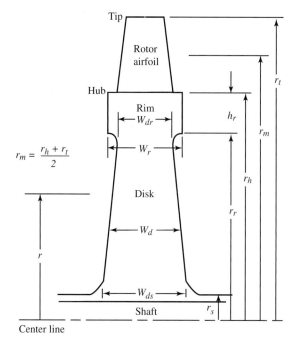

Fig. 8.17   Turbomachinery rotor nomenclature.

can cause failures in localized regions of high distress, the temperature distribution of critical parts must be accurately known for the structural analysis to be reliable.

Creep will be a limiting factor for many likely future engine applications. These include long-range supersonic transports, business jets, and attack aircraft, and long-endurance unpiloted air vehicles. You may therefore find the Larson–Miller parameter very handy in the years to come.

We now turn to the development of several important structural design tools. These analyses will be based on the nomenclature and terminology found in Figs. 8.17 and 8.18. It is most convenient to start at the outer radius and work inward because the stress is known to be zero at the blade tips and because each succeeding part must restrain or support all of the material beyond its own radial location.

8.2.3.2   Rotor airfoil centrifugal stress σ_c.
Because each cross-sectional area of the rotor airfoil must restrain the centrifugal force on all of the material beyond its own radial location (see Figs. 8.17 and 8.18), the hub or base of the airfoil must experience the greatest force. The total centrifugal force acting on A_h is

$$F_c = \int_{r_h}^{r_t} \rho\omega^2 A_b r \, dr \qquad (8.59)$$

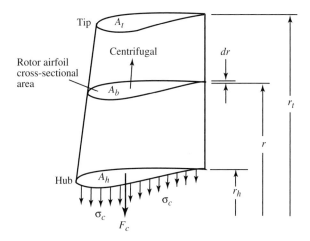

Fig. 8.18   Rotor airfoil centrifugal stress nomenclature.

so that the principal tensile stress is

$$\sigma_c = \frac{F_c}{A_h} = \rho\omega^2 \int_{r_h}^{r_t} \frac{A_b}{A_h} r \, dr \qquad (8.60)$$

The airfoil cross-sectional area usually tapers down or diminishes with increasing radius, which, according to Eq. (8.60), has the effect of reducing σ_c. If the taper is "linear," then

$$\frac{A_b}{A_h} = 1 - \left(1 - \frac{A_t}{A_h}\right)\left(\frac{r - r_h}{r_t - r_h}\right) \qquad (8.61)$$

and Eq. (8.60) becomes

$$\sigma_c = \rho\omega^2 \left[\frac{A}{2\pi} - \int_{r_h}^{r_t}\left(1 - \frac{A_t}{A_h}\right)\left(\frac{r - r_h}{r_t - r_h}\right) r \, dr\right] \qquad (8.62)$$

where A is the usual flowpath throughflow or annulus area $\pi(r_t^2 - r_h^2)$. Although Eq. (8.62) can be directly integrated for any particular case, a useful and slightly conservative result is obtained by taking $r = (r_h + r_t)/2$, which leads to the desired relationship

$$\sigma_c = \frac{\rho\omega^2 A}{4\pi}\left(1 + \frac{A_t}{A_h}\right) \qquad (8.63)$$

which can be employed directly in any situation to calculate the rotor airfoil centrifugal stress. A_t/A_h is known as the taper ratio and is usually in the range of 0.8–1.0. For example, after choosing the values of rotor airfoil materials shown in Table 8.7, Eq. (8.63) yields $\sigma_c = 17,900$ and $14,900$ psi for the compressor and turbine, respectively.

Table 8.7   Example values of rotor airfoil materials

Item	Compressor	Turbine
ρ, slug/ft^3	9.0	15.0
ω, rad/s	1000	1000
A, ft^2	2.0	1.0
A_t/A_h	0.8	0.8

Moreover, since $AN^2 = A\omega^2(30/\pi)^2$, then Eq. (8.63) can be rearranged into

$$AN^2 = \frac{3600}{\pi(1 + A_t/A_h)} \frac{\sigma_c}{\rho} \tag{8.64}$$

Thus, for a taper ratio (A_t/A_h) of 0.8, a strength-to-weight ratio (σ_c/ρ) of 3 ksi/(slug/ft^3) corresponds to an AN^2 value of 4×10^{10} in.^{2}-rpm^2.

It is important for you to know that the accepted practice is to use Eq. (8.64) to calculate the allowable AN^2 using material properties such as those of Fig. 8.16 and to compare that with the value actually required by the engine rotating parts. This quantity, referred to simply as "AN^2," is thereby transformed into a surrogate for the allowable airfoil material specific strength. Put simply, if the required AN^2 exceeds the allowable AN^2, a superior material must be found or the flowpath design must be changed. In fact, designers often express their design capabilities to each other in terms of AN^2 and usually omit the units and the 10^{10} factor in conversations as a matter of convenience. For these reasons, the COMPR and TURBN computer programs present AN^2 for each stage so you may use it for airfoil material selection. You may find Fig. 8.19 helpful for converting specific strength into AN^2.

It should be obvious by now that anything that reduces the amount of material beyond the hub or base of the rotating airfoil will reduce the centrifugal stress there or, conversely, increase the allowable AN^2 of the airfoil. This explains the great attraction of hollow fan blades, which, although extraordinarily expensive to manufacture, are an essential ingredient of modern engines.

8.2.3.3 Rim web thickness W_{dr}.

The rotating airfoils are inserted into slots in an otherwise solid annulus of material known as a rim (see Fig. 8.17), which maintains their circular motion. The airfoil hub tensile stress σ_c is treated as though "smeared out" over the outer rim surface, so that

$$\bar{\sigma}_{blades} = \frac{\sigma_c N_b A_h}{2\pi r_h W_r} \tag{8.65}$$

where N_b is the number of blades on the "wheel."

Making the conventional assumption of uniform stress within the rim (σ_r), the force diagram of Fig. 8.20 may be used to determine the dimension W_{dr} necessary to balance the blade and rim centrifugal forces. Please note that W_r and h_r are simply sensible initial choices, where W_r approximates the axial chord of the airfoil and h_r is similar in magnitude to W_r. It is very important to realize that it will always be possible to design a rim large enough to "carry" the airfoils. The real question is whether the size of the rim is practical from the standpoint of the space

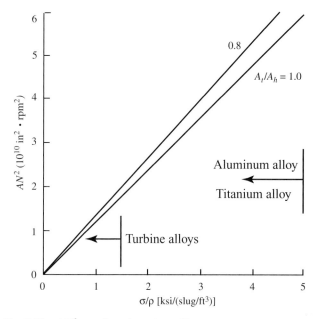

Fig. 8.19 AN^2 **as a function of specific strength and taper ratio.**

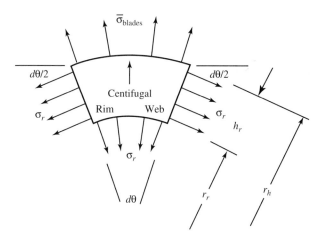

Fig. 8.20 Rim segment radial equilibrium nomenclature.

Table 8.8   Example values of disk materials

Item	Compressor	Turbine
$\bar\sigma_{blades}/\sigma_r$	0.10	0.20
h_r/r_r	0.05	0.10
$\rho(\omega r_r)^2/\sigma_r$	6.0	4.0

required, weight, and manufacturing cost. Thus, there is no absolute solution, and the final choice must be based on experience and a sense of proportion.

The radial force balance leads to the equation for the minimum W_{dr}

$$\bar\sigma_{blades}\, r_h\, W_r\, d\theta + \rho\omega^2 h_r\, W_r \left(r_r + \frac{h_r}{2}\right)^2 d\theta = \sigma_r r_r W_{dr}\, d\theta + 2\sigma_r h_r\, W_r \sin\frac{d\theta}{2}$$

which, for an infinitesimal $d\theta$, becomes

$$\frac{W_{dr}}{W_r} = \left[\frac{\bar\sigma_{blades}}{\sigma_r}\left(1 + \frac{r_r}{h_r}\right) + \frac{\rho(\omega r_r)^2}{\sigma_r}\left(1 + \frac{h_r}{2r_r}\right)^2 - 1\right]\frac{h_r}{r_r} \qquad (8.66)$$

which can be employed directly in any situation to calculate the rotor airfoil centrifugal stress. If σ_r is sufficiently large, Eq. (8.66) clearly shows that W_{dr} can be zero or less, which means that the rim is "self-supporting." Nevertheless, a token disk will still be required in order to transfer torque to the shaft and, of course, to keep the rim and airfoils in their correct axial and radial positions. For example, after choosing the values of disk materials shown in Table 8.8, then Eq. (8.66) yields $W_{dr}/W_r = 0.37$ for the compressor and 0.56 for the turbine.

8.2.3.4   *Disk of uniform stress.*

The disk supports and positions the rim while connecting it to the shaft (see Fig. 8.17). Its thickness begins with the value W_{dr} at the inside edge of the rim and generally grows as the radius decreases because of the accumulating centrifugal force that must be resisted. Just as was discovered for the rim, a disk that will perform the required job can always be found, but the size, weight, and/or cost may be excessive. Thus, the final design choice usually involves trial-and-error and judgment.

It is impossible to overemphasize the importance of ensuring the structural integrity of disks, particularly the large ones found in cooled high-pressure turbines. Because they are very difficult to inspect and because the massive fragments that fly loose when they disintegrate cannot be contained, they must not be allowed to fail.

The most efficient way to use available disk materials is to design the disk for constant radial and circumferential stress. Because the rim and disk are one continuous piece of material, the design stress would be the same throughout ($\sigma_r = \sigma_d$).

Applying locally radial equilibrium to the infinitesimal element of the disk of Fig. 8.21 leads to the equation

$$\rho(\omega r)^2 W_d\, dr\, d\theta = \sigma_d\left[\left(r - \frac{dr}{2}\right)\left(W_d - \frac{dW_d}{2}\right)d\theta\right.$$
$$\left. - \left(r + \frac{dr}{2}\right)\left(W_d + \frac{dW_d}{2}\right)d\theta + 2W_d\, dr\sin\frac{d\theta}{2}\right]$$

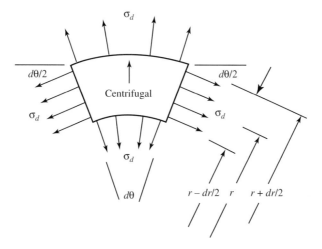

Fig. 8.21   Disk element radial equilibrium nomenclature.

which becomes in the limit

$$\frac{dW_d}{W_d} + \frac{\rho\omega^2}{\sigma_d} \, d\left(\frac{r^2}{2}\right) = 0$$

This equation may be integrated, starting from $r = r_d$ and $W_d = W_{dr}$, to yield the desired result:

$$\frac{W_d}{W_{dr}} = \exp\left\{ \frac{\rho(\omega r_r)^2}{2\sigma_d} \left[1 - \left(\frac{r}{r_r}\right)^2 \right] \right\} \tag{8.67}$$

The main feature of Eq. (8.67) is that the disk thickness grows exponentially in proportion to $(\omega r_r)^2$, which is the square of the maximum or rim velocity of the disk.

What does Eq. (8.67) look like? Figure 8.22 shows the disk thickness distribution for typical values of the disk shape factor (*DSF*):

$$DSF = \rho(\omega r_r)^2/2\sigma_d \tag{8.68}$$

Judging by the looks of these thickness distributions, the maximum allowable value of *DSF* is not much more than two, so that

$$[\omega r_r]_{\max} \cong \sqrt{4\sigma_d/\rho} \tag{8.69}$$

which, for typical compressor disk values of $\sigma_d = 30{,}000$ psi and $\rho = 9.0$ slug/ft^3, is about 1400 ft/s, whereas for typical turbine disk values of $\sigma_d = 20{,}000$ psi and $\rho = 16.0$ slug/ft^3 it is about 850 ft/s. Why does W_d/W_{dr} grow more slowly as r approaches zero?

It is important for you to know that $[\omega r_r]_{\max}$, known to designers as the "allowable wheel speed," is a surrogate for the allowable disk material specific strength. For this reason, the COMPR and TURBN computer programs present

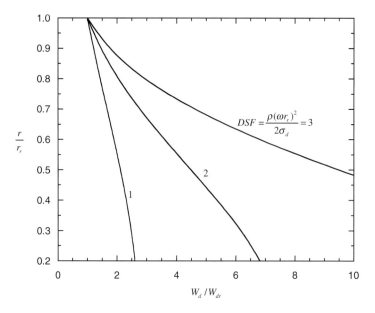

$$DSF = \frac{\rho(\omega r_r)^2}{2\sigma_d} = 3$$

Fig. 8.22   Disk thickness distributions.

$[\omega r_r]_{max}$ for each stage for $DSF = 2$ so you may use it for disk material selection. Figure 8.23 shows the allowable wheel speed $\{[\omega r_r]_{max}\}$ vs specific strength (σ_d/ρ) and several values of DSF with ranges indicated for high-pressure compressors and turbines.

We may now draw some important general conclusions based on the preceding analyses. Because the annulus area A is largest on the low-pressure spool, and particularly for the first fan stage of high bypass ratio engines, the rotational speed ω will most likely be limited by allowable blade centrifugal stress [see Eq. (8.63)]. In fact, the practical processing and fabrication of titanium was developed specifically to make possible the manufacturing of modern fan airfoils. Conversely, on the high-pressure spool, where the annulus flow area is considerably smaller but the temperatures are higher, the rotational speed will most likely be limited by allowable wheel speed [see Eq. (8.69)]. Because high rotor blade speeds are desirable because they reduce the required number of compressor and turbine stages (see Sec. 8.2.2), the inevitable push and pull between the AN^2 and ωr design criteria becomes the basis for many important design decisions. Two of the most frequently encountered situations are described next.

In the case of high bypass turbofan engines, the rotational speed of the low-pressure or fan spool is dominated by the allowable value of AN^2 for fan blades and the fact that A is fixed in advance by cycle computations. Thus, the fan designer works at the maximum resulting value of N and places the fan hub at the largest possible radius. The latter will be determined by other factors, such as the largest reasonable fan tip radius or the minimum acceptable fan blade aspect ratio. This choice provides the low-pressure turbine the highest allowable value of N. The low-pressure turbine designer also places the blade hubs at the largest possible

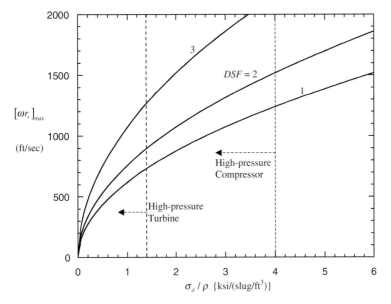

Fig. 8.23 Allowable wheel speed.

radius, the limitation usually being either the largest reasonable blade tip radius or radial displacement from the high-pressure turbine exit.

In the case of the high-pressure spool, the rotational speed is often determined by the allowable value of ωr for the first turbine disk. Thus, the turbine designer works at the minimum reasonable value of hub radius. The latter will be determined by other factors, such as the minimum radius required for the internal functions of the engine (for example, shafts, bearings, cooling flows, and lubricant flows) or the largest reasonable radial displacement from the high-pressure compressor exit or the low-pressure turbine entrance. This choice provides the high-pressure compressor the highest allowable value of ω. The high-pressure compressor designer places the blade hubs at the largest possible radius, the limitation usually being the allowable value of ωr for the compressor disks, the height of the rear airfoils, or radial displacement from the high-pressure turbine entrance.

Many other situations are, of course, possible. This is one of the things that makes design interesting.

8.2.3.5 Disk torsional stress τ_d.

The tangential disk shear stress required to transfer the shaft horsepower to the airfoils is easily calculated since

$$HP = \text{shear stress} \times \text{area} \times \text{velocity}$$

$$HP = \tau_d \times 2\pi r W_d \times \omega r$$

whence

$$\tau_d = \frac{HP}{2\pi r^2 W_d \omega} \tag{8.70}$$

For example, by choosing the following typical values of disk properties

$$HP = 10{,}000 \text{ hp}$$

$$r = 0.30 \text{ ft}$$

$$W_d = 0.10 \text{ ft}$$

$$\omega = 1000 \text{ rad/s}$$

then Eq. (8.70) shows that $\tau_d = 675$ psi, which makes a relatively small contribution to the overall stress.

8.2.3.6 Disk thermal differential stress σ_t.

It was noted earlier that differential thermal stresses are often more important than one might think. Although it is difficult to provide the type of complex analysis required for LCF life estimation, the following classical example makes the point clearly enough.

Considering a circular disk of constant thickness with no center hole and a temperature distribution that depends only on radius [$T = T(r)$], it can be shown[18] that the radial tensile stress is

$$\sigma_{tr} = \alpha E \left\{ \frac{1}{r_h^2} \int_0^{r_h} Tr \, dr - \frac{1}{r^2} \int_0^r Tr \, dr \right\} \tag{8.71}$$

where α is the coefficient of linear thermal expansion and E is the modulus of elasticity, and the tangential tensile stress is

$$\sigma_{t\theta} = \alpha E \left\{ \frac{1}{r_h^2} \int_0^{r_h} Tr \, dr + \frac{1}{r^2} \int_0^r Tr \, dr - T \right\} \tag{8.72}$$

both of which are zero if the temperature is constant. An interesting illustrative case is that of the linear temperature distribution $T = T_0 + \Delta T(r/r_h)$, for which Eq. (8.71) becomes

$$\sigma_{tr} = \frac{\alpha E \, \Delta T}{3} \left(1 - \frac{r}{r_h} \right) \tag{8.73}$$

and Eq. (8.72) becomes

$$\sigma_{t\theta} = \frac{\alpha E \, \Delta T}{3} \left(1 - 2\frac{r}{r_h} \right) \tag{8.74}$$

both of which have a maximum magnitude of $aE \, \Delta T/3$ at $r = 0$. For example, by choosing typical values of

$$\alpha = 1 \times 10^{-5} \, 1/°\text{F}$$

$$E = 20 \times 10^6 \text{ psi}$$

$$\Delta T = 100°\text{F}$$

then Eqs. (8.73) and (8.74) show that the maximum magnitude of σ_{tr} and $\sigma_{t\theta}$ is 6700 psi! This simple case demonstrates forcefully that thermal stresses can be

Table 8.9   Airfoil aspect ratio

Component	Axial aspect ratio
Fan	3–6
Compressor	1–5
High-pressure turbine	1–3
Low-pressure turbine	2–4

very large and, therefore, must be carefully accounted for and reduced as much as possible. This is especially true during transient operation.

With this perspective, it is possible to imagine that truly enormous stresses could be generated in the thin outer walls of the cooled turbine airfoils, if they are not very carefully designed. Because such stresses will be proportional to the temperature difference between the mainstream and the cooling air, there is also a limit to how cold a coolant may be used before it no longer truly "protects" the material. Furthermore, the frequently cited materials limitations on T_{t3} or T_{t4} are often caused by the transient tangential thermal differential stresses that arise at the hot rims of the high-pressure compressor and turbine disks when the throttle is retarded and the temperature of the adjacent airflow is suddenly reduced.

8.2.3.7   Airfoil aspect ratio.

At some point in the analysis, it becomes important to be able to estimate h_r and W_r (see Fig. 8.17), both of which approximate the axial chord at the hub of the rotating airfoil. Because the latter results from much more elaborate calculations, a rule of thumb based on many successful designs is used in COMPR and TURBN for preliminary calculations. The rule of thumb is that the "axial aspect ratio" of the rotating airfoils [that is, height to hub axial chord or $(r_t - r_h)/h_r$] depends largely on the component under consideration, as shown in Table 8.9.

8.3   Example AAF Engine Component Design: Rotating Turbomachinery

We will now design the rotating components for the AAF Engine (see Sec. 6.5). This example will illustrate the preliminary design of the axial flow fan, high-pressure compressor (HPC), high-pressure turbine (HPT), and low-pressure turbine (LPT). The designs will be based on the methods of Sec. 8.2. The design point and off-design component performance data, which provide the starting point for the designs, were assembled before in the following figures and tables: Fig. 7.1 AAF Engine design point performance data; Table 7.E1 AAF Engine design point interface quantities; Fig. 7.E1 Fan performance—fan pressure ratio; Fig. 7.E2 HPC performance—HP compressor pressure ratio; Fig. 7.E3 Low-pressure turbine performance—pressure ratio; Table 7.E3 AAF Engine turbomachinery performance at $\theta_0 = \theta_{0\,break}$, sea level, standard day ($M_0 = 0.612$); Fig. 7.E10 AAF Engine fan operating line; Fig. 7.E11 AAF Engine high-pressure compressor operating line; and Fig. 7.E9 AAF Engine high- and low-pressure turbine operating lines.

Further supportive data to be used in the selection of materials for the various component parts are contained in Table 8.5 and Figs. 8.16 and 8.17. As already noted, it is initially assumed that the AAF is twin-engined and that it will be powered by two AAF Engines having the general configuration shown in Fig. 4.la.

Following the preceding reasoning, it is presumed that the maximum mechanical speeds of the low- and high-pressure spools are determined by the structurally acceptable mechanical speeds for the fan and the high-pressure turbine, respectively. Consequently, the design of these two components is considered first followed by the high-pressure compressor and the low-pressure turbine in that order. These presumptions are, of course, subject to later examination and, if necessary, reconsideration.

8.3.1 Fan Design—AAF Engine

The process begins with the selection of the fan design point and the determination of the number of fan stages. Design choices are then made for the stage parameters D, M_0, σ, and e_c and the aerodynamic definition of each stage fixed. Next, rotating airfoil material and taper ratio choices are selected; the rotational speed of the low-speed spool is found from centrifugal stress considerations; and the airfoil radii are calculated. Finally, the wheel material is selected; the wheel parameters h_r and $\bar{\sigma}_{blades}/\sigma_r$ are estimated; and the wheel speed, disk shape factor, and rim web thickness are determined by rim and disk stresses considerations.

8.3.1.1 Design point.   A single design point for the fan is selected with the help of the fan map of Fig. 7.E10, reproduced here as Fig. 8.E1. This map reveals that the fan must operate over a wide range of pressure ratios and corrected fan inlet mass flow rates. The most demanding operating points in terms of approach

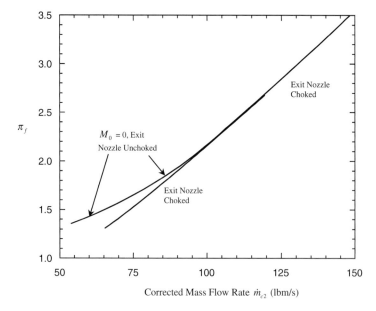

Fig. 8.E1   AAF Engine fan operating line.

Station	m dot (1bm/s)	gamma	Pt (psia)	Tt (R)
0	176.95	1.4000	18.923	557.54
1	176.95	1.4000	18.923	557.54
2	176.95	1.4000	18.166	557.54
13	176.95	1.4000	63.507	833.26
bypass	76.01	1.4000	63.507	833.26
2.5	100.94	1.4000	63.507	833.26
3	100.94	1.4000	509.015	1613.34
3.1	89.84	1.4000	509.015	1613.34
3.2	89.84	1.4000	503.925	1613.34
MB fuel	2.5064			
4	92.34	1.3000	483.564	3199.99
4.1	97.39	1.3000		3101.86
4.4	97.39	1.3000		2435.95
4.5	102.44	1.3000	149.089	2380.29
5	102.44	1.3000	63.078	1990.88
6	102.44	1.3000	63.078	1990.88
16	76.01	1.4000	63.507	833.26
6A	178.45	1.3360	60.769	1554.97
AB fuel	6.6782			
7	185.13	1.3000	57.731	3600.00
8	185.13	1.3000	57.731	3600.00
9	185.13	1.3000	55.999	3600.00

Fig. 8.E2   AAF Engine station test results at $\theta_0 = \theta_{0\,break}$, sea level, standard day (M_0 = 0.612).

to stall and/or surge and maximum flow are often those associated with full throttle (maximum T_{t4}). And of those, the operating point requiring the highest π_f and corrected mass flow rate correspond to full throttle flight conditions at $\theta_0 = \theta_{0\,break}$, where $\pi_f = 3.50$ (see Table 7.E3). To be certain that the fan can meet this most stringent condition, this will be chosen as the design point. Further, because the highest rotor mechanical speeds and centrifugal stresses occur at the highest value of θ_0 for a given fan pressure ratio, the fan will be designed at the theta break. Of all of the possible theta break flight conditions for design, sea level is selected because it corresponds to the largest mass flow rate and inlet pressure. Hence, the key parameters for the fan design are obtained from Fig. 8.E2, which presents the flow properties at the most demanding operating point at sea level as obtained from the AEDsys program.

The fan design parameters (0.612M/sea level) are therefore as follows:

$\dot{m}_2 = 177.0$ lbm/s $P_{t2} = 18.17$ psia $T_{t2} = 557.5°R$

$\Delta T_t = 275.7°R$ $\pi_f \geq 3.5$ $\eta_f \geq 0.8693$ (Fig. 7.1)

$\gamma_c = 1.4$ $g_c c_{pc} = 6006$ ft^2/s^2-°R $R = 53.34$ ft-lbf/lbm-°R

8.3.1.2 Number of stages.   Table 8.1 lists the fan temperature rise per stage as the range between 60 and 100°F. Based on this estimate, the design temperature rise of 275.7°F for the fan will require either three or four stages. The change in total temperature for each stage is constant for the repeating stage, repeating row, mean-line design [see. Eq. (8.11)]. Assuming three stages, a total temperature increase of 91.9°F is required in each stage, and the required first stage total pressure ratio obtained from Eq. (4.9a-CPG) is

$$\pi_s = (\tau_s)^{\frac{\gamma_c e_f}{\gamma_c - 1}} = \left(\frac{557.5 + 91.9}{557.5}\right)^{3.5 \times 0.89} = (1.1648)^{3.115} = 1.6083$$

If we assume a stage inlet Mach number $M_1 = 0.6$, a diffusion factor $D = 0.5$, a solidity $\sigma = 1.0$, and a polytropic efficiency $e_f = 0.9$, Fig. 8.2a shows that an excessively large inlet flow angle $\alpha_1 > 70$ deg is required. To obtain the required stage temperature rise and keep the size of inlet flow angle α_1 reasonable, increases will be needed in the diffusion factor D, the solidity σ, and/or inlet stage Mach number M_1.

We therefore calculated the temperature rise per stage over a range of inlet flow angles α_1, diffusion factor D, and solidity σ for assumed values of inlet stage Mach number M_1 and polytropic efficiency e_f, and summarized the important results in Table 8.E1. They were obtained using Eqs. (8.6–8.17). (The same results can be obtained using the COMPR program.) Note that a mean-line design with a stage inlet Mach number $M_1 = 0.6$, a diffusion factor $D = 0.55$, a solidity $\sigma = 1.1$, polytropic efficiency e_f of 0.89 (see Table 8.E1), and an inlet flow angle $\alpha_1 = 30$ deg has a temperature rise of 92.6°F. This would allow the fan to be designed with three stages. Similar results are obtained for inlet flow angles $\alpha_1 = 40$ deg and solidity $\sigma = 1.0$ but at a higher mean rotor speed ωr_m, which would make the structural design more difficult.

8.3.1.3 Aerodynamic definition.
Consequently, the three-stage fan design is based on the analysis of Sec. 8.2.1 and the following assumptions: $D = 0.55$ (see Fig. 8.26); $M_1 = 0.6$ (first stage choice to increase stage temperature rise); $\sigma = 1.1$ (allows higher τ_s and π_s, see Fig. 8.2c); and $e_c = 0.89$ (used in all cycle calculations).

Table 8.E1   Summary of repeating stage, repeating row, mean-line design properties ($M_1 = 0.6$, $e_c = 0.89$, and $T_{t1} = 557.5°R$)

D	σ	α_1, deg	α_2, deg	τ_s	ΔT_t, °F	π_s	$\omega r_m / V_1$	ωr_m, ft/s	M_{1R}
0.50	1.0	30	51.79	1.1290	71.9	1.4591	1.6000	1073	0.840
0.50	1.0	40	57.67	1.1413	78.8	1.5093	1.8532	1243	0.859
0.55	1.0	30	53.76	1.1539	85.8	1.5621	1.6815	1128	0.879
0.55	1.0	40	59.32	1.1685	93.9	1.6244	1.9342	1297	0.901
0.50	1.1	30	52.59	1.1386	77.3	1.4982	1.6321	1095	0.855
0.50	1.1	40	58.29	1.1510	84.2	1.5495	1.8825	1263	0.875
0.55	1.1	30	54.62	1.1661	92.6	1.6141	1.7194	1153	0.897
0.55	1.1	40	59.99	1.1808	100.8	1.6783	1.9693	1321	0.919

The required stage total temperature rise of 91.9°F can be obtained with an inlet flow angle $\alpha_1 = 29.2$ deg with the following results:

$$\alpha_1 = 29.20 \qquad \text{assumed}$$

$$\Gamma = 2.666 \qquad \text{Eq. (8.7)}$$

$$\alpha_2 = 54.20 \qquad \text{Eq. (8.6)}$$

$$\Delta\alpha = 25.00 \qquad \alpha_2 - \alpha_1$$

$$\tau_s = 1.153 \qquad \text{Eq. (8.12)}$$

$$\Delta T_t = 91.90°\text{F} \qquad T_{t1}(\tau_s - 1)$$

$$\pi_s = 1.165 \qquad \text{Eq. (8.13)}$$

$$V_1 = M_1 a_1 = M_1 a_{std} \sqrt{\frac{T_{t1}/T_{std}}{1 + (\gamma_c - 1)M_1^2/2}} = 670.7 \text{ ft/s}$$

$$\frac{\omega r_m}{V_1} = 1.698 \qquad \text{Eq. (8.16)}$$

$$\omega r_m = 1139 \text{ ft/s}$$

$$M_{1R} = 0.895 \qquad \text{Eq. (8.17)}$$

so that

$$\tau_f = 1.495 \qquad \text{(vs 1.495 of cycle analysis calculation)}$$

$$\pi_f = 3.496 \qquad \text{(vs 3.500 of cycle analysis calculation)}$$

$$\eta_f = 0.8694 \qquad \text{(vs 0.8693 of cycle analysis calculation)}$$

Because these results seem satisfactory, the annulus area A at the inlet and exit from each stage is calculated using Eq. (8.20), and the results are shown in Table 8. E2.

8.3.1.4 Airfoil centrifugal stress.

A conservative analysis will be performed here by using the largest (that is, the inlet) annulus area for each stage. Recognizing that the shaft rotational speed will be limited by the stage with the largest area (that is, the first stage) and assuming that advanced titanium will be

Table 8.E2   AAF Engine fan stage annulus areas

Quantity/stage no.	1	2	3	Fan exit
T_t, °R	557.5	649.4	741.3	833.2
P_t, psia	18.12	29.22	44.13	63.51
M_1, Eq. (8.13)	0.600	0.553	0.516	0.485
A, in.^{2}	588.8	415.8	308.4	237.3

used with the properties (see Table 8.5 and Fig. 8.15)

$$\sigma_c = 50{,}000 \text{ psi} \qquad (\text{first stage } T_{t1R} = 603°\text{R})$$

$$\rho = 9.08 \text{ slug/ft}^3$$

$$A_t/A_h = 0.8$$

Rearranging Eq. (8.63) to find the allowable rotational speed

$$\omega = \sqrt{\frac{4\pi\sigma_c}{\rho A(1 + A_t/A_h)}} \qquad (8.E1)$$

reveals that

$$\omega = 1160 \text{ rad/s}$$

$$N = 11{,}070 \text{ rpm}$$

This corresponds to a value of 6.49×10^{10} in.^{2}-rpm^2 for AN^2 (see Fig. 8.19). The COMPR program gives a slightly different value of AN^2 (6.14×10^{10} in.^{2}-rpm^2) because it uses the average annulus flow area of the rotor airfoil and a blade taper ratio (A_t/A_h) of 1.0 in its calculation.

The mean radius can now be calculated from

$$r_m = \frac{\omega r_m}{\omega} = \frac{1139}{1160} = 0.982 \text{ ft} = 11.78 \text{ in.}$$

It is now possible to determine many properties of the airfoils using Fig. 8.4, Eq. (8.63), and the following relationship:

$$A = 2\pi r_m h = \pi(r_t^2 - r_h^2)$$

The results are summarized in Table 8.E3. Note, however, that even the third stage has $\sigma_c = 26{,}200$ psi, indicating that titanium airfoils are required on every fan rotor (see Fig. 8.15).

It should be evident at this point that the main advantage of increasing σ_c/ρ is to increase ω and thus reduce r_m, which reduces the frontal area, volume, and weight of the engine. An important virtue of the large ω is that the low-pressure turbine, which drives the fan, can produce more power per stage and hence will need fewer stages.

Table 8.E3 AAF Engine fan airfoil centrifugal stresses

Quantity/stage no.	1	2	3	Fan exit
A, in.^{2}	588.8	415.8	308.4	237.3
h, in.	7.95	5.62	4.17	3.21
r_t, in.	15.76	14.59	13.87	13.39
r_h, in.	7.81	8.98	9.70	10.18
T_{t1R}, °R	603	695	787	——
AN^2, 10^{10} in.^{2}-rpm^2	6.49	5.09	3.78	——
σ_c, ksi	50.0	35.3	26.2	——

Table 8.E4   AAF Engine fan rim and disk results

Quantity/stage no.	1	2	3
T_{t1R}, °R	603	695	787
σ_r, σ_d, ksi	50.0	45.0	40.0
ρ, slug/ft^3	9.08	9.08	9.08
σ_r/ρ, ksi/(slug/ft^3)	5.5	5.0	4.4
$\bar{\sigma}_{blades}/\sigma_r$	0.10	0.10	0.10
h, in. $(= r_t - r_h)$	7.95	5.61	4.17
r_h, in.	7.81	8.98	9.70
h_r, in. (selected)^a	2	1.5	1.0
r_r, in. $(= r_h - h_r)$	5.81	7.48	8.70
h_r/r_r	0.344	0.201	0.115
ωr_r, ft/s (wheel speed)	562	723	841
$\rho(\omega r_r)^2/2\sigma_d$ (disk shape factor)	0.199	0.363	0.558
W_{dr}/W_r (rim web thickness)	−0.022	0.096	0.140

^{a}Selected h_r can be obtained in COMPR program by entering the appropriate value of h_r/W_r in stage sketch data window.

8.3.1.5   Rim web thickness/allowable wheel speed.   Supporting the rotating airfoils at the front or cool end of the engine is seldom difficult. In this case, the rim is a continuation of the disk, and so the same advanced titanium material properties are used in both. Thus, if the material properties σ_r and ρ [or specific strength (σ_r/ρ)], $\bar{\sigma}_{blades}/\sigma_r$, h_r, and r_h are as given in Table 8.E4 for stages 1, 2, and 3, the values of r_r, h_r/r_r, wheel speed ωr_r (Fig. 8.23), disk shape factor (Fig. 8.22), and rim web thickness [Eq. (8.67)] tabulated there are obtained. These results are all reasonable and acceptable. Note in particular that the disks will either be insignificant (stage 3) or nonexistent/self-supporting (stage 1). This often occurs in practice, as can be confirmed by examining cross-sectional views of current fan configurations in the AEDsys Engine Pictures files. The COMPR program gives similar but slightly different results because some of the information is entered in ratio form. For example, the results given in Table 8.E4 are based on selected hub heights h_r, whereas the COMPR program uses input values of blade chord-to-height ratio c/h, rim width-to-blade axial chord ratio W_r/c_x, and rim height-to-width ratio h_r/W_r to determine the rim height h_r and the resulting rim and disk dimensions.

8.3.1.6   Radial variation.   The fan blades have low hub/tip radius ratios that indicates large radial variations in both airflow and blade shape. Based on free vortex swirl distribution, the COMPR program calculations for the hub of the first stage fan give a near zero degree of reaction and very high exit swirl velocity, which are undesirable. Sophisticated CFD methods would be employed to design these blades and alleviate these problems.[19] Although the degrees of reaction at the hubs of the latter fan stages are acceptable, they would also be designed with CFD. Please note the commonsense result that, because the hub/tip radius ratio decreases as the total pressure increases, the magnitudes of the radial variations also diminish.

8.3.1.7 Fan design summary. The AAF engine fan design found here is sufficiently capable and sound as to constitute a confident starting point for more detailed studies. The results obtained are certainly very encouraging and suggest that a three-stage fan capable of doing the required job can be built with modern technology. The next step would be to use the results of the repeating stage/repeating row design as a starting point in COMPR for a final design having a constant tip radius in order to maximize the value of the rotational speed and minimize the possibility of rubbing between rotor blade tips and air seals during axial shifting.

The design status may be conveniently captured in the pictorial form of Fig. 8.E3 (from the cross-section sketch results of the COMPR program) in order to reveal the proportions of the selected three-stage fan. The pictured fan design includes inlet guide vanes with an entry Mach number of 0.5, solidity σ of 0.5, and chord-to-height ratio $c/h = 0.3$. A chord-to-height ratio $c/h = 0.4$ was used for both the rotor and stator blades. In addition, a rim width-to-blade axial chord ratio $W_r/c_x = 1.1$ and rim height-to-width ratio $h_r/W_r = 0.625$, 0.65, and 0.6 were used for the first, second, and third stages, respectively, in order to obtain the assumed values of the rim height h_r. The overall length of the three-stage fan including the inlet guide vanes is estimated to be 16.9 in.

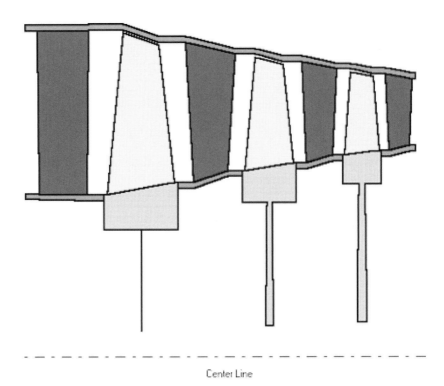

Center Line

Fig. 8.E3   AAF Engine fan cross section (COMPR screen capture).

One is always tempted to remark at this point that the design "looks like" a fan. This should not be the least bit surprising, but rather should be expected because the shape of the fan is determined by the physics of the situation, and not by the whim or fancy of the designer. You will find this to be equally true for the other AAF Engine components.

8.3.2 High-Pressure Turbine Design—AAF Engine

The process begins with the selection of the turbine design point and the turbine disk material. An initial estimate of the mean wheel speed is made based on the allowable wheel speed calculated for a disk shape factor (DSF) value of two. The number of stages are chosen and their temperature ratios determined. Design choices are then made for the stage parameters M_2 and M_{3R} and the aerodynamic definition of each stage fixed. Next, rotating airfoil material and taper choices are selected; the rotational speed of the high-speed spool is found from centrifugal stress considerations; and the airfoil radii are calculated. Finally wheel parameters h_r and $\bar{\sigma}_{blades}/\sigma_r$ are estimated; and the wheel speed, disk shape factor, and rim web thickness are determined by rim and disk stresses considerations.

8.3.2.1 Design point.
The highest rotor mechanical speeds and centrifugal stresses occur at the highest value of θ_4 for a given turbine temperature ratio. Thus the high-pressure turbine design will be at a flight condition where T_{t4} is maximum. The design requirements of the high-pressure compressor place its design point at full throttle flight conditions where $\theta_0 = \theta_{0\,break}$, and this condition at sea level is selected for the high-pressure compressor design because it corresponds to the largest mass flow rate and inlet pressure. Because the high-pressure turbine drives the high-pressure compressor, the high-pressure turbine design point corresponds to the same flight conditions.

From Table 7.E3 and Fig. 8.E2, the high-pressure turbine design point parameters (0.612M/sea level) are as follows:

$$\tau_{tH} = 0.7853 \quad P_{t4.1} = 483.6 \text{ psia} \quad \gamma_t = 1.300$$

$$\pi_{tH} = 0.3083 \quad T_{t4.1} = 3102°R \quad g_c c_{pt} = 7378 \text{ ft}^2/\text{s}^2\text{-}°R$$

$$\eta_{tH} = 0.9028 \quad \dot{m}_{4.1} = 97.39 \text{ lbm/s} \quad R_t = 53.0 \text{ ft-lbf/lbm-}°R$$

8.3.2.2 Initial estimate of wheel speed.
Presuming that advancing technology will make disk materials available for the AAF engine that provide (see Table 8.5 and Fig. 8.15)

$$\sigma_d = 30,000 \text{ psi} \quad \text{and} \quad \rho = 16.0 \text{ slug/ft}^3$$

under the anticipated environmental conditions, and applying Eq. (8.69) with an assumed DSF of 2 (see Fig. 8.23), then

$$\omega r_r = \sqrt{4\sigma_d/\rho} = 1040 \text{ ft/s}$$

which allows the initial estimate of the mean wheel speed

$$\omega r_m = 1150 \text{ ft/s}$$

This result must be checked later.

8.3.2.3 Aerodynamic design. It is important, particularly in the complex, expensive, and heavy high-pressure turbine, to reduce as much as reasonably possible the number of stages. A first guess is that the turbine will have only one stage, whence

$$\tau_{ts} = \tau_{tH} = T_{t4.4}/T_{t4.1} = 0.7853 \quad \Omega = \frac{\omega r_m}{\sqrt{g_c c_{pt} T_{t4.1}}} = 0.240$$

Placing this point on Fig. 8.8 reveals that a single-stage design of this type would require both a large M_2 and a value of $\alpha_2 > 80$ deg, making efficient aerodynamic design impossible (see Sec. 8.2.2). However, a two-stage design with each τ_{ts} between 0.85 and 0.90 falls well within the "safe" region and thus will be attempted next.

8.3.2.4 Stage temperature ratios. A reasonable approach to efficient stage design is to have the inlet flow angle α_2 and exit relative Mach number M_{3R} the same for both stages. However the Mach number leaving the first stage turbine nozzles needs to be supersonic ($M_2 > 1$), whereas that leaving the second stage needs to be subsonic ($M_2 < 1$). For the first stage, $\Omega_{stage\ 1} = 0.240$ and, assuming $\alpha_2 = 60$ deg, $M_2 = 1.0$, and $M_{3R} = 0.9$, then Fig. 8.8 gives $(\tau_{ts})_{stage\ 1} = 0.88$. For the second stage, assuming $\alpha_2 = 60$ deg, $M_2 = 0.9$, and $M_{3R} = 0.9$ with

$$\Omega_{stage\ 2} = \frac{\omega r_m}{\sqrt{g_c c_{pt}(\tau_{ts})_{stage\ 1} T_{t4.1}}} = \frac{\Omega_{stage\ 1}}{\sqrt{(\tau_{ts})_{stage\ 1}}} = 0.256,$$

then Fig. 8.8 gives $(\tau_{ts})_{stage\ 2} = 0.89$. Because $(\tau_{ts})_{stage\ 1}(\tau_{ts})_{stage\ 2} = 0.783$, a two-stage high-pressure turbine with the required total temperature ratio of 0.7853 is easily obtainable. The assumed stage data just noted will be used as the starting point in the design of the two-stage high-pressure turbine either using Eqs. (8.37–8.52) or the AEDsys TURBN program (unknown: α_3; known: α_2, M_2, and M_{3R}).

8.3.2.5 Aerodynamic definition. Directly applying the methods of Sec. 8.2.2 for constant axial velocity, selected Mach number, mean-line stage design to the proposed two stage design for a mean rotor speed (ωr_m) of 1150 ft/s, M_{3R} of 0.8, and polytropic efficiency of 0.89 (used in all cycle calculations) leads to the results in Table 8.E5.

Thus

$$\tau_{tH} = 0.7853 \quad \text{(same as cycle calculations)}$$

$$\pi_{tH} = 0.3083 \quad \text{(same as cycle calculations)}$$

and

$$\eta_{tH} = 0.9028 \quad \text{(same as cycle calculations)} \quad \text{(4.9d-CPG)}$$

Two points are worthy of special mention here. First, because both stages are rather lightly loaded, one is tempted to shift work either to or from the high-pressure spool in order to make more use of the hardware or to increase τ_{tH} enough that a single-stage high-pressure turbine will suffice. Second, the resulting (not imposed) values of stage loading ψ are in line with those of Tables 8.4a and 8.4b.

Table 8.E5   AAF Engine high-pressure turbine aerodynamic results

Quantity/stage no.	1	2
$T_{t2},°R$	3102	2720
M_2	1.0	0.9
$\Omega = \omega r_m / \sqrt{g_c c_{pt} T_{t2}}$	0.2400	0.2563
α_2, deg (selected)	60.0	52.9
β_2, Eq. (8.43)	38.38	22.26
T_{t2R}, °R, Eq. (8.44)	2862	2551
β_3, deg, Eq. (8.45)	50.56	46.15
$\beta_2 + \beta_3$, deg	88.94	68.41
α_3, deg, Eq. (8.48)	15.43	7.30
τ_{ts}, Eq. (8.50)	0.8769	0.8956
$°R_t$, Eq. (8.51)	0.2254	0.3459
π_{ts}, Eq. (8.53)	0.5275	0.5846
ψ, Eq. (8.57)	2.136	1.589

8.3.2.6 Airfoil centrifugal stress.   A conservative analysis will be performed here, by using both the average rotor annulus area for the first stage and assuming that $A_t/A_h = 1.0$. The annulus area at inlet and exit of each stage is calculated using Eq. (8.20) where the mass flow parameter (MFP) is given by Eq. (1.3). The results are summarized in Table 8.E6.

Employing Eq. (8.E1) at the average rotor annulus area of 47.56 in.^{2} for stage one

$$\omega = \sqrt{\frac{4\pi\sigma_c}{\rho A(1 + A_t/A_h)}}$$

with

$$\sigma_c = 21,000 \text{ psi}\quad \text{(advanced material, cf. Fig. 8.15)}$$

Table 8.E6   AAF Engine high-pressure turbine annulus area

Stage no.		One			Two	
Stage station	1	2	3/1	2		3
Engine station	4.0	4.1	——	——		4.4
Quantity						
$\dot{m}$, lbm/s	92.34	97.39	97.39	97.39		97.39
T_t, °R	3200	3102	2720	2720		2436
T_{tR}, °R	——	2862	2862	2551		2551
M	0.2	1.0	0.53	0.9		0.56
P_t, psia	483.6	——	255.1	——		149.2
α, deg	0	60.0	15.43	52.9		7.3
A, in.^{2}	61.25	43.54	51.58	64.58		78.02

Table 8.E7   AAF Engine high-pressure turbine airfoil centrifugal stresses

Stage no.		One		Two	
Stage station	1	2	3/1	2	3
Engine station	4.0	4.1	——	——	4.4
Quantity					
r_t, in.	7.69	7.50	7.56	7.72	7.86
r_m, in.	7.00	7.00	7.00	7.00	7.00
r_h, in.	6.31	6.50	6.44	6.26	6.14
$h = r_t - r_h$, in.	1.38	1.00	1.12	1.44	1.72
σ_c, kpsi	——	——	21.0/——	——	32.4
AN^2, 10^{10} in.^{2}-rpm^2	——	——	1.65/——	——	2.47

and

$$\rho = 15.00 \text{ slug/ft}^3 \qquad \text{(Table 8.5)}$$

then

$$\omega = 1970 \text{ rad/s}$$

$$N = 18{,}800 \text{ rpm}$$

$$r_m = (\omega r_m)/\omega = 1150/1970 = 7.00 \text{ in.}$$

Assuming that the airfoils have a common mean radius of 7 in. the airfoil properties are as shown in Table 8.E7.

Airfoils of such small heights are challenging from the standpoint of both effective cooling and high aerodynamic efficiency, but are certainly possible. To reduce r_m and thus increase their height, the foregoing calculations can be traced back to reveal that the rotational speed N may have to increase in order to maintain Ω, thus requiring an even stronger blade material. The present design is, however, perfectly adequate and will be pursued further.

8.3.2.7 *Rim web thickness/allowable wheel speed.*   Because the rim is part of the disk, the same advanced of material properties are used. Thus, if the material properties (σ_r, ρ) [or specific strength (σ_r/ρ)], $\bar{\sigma}_{blades}/\sigma_r$, h_r, and r_h are as given in Table 8.E8, then the listed values of r_r, h_r/r_r, wheel speed ωr_r (Fig. 8.23), disk shape factor (Fig. 8.22), and rim web thickness [Eq. (8.66)] are obtained.

The results of Table 8.E8 indicate that the wheel speed is less than the initial estimate of 1040 ft/s, the disk shape factor is less than 2.0, and the rim web thickness ratio is less than 1.0. All are satisfactory values (see Figs. 8.22 and 8.23). This is evidently a situation where the high-pressure spool rotational speed is dictated by the turbine airfoil centrifugal stress.

8.3.2.8 *Radial variation.*   The high-pressure turbine blades have high hub/tip radius ratios that produce small radial variations in both airflow and blade

Table 8.E8   AAF Engine high-pressure turbine rim and disk results

Quantity/stage no.	1	2
T_{t2R}, °R	2862	2551
σ_r, σ_d, ksi	30.0	30.0
ρ, slug/ft^3	16.0	16.0
σ_r/ρ, ksi/(slug/ft^3)	1.88	1.88
$\bar{\sigma}_{blades}/\sigma_r$,	0.20	0.20
r_h, in.	6.50	6.27
h_r, in. (selected)[a]	1.0	1.0
r_r, in. ($= r_h - h_{Rim}$)	5.5	5.27
h_r/r_r	0.182	0.190
ωr_r, ft/s (wheel speed)	900	870
$\rho(\omega r_r)^2/2\sigma_d$ (DSF)	0.678	0.668
W_{dr}/W_r (rim web thickness)	0.353	0.349

[a] Selected h_r can be obtained in TURBN program by inputting appropriate value of h_r/W_r in stage sketch data window.

shape. Based on free vortex swirl distribution, the TURBN program calculations of the first stage give degree of reactions for the hub and tip of 0.10 and 0.32, respectively. These are acceptable variations.

8.3.2.9   High-pressure turbine design summary.

This AAF engine high-pressure turbine design is sufficiently sound and balanced that it represents an entirely satisfactory starting point. Thus, no other iteration will be carried out. The TURBN cross section results displayed in Fig. 8.E4 reveal the basic configuration of the two-stage high-pressure turbine. The fact that the rotor airfoils have an almost constant tip radius is an advantage from the standpoint of sealing against tip leakage because unavoidable axial motion has little effect on clearance. The complete turbine stage computations of TURBN could be used now, for example, to trim this design to have an exactly constant tip radius. The turbine has an approximate overall length of 7.0 in. Comparison with examples in the AEDsys Engine Pictures file will convince you that it looks like many of its brethren.

8.3.2.10   Spool design speeds comment.

Before proceeding with the design of the remaining two rotating machines, the high-pressure compressor and the low-pressure turbine, special note should be taken regarding the assumptions about their design mechanical speeds.

The fan and high-pressure compressor are initially designed to their highest required pressure ratios. Given normal map behavior, these will also correspond to their highest required mechanical speeds. The turbines that share their respective shafts must be designed to perform reliably at the same mechanical speeds. It may be safely assumed that, because turbine efficiency varies slowly around the map, the exact choice of the turbine aerodynamic design point is not critical.

In the case of the high-speed spool, the high-pressure turbine has been designed to operate at its almost constant design point at a structurally acceptable mechanical

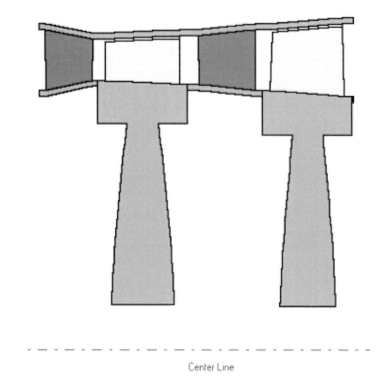

Fig. 8.E4   AAF Engine two stage high-pressure turbine cross section (TURBN screen capture).

speed (that is, 18,800 rpm). The high-pressure compressor may therefore not exceed this value, and logic indicates that the highest required pressure ratio should occur at the same mechanical speed.

On the low-speed spool, similar reasoning applies. The maximum mechanical speed of the shaft has already been determined for the fan (that is, 11,070 rpm), and this cannot be exceeded by the low-pressure turbine. The corresponding aerodynamic design point of the low-pressure turbine must be chosen to be some representative condition, the exact one being less critical because of the forgiving nature of the turbine efficiency. To illustrate this, the low-pressure turbine will be designed for the engine design point at the maximum allowable mechanical speed.

Other approaches are, of course, possible, but all will lead to iterations that converge on the best answer. What is important are the means to get started and the tools to do the work. This example has provided the first approximation and some indications of the direction that will yield improvement. In the end, everything must work well together. Hence

$$N_L = 11,070 \text{ rpm}$$

$$N_H = 18,800 \text{ rpm}$$

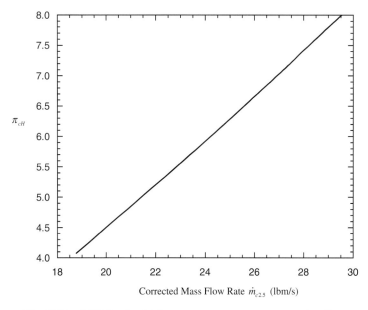

Fig. 8.E5   AAF Engine high-pressure compressor operating line.

8.3.3 High-Pressure Compressor Design—AAF Engine

Because this process parallels that of the fan design, other than the fact that the mechanical rotational speed is known in advance, only the outline will be repeated here.

8.3.3.1 *Design point.*   The high-pressure compressor (a.k.a. "compressor") operating line of Fig. 7.E11, reproduced here as Fig. 8.E5, reveals that the compressor must operate over a wide range of pressure ratios and corrected inlet mass flow rates, although the variations are not as large as for the fan. The operating point requiring the highest pressure ratio again corresponds to full throttle flight conditions at $\theta_0 = \theta_{0\,break}$, where π_{cH} is 8.0 (see Table 7.E3). To be certain that the high-pressure compressor can meet this most stringent condition, this will be chosen as the design point. Of all of the possible theta break flight conditions for design, sea level is selected because it corresponds to the largest mass flow rate and inlet pressure. Hence, the key parameters are obtained from Fig. 8.E2, which presents the flow properties at the most demanding operating point obtained from the AEDsys program.

The high-pressure compressor design parameters (0.612M/sea level) are as follows:

$\dot{m}_{2.5} = 100.9\,\text{lbm/s}$ $P_{t2.5} = 63.51\,\text{psia}$ $T_{t2.5} = 833.3°\text{R}$

$\Delta T_t = 780.0°\text{R}$ $\pi_{cH} \geq 8.0$ $\eta_{cH} \geq 0.8678\,(\text{Fig. 7.1})$

$\gamma_c = 1.4$ $g_c c_{pc} = 6006\,\text{ft}^2/\text{s}^2\text{-}°\text{R}$ $R = 53.34\,\text{ft-lbf/lbm-}°\text{R}$

and

$$\omega_H = 1970 \text{ rad/s}, \quad N_H = 18{,}800 \text{ rpm}$$

8.3.3.2 Number of stages. Table 8.1 gives the ΔT_t per stage range of design values for high-pressure compressors as 60–90°R. To achieve an overall ΔT_t of 780.0°R with a compressor having n repeating stages, the following stage total temperature increases are required:

Number of stages, n	Stage ΔT_t, °R
8	97.5
9	86.7
10	78.0

An initial choice of $n = 9$ gives a stage ΔT_t of 86.7°R (upper range of design range from Table 8.1) that is slightly more conservative than the fan, thus reducing the development risk of the system.

8.3.3.3 Aerodynamic definition. The analysis of Sec. 8.2.1 on repeating stage, repeating row mean-line design is used with the following assumptions: $D = 0.5$ (conventional technology); $M_1 = 0.5$ (upper range of corrected mass flow/area in Table 8.1); $\sigma = 1.0$ (conventional technology); and $e_c = 0.90$ (used in all cycle calculations).

The required stage total temperature rise of 86.7°F can be obtained with an inlet flow angle (α_1) of 45.2 deg with the following results:

$$\alpha_1 = 45.2 \text{ deg} \qquad \text{assumed}$$
$$\Gamma = 3.845 \qquad \text{Eq. (8.7)}$$
$$\alpha_2 = 60.85 \text{ deg} \qquad \text{Eq. (8.6)}$$
$$\Delta\alpha = 15.65 \text{ deg} \qquad \alpha_2 - \alpha_1$$
$$\tau_s = 1.104 \qquad \text{Eq. (8.12)}$$
$$\Delta T_t = 86.67°\text{F} \qquad T_{t1}(\tau_s - 1)$$
$$\pi_s = 1.366 \qquad \text{Eq. (8.13) – First stage}$$

$$V_1 = M_1 a_1 = M_1 a_{std} \sqrt{\frac{T_{t1}/T_{std}}{1 + (\gamma_c - 1)M_1^2/2}} = 690.4 \text{ ft/s}$$

$$\omega r_m / V_1 = 1.973 \qquad \text{Eq. (8.16)}$$
$$\omega r_m = 1362 \text{ ft/s}$$
$$M_{1R} = 0.723 \qquad \text{Eq. (8.17)}$$

Table 8.E9   AAF Engine high-pressure compressor annulus areas

Quantity/ stage no.	1	2	3	4	5	6	7	8	9	Exit
$T_t, °R$	833.3	920.0	1007	1093	1180	1267	1353	1440	1527	1613
P_t, psia	63.5	86.7	100.1	149.4	190.0	237.5	292.6	355.8	427.7	508.9
M_1, Eq. (8.13)	0.500	0.475	0.453	0.434	0.417	0.402	0.389	0.376	0.365	0.355
A, in.^{2}	164.0	131.0	106.9	88.8	74.8	63.9	55.1	48.0	42.2	37.3

so that

$$\tau_{cH} = 1.936 \quad \text{(vs 1.935 of cycle analysis calculation)}$$

$$\pi_{cH} = 8.013 \quad \text{(vs 8.000 of cycle analysis calculation)}$$

$$\eta_{cH} = 0.8678 \quad \text{(vs 0.8678 of cycle analysis calculation)}$$

These results are satisfactory, and so the annulus area at the inlet and exit from each stage can be calculated using Eq. (8.20). The results are summarized in Table 8.E9. The mean radius is 8.3 in. $[(\omega r_m)]/\omega = 1362/1970]$. Special note should be taken of the fact that $T_{t3} = 1613°R$ is close to the rule-of-thumb upper limit for compressor discharge temperature of $1700°R$ ($1240°F$) of Table 8.1.

8.3.3.4   Airfoil centrifugal stress. With ω known, and assuming constant mean radius and $A_t/A_h = 1.0$ and an advanced titanium (see Table 8.5 and Fig. 8.15) having $\rho = 9.08$ slug/ft^3, the results in Table 8.E10 may be directly calculated.

Two observations are important here. First, the diminishing area more than compensates for the effect of increasing temperature on allowable AN^2 or σ_c through the compressor. The result is that it will be possible to manufacture all of the rotor airfoils from titanium. Second, the exit blade height of 0.81 in., although

Table 8.E10   AAF Engine high-pressure compressor airfoil centrifugal stresses

Quantity/ stage no.	1	2	3	4	5	6	7	8	9
A, in.^{2}	164.0	131.0	106.9	88.8	74.8	63.9	55.1	48.0	42.2
AN^2, $\times 10^{10}$ in.^{2}-rpm^2	5.80	4.63	3.78	3.14	2.64	2.26	1.95	1.70	1.49
h, in.	3.15	2.51	2.05	1.71	1.43	1.23	1.06	0.92	0.81
r_t, in.	9.87	9.55	9.32	9.15	9.01	8.91	8.83	8.76	8.70
r_h, in.	6.72	7.04	7.27	7.44	7.58	7.68	7.77	7.84	7.89
$T_{t1R}, °R$	877	963	1050	1137	1223	1310	1397	1483	1570
σ_c/ρ, [ksi/(slug/ft^3)]	4.89	3.90	3.18	2.64	2.22	1.91	1.64	1.43	1.26
σ_c, ksi	44.4	35.4	28.9	24.0	20.2	17.3	14.9	13.0	11.4

Table 8.E11   AAF Engine high-pressure compressor rim and disk results

Quantity/stage no.	1	9
σ_r, σ_d, ksi	25.0	25.0
ρ, slug/ft^3	9.08	9.08
σ_r/ρ, ksi/(slug/ft^3)	2.75	2.75
$\bar{\sigma}_{blades}/\sigma_r$	0.10	0.10
h, in. $(= r_t - r_h)$	3.15	0.81
r_h, in.	6.72	7.89
h_r, in. (selected)[a]	1	0.5
r_r, in. $(= r_h - h_r)$	5.72	7.39
h_r/r_r	0.175	0.067
ωr_r, ft/s (wheel speed)	939	1213
$\rho(\omega r_r)^2/2\sigma_d$ (disk shape factor)	1.145	1.866
W_{dr}/W_r (rim web thickness)	0.411	0.308

[a]Selected h_r can be obtained in COMPR program by entering appropriate value of h_r/W_r in stage sketch data window.

seemingly small, is similar to those found in many contemporary machines and therefore quite practical to manufacture.

8.3.3.5 Rim web thickness/allowable wheel speed.
An advanced titanium material is selected for the disk (see Table 8.5 and Fig. 8.15). Thus, if the material properties (σ_r, ρ) [or specific strength (σ_r/ρ)], $\bar{\sigma}_{blades}/\sigma_r$, h_r, and r_h are as given in Table 8.E11 for stages 1 and 9, the listed values of r_r, h_r/r_r, wheel speed ωr_r (Fig. 8.23), disk shape factor (Fig. 8.22), and rim web thickness [Eq. (8.66)] are obtained.

The wheel speed, disk shape factor, and the ratio W_{dr}/W_r remain in reasonable ranges (see Figs. 8.22 and 8.23) throughout the compressor, indicating that modest disks are required. This can also be confirmed by examining cross-sectional views of existing engines.

8.3.3.6 Radial variation.
The high-pressure compressor blades of the first three stages have hub/tip radius ratios from 0.68 to 0.78 that indicate moderate radial variations in both airflow and blade shape. Based on free vortex swirl distribution, the COMPR program calculations for the hub of the first, second, and third compressor stages give a degree of reaction of 0.28, 0.33, and 0.37, respectively, and diffusion factors less than 0.56. All are within reason. As anticipated, the latter stages of the high-pressure compressor experience smaller radial variations as a result of their higher hub/tip radius ratios.

8.3.3.7 High-pressure compressor design summary.
The AAF engine high-pressure compressor design found here is sufficiently capable and sound as to constitute a confident starting point for more detailed studies. The results obtained are certainly very encouraging and suggest that a high-pressure compressor capable of doing the required job can be built with modern technology. The next step would

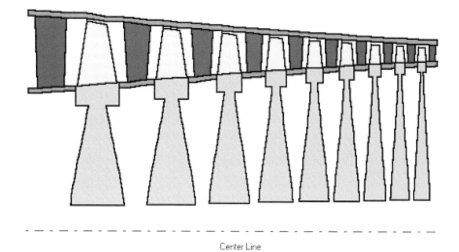

Center Line

Fig. 8.E6   AAF Engine high-pressure compressor cross section (COMPR screen capture).

be to use the results of the repeating stage/repeating row design as a starting point in COMPR for a final design having a constant tip radius in order to maximize the value of the rotational speed and minimize the possibility of rubbing between rotor blade tips and air seals during axial shifting.

The design status may be conveniently captured in the pictorial form of Fig. 8.E6 (from the cross-section sketch results of the COMPR program) in order to reveal the proportions of the selected nine-stage high-pressure compressor. The pictured high-pressure compressor design includes inlet guide vanes with an entry Mach number of 0.35, solidity σ of 0.5, and chord-to-height ratio $c/h = 0.5$. A chord-to-height ratio $c/h = 0.6$ was used for both the rotor and stator blades and a rim width-to-blade axial chord ratio $W_r/c_x = 1.1$ was used. In addition, the value of the rim height-to-width ratio h_r/W_r varied from 0.625 for stage one to 1.36 for stage nine in order to obtain the assumed rim height h_r of 1 in. for stage one and 1/2 in. for stage nine. The overall length of the nine-stage compressor is estimated to be 17.0 in.

Once again, it is pleasing, but no longer surprising, to discover that the design "looks like" a compressor.

8.3.4   Low-Pressure Turbine Design—AAF Engine

Because this process parallels that of the high-pressure turbine, other than the fact that the mechanical rotational speed is known in advance, only the outline will be repeated here. The process begins with the selection of the turbine design point and the turbine disk material. An initial estimate of the mean wheel speed is made based on the allowable wheel speed calculated for a disk shape factor (*DSF*) value of two. The number of stages are chosen and their temperature ratios determined. Design choices are then made for the stage parameters M_2 and M_{3R}

and the aerodynamic definition of each stage fixed. Next, rotating airfoil material and taper choices are selected, the rotational speed of the high-speed spool is found from centrifugal stress considerations, and the airfoil radii are calculated. Finally the wheel parameters h_r and $\bar{\sigma}_{blades}/\sigma_r$ are estimated; and the wheel speed, disk shape factor, and rim web thickness are determined by rim and disk stresses considerations.

8.3.4.1 Design point.
From Table 7.E3 and Fig. 8.E2, the low-pressure turbine design point parameters (0.612M/sea level) are as follows:

$$\tau_{tH} = 0.8366 \quad P_{t4.5} = 149.1 \text{ psia} \quad \gamma_t = 1.300$$

$$\pi_{tH} = 0.4236 \quad T_{t4.5} = 2380°\text{R} \quad g_c c_{pt} = 7378 \text{ ft}^2/\text{s}^2\text{-}°\text{R}$$

$$\eta_{tH} = 0.9087 \quad \dot{m}_{4.5} = 102.44 \text{lbm/s} \quad R_t = 53.0 \text{ ft-lbf/lbm-}°\text{R}$$

and

$$\omega_L = 1160 \text{ rad/s}, \quad N_L = 11,070 \text{ rpm}$$

8.3.4.2 Disk consideration.
Because of lower temperatures and lower rotational speeds that are found in low-pressure turbines, disk design is never a fundamental limitation. However, the same care for durability and safety must be applied as in the high-pressure turbine. Since r_r will probably be less than 8 in., it follows that the rim speed $\omega_L r_r$ will not exceed 780 ft/s, well within the capability of existing disk materials (cf. Fig. 8.23).

8.3.4.3 Number of stages.
It is particularly important in the slowly rotating low-pressure turbine to reduce the number of stages as much as humanly possible. Referring to the AEDsys Engine Pictures file, you can easily find engines with as many as six low-pressure turbine stages. These are bound to be heavy and expensive machines.

A first guess is that the turbine will have only one stage with a mean radius of 9 in., whence

$$\tau_{ts} = \tau_{tL} = T_{t5}/T_{t4.5} = 0.8366 \quad \Omega = \frac{\omega r_m}{\sqrt{g_c c_{pt} T_{t4.5}}} = 0.2075$$

The story is quite similar to that of the high-pressure turbine. Placing this point on Fig. 8.8 reveals that a single-stage design of this type would require values of α_2 and M_2 so large that high aerodynamic efficiency could not be achieved. However, a two-stage design with each τ_{ts} between 0.85 and 0.90 falls well within the "safe" region and thus will be attempted next.

8.3.4.4 Stage temperature ratios.
A reasonable approach to efficient stage design is to have the inlet flow angle α_2 and exit relative Mach number M_{3R} the same for both stages. However the Mach number leaving the first stage turbine nozzles needs to be supersonic ($M_2 > 1$), whereas that leaving the second stage needs to be subsonic ($M_2 < 1$). For the first stage, $\Omega_{stage\ 1} = 0.208$ and assuming

Table 8.E12   AAF Engine low-pressure turbin aerodynamic results

Quantity/stage no.	1	2
T_{t2}, °R	2380	2105
$M_2, \backslash M_{3R}$	1.05\0.8	0.7\0.6
$\Omega = \omega r_m / \sqrt{g_c c_{pt} T_{t2}}$	0.2075	0.2594
α_2, deg (selected)	60.0	47.8
β_2, deg, Eq. (8.43)	43.63	12.16
T_{t2R}, °R, Eq. (8.44)	2203	2029
β_3, deg, Eq. (8.45)	48.59	37.73
$\beta_2 + \beta_3$, deg	92.22	49.89
α_3, deg, Eq. (8.48)	19.55	−6.49
τ_{ts}, Eq. (8.50)	0.8847	0.9458
$°R_t$, Eq. (8.51)	0.1160	0.3145
π_{ts}, Eq. (8.53)	0.5543	0.7646
ψ, Eq. (8.57)	2.694	1.132

$\alpha_2 = 60$ deg, $M_2 = 1.1$, and $M_{3R} = 0.9$, then Fig. 8.8 gives $(\tau_{ts})_{stage\ 1} = 0.87$. For the second stage, assuming $\alpha_2 = 60$ deg, $M_2 = 0.9$, and $M_{3R} = 0.9$ with

$$\Omega_{stage\ 2} = \frac{\omega r_m}{\sqrt{g_c c_{pt}(\tau_{ts})_{stage\ 1} T_{t4.1}}} = \frac{\Omega_{stage\ 1}}{\sqrt{(\tau_{ts})_{stage\ 1}}} = 0.223,$$

then Fig. 8.8 gives $(\tau_{ts})_{stage\ 2} = 0.88$. Because $(\tau_{ts})_{stage\ 1}(\tau_{ts})_{stage\ 2} = 0.766$, a two-stage low-pressure turbine with the required total temperature ratio of 0.8366 is easily obtainable. The assumed stage data just noted will be used as a starting point in the design of the high-pressure turbine using Eqs. (8.37–8.52) or the TURBN program (unknown: α_3; known: α_2, M_2, and M_{3R}).

Because neither of these stages is very highly loaded, remarks similar to those made about the high-pressure turbine apply. There appears, in fact, to be an opportunity to reduce the total number of turbine stages from four to three, but that would require a complete engine cycle iteration.

8.3.4.5 Aerodynamic definition.

Directly applying the methods of Sec. 8.2.2 on constant axial velocity, selected Mach number, mean-line stage design to the proposed two-stage design for a mean rotor speed (ωr_m) of 870 ft/s, and polytropic efficiency of 0.90 (used in all cycle calculations) leads to the results of Table 8.E12.

Thus

$$\tau_{tL} = 0.8366 \quad \text{(same as cycle calculations)}$$

$$\pi_{tL} = 0.4236 \quad \text{(same as cycle calculations)}$$

and

$$\eta_{tL} = 0.9087 \quad \text{(same as cycle calculations)} \quad \text{(4.9e-CPG)}$$

The resulting stage loading ψ is consistent with the data of Table 8.4b. Can you explain how and why the stage loading of low-pressure turbines is so high?

Table 8.E13   AAF Engine low-pressure turbine airfoil centrifugal stresses

Stage no.	One			Two	
Stage station	1	2	3/1	2	3
Engine station	4.5	—	—	—	5
Quantity					
$\dot{m}$, lbm/s	102.44	102.44	102.44	102.44	102.44
T_t, °R	2380	2380	2105	2105	1991
T_{tR}, °R	—	2203	2203	2029	2029
M	0.30	1.05	0.56	0.7	0.48
P_t, psia	149.1	—	82.6	—	63.1
α, deg	0	60.0	19.55	47.80	−6.49
A, in.^{2}	132.59	130.48	144.45	179.66	195.24
AN^2, × 10^{10} in.^{2}-rpm^2	—	—	1.68/—	—	2.30

8.3.4.6   Airfoil centrifugal stress.   A conservative analysis is performed and the results presented in Table 8.E13, by using both the average rotor annulus area for the first stage and that of $A_t/A_h = 1.0$. The annulus area at inlet and exit of each stage is calculated using Eq. (8.20) where the *MFP* is given by Eq. (1.3).

Employing Eq. (8.64) at the average rotor annulus area for each stage with $A_t/A_h = 1.0$ and $\rho = 17.00$ slug/ft^3 yields the stresses given in Table 8.E14, which is well within current capabilities (cf. Table 8.5 and Fig. 8.15). Assuming that the airfoils have a common r_m, the results of Table 8.E14 follow.

Airfoils of these dimensions are common in modern gas turbines. The present design is, therefore, perfectly adequate and will be pursued further.

8.3.4.7   Rim web thickness/allowable wheel speed.   Because the rim is part of the disk, the same type of material properties are used. Thus, if the material properties (σ_r, ρ) [or specific strength (σ_r/ρ)], $\bar{\sigma}_{blades}/\sigma_r$, h_r, and r_h are as given in Table 8.E15, then the listed values of r_r, h_r/r_r, wheel speed ωr_r (Fig. 8.23), disk shape factor (Fig. 8.22), and rim web thickness [Eq. (8.66)] are obtained.

Table 8.E14   AAF Engine low-pressure turbine airfoil results

Stage no.	One			Two	
Stage station	1	2	3/1	2	3
Engine station	4.5	—	—	—	5.0
Quantity					
r_t, in.	10.17	10.15	10.28	10.59	10.73
r_m, in.	9.00	9.00	9.00	9.00	9.00
r_h, in.	7.83	7.85	7.72	7.41	7.27
$h = r_t - r_h$, in.	2.34	2.30	2.56	3.18	3.46
σ_c/ρ [ksi/(slug/ft^3)]	—	—	1.42/—	—	1.94
σ_c, kpsi	—	—	24.1/—	—	32.9

Table 8.E15   AAF Engine low-pressure turbine rim and disk results

Quantity/stage no.	1	2
T_{t2R}, °R	2203	2029
σ_r, σ_d, ksi	32.0	32.0
ρ, slug/ft^3	17.0	17.0
σ_r/ρ, ksi/(slug/ft^3)	1.88	1.88
$\bar{\sigma}_{blades}/\sigma_r$	0.20	0.20
r_h, in.	7.85	7.41
h_r, in. (selected)[a]	1.0	1.0
r_r, in. ($= r_h - h_{Rim}$)	6.85	6.41
h_r/r_r	0.146	0.156
ωr_r, ft/s (wheel speed)	660	620
$\rho(\omega r_r)^2/2\sigma_d$ (disk shape factor)	0.808	0.748
W_{dr}/W_r (rim web thickness)	0.356	0.341

[a]Selected h_r can be obtained in TURBN program by entering the appropriate value of h_r/W_r in stage sketch data window.

The wheel speed is less than 700 ft/s, the disk shape factor less than 2.0, and the rim web thickness ratio less than 1.0. All are satisfactory values.

8.3.4.8   Radial variation.

The low-pressure turbine blades have low hub/tip radius ratios that indicate large radial variations in both airflow and blade shape. Based on free vortex swirl distribution, the TURBN program calculations for the degree of reaction at the hub of the first- and second-stage turbine give −0.16 and −0.01, respectively, which are undesirable. Sophisticated CFD methods would be employed to design these blades and alleviate this problem (Chapter 4 of Ref. 1).

8.3.4.9   Low-pressure turbine design summary.

This AAF Engine low-pressure turbine design is sufficiently sound and balanced so that it represents an entirely satisfactory starting point. Thus, no other iteration will be carried out. The TURBN cross section results displayed in Fig. 8.E7 reveal the basic configuration of the two-stage low-pressure turbine. The fact that the rotor airfoils have an almost constant tip radius is an advantage from the standpoint of sealing against tip leakage because unavoidable axial motion has little effect on clearance. The two-stage low-pressure turbine has exit guide vanes with exit Mach number of 0.4 and an approximate overall length of 10.3 in. Comparison with examples in the AEDsys Engine Pictures file will convince you that it looks like many of its brethren.

The low-pressure turbines' mean radius is 2 in. larger that that of the high-pressure turbine and will require a transition duct. The TURBN program could be used to better align these two turbines.

8.3.5   AAF Engine Turbomachinery Design Closure

The present design status is summarized by Fig. 8.E8a, which combines the fan and high-pressure compressor, and Fig. 8.E8b, which combines the high-pressure and low-pressure turbines. Although this is a satisfactory start and no important technological or geometrical barriers to a successful design have been encountered, further iteration would focus on the following points: 1) redistributing the stage

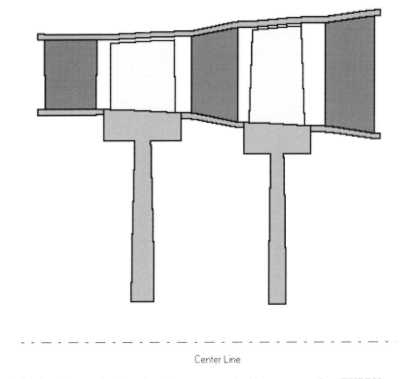

Fig. 8.E7   AAF Engine two-stage low-pressure turbine cross section (TURBN screen capture).

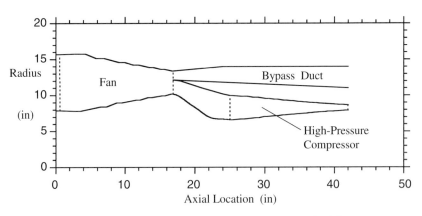

Fig. 8.E8a   General arrangement of the AAF Engine fan and high-pressure compressor.

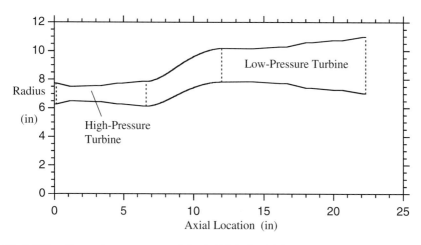

Fig. 8.E8b   General arrangement of the AAF Engine high-pressure and low-pressure turbines.

temperature rise in the high-pressure compressor (more in the rear stages and less in the front) in order to raise r_m at the rear (approach a constant tip radius) and possibly reduce the number of stages; 2) exploring aerodynamic and/or materials approaches that can increase r_m for the high-pressure turbine in order to straighten out the main burner and the aft transition duct; and 3) evaluating different work splits between the low- and high-pressure compressors in order to remove one turbine stage.

It is our intention and hope that this exercise carries lessons far beyond the actual design of these components. For one thing, it should convince you that a successful design rests upon the simultaneous solution of interdependent aerodynamic, thermodynamic, materials, and structural problems. For another, it should clearly demonstrate the importance of advanced technology to the solution of these problems. Finally, it should show that judgment and iteration are necessary partners in the search for the best answer.

References

[1]Oates, G. C. (ed.), *Aerothermodynamics of Aircraft Engine Components*, AIAA Education Series, AIAA, Reston, VA, 1985.

[2]Wilson, D. G., *The Design of High Efficiency Turbomachinery and Gas Turbines*, 2nd ed., MIT Press, Cambridge, MA, 1998.

[3]Horlock, J. H., *Axial Flow Compressors*, Krieger, Malabar, FL, 1973.

[4]Johnsen, I. A., and Bullock, R. O. (eds.), *Aerodynamic Design of Axial-Flow Compressors*, NASA SP-36, 1965.

[5]Dixon, S. L., *Thermodynamics of Turbomachinery*, 4th ed., Pergamon, New York, 1998.

[6]Cumpsty, N. A., *Compressor Aerodynamics*, Longman Scientific and Technical, London, 1989.

[7]Horlock, J. H., *Axial Flow Turbines*, Krieger, Malabar, FL, 1973.

[8]Glassmann, A. J. (ed), *Turbine Design and Application*, Vols. 1–3, NASA SP-290, 1972.

[9]Kerrebrock, J. L., *Aircraft Engines and Gas Turbines*, 2nd ed. MIT Press, Cambridge, MA, 1992.

[10]Oates, G. C., *The Aerothermodynamics of Gas Turbine and Rocket Propulsion*, 3rd ed., AIAA Education Series, AIAA, Reston, VA, 1997.

[11]Mattingly, J. D., *Elements of Gas Turbine Propulsion*, McGraw–Hill, New York, 1996.

[12]Zweifel, O., "The Spacing of Turbomachinery Blading, Especially with Large Angular Deflection," *Brown Boveri Review*, Vol. 32, 1945, p. 12.

[13]Dorman, T. E., Welna, H., and Lindlauf, R. W., "The Application of Controlled-Vortex Aerodynamics to Advanced Axial Flow Turbines," *Journal of Engineering for Power*, Ser. A, Vol. 98, Jan. 1976.

[14]Hiroki, T., and Katsumata, I., "Design and Experimental Studies of Turbine Cooling," American Society of Mechanical Engineer Paper 74-GT-30, 1974.

[15]Hertzberg, R. W., *Deformation and Fracture Mechanics of Engineering Materials*, 4th ed., Wiley, New York, 1996.

[16]Budynas, R., *Advanced Strength and Applied Stress Analysis*, 2nd ed., McGraw–Hill, New York, 1998.

[17]*Aerospace Structural Metals Handbook*, Battelle Memorial Inst., Columbus Lab., Columbus, OH, 1984.

[18]Sorensen, H. A., *Gas Turbines*, Ronald, New York, 1951.

[19]Von Kármán Inst., *Turbomachinery Blade Design Systems*, AIAA, Reston, VA, 1999.

9
Engine Component Design: Combustion Systems

9.1 Concept

> With several others, I was sent on loan from the Royal Aircraft Establishment
> to lead a group on combustion at Power Jets [in 1940]. I had done my thesis on
> laminar and turbulent diffusion flames and knew the importance of aerodynamics
> in the combustion process. It surprised me that others did not see that as much
> care was required in characterising the aerodynamic features of a combustion
> chamber as in the design of a blade for a compressor or turbine.
>
> —Sir William Hawthorne, "The Early History
> of the Aircraft Gas Turbine in Britain," (Ref. 1).

The purpose of the combustion systems of aircraft gas turbine engines is to increase the thermal energy of a flowing gas stream by combustion, which is an exothermic chemical reaction between the onboard hydrocarbon fuel and the oxygen in the ingested airstream. The two engine components in which this "heat addition" is made to occur are the main burner (also called the combustor) and the afterburner (also called the augmentor or reheater.) Both are covered in this chapter, as they have many basic processes in common, and means are provided for preliminary design of both.

The design of the main burner and afterburner of an airbreathing engine differs in many ways from that of stationary combustion devices. Space (especially length) is at a premium in aircraft applications. The combustion intensity (rate of thermal energy released per unit volume) is very much greater for the main burner of a turbojet (40,000 Btu/s-ft^3) than, for example, the furnace of a typical steam power plant (10 Btu/s-ft^3).

The following properties of the main burner or combustion chamber are desired: 1) complete combustion; 2) moderate total pressure loss; 3) stability of combustion process (freedom from flameout); 4) in-flight relight ability; 5) proper temperature distribution at exit with no "hot spots"; 6) short length and small cross section; 7) wide operating range of mass flow rates, pressures, and temperatures; and 8) satisfaction of established environmental limits for air pollutants.

Unfortunately, every one of these desirable characteristics is in conflict with one or more of the others. For example, complete combustion requires a large size, but moderate total pressure loss requires a small size. Design choices that minimize the generation of air pollutants severely impact combustion stability and narrow the range of stable operating parameters. As with many complex engineering systems, the design of the main burner or afterburner is necessarily an engineering design compromise.

Of the three principal components of a gas turbine engine—the compressor, combustor, and turbine—the combustor is usually perceived to be the least understood, perhaps even a "black art," component, and the same can be said of the fourth component of some engines, the afterburner. This is because most propulsion-oriented students and engineers have not had the opportunity to study all of the engineering subjects that are required to understand, analyze, and design combustors and afterburners.

Because there are no rotating parts in the combustor and afterburner to transfer external work to or from the gas stream, the only work and power relations required are those which determine how much mechanical power must be dissipated in order to cause the vigorous mixing required by the combustion process. Consequently, students who are familiar with the analysis and design of rotating machinery will be reasonably comfortable dealing with the processes of velocity diffusion, liner wall cooling, jet mixing, total pressure loss, and air partitioning in the combustor.

However, in order to understand the equally essential processes of heat release, flameholding, and pollutant formation and control, students must have some background in three additional engineering subjects, namely, 1) chemical thermodynamics of ideal gases, 2) gas-phase chemical kinetics, and 3) chemical reactor theory. Essential concepts from these three topics are presented in summary form in this chapter. Supporting design and analysis computer programs are included in AEDsys, the suite of software tools that accompanies this textbook.

Unlike the study of rotating machinery, there are surprisingly few resources in the open literature that deal with the design of main burners and afterburners in airbreathing propulsion systems. For more in-depth information two recommended sources are Arthur Lefebvre's *Gas Turbine Combustion*[2] for the main burner and Edward E. Zukoski's "Afterburners."[3]

9.1.1 Combustion Systems Components

9.1.1.1 Main burner or combustor. Figure 9.1 shows schematically the principal features of a main burner and illustrates the general pattern of recirculating and mixing flow patterns. These features are present in both axisymmetric and annular main burners.

Inflowing air enters the main burner at station 3.1. Because the airstream velocity leaving the stator of the last compressor stage is undesirably high, the flow must be diffused to a lower subsonic velocity. This is done by the expanding shape of the inner and outer casing, which is the pressure vessel of the main burner. The entering airflow is diffused to station 3.2, which is by definition the reference station for the main burner. A "snout" or splitter stabilizes the diffusing airstream and divides it for distribution to the liner and annulus. The central part of the divided airstream flows through an air swirler into the primary zone, where it mixes with atomized and/or vaporized fuel and with recirculated, partially burned gases. The remaining air flows into the inner and outer annulus, then flows into the liner through various holes and cooling slots punched or drilled into the walls of the liner.

The primary zone is where the action is! Inflowing fuel is atomized, and partially or completely vaporized, by the fuel nozzle. The vaporized fuel is entrained by and mixed into the primary air, which entered through the air swirler. Both the primary air and fuel streams are mixed with partially burned combustion products that are trapped in the recirculation "bubble" in the primary zone. This "backmixing" of partially burned gases with fresh reactants is responsible for the continuous

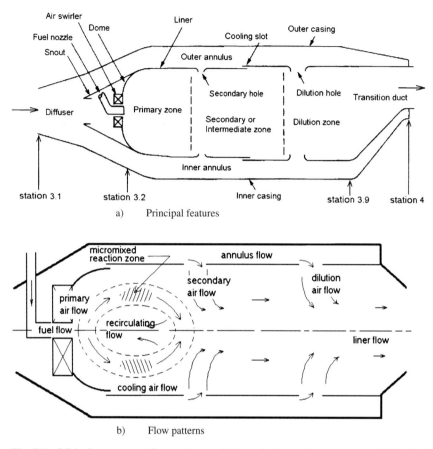

Fig. 9.1   Main features and flow patterns of the main burner/combustor: a) Principal features; b) Flow patterns.

self-ignition process called flameholding, so that an external source of ignition, such as a spark plug, is not required. (However, an external ignition source is required for starting the flameholding process.) Chemical reaction occurs primarily in the micromixed reaction zone, within which reactants have been mixed to near-molecular homogeneity.

From the primary zone the mixture of partially mixed, actively burning, and incompletely burned gases flows downstream into the secondary or intermediate zone, where they continue to burn towards completion while mixing with inflowing air from the secondary holes. Two processes must occur in parallel in the secondary/intermediate zone: 1) the primary zone effluent gases must continue to burn out, and 2) the in-mixing secondary air must "lean out" (reduce the fuel-air ratio of) the liner gas stream. These two processes must be balanced in such a way that the temperature rise which would otherwise occur from continued burnout is offset by a temperature decrease which would otherwise occur as a result of the decrease in fuel-air ratio. Consequently, the liner gases flow through the intermediate zone at essentially constant temperature, and combustion should be complete when the liner gas reaches the downstream end of the intermediate zone.

The dilution zone process, by comparison with the complex chemical and physical processes occuring in the primary and intermediate zones, is a "no-brainer." All that is required of the dilution zone is that any remaining annulus airflow be dumped through the dilution holes into the liner hot gas stream, with just sufficient stirring to avoid hot spots forming on the first-stage high-pressure turbine stators (nozzles).

After the hot gases exit the combustor liner at station 3.9, they are accelerated through a converging transition duct until they are choked at the throat of the first stage high-pressure turbine nozzles downstream of station 4.

9.1.1.2 Afterburner or augmenter.
Figure 9.2a shows schematically the principal features of an afterburner, and Fig. 9.2b illustrates the general pattern of recirculating and mixing flow patterns. The geometry in Fig. 9.2a is axisymmetric about the engine axis, but Fig. 9.2b is planar.

As shown in Fig. 9.2a, the core gas and bypass air enter the mixer at station 6 and station 16, respectively. The core gas is composed of combustion products. Although the core gases have given up a considerable amount of thermal energy to work extraction in the turbine, they still contain a considerable amount of thermal energy and excess oxygen. Mixing the bypass air with the core gas increases the mol fraction of oxygen available for reburning, and the hotter core gas warms up the cooler bypass air as well. The two gas streams are mixed adiabatically and slightly diffused by station 6A.

While the (core gas + bypass air) mixture is being slowed in the diffuser, fuel is injected and atomized by the spray rings. The flow rate of fuel is designed to produce the highest possible temperature at the afterburner exit. By the time the (fuel + core gas + bypass air) mixture enters the afterburner flameholding region at station 6.1, it is well-mixed to near-molecular level, so that combustion can take place.

As shown in Fig. 9.2b, after the combustible gas mixture passes over the downstream edge of the vee-gutter flame holders, it then entrains fully burned, hot combustion products from the recirculation zone in a shear-driven mixing layer. At some point sufficiently far downstream, a standing flame front is established. Just downstream of the standing flame front, the shear-driven mixing layer disentrains a portion of the burning gases. The disentrained gases then reverse direction and flow upstream inside the bubble of the recirculation zone, where there is sufficient residence time for them to burn to near completion. The remaining, outer portion of the burning gases behind the standing flame front propagates a turbulent flame front outward through the bypassing gas stream.

As the flame front propagates outward, the flow into which it is propagating is closing in behind the vee-gutter wake, which initially draws the flame front inward and away from the walls, following which its outward progress continues. As a result, it is often the case that the outward-propagating turbulent flame front fails to reach the walls before exiting the afterburner at station 7. When this happens, a visible, burning external plume extends well downstream from the exit of the thrust nozzle.

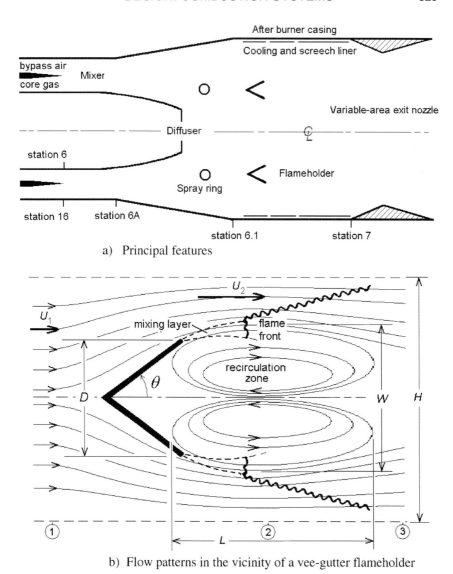

a) Principal features

b) Flow patterns in the vicinity of a vee-gutter flameholder

Fig. 9.2   Principal features and flow patterns of the afterburner: a) Principal features; b) Flow patterns in the vicinity of a vee-gutter flameholder.

At first glance the mechanism of flameholding in the afterburner appears to be very similar to that of the main burner (Fig. 9.1). However, there are subtle but important differences between the two. In the main burner primary zone the recirculation bubble is fueled from the inside and is confined by the combustor dome and liner walls so that all primary zone combustion is forced to take place within the confines of the recirculation bubble. Consequently, there is no discernable flame front, and spatially homogeneous combustion occurs within the micromixed reaction zone. In the afterburner, however, the recirculation zone is fueled from the outside, so that a discrete, standing turbulent flame front is established in the shear-driven mixing layer at the outer edge of the recirculation bubble. The chemical reactions responsible for flameholding occur in a very small micromixed reaction zone immediately behind the upstream-propagating flame front. By the time the burning gases, which are disentrained into the recirculation bubble, flow back upstream to be reentrained in the mixing layer, combustion is nearly complete. There is negligible chemical reaction within the hot recirculation zone, as it is composed of almost completely burned products. The hot recirculated gases that are mixed in with the external flow merely help to stabilize the axial location of the standing turbulent flame front.

9.1.2 The Combustion Process

9.1.2.1 Stoichiometry.
The stoichiometric or "ideal" fuel/air mixture ratio f_{st} is of interest because that is the fuel/air ratio which usually results in the greatest liberation of sensible energy from the breaking of molecular bonds. Although there exist general rules of stoichiometry for combustion of arbitrary reactants, attention will be restricted to hydrocarbon fuels in current use for the propulsion of aircraft. The only oxidizer of interest is air, which will be assumed to be 21% oxygen (O_2) and 79% nitrogen (N_2) by volume.

The maximum combustion temperature occurs when hydrocarbon fuel molecules are mixed with just enough air so that all of the oxygen atoms are consumed, all of the hydrogen atoms form water vapor H_2O, and all of the carbon atoms form carbon dioxide CO_2. This ideal mixture of fuel and air is represented by a general atom-balance equation for "complete combustion" called the stoichiometric equation, given by

$$C_x H_y + \left(x + \frac{y}{4} \right) \left[O_2 + \frac{79}{21} N_2 \right] \rightarrow x CO_2 + \frac{y}{2} H_2O + \frac{79}{21} \left(x + \frac{y}{4} \right) N_2 \quad (9.1)$$

Note that in Eq. (9.1) the nitrogen (N_2) acts merely as an inert diluent, absorbing some of the sensible thermal energy released by combustion by virtue of its specific heat capacity.

The stoichiometric fuel-air ratio can be determined readily from the ratio of molar coefficients of the reactants appearing on the left-hand side of Eq. (9.1). The stoichiometric fuel/air ratio expressed as a volume or mol ratio is

$$f_{st} = \frac{1}{\left(x + \frac{y}{4} \right) \left[1 + \frac{79}{21} \right]} = \frac{84}{100 \, (4x + y)} \text{ lbmols } F/\text{lbmol } A$$

where F stands for fuel and A for air.

The stoichiometric mass-basis fuel-air ratio is given by

$$f_{st} = \frac{36x + 3y}{103\,(4x + y)} \text{ lbm } F/\text{lbm } A \tag{9.2}$$

A representative or generic molecule representing jet fuels is $C_{12}H_{23}$. Solving Eq. (9.2) for $x = 12$ and $y = 23$ gives $f_{st} = 0.0685$ lbm $C_{12}H_{23}$/lbm A. Because the fuel-air ratio in use f is always less than f_{st} and f_{st} is much less than unity, it is often convenient to neglect the mass flow rate of fuel compared to the mass flow rate of air in performance calculations.

When considering off-stoichiometric mixtures of fuel and air, it is conventional to speak of "fuel-rich" and "fuel-lean" mixtures. To quantify this, the fuel/air equivalence ratio, or simply the equivalence ratio, is defined as the ratio of the actual fuel/air ratio to the stoichiometric fuel/air ratio:

$$\phi \doteq \frac{f}{f_{st}} \tag{9.3}$$

The utility of the equivalence ratio ϕ is that it permits representation of either fuel-rich or fuel-lean mixtures by multiplying the fuel term in the atom-balance equation by ϕ:

$$\phi C_x H_y + \left(x + \frac{y}{4}\right)\left[O_2 + \frac{79}{21}N_2\right] \rightarrow \text{products} \tag{9.4}$$

The "complete combustion" assumption behind Eq. (9.1) does not imply that, in actual practice, a stoichiometric mixture of fuel and air will yield only CO_2 and H_2O as combustion products. In reality, the CO_2 and H_2O molecules will dissociate into other molecular fragments at elevated temperature, just as happens with air alone at high temperature. Further, for reasons to be shown in Sec. 9.1.3, it is desireable to have very incomplete combustion occur in the turbojet combustor primary zone, so that the actual gases leaving the primary zone will be a mixture of reactants (fuel plus air), reaction intermediate species, dissociated products, and incompletely oxidized fuel molecules. In addition, at elevated temperatures a very small fraction of the atmospheric nitrogen is in fact oxidized, forming the air pollutant gases nitric oxide (NO), nitrous oxide (N_2O), and nitrogen dioxide (NO_2). The oxidized nitrogen species NO and NO_2 are collectively referred to as NO_x.

Finally, off-stoichiometric fuel/air ratios, as characterized by the equivalence ratio $\phi \neq 1$, affect the type and distribution of combustion products, as well as the temperature. As a practical guideline, equivalence ratios must be in the range 0.2 to 2 for combustion to occur, and equivalence ratios near or greater than unity are of little or no interest for airbreathing aircraft propulsion applications.

For off-stoichiometric mixtures, and also for possibly incomplete combustion, the atom-balance equation can be generalized as

$$\phi C_x H_y + \left(x + \frac{y}{4}\right)\left[O_2 + \frac{79}{21}N_2\right] \rightarrow n_{CO_2}CO_2 + n_{CO}CO + n_{H_2O}H_2O + \cdots$$

$$\cdots + n_{O_2}O_2 + n_O O + n_{NO_2}NO_2 + n_{N_2O}N_2O + \cdots \text{etc.} \tag{9.5}$$

where etc. indicates that the list of possible product gases may be as many combinations of O, H, C, and N atoms as exist in nature. If NS is used to denote the total number of product species that may appear on the right-hand side of Eq. (9.5), the messy right-hand side of Eq. (9.5) can be represented with the notation

$$\phi C_x H_y + \left(x + \frac{y}{4}\right)\left[O_2 + \frac{79}{21}N_2\right] \rightarrow \sum_{i=1}^{NS} n_i A_i \tag{9.6}$$

where A_i represents the chemical formula of the ith gas molecule appearing in the NS product gases. Methods for finding the actual composition of the post-combustion product gases, as represented by the set of mole numbers $\{n_i\}$ in Eq. (9.6), by assuming either chemical equilibrium or finite-rate chemistry (chemical kinetics), are provided in the AEDsys software programs EQL and KINETX, respectively.

9.1.2.2 Heat of reaction and adiabatic flame temperature.
With the initial composition and state of the fuel/air mixture given or known, as well as at what pressure burning will occur, it is desired to find what the temperature will be after combustion. Assuming that combustion occurs at constant pressure, without either heat or work transfer with the surroundings, then the total enthalpy of the (final) products will be the same as the (initial) reactants, and that value is known.

When molecular collisions result in the exchange of atoms between molecules, the number of molecules of each kind changes. Exothermic reactions result in the release of chemical bonding energy, which appears in the gas mixture as sensible thermal energy. These two kinds of energy associated with each molecule are represented in the static enthalpy for each species,

$$h_k^0 = \left(\Delta h_{f_k}^0\right)_{536} + \int_{536}^{T} c_{p_k} \, dT' \tag{9.7}$$

where the first term on the right-hand side of Eq. (9.7) is the enthalpy of formation of the kth gas, which is the sum of the molecular bond energy and the sensible enthalpy at 536°R (or 298 K), and the other term in Eq. (9.7) is the sensible enthalpy above 536°R. Enthalpies of formation for many of the gases of interest in combustion are given in Table 9.1.

The static enthalpy of a mixture of gases is given by

$$H = \sum_{k=1}^{NS} n_k h_k \tag{9.8}$$

and for the particular mixtures representing the reactants (fuel plus air) and products, that is, those gases appearing on the left-hand side and on the right-hand side of Eq. (9.6), respectively,

$$H_R = \sum_{k=1}^{NS} (n_k)_R h_k \quad \text{and} \quad H_P = \sum_{k=1}^{NS} (n_k)_P h_k \tag{9.9}$$

If the reactants are ignited and allowed to burn to the final equilibrium state without heat being added or removed during the process, the final equilibrium temperature is called the adiabatic flame temperature (AFT). For example, consider a case where the reactants are initially at 536°R. Because combustion occurs

Table 9.1 Enthalpy of formation $(\Delta h^0_{f_k})_{536}$ for some reactant and product gases

Gas	BTU/lbmol
Methane, CH_4	$-32{,}192$
Ethane, C_2H_6	$-36{,}413$
Hexane, C_6H_{14}	$-71{,}784$
Octane, C_8H_{18}	$-89{,}600$
Jet-A, $C_{12}H_{23}$	$-152{,}981$[a]
Carbon monoxide, CO	$-47{,}520$
Carbon dioxide, CO_2	$-169{,}181$
Atomic hydrogen, H	$93{,}717$
Hydrogen, H_2	0
Water vapor, H_2O	$-103{,}966$
Atomic oxygen, O	$107{,}139$
Oxygen, O_2	0
Hydroxyl, OH	$16{,}967$
Atomic nitrogen, N	$203{,}200$
Nitrogen, N_2	0
Nitrous oxide, N_2O	$35{,}275$
Nitric oxide, NO	$38{,}817$
Nitrogen dioxide, NO_2	$14{,}228$

[a]For heating value $h_{PR} = 18{,}400$ BTU/lbm.

adiabatically, releasing sensible thermal energy, and neglecting the difference between the kinetic energy of the reactants and products, the AFT is found by solving the algebraically implicit equation

$$H_P = H_R \tag{9.10}$$

Figure 9.3 illustrates the solution of Eqs. (9.9) and (9.10). At the initial temperature, assumed here to be 536°R, H_P is less than H_R. This is because the principal product molecules have larger negative values of enthalpy of formation than reactant molecules, as can be seen from Table 9.1.

If the fuel/air reactant mixture temperature is initially 536°R, as illustrated in Fig. 9.3, and if the fuel and air are in stoichiometric proportion, so that $\phi = 1$ in Eq. (9.6), then the stoichiometric AFT is found from the solution of Eq. (9.10).

If the products are subsequently cooled at constant composition and pressure until the product mixture temperature is brought back to 536°R, then the amount of heat removed is called the heating value or heat of reaction h_{PR}. Because the end states of the overall process (adiabatic burning followed by cooling) are both at the reference temperature 536°R, the relationship between the enthalpies of formation of each species and the heating value of the fuel is determined from an energy balance for the overall process:

$$h_{PR} = (H_R)_{536} - (H_P)_{536} = \sum_{i=1}^{NS} (n_i)^R \left(\Delta h^0_{f_i}\right)_{536} - \sum_{i=1}^{NS} (n_i)^P \left(\Delta h^0_{f_i}\right)_{536} \tag{9.11}$$

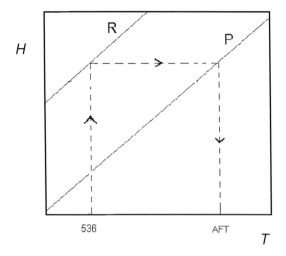

Fig. 9.3 Enthalpy-temperature diagram illustrating relationship between enthalpies of reactants H_R and products H_P and between initial reactants temperature (example shown as $536°R$) and the equilibrium AFT.

If the fuel and air are initially at a temperature greater than $536°R$, the solution of Eq. (9.10) will give a proportionately greater AFT, and Eq. (9.11) will give a value for h_{PR} that differs slightly from the standard value defined at $536°R$.

Using the enthalpies of formation listed in Table 9.1, Eq.(9.11) can be used to calculate the heating values of fuels listed in Table 9.1. The results are presented in Table 9.2.

Sometimes, h_{PR} is called the lower heating value (LHV). This is done to distinguish it from the higher heating value (HHV), which would be realized if, in addition to cooling the product gases to $536°R$, the latent heat of vaporization were extracted by condensing all of the water vapor in the product gases. The HHV is not relevant for propulsion applications, as combustion products are never cooled to ambient temperatures while inside the engine. The water condensation streams or "contrails" that mark the sky occur outside the nozzle and thus have no effect on engine thrust or performance.

Table 9.2 Molecular weights and heating values h_{PR} for gaseous fuels in Table 9.1

Gas	lbm/lbmol	BTU/lbmol	BTU/lbm
Methane, CH_4	16	334,921	21,558
Ethane, C_2H_6	30	613,847	20,462
Hexane, C_6H_{14}	86	1,671,063	19,431
Octane, C_8H_{18}	114	2,199,516	19,294
Jet-A, $C_{12}H_{23}$	167	3,072,800	18,400
Carbon monoxide, CO	28	121,660	4,345
Hydrogen, H_2	2	103,966	51,983

The AEDsys program EQL finds the equilibrium AFT for the fuels listed in Table 9.2.

9.1.2.3 Chemical kinetics.

Both the adiabatic flame temperature and heat of reaction, defined by Eqs. (9.8–9.11), are end-state quantities calculated on the basis of static change from the known/given reactant mol numbers $\{n_i\}_R$ to the set of product mol numbers $\{n_i\}_P$. The product mol numbers can be calculated either from assumed complete combustion or chemical equilibrium. However, neither result considers the instantaneous rates of change of mol numbers, nor the integrated values of mol numbers that may exist at specific moments. Because fluid particle residence times in any subcomponent of a gas turbine or ramjet engine are less than a millisecond (10^{-3} s), it is very often the case that insufficient time is available for the exothermic combustion reactions to reach chemical equilibrium. Further, minimizing the production of air pollutants formed in the combustion process depends entirely on differential control of varying chemical kinetic rates of different species. Consequently, it is necessary to study the rate at which chemical reactions proceed. For purposes of mathematically modeling finite-rate chemical kinetics for homogeneous gas-phase chemical reaction, it is assumed that very many individual, reversible, "elementary physical-chemical" collision reactions of the form $CO + OH \rightarrow CO_2 + H$ occur. By convention, species appearing on the left-hand side of each such reaction are called reactants, and those on the right-hand side are called products. Note that the example reaction could just as well have been written $CO_2 + H \rightarrow CO + OH$, in which case CO_2 and H would be called the reactants, rather than CO and OH.

With a suitable collection of such reactions, it is possible to approximately describe the time rates of change of all species and, by summing them up, calculate the rates of change of mixture properties such as density and temperature. Such a set of individual reactions is referred to as a reaction mechanism. Table 9.2 is such a mechanism for combustion of the gaseous jet fuel surrogate $C_{12}H_{23}$ with air.

The system of partial differential equations describing the adiabatic, homogeneous, one-dimensional, ideal-gas phase chemical reaction without axial molecular or turbulent diffusion is given by[4,5]

$$\frac{\partial n_i}{\partial t} + U \frac{\partial n_i}{\partial x} = f_i(n_k, T) \qquad i, k = 1, NS \quad (9.12)$$

where

$$f_i = -\rho^{-1} \sum_{j=1}^{JJ} (\alpha'_{ij} - \alpha''_{ij})(R_j - R_{-j}) \qquad (9.13)$$

In Eq. (9.13) R_j and R_{-j} ($j = 1, JJ$) are modified Arrhenius expressions for the forward and reverse rates of the jth reaction,

$$R_j = k_j \prod_{k=1}^{NS} (\rho n_k)^{\alpha'_{kj}} \qquad (9.14)$$

and

$$R_{-j} = k_{-j} \prod_{k=1}^{NS} (\rho n_k)^{\alpha''_{kj}} \qquad (9.15)$$

In Eqs. (9.12–9.15) n_i is the mass-specific mole number of the ith species ($i = 1, NS$); T is the temperature; ρ is the mixture mass density, α'_{ij} and α''_{ij} are the stoichiometric coefficients of species i ($i = 1, NS$) in reaction j ($j = 1, JJ$) as a reactant and as a product species, respectively; k_j and k_{-j} are the forward and reverse rate constants in the modified Arrhenius rate expressions for R_j and R_{-j}, which in turn are the forward and reverse rates of the jth reaction ($j = 1, JJ$). NS is the total number of distinct chemical species in the gas mixture, and JJ is the total number of independent chemical reactions prescribed in the reaction mechanism. A typical form for k_j is given in Table 9.3.

Table 9.3 presents a 30-step reaction mechanism devised by Reiner Kollrack in 1976 for modeling combustion of "jet fuel," represented as $C_{12}H_{23}$, including

Table 9.3 Kollrack's two-step pyrolysis mechanism for jet fuel kinetics (Ref. 5)

A	B	C	D	E	F	B	N	T_{act}
$C_{12}H_{23}$	O_2	—	$5C_2H_4$	C_2H_3	O_2	4.48	1.5	7900
$C_{12}H_{23}$	OH	—	$6C_2H_4$	O	—	7.3	1.0	4500
C_2H_4	H	—	C_2H_3	H_2	—	10.48	0.0	9500
H	H	M	H_2	—	M	12.30	−1.0	0.0
O	O	M	O_2	—	M	11.0	−1.0	0.0
H	OH	M	H_2O	—	M	13.85	−1.0	0.0
H	O_2	—	OH	O	—	11.35	0.0	8400
O	H_2	—	OH	H	—	10.24	0.0	4730
CO	OH	—	CO_2	H	—	−14.75	7.0	−7000
H	H_2O	—	OH	H_2	—	10.92	0.0	10050
CH_3	O_2	—	CH_2O	OH	—	9.0	0.0	4000
HO_2	—	M	H	O_2	M	12.32	0.0	23000
HO_2	H	—	OH	OH	—	9.89	0.0	950
CH_2O	OH	—	H_2O	HCO	—	10.90	0.0	2120
O	H_2O	—	OH	OH	—	10.76	0.0	9000
N_2	O	—	NO	N	—	9.00	0.0	25000
N	O_2	—	NO	O	—	5.00	1.0	2000
N	OH	—	NO	H	—	9.00	0.0	0.0
HCO	O_2	—	HO_2	CO	—	10.48	0.0	7000
HCO	OH	—	H_2O	CO	—	10.30	0.0	0.0
C_2H_4	OH	—	C_2H_3	H_2O	—	9.78	0.0	1750
CH_2O	HO_2	—	HCO	OH	OH	9.0	0.0	4500
C_2H_2	HO_2	—	HCO	CH_2O	—	9.30	0.0	5500
C_2H_3	O_2	—	C_2H_2	HO_2	—	9.23	0.0	5000
NO	HO_2	—	NO_2	OH	—	3.00	1.0	0.0
C_2H_4	O	—	CH_3	HCO	—	9.93	0.0	1500
C_2H_4	HO_2	—	CH_3	HCO	OH	9.90	0.0	5000
H_2	CH_3	—	CH_4	H	—	7.0	−1.5	7140
C_2H_2	OH	—	CH_3	CO	—	8.2	0.0	2500
CH_3	O	—	CH_2O	H	—	11.11	0.0	1000

$A + B + C \rightarrow D + E + F,\ k = 10^{B}T^{N}\exp\left(-T_{act}/T\right)$; (SI units: kmol, m^3, K, s)

production of NO_x (Ref. 5). The first two reactions in Table 9.3 are not elementary physico-chemical reactions, but are "global" reactions, devised to represent a very great number of complex and largely unknown steps in the pyrolysis of the fuel molecules to smaller molecular fragments. In Table 9.3 the symbol M stands for "third body," meaning any species acting as a gas-phase catalyst.

For adiabatic and no-work reaction, conservation of static enthalpy, Eq. (9.10), constitutes an algebraic constraint on Eqs. (9.12) to (9.15). The mass density ρ in Eqs. (9.13–9.15) is determined from the temperature and pressure by the equation of state for an ideal gas, $\rho = P/(\bar{R}Tn_m)$, where $\bar{R}$ is the universal gas constant and n_m is the sum of the mole numbers, $n_m \doteq \sum_{i=1}^{NS} n_i$.

Constant-pressure batch reaction. Consider an initially quiescent uniform mixture of fuel and air in a shock tube. At time zero a shock wave passes quickly through the mixture, rapidly raising the pressure and temperature well above the ignition limits. The experiment is designed so that the pressure remains constant until chemical equilibrium is approached. Because there is no mass convection, Eq. (9.12) simplifies to

$$\frac{dn_i}{dt} = f_i(n_k, T) \qquad\qquad i, k = 1, NS \quad (9.16)$$

The subsequent events leading to release of sensible thermal energy occur in three distinctly different chemical-physical periods, as illustrated in Fig. 9.2. These three periods or regimes are called the induction, heat release, and equilibration regimes.

The induction period is the time interval immediately following some form of homogeneous bulk ignition. In the homogeneous (completely micromixed) case under consideration, ignition occurs as a result of shock compression, but such ignition occurs only if fuel and air are micromixed to flammable proportions $(0.2 < \phi < 2.0)$. During the induction period, the mole numbers of reaction intermediates or chain carriers, such as O, H, OH, HO_2, and H_2O_2, increase by many orders of magnitude from near-zero values in the initial mixture. During this period, the coupling with the enthalpy equation Eq. (9.10) is very weak, so that the induction process is essentially isothermal as well as adiabatic, that is, no sensible energy is released. When the intermediate species have reached some critical value of concentration sufficient to begin to react with fuel and oxygen molecules, the process of releasing sensible thermal energy can begin. Therefore, the induction period ends when the mixture temperature begins to rapidly increase. In the methane/air example illustrated in Fig. 9.4, the induction time (also called the ignition delay time) is about 8×10^{-6} s.

During the heat release period, very rapid changes in temperature and species mol numbers occur. During this period, the species equations and the energy conservation equations are all very strongly coupled. The heat release period ends when the reaction intermediates have all passed their peak values, at about 1×10^{-5} s in Fig. 9.4.

The equilibration period begins when all species mole numbers begin a decaying-exponential approach toward their respective equilibrium values. The equilibration process does not have a clearly defined termination, because of the asymptotic nature of the approach to the chemical equilibrium state. However, because equilibrium values of temperature and species concentration can be determined in

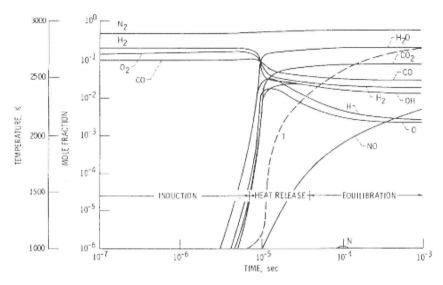

Fig. 9.4   Regimes of combustion in isobaric batch reaction of stoichiometric methane (pyrolyzed to CO and H_2) and air. Initial conditions are: $P = 10$ atm and, $T = 1000$ K ($1800°R$). Reaction mechanism includes 12 reactions and 11 species.[6]

advance, the end of the equilibration period can be defined as the time at which all of the mole numbers and the temperature are within (say) 1% of their chemical equilibrium values, at about 5×10^{-4} s in Fig. 9.4.

Note that Fig. 9.4 is presented on log-log coordinates. This choice of scale tends to obscure the many orders-of-magnitude variation in mol fractions of the various species. In addition, note that each of the three sequential combustion periods requires an order-of-magnitude longer time than the preceding period. The implications of this slowing down of chemical reaction rates are of obvious concern to achieving high combustion efficiency.

Steady-state "plug flow" reaction.   For time-steady one-dimensional flows without axial diffusion of mol number, Eq. (9.12) simplifies to a coupled set of ordinary differential equations (ODE),

$$U \frac{dn_i}{dx} = f_i(n_k, T) \qquad\qquad i, k = 1, NS \quad (9.17)$$

which corresponds to "plug flow" in tubes or ducts. Plug-flow reactors (PFR) will be explained in more detail in Sec. 9.1.3. The mole fractions of various species are distributed along the x axis, rather than a time axis as in Fig. 9.4. This initial value problem type can readily be solved by any of a number of widely available ODE solvers.[6]

Stationary-state "well-stirred reactor" reaction.   For flows that are time-steady, and for which the axial gradient term in Eq. (9.12) can be approximated by the finite difference formula

$$U \frac{dn_i}{dx} \approx u \frac{\Delta n_i}{\Delta x} \qquad\qquad i = 1, NS$$

So that Eq. (9.12) can be rewritten as

$$\rho U A \frac{(n_i - n_i^*)}{A \Delta x} = \rho f_i(n_k, T) \qquad i, k = 1, NS \quad (9.18)$$

where n_i^* refers to the upstream or entry value of n_i into the control volume of volume $V = A \Delta x$ and $\rho A u = \dot{m}$. With this notation the resulting well-stirred reactor (WSR) equations become[4]

$$\frac{\dot{m}}{V}(n_i - n_i^*) = \rho f_i(n_k, T) \qquad i, k = 1, NS \quad (9.19)$$

Note that Eq. (9.19) can also be derived directly from an elementary control volume mass balance.

The WSR model for combustion will be further explained in Sec. 9.1.3. For present purposes, it is sufficient to just point out that WSR solutions have features that are markedly and significantly different from PFR solutions. For one, the WSR equations are a coupled set of nonlinear algebraic equations, rather than ordinary differential equations, and therefore require different numerical methods for their solution. In addition, WSR solutions feature multiple stationary states, and decisions must be made as to which of those solutions are desireable or achievable in practice. The real-world implications of these features will be dealt with in Sec. 9.1.3.

The AEDsys program KINETX solves the WSR equations using the Kollrack mechanism given in Table 9.3.

9.1.3 Combustion Stability and Flameholding

It has long been known that it is possible to sustain a self-propagating (that is, continuously self-igniting) flame in a steady-flow combustor, even when the velocity of reactants entering greatly exceeds the turbulent flame speed of a stoichiometric mixture of fuel and air at combustor entrance temperatures and pressures. For example, while the fastest measured turbulent flame speeds for hydrocarbon-air combustion are in the range 10–15 ft/s, combustor entry airspeeds are typically 200–300 ft/s.

How is it possible for the mean combustor flow velocity to be more than one order of magnitude greater than the highest known turbulent flame speed? This is made possible by the insertion of a flameholder, which may be a "bluff body" or "vee-gutter," or some other form of flow blockage, into the stream.[3,7] The separated flow in the aerodynamic wake behind the flameholder causes the flow to recirculate from downstream to upstream, so that some fraction of the reactants can reside for a sufficiently long time to mix with hot product gases, thereby sustaining a continuous combustion reaction.

9.1.3.1 Chemical reactor theory. The interplay of mixing and chemical processes that enable flameholding in a wake region can be better understood by using chemical engineering concepts called reaction engineering or chemical reactor theory.[8]

Steady-flow chemical reactors may be represented by a spectrum of mixing models, varying between two idealized extremes: the zero-dimensional WSR and the one-dimensional PFR. In theory, the two extreme reactor types may be characterized by means of a hypothetical tracer-response experiment, in which a step function concentration of tracer substance is introduced into the feed stream at some instant, and the subsequent concentration of tracer at reactor exit (the response) is monitored. The WSR response to such an input step function would be a decaying-exponential rise in tracer concentration, with no time delay from inlet step change to the initial rise of response signal at exit. The PFR response would be simply the appearance of the same step change at exit, precisely one mean residence time later. The negative time derivative of the response function to a step input function is called the residence time distribution function and can be shown to be the probability density for a fluid particle, having entered at time t_0, to exit at time $(t - t_0)$.[8]

PFRs offer no conceptual difficulties—the concept is familiar, because all steady-flow systems feature an inflow at one end and outflow at the other, so that one can readily envision a "plug" of fluid entering and leaving without axial mixing.

The WSR concept is somewhat less familiar. The WSR is an idealization of flow systems in which the flow stream is recirculated in some way to promote gross mixing of products, reactants, and reaction intermediates. The physical reactor being modeled is usually referred to as a backmixed or jet-stirred reactor. In terms of turbulent mixing theory, the WSR assumption implies that the gross recirculating flow velocity is so great, and the turbulent diffusion across streamlines so rapid, that every entering fluid particle has instantaneous access to every other fluid particle. This assumption, however, does not require that mass or energy transfer caused by molecular diffusion will necessarily occur between the fluid particles. WSRs may therefore be subdivided into two important subclasses: micromixed and macromixed, as illustrated in Fig. 9.5.

The micro-WSR assumption is that mixing is complete on the molecular scale. Thus, combustion reactions in this context are volume burning in nature, and such terms as "flame front," "post- or pre-flame," and "induction time" are meaningless. Chemical reactions are necessarily "parallel" in a micro-WSR, as opposed to the "series" nature of processes in a PFR. Reaction rate equations are therefore regarded as simultaneous algebraic equations in micro-WSR analysis, as shown by Eq. (9.19), whereas they are regarded as differential equations in PFR analysis, as in Eq. (9.17).[9]

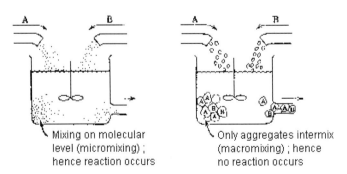

Fig. 9.5   **Well-stirred reactor with feeds of reactants A and B.[8] Chemical reaction can occur only when *molecules* of A interact with *molecules* of B.**

The macro-WSR model assumes mixing to be complete on a scale small by comparison with reactor dimensions, but large on a molecular scale. The small macrovolumes are assumed to retain their individual molecular integrity, acting as little batch reactors, but are uniformly distributed throughout the vessel instantaneously upon entry. The theoretical decaying-exponential response curve that characterizes a WSR cannot in principle discriminate between the micro- and macromixed condition.

The micro-WSR concept has meaning only for homogeneous or single-phase flow systems, whereas the macro-WSR concept has utility when dealing with two-phase flows. In this case the macrovolume may represent a liquid droplet or a solid particle. For homogeneous fluid flow the macrovolumes may represent idealized turbulent eddies or "turbules." In the context of homogeneous gas flows, the micro-WSR assumption is equivalent to assuming that turbulence is generated, cascades through the diminishing spectrum of eddy sizes, and dissipates—all this on a timescale very small compared with the mean residence time. The macro-WSR assumption corresponds to assuming that the turbulent eddies enter in the feed stream already formed and reside in the reactor in too short an interval to undergo coalescence, dispersion, or dissipation prior to exiting the reactor. In designing and analyzing both combustors and afterburners, both mixing models will be used. In the micromixed reacting zones shown as cross-hatched areas in Figs. 9.1 and 9.2, combustion chemical reactions will be assumed to occur as in a micromixed WSR. In the dilution zone of the main burner, on the other hand, because no further chemical reactions occur the flow can be assumed to be macromixed.

The Bragg criterion.   A self-stabilized, steady-state, steady flow combustion system, such as that in a gas turbine engine, requires two distinct subregions, known as the primary and secondary zones. An idealized main burner with a WSR primary zone and a PFR secondary zone is known as a "Bragg combustor" and is illustrated in Fig. 9.6.

As the actual primary zone is a region of intense backmixing or recirculation, it is idealized or modeled as a WSR, within which inflowing reactants are mixed with previously burned gases that are continuously recirculated within the primary zone. The effluent from the primary zone, being a mixture of reactants, products, and reaction intermediates, is necessarily at a combustion efficiency of (typically) less than 80%.

The main function of the secondary zone, which is idealized as a PFR, is to allow sufficient convective residence time or "stay time" for the primary zone effluent to burn out (approach 100% combustion efficiency) before exiting the combustor.

In aircraft gas turbine design, where combustor volume, weight, and frontal area are limited by airframe considerations, this question naturally arises: "Given

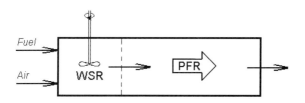

Fig. 9.6   Bragg combustor, an idealized gas turbine combustor with WSR primary zone and PFR secondary zone.

a fixed axial distance and/or spatial volume within which combustion must take place, what is the optimal division of this space between primary and secondary zones?" The answer, arrived at first through chemical reactor modeling and later verified in practice, was summarized in the late 1940s by S.L. Bragg, a pioneer in British gas turbine development, in what has become known as the Bragg criterion: *The maximum overall combustor efficiency occurs when the primary zone is operating at incipient blowout.*[10]

This is not intuitively obvious, as the smallest value of primary zone combustion efficiency occurs at incipient blowout! However, at incipient blowout the chemical reaction rate in the primary zone is at its maximum value, and also the primary zone effluent has its highest concentration of reaction intermediates. In addition, the maximum secondary zone volume provides the greatest convective stay time possible to promote near-complete combustion at secondary zone exit. However, in actual practice combustors are never operated at incipient blowout because experience shows that incipient blowout means eventual blowout!

Blowout. To illustrate these flameholding concepts, a greatly simplified version of the atom-balance equation [Eq. (9.5)], will be employed, in which it is assumed that, for fuel-lean mixtures only ($\phi < 1$), the excess air remaining after CO_2 and H_2O are formed is simply present as a diluent:

$$\phi C_x H_y + \left(x + \frac{y}{4}\right)\left\{O_2 + \frac{79}{21}N_2\right\}$$

$$\rightarrow x\phi CO_2 + \frac{y}{2}\phi H_2O + \left(x + \frac{y}{4}\right)\left\{(1 - \phi)O_2 + \frac{79}{21}N_2\right\} \quad (9.20)$$

Also, for incomplete combustion, the atom-balance equation Eq. (9.20) may be further generalized as

$$\phi C_x H_y + \left(x + \frac{y}{4}\right)\left\{O_2 + \frac{79}{21}N_2\right\}$$

$$\rightarrow \phi(1 - \varepsilon)C_x H_y + x\phi\varepsilon CO_2 + \frac{y}{2}\phi\varepsilon H_2O + \left(x + \frac{y}{4}\right)\left\{(1 - \phi\varepsilon)O_2 + \frac{79}{21}N_2\right\}$$

$$(9.21)$$

where ε is the "fraction reacted" or combustion reaction progress variable, also commonly known as the combustion efficiency.

When $\varepsilon = 1$ in Eq. (9.21), the maximum value of T, the adiabatic flame temperature T_{AFT}, is realized. This temperature is determined by the energy balance equation, Eqs. (9.9) and (9.10), which may be very well approximated by the linear equation

$$T_{AFT} \approx T_i + \frac{\phi f_{st} h_{PR}}{c_p} = T_i + \phi \Delta T_{max} \quad (9.22)$$

where ΔT_{max} is the maximum temperature rise when both $\phi = 1$ and $\varepsilon = 1$. The static temperature T and the reaction progress variable ε can be similarly represented by the linear equation

$$T = T_i + \varepsilon(T_{AFT} - T_i) = T_i + \varepsilon\left(\frac{\phi f_{st} h_{PR}}{c_p}\right) = T_i + \varepsilon\phi \Delta T_{max} \quad (9.23)$$

The volumetric mass rate of consumption of the fuel (lbm fuel/s-ft^3) can be expressed by a modified Arrhenius equation for the overall combustion reaction

$$RR_f = M_f A e^{-T_{act}/T} [C_x H_y][O_2] \text{ lbm fuel/s-ft}^3 \qquad (9.24)$$

where $M_f = 12x + y$ is the apparent molecular weight of the fuel, A is the pre-exponential factor, T_{act} is the activation temperature of the reaction, and the square-bracket terms denote the concentration (mols per unit volume) of fuel and of oxygen, respectively.

The concentrations of fuel and oxygen may be expressed in terms of their respective mol fractions Y, the mixture static temperature T, static pressure P, molar density $\bar{\rho}$, and the universal gas constant $\bar{R}$, by

$$[C_x H_y] = \bar{\rho} Y_{C_x H_y} = \left(\frac{P}{\bar{R}T}\right) Y_{C_x H_y} \quad \text{and} \quad [O_2] = \bar{\rho} Y_{O_2} = \left(\frac{P}{\bar{R}T}\right) Y_{O_2}$$

The volumetric mass rate of disappearance of the fuel may then be rewritten as

$$RR_f = M_f A e^{-T_{act}/T} \left(\frac{P}{\bar{R}T}\right)^2 Y_{C_x H_y} Y_{O_2} \qquad (9.25)$$

The sum of the product mol numbers on the right-hand side (RHS) of Eq. (9.21) is given by

$$\Sigma N_P = \frac{100}{21}\left(x + \frac{y}{4}\right) + \phi\left[1 + \left(\frac{y}{4} - 1\right)\varepsilon\right] \qquad (9.26)$$

so that the mole fractions of fuel and oxygen may be written from the RHS of Eq. (9.21) as

$$Y_{C_x H_y} = \frac{\phi(1-\varepsilon)}{\Sigma N_P} \quad \text{and} \quad Y_{O_2} = \frac{\left(x + \frac{y}{4}\right)(1 - \phi\varepsilon)}{\Sigma N_P}$$

respectively. With these subsitutions for mole fractions, Eq. (9.25) becomes

$$RR_f = M_f\left(x + \frac{y}{4}\right)\phi A e^{-T_{act}/T}\left(\frac{P}{\bar{R}T\Sigma N_P}\right)^2 (1-\varepsilon)(1-\phi\varepsilon) \qquad (9.27)$$

With the substitution of Eq. (9.26) for ΣN_P and Eq. (9.23) for T, Eq. (9.27) can be written with only the reaction progress variable ε as an independent variable.

Note the limiting values of RR_f in Eq. (9.27) for varying values of the reaction progress variable ε. Clearly, RR_f approaches zero as ε approaches 1. However, note that RR_f does not approach zero as ε approaches zero, but rather to a small positive value. Equation (9.27) is plotted on Fig. 9.7.

From inspection of Fig. 9.7, it can be seen that there is an optimal value of ε between 0 and 1 (and corresponding temperature between T_i and T_{AFT}) for which RR_f is a maximum. As one might guess, a design goal for afterburners and combustor primary zones is to achieve as nearly as possible this maximum value of RR_f at some location in the combustion device.

The next question to be addressed is: Which operating point on Fig. 9.7 will be realized in practice? To answer this, the principle of conservation of fuel mass is

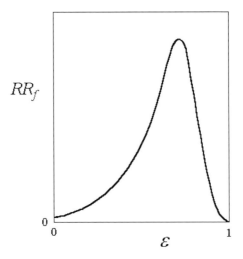

RR_f

0

0   1

ε

Fig. 9.7   Variation of volumetric rate of consumption of fuel RR_f with combustion progress variable ε [Eq. (9.27)] (not to scale).

invoked, applied to a steady flow, steady-flow well-stirred reactor that represents the primary or flameholding zone:

$$\dot{m}_{f_{in}} = \dot{m}_{f_{out}} + V\, RR_f \tag{9.28}$$

where V is the volume of the WSR modeling the combustor primary zone. By definition of the reaction progress variable, $\dot{m}_{f_{out}} = (1 - \varepsilon)\,\dot{m}_{f_{in}}$. Further, by definition of the equivalence ratio ϕ and the stoichiometric fuel-air ratio f_{st}, $\dot{m}_{f_{in}} = \phi f_{st} \dot{m}_A$, where $\dot{m}_A$ is the mass feed rate of air into the WSR. With these two substitutions Eq. (9.28) may be rewritten as

$$RR_f = \left(\frac{\phi f_{st} \dot{m}_A}{V} \right) \varepsilon \tag{9.29}$$

Equation (9.29) is plotted on Fig. 9.8, together with Eq. (9.27) from Fig. 9.7.

For fixed values of the parameters ϕ, f_{st}, and V in Eq. (9.29), the slopes of the three lines shown on Fig. 9.8 are directly proportional to the air mass flow rate $\dot{m}_A$.

For line a, which has the lowest value of $\dot{m}_A$, there is only one intersection with the curve of RR_f of Eq. (9.27). It can be seen that, for vanishingly small values of $\dot{m}_A$, the progress variable ε approaches 1 asymptotically. Line b, however, has three intersections with the RR_f curve. Which of these three states can or will be established in the WSR, for this increased value of $\dot{m}_A$?

It can be shown that the middle branch solution is thermodynamically unstable, but that either of the other two solutions may be realized in practice.[7,8] The lower branch, "cold flow" solution represents the case where the air-fuel mixture is flowing steadily through the WSR, but no ignition source has been introduced. The upper branch solution represents the case of interest, namely, the stable "hot flow" solution, which is established following ignition and subsequent removal of the ignition source.

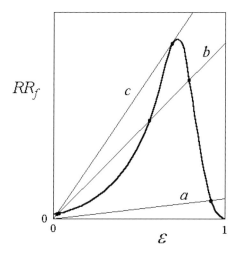

Fig. 9.8 Superimposed plots of Eqs. (9.27) and (9.29).

For stable upper branch solutions, further increases in $\dot{m}_A$ beyond that of line b result in decreasing values of ε, up to that value of $\dot{m}_A$ which results in a solution corresponding to the maximum value of RR_f. Further small increases of $\dot{m}_A$ are permitted up to the case shown as line c, which is tangent to the RR_f curve. It can be seen that any further increase in $\dot{m}_A$ will cause a jump to a unique lower branch solution! This observeable phenomena of abrupt flame extinction is called blowout or flameout.

In practice, it is not possible to reignite the flameholding region, represented in our model by a WSR, simply by reducing $\dot{m}_A$ to its former value just prior to blowout. It is necessary to reduce $\dot{m}_A$ to a much lower value, say that of line a, so that the same ignition source used for initial startup can be employed. This hysteresis effect is known in practice as the in-flight restart problem.

9.1.3.2 Combustor loading parameter.

The intersections of the two curves on Fig. 9.8 graphically represent equating the two equations for RR_f given by Eqs. (9.27) and (9.29):

$$RR_f = M_f \left(x + \frac{y}{4}\right) \phi A e^{-T_{act}/T} \left(\frac{P}{RT\Sigma N_p}\right)^2 (1 - \varepsilon)(1 - \phi\varepsilon) = \left(\frac{\phi f_{st} \dot{m}_A}{V}\right) \varepsilon$$

$$(9.30)$$

When the term RR_f is eliminated by equating the two right-most terms in Eq. (9.30), and by rearranging terms, one can obtain the relation

$$I \doteq \frac{\dot{m}_A}{VP^2} = \frac{M_f \left(x + \frac{y}{4}\right) A e^{-T_{act}/T} (1 - \varepsilon)(1 - \phi\varepsilon)}{\varepsilon f_{st}(RT\Sigma N_p)^2}$$

$$(9.31)$$

The grouping of terms on the left-hand side (LHS) of Eq. (9.31) is called the "air loading" I, or simply the "loading," in gas turbine combustion terminology.

Note the strange, mixed units: lbms air per second per unit volume per pressure squared.

In gas turbine practice the air loading concept is applied not to the primary zone volume as in the present analysis, but rather to the volume of the entire combustor. When so applied, it is called the combustor loading parameter (CLP), defined by

$$CLP \doteq \frac{\dot{m}_A}{VP^n} \text{ lbm/s-ft}^3\text{-(atm)}^n \tag{9.32}$$

The exponent n in Eq. (9.32) has been found empirically to be closer to 1.8 than 2. Because the entire combustor as a whole does not satisfy the assumptions necessary to model the primary zone as a WSR, it should not be surprising that this minor disagreement between theory and practice exists.

The value of the CLP defined by Eq. (9.32) is that it reflects the influence of the most important parameters affecting combustion flame stability, namely, airflow rate, combustor volume, and static pressure. Although the combustor volume is a design parameter, both the airflow rate and combustor pressure are operating parameters, controlled in practice by throttle setting and flight altitude.

9.1.3.3 Combustor stability map.
Note that the right-hand side of Eq. (9.31) contains all six of the WSR parameters—A, T_{act}, M_f, f_{st}, R, and ϕ—and the two independent variables ε and T, which, as has been shown, are related through the approximate energy conservation Eq. (9.23). By fixing all six parameters, and then varying ε systematically, Eq. (9.31) can be solved for the corresponding values of air loading $I = \dot{m}/VP^2$. By repeating the calculation for varying ϕ, a complete performance and stability map of the primary zone can be constructed, as shown in Fig. 9.9.

It has been mentioned in connection with Eq. (9.19) that solutions to the chemical kinetic WSR equations solutions have features not present in ODE solutions, such as multiple stationary states and attendant hysteresis phenomena. Figure 9.10 illustrates stationary-state solutions of the WSR kinetic equations for varying values of the loading parameter $I = \dot{m}/VP^2$, superimposed on the equilibrium solutions illustrated in Fig. 9.3. In the limit as $I \to 0$, the residence time in the control volume is infinite, and so there is ample time for the chemical reactions to reach equilibrium. At the other limit, $I \to \infty$, there is zero residence time for

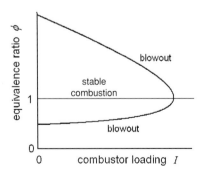

Fig. 9.9   Performance and stability map of a WSR, from Eq. (9.31) (not to scale).

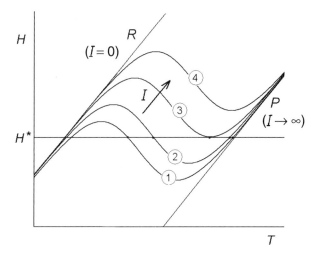

Fig. 9.10   Variation of WSR chemical kinetic stationary states with loading parameter
$I = \dot{m}/VP^2$ **(Ref. 9).**

the reactions to occur, so that the reactants simply exit the control volume without chemical change, with combustion efficiency ε given by Eq. (9.23).

As the loading is increased from zero to I_1, there is now finite residence time in the control volume, and so the reactions fail to reach the equilibrium state, and their temperature is lower than the AFT, as illustrated by curve 1 in Fig. 9.10. Further increasing the loading to I_2 causes further reduction in stationary-state temperature as a result of incomplete combustion.

9.1.4   Stirring and Mixing

In the main burner, round jets and swirling annular jets are utilized to mix fuel and air to flammable proportions, and to mix burned gases with fresh reactant gases, for both flameholding and burnout to completion. In the afterburner, these same ends are achieved by shear layer mixing between co-flowing streams. In this section the fluid mechanics and aerodynamics of these three fluid mixing systems are presented in order.

9.1.4.1   Round jets.
Consider the turbulent jets of fluid issuing from sharp-edged, round holes, such as those shown in Fig. 9.1, for admitting air into the secondary and dilution zones of the main burner.

In Fig. 9.11 the annulus and liner regions are assumed to be semi-infinite reservoirs containing two different fluids having mass densities ρ_A and ρ_L, respectively. The fluids will be assumed to be "Boussinesq" fluids, that is, they are incompressible, with mass densities that vary with temperature but not with pressure.[11]

If the liner region has a lower static pressure than the annulus region above, the pressure difference causes a jet to flow through the hole of area $A_h = \pi d_h^2/4$. As the locally reduced pressure around the hole draws the fluid into the opening, a vena contracta forms, so that the entering jet velocity V_j occurs at the reduced

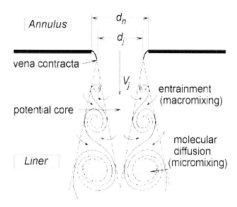

Fig. 9.11   Turbulent jet issuing through a round hole between two fluid reservoirs.

flow area $A_j = \pi d_j^2/4$. For a sharp-edged "plain" hole, as shown in Fig. 9.11, the vena contracta diameter ratio is approximately $d_j = 0.8d_h$. For a round-edged "plunged" hole, as shown in Fig. 9.12, the vena contracta diameter ratio is about $d_j = 0.9d_h$. The corresponding jet-to-hole-area ratio is called the discharge coefficient[12]:

$$C_{D90°} = \begin{cases} 0.64 & \text{for plain holes} \\ 0.81 & \text{for plunged holes} \end{cases} \qquad (9.33)$$

Because the flow is isentropic from the upper reservoir to the vena contracta, Bernoulli's equation is applicable. The jet velocity V_j is therefore uniquely determined by the static pressure difference across the orifice:

$$P_A = P_j + \frac{1}{2}\rho_j V_j^2 \qquad (9.34)$$

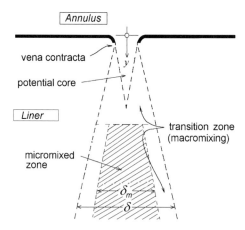

Fig. 9.12   Time-averaged properties of a turbulent round jet.

The static pressure at the vena contracta is equal to that of the liner (lower) region, and the mass density is equal to that from the annulus (upper) reservoir, and so the jet velocity V_j may be written as follows:

$$V_j = \sqrt{2\left(\frac{P_A - P_L}{\rho_A}\right)} \tag{9.35}$$

Downstream of the vena contracta, all of the kinetic energy in the jet is converted to thermal energy by turbulence and subsequent viscous dissipation. Because both reservoirs are at rest far from the orifice and jet, the total pressure drop for the flow from annulus to liner is equal to the static pressure drop:

$$\Delta P_t \doteq P_{tA} - P_{tL} = \frac{1}{2}\rho_A V_j^2 = q_j \tag{9.36}$$

An annular shear layer forms at the interface between the jet and the surrounding fluid, which causes ring vortices to form at the fluid/jet interface. The onset of Kelvin–Helmholtz instability causes them to intermittently form into distinct "smoke ring"-like structures, which grow in size as they are washed downward by the action of the jet momentum and viscous shear forces. As the shear layer grows inward towards the jet centerline, the potential core is finally consumed.

The rolling up of the ring vortices engulfs or entrains pockets of the liner fluid into the annulus fluid, stretching the interface between the two fluids, thereby reducing the "scale of segregation"[13] between the two mixants. This process of scale reduction is called "stirring," "near-field mixing," or "macromixing."[8,9]

After a sufficiently long convective time (that is, distance) downstream of jet entry, the stretching of the mixant interface has reduced the scale of segregation to the point that molecular diffusion can complete the process of molecular-scale mixing. The result of molecular diffusion is to eliminate the mixant interface and produce a molecularly homogeneous mixture, at whatever mixture ratio the system dynamics dictates. This latter process is called "far-field mixing" or "micromixing".

Figure 9.12 shows the time-averaged properties of the mixing jet. The length of the potential core varies from about $5\,d_j$ to $7\,d_j$ as the jet Reynolds number varies from 10^4 to 10^5 (Ref. 14), it can be taken to be $\sim 6\,d_j$ for purposes of preliminary design. The mixing transition point, the point at which a significant amount of micromixing has occurred, is about $10\,d_j$ downstream of the vena contracta.

Downstream of the potential core, the jet grows linearly with y at a conical half-angle $\sigma \sim 7\,\mathrm{deg}$, so that the jet width δ varies with y as $\delta = d_j + 2y \times \tan\sigma \sim 2y\tan\sigma$ where, for y sufficiently large, d_j can be neglected compared to $2y\tan\sigma$ (Ref. 14).

The micromixed region occupies about one-half the jet width, so that the part of the jet that has both entrained and micromixed the two fluids grows approximately as

$$\delta_m \cong y\tan\sigma = 0.123y \tag{9.37}$$

Assuming that the y momentum in the jet is conserved,

$$\rho_j v_j^2 \delta^2 = \rho_A V_j^2 d_j^2 = \text{const.} \tag{9.38}$$

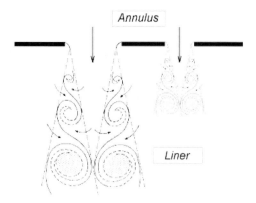

Fig. 9.13   Two round jets with same velocity, but with hole diameters different by a factor of 2.

then the average y component of the jet velocity v_j varies inversely with y as

$$v_j = \sqrt{\frac{\rho_A}{\rho_j}} \frac{V_j d_j}{2 \tan \sigma} \frac{1}{y} \tag{9.39}$$

In Fig. 9.13 a pair of jets are shown issuing through two round holes, the diameter of the hole on the left being two times that of the hole on the right.

Figure 9.13 illustrates that, although the pressure difference between the reservoirs uniquely determines the jet velocity and total pressure loss [Eqs. (9.35) and (9.36)], the hole diameter uniquely determines the penetration depth and structure of the jet [Eqs. (9.37–9.39)]. For the case shown, the mass flow rate through the larger hole is four times that of the smaller hole.

9.1.4.2   Jet flowing into a cross stream.   Figure 9.14 is a schematic drawing of a turbulent round jet flowing from the upper annulus reservoir into the liner

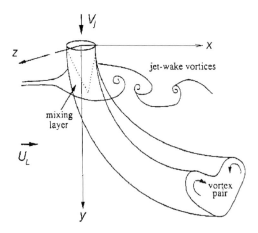

Fig. 9.14   Jet issuing from a reservoir into a cross stream.[15]

region, as before. However, the liner fluid is now also in motion, flowing from left to right with a velocity U_L. The cross-stream flow sees the vertical jet as a cylindrical obstruction in the flow, and so it exerts an aerodynamic drag force upon it. The jet, being a compliant structure rather than a rigid cylinder, deforms in response to the drag force and is bent up horizontally as it is washed downstream.

In addition to the jet entrainment as a result of the sequence of ring vortices, as sketched in Fig. 9.11, there is now an additional set of horseshoe vortices, as depicted in Fig. 9.14, which have vertical vortex filaments, established in the wake of the jet.[15] This creates a second mixing system extending in the x direction—that is, downstream in the sense of U_L—in addition to the jet mixing region as a result of the ring vortices, which extends in the y direction, downstream in the sense of V_j.

An expression for the trajectory of the jet centerline is given by Lefebvre[2]:

$$\frac{Y}{d_j} = 0.82 \, J^{0.5} \left(\frac{X}{d_j}\right)^{0.33} \quad \text{where} \quad J \doteq \frac{\rho_A V_j^2}{\rho_L U_L^2} = \frac{q_j}{q_L} \quad (9.40)$$

A derivation of Eq. (9.40) can be found in Ref. 14.

As the jet mixes out into the flowing stream, the jet centerline must eventually become parallel to the velocity U_L. However, the one-third power exponent in Eq. (9.40) does not approach an asymptote for Y as X increases, so Eq. (9.40) describes the jet trajectory only in the near field. Lefebvre gives an empirical equation for the asymptote, namely, the maximum jet penetration depth,[2]

$$\frac{Y_{\max}}{d_j} = 1.15 \, J^{0.5} \quad (9.41)$$

9.1.4.3 Jet from a crossflowing annulus.

If the fluid in the annulus is moving from left to right at velocity U_A, as depicted in Fig. 9.15, then the fluid entering the jet carries with it its axial momentum flux $\rho_A U_A^2$ in addition to the

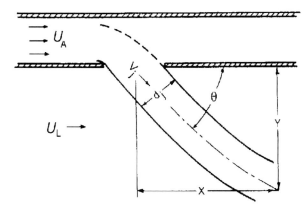

Fig. 9.15 Jet issuing from an annulus with velocity U_A into a stream with velocity U_L (Ref. 2).

y direction (vertically downward) momentum flux $\rho_A V_j^2$ generated by the difference in static pressure between the annulus and liner regions. Consequently, the entering velocity $V_j = \sqrt{2\Delta P_t / \rho_A}$ is now inclined at an angle θ as shown, where $\theta = \cos^{-1}(U_A / V_j)$. Obviously, the inclination of the jet at entry must affect both the discharge coefficient C_D and the jet penetration trajectory $Y(X)$.

The discharge coefficients of Eq. (9.33) are corrected for jet inclination by[16]

$$C_D = C_{D90°} \left(1 - \frac{U_A^2}{V_j^2} \right) = C_{D90°} \left(1 - \frac{q_A}{q_j} \right) = C_{D90°} \sin^2 \theta$$

$$0 < \theta \leq 90 \deg \quad (9.42)$$

and, according to Lefebvre,[2] the jet trajectory Eqs. (9.40) and (9.41) must be corrected as well, by multiplying them by $\sin \theta$:

$$\frac{Y}{d_j} = 0.82 \, J^{0.5} \left(\frac{X}{d_j} \right)^{0.33} \sin \theta = 0.82 \left(\frac{X}{d_j} \right)^{0.33} \sqrt{\frac{q_j}{q_L} \left(1 - \frac{q_A}{q_j} \right)} \quad (9.43)$$

and

$$\frac{Y_{max}}{d_j} = 1.15 \, J^{0.5} \sin \theta = 1.15 \sqrt{\frac{q_j}{q_L} \left(1 - \frac{q_A}{q_j} \right)} \quad (9.44)$$

Finally, note that these jet trajectory and penetration depth estimates are for a single jet. If many jets are located near to each other, their collective jet penetration is less than that given by Eq. (9.44).[2]

9.1.4.4 Swirling annular jets.
The primary combustion air in the main burner enters axially through an annular swirling jet, with sufficient swirl to cause a strong flow reversal on the axis of symmetry immediately downstream of the annular jet. By design, the air swirler surrounds the fuel injector or atomizer, so that all of the main burner fuel is captured, vaporized, and mixed with primary air in the swirler-induced recirculating flow. In addition, the combustor dome is usually shaped so that all or mostly all of the swirling air is also captured in the recirculation eddy, unlike the open-face swirl burner illustrated in Fig. 9.16.

If swirl were not present in the annular jet, a small bluff-body recirculation zone would still be established behind the aft surface of the air-blast atomizer at the core of the assembly. Because the geometry is axisymmetric, there would be no preferred direction for the recirculating flow, and so velocities in the wake region would probably be random or chaotic—not a good basis for establishing a stable flame.

The addition of a sufficient amount of swirl to the annular air flow changes all that. The tangential component of velocity of the swirled air creates a toroidal shear region, and if the swirl is sufficiently strong, centrifugal pressure gradients are set up of sufficient strength to induce a reverse (downstream-to-upstream) flow on the symmetry axis. The two effects combine to form a toroidal vortex system, with a small toroidal region of micromixed fuel and air at its core.

The geometry of a single annular swirler looks just like that of a compressor inlet guide vane, except that the annulus radii are measured from the axis of symmetry

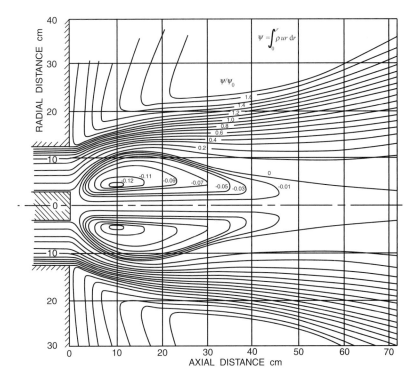

$$\psi = \int_0^r \rho\, ur\, dr$$

ψ/ψ_0

Fig. 9.16 Streamlines of recirculation eddy in swirling annular jet, for swirl number
$S' = 1.57$ (Ref. 17).

of the atomizer/swirler assembly, and not from the engine axis. Denoting the inner
("hub") radius of the annular area by r_h and the outer ("tip") radius by r_t, the axial
flow area of each swirler is simply $A_{sw} = \pi(r_t^2 - r_h^2)$, neglecting the thickness of
the swirl vanes.

The swirler vanes are designed with a solidity of about one, at an off-axial angle
α_{sw} such that the air leaving the swirler at velocity V_j has axial and tangential
velocity components $U = V_j \cos \alpha_{sw}$ and $W = V_j \sin \alpha_{sw}$, respectively. Note
well that this value of V_j is precisely the same jet velocity determined by the
combustor total pressure drop given by Eq. (9.36),

$$\Delta P_t \doteq P_{tr} - P_{tL} = \frac{1}{2}\rho_r V_j^2$$

and that the discharge coefficient for the annular jet is simply $C_D = C_{D90°} \cos \alpha_{sw}$,
where $C_{D90°}$ is the sharp-edged hole discharge coefficient given by Eq. (9.33).

The amount or degree of swirl imparted to the flow is quantified by the swirl
number S', defined by[17]

$$S' \doteq G_\phi / G_x' r_t \tag{9.45}$$

where G_ϕ and G'_x are the axial fluxes of tangential and axial momentum, respectively,

$$G_\phi \doteq \int_{r_h}^{r_t} (Wr)\, \rho U (2\pi r)\, dr = (U \tan \alpha) 2\pi \rho U \int_{r_h}^{r_t} r^2\, dr = \frac{2}{3}\pi \rho U^2 \left[r_t^3 - r_h^3\right]$$

(9.46)

and

$$G'_x \doteq \int_{r_h}^{r_t} (U)\, \rho U (2\pi r)\, dr = (U) 2\pi \rho U \int_{r_h}^{r_t} r\, dr = \pi \rho U^2 \left[r_t^2 - r_h^2\right] \quad (9.47)$$

so that the swirl number is given by

$$S' = \frac{2}{3}\tan \alpha_{sw} \left[\frac{1 - (r_h/r_t)^3}{1 - (r_h/r_t)^2}\right]$$

(9.48)

It has been found experimentally that a swirl number of at least 0.6 is required to cause on-axis recirculation. Increasing the swirl number beyond 0.6 increases the axial length of and rate of entrainment into the recirculation zone, but does not significantly increase its width. The rate of entrainment of swirler air into the recirculation zone is given approximately by the recirculation ratio[2]

$$\frac{\dot{m}_{recirc}}{\dot{m}_{sw}} \cong 0.1(S')^3 \quad \text{for} \quad S' < 2.5$$

(9.49)

from which it can be seen that the reverse mass flow rate in the bubble can actually exceed the flow through the swirler vanes, for swirl numbers just a little greater than 2.

However, because the Bragg criterion says that the primary zone should be as short as possible, S' between 0.6 and 1.0 would appear to be optimal.

Because the hub-to-tip ratio of the axial swirler will likely be in the range 0.7–0.9, it can be estimated from Eq. (9.48) that, for a swirl number $S' = 0.6$–1.0, a vane angle in the range $\alpha_{sw} = 35$ to 50 deg will be required.

The volume of the recirculation bubble may be estimated by $\text{Vol} \sim L\pi r_t^2$, where L is the axial length of the recirculation bubble and r_t is the tip radius of the swirl vanes, and L in turn is estimated by

$$L \sim 2S'r_t$$

(9.50)

from inspection of the sparse swirler data available, namely, Figs. 9.16 and 9.17.

The mean residence time or "stay time" for the air, fuel, and hot gases in the recirculation bubble is estimated as

$$t_s = \frac{\rho_r \text{Vol}}{\dot{m}_{PZ}} = \frac{\rho_r \pi r_t^2 L}{\rho_r A_{sw} U} \approx \frac{2S'\pi r_t^3}{\pi \left(r_t^2 - r_h^2\right) U} = \frac{2S'r_t}{\left(1 - r_h^2/r_t^2\right) V_j \cos \alpha_{sw}}$$

(9.51)

Note that the mass flow rate of the fuel has been neglected in arriving at these estimates.

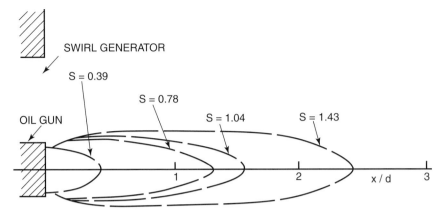

Fig. 9.17   Size of recirculation zone as function of swirl number S'.[17]

Finally, it may be assumed that the micromixed portion within the toroidal vortex is only about one-eighth of the volume of the primary zone recirculation bubble. This very rough estimate will be the residence time of the primary zone WSR used for chemical kinetics flame stability calculations in the KINETX program.

9.1.4.5 Shear layers.   The afterburner utilizes turbulent shear layers for both flameholding and flame spread, as depicted in Fig. 9.2. To understand this method of mixing, consider two uniform, parallel flowing streams of gas flowing continuously over a splitter plate, as shown in Fig. 9.18. Immediately downstream of the splitter plate, the axial velocities are U_1 and U_2. For clarity, it is initially assumed that the pressures and densities of both streams are equal and constant, and that boundary layers on the splitter plate and duct walls can be ignored.[18]

If the two velocities differ, for example if $U_1 > U_2$, a shear layer is generated at the interface between the two streams, in which momentum is transported laterally from the faster to the slower stream. Not only are vorticity and momentum transported laterally within a shear layer, but also thermal and mechanical energy,

Fig. 9.18   Mixing of parallel streams of air and gaseous fuel in a shear layer for $U_1 > U_2$. Dashed curves at mixant boundaries indicate molecular diffusion. Cross-hatched area represents fully micromixed region.

and mass (molecules) may be transported laterally as well. If the two streams have different molecular identities, the shear layer is also a mixing layer. By analogy with the definition of boundary layer thickness, the mixing layer thickness δ_m is defined as the region within which the mole fractions of mixant gases differ by 1% or more from their respective values in the unmixed streams.

The velocity ratio $r = U_2/U_1$ and the velocity difference $\Delta U = U_1 - U_2$ are related to the mean convective velocity $U_c = (U_1 + U_2)/2$ by

$$\Delta U = 2U_c \left(\frac{1-r}{1+r}\right) \tag{9.52}$$

For very small ΔU the shear layer may be laminar and time steady. As the velocity difference ΔU between the two streams is increased, the laminar shear layer becomes unstable, and large vortices are periodically formed between the two streams, just as in the case for round jets, as shown schematically in Fig. 9.18.

The cross-hatched area shown in the third vortex structure in Fig. 9.18 represents the fully micromixed region. Of course, molecular diffusion occurs continuously at the fuel-air interface immediately after the splitter plate, and the fully micromixed end state is simply the cumulative result of interfacial diffusion.

The time-mean growth rate of a turbulent shear layer is given approximately by[19]

$$\frac{\delta}{x} = 3B^2 \left(\frac{1-r}{1+r}\right) \tag{9.53}$$

where δ is the local shear layer width at a distance x downstream of the splitter plate, and where B is the ratio of the Prandtl mixing length ℓ_m to the shear layer width, $B = \ell_m/\delta$. The ratio B is an empirical constant and can only be determined from experimental data.[19] A time-averaged picture of the growth of the shear layer and embedded mixing layer is shown in Fig. 9.19.

In a recent survey of post-1970 research on turbulent mixing layers by Dimotakis,[18] the time-mean shear layer growth rate for constant and equal densities was found by many researchers to be given by

$$\frac{\delta}{x} = C_\delta \left(\frac{1-r}{1+r}\right) \tag{9.54}$$

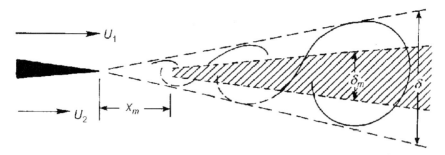

Fig. 9.19   Growth of time-averaged shear layer thickness δ and of micromixed mixing layer thickness δ_m, following mixing transition.

where C_δ was reported as varying from 0.25 to 0.45. Note that Eqs. (9.54) and (9.53) are of the same form and differ only in the representation of the proportionality constant.

When the mass densities in the two streams are different, the convective velocity U_c is given by[18]

$$U_c = \frac{U_1 + s^{1/2}U_2}{1 + s^{1/2}} \tag{9.55}$$

where $s = \rho_2/\rho_1$. The corresponding growth rate of the shear layer is also considerably more complex than Eq. (9.54):

$$\frac{\delta}{x} = C_\delta \left(\frac{1-r}{1+s^{1/2}r}\right)\left(\frac{1+s^{1/2}}{2}\right)\left\{1 - \frac{\left(1-s^{1/2}\right)/\left(1+s^{1/2}\right)}{1 + 1.29(1+r)/(1-r)}\right\} \tag{9.56}$$

Note that Eq. (9.56) reduces to Eq. (9.54) when $s = 1$.

By inspection of Fig. 9.18, it is apparent that, at any axial station, micromixing (indicated by dashed lines) is not complete throughout the shear layer. In fact, for the first one or two vortices sketched in Fig. 9.18, it may be seen that comparatively little micromixing has yet occurred. The distance downstream of the splitter plate at which significant amount of mixed fluid is first present is called the mixing transition point. The mixing transition occurs approximately at the point where

$$\frac{(U_1 - U_2)\delta}{\nu} \approx 10 \tag{9.57}$$

where ν is a representative average value of the molecular kinematic viscosity within the shear layer. Following the mixing transition, the time-averaged micromixing layer is observed to grow approximately as a constant fraction of the shear layer,

$$\frac{\delta_m}{\delta} \approx 0.49 \tag{9.58}$$

as illustrated in Fig. 9.19.

The composition of the gases within the mixing layer is characterized by the volumetric entrainment ratio E_v, defined as the volume ratio of high-speed fluid to low-speed fluid entrained within each vortex structure, that is, "wrapped up" into each vortex or "jelly-roll" structure as shown in Fig. 9.18. The volumetric entrainment ratio is observed to depend on both the density ratio and velocity ratio[18] as

$$E_v \cong s^{1/2}\left\{1 + 0.68\left(\frac{1-r}{1+r}\right)\right\} \tag{9.59}$$

The corresponding mass-basis and mole-basis entrainment ratios E_m and E_n are given by

$$E_m = \frac{E_v}{s} \quad \text{and} \quad E_n = \frac{M_2}{M_1}E_m \tag{9.60}$$

where M_1 and M_2 are the mean or apparent molecular weights of the gases in streams 1 and 2, respectively.[18]

9.1.5 Total Pressure Loss

The main burner or combustor is the engine component immediately downstream of the high-pressure compressor. For reasons to be shown presently, the main burner requires an inlet velocity which is much lower than that leaving the high-pressure compressor, so that the flow velocity must be greatly reduced between these two components. As the required flow diffuser inserted into the flowpath is a passive device, adding neither mechanical nor thermal energy to the flow, it is not clear from a strictly logical point of view where design responsibility for this component should lie. Historically, it has been regarded as a part of the main burner, and so it is included here.

In this section it will first be shown how to estimate the main burner diffuser total pressure loss. Next, the principal source of total pressure loss in the main burner liner (see Fig. 9.1) namely, stirring and mixing with jets, will be considered. Finally, the total pressure loss in the afterburner (see Fig. 9.2) will be analyzed.

A number of assumptions will be made in common for all of the derivations to follow. They are as follows: 1) flow is quasi-one dimensional, 2) mass density varies with temperature, but not with pressure,[11] 3) combustion in the main burner is at constant pressure, and 4) the mass flow rate of fuel is neglected compared to that of air.

9.1.5.1 Flat-wall diffuser.
Although the purpose of a flow diffuser is to reduce axial velocity in order to gain static pressure, this must be accomplished in a very short axial distance and with a minimal loss of total pressure. As with the diffusing flow in compressor blade passages, this is not easily accomplished without flow separation. The geometry and nomenclature of a generic flat wall diffuser with flow-straightening section are shown in Fig. 9.20. The entry and exit stations of Fig. 9.20 correspond to compressor outlet, station 3.1, and burner inlet, station 3.2, respectively, in Fig. 9.1. Typically, an area ratio $AR = A_2/A_1$ of 3 to 5 is required to diffuse the flow, although an area ratio as great as 10 or even 20 may be required for some engine designs. A "tailpipe" of length L_d can be added for improved performance.

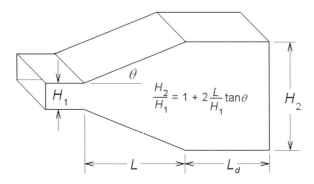

$$\frac{H_2}{H_1} = 1 + 2\frac{L}{H_1}\tan\theta$$

Fig. 9.20   Geometry of a flat-wall diffuser with tailpipe.[20,21]

Strictly speaking, both the main burner and afterburner diffusers are annular diffusers, rather than the planar diffuser pictured in Fig. 9.20. Because an annular flow passage has inner and outer radii r_i and r_o, respectively, the geometrical variables that define the shape of an annular (quasi-flat-wall) diffuser are given by

$$AR \doteq \frac{A_2}{A_1} = \frac{H_2 \, r_{m2}}{H_1 \, r_{m1}} = 1 + 2\frac{r_{m2}}{r_{m1}} \frac{L}{H_1} \tan \theta$$

or

$$\frac{L}{H_1} = \left(\frac{r_{m1}}{r_{m2}}\right) \frac{(AR - 1)}{2 \tan \theta} \tag{9.61}$$

where H is the radial height $H = (r_o - r_i)$ and r_m is the mean radius, $r_m = (r_o + r_i)/2$. Note that when the inlet and exit mean radii are equal Eq. (9.61) reduces to the geometrical relationship for a planar flat-wall diffuser given on Fig. 9.20.

There are a number of measures used to characterize the performance of a diffuser. The pressure recovery coefficient C_P is defined by[20,21]

$$C_P \doteq \frac{P_2 - P_1}{q_1} \tag{9.62}$$

In the case of isentropic flow, that is, flow with neither wall friction nor flow separation, and with the assumptions listed at the beginning of this section, conservation of mass leads immediately to the ideal pressure recovery coefficient C_{Pid}:

$$C_{Pid} \doteq \frac{(P_2 - P_1)_{isen}}{q_1} = \frac{q_1 - q_{2isen}}{q_1} = 1 - \frac{1}{AR^2} \tag{9.63}$$

The ratio of actual-to-ideal pressure recovery is a logical measure of diffuser performance and is called the diffuser effectiveness or diffusion efficiency η_D,

$$\eta_D \doteq \frac{C_P}{C_{Pid}} \tag{9.64}$$

It is interesting to note that η_D defined by Eq. (9.64) is identical to the isentropic diffuser efficiency η_D defined by the ratio of ideal-to-actual enthalpy change,[22]

$$\eta_D \doteq \frac{h_{2s} - h_1}{h_2 - h_1} \tag{9.65}$$

The total pressure loss coefficient is defined by

$$\left(\frac{\Delta P_t}{q_1}\right)_D \doteq \frac{P_{t1} - P_{t2}}{q_1} = C_{Pid} - C_P = \left(1 - \frac{1}{AR^2}\right)(1 - \eta_D) \tag{9.66}$$

and the related total pressure ratio π_D is

$$\pi_D \doteq \frac{P_{t2}}{P_{t1}} = 1 - \frac{(\Delta P_t/q_1)_D}{1 + 2/\gamma M_1^2} = 1 - \frac{(1 - 1/AR^2)(1 - \eta_D)}{1 + 2/\gamma M_1^2} \tag{9.67}$$

All of the preceding figures of merit are useful, depending on the perspective or interest of the designer. If the primary design goal of the diffuser is maximum

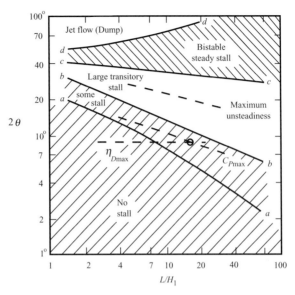

Fig. 9.21   Operating regimes of a flat-wall diffuser without tailpipe.[20,21]

static pressure recovery, then both C_p and η_D are of interest. If a design goal is to minimize adiabatic irreversibility (entropy rise or, equivalently, total pressure loss), then η_D, $(\Delta P_t / q_r)_D$, and π_D are all of interest.

The operating regimes of a flat-wall diffuser without tailpipe are shown in Figs. 9.21 and 9.22. It can be seen from Fig. 9.21 that the possible operating regimes for a flat-wall diffuser are a veritable snake's nest of flow phenomena. In the "no stall" region below curve a-a, flow remains attached to the walls, but performance is suboptimal because of excessive friction resulting from very long walls. The best performance occurs in the "some stall" region, bounded by a-a and b-b, even though the flow in this regime is in mild transitory stall, that is, alternately separating and reattaching to the walls. In the "large transitory stall" region bounded by b-b and c-c, the flow is oscillating so vigorously from wall to wall that the flow patterns are highly unstable, and total pressure loss is consequently excessive. In the "bistable steady stall" region bounded by c-c and d-d, the flow separates completely from one wall and attaches to the opposite wall. Finally, above d-d, the flow is separated from both walls and enters the diffuser as a core jet flow, which eventually reattaches to the downstream walls, if there is sufficient axial length to do so, as for example a tailpipe of some length L_d as shown in Fig. 9.20. When operating in the jet flow regime, the diffuser is called a "dump" diffuser.

There is a "sweet spot" in the operating map, represented by the "bullseye" in Figs. 9.21 and 9.22. For this particular geometry, namely, $2\theta \sim 9$ deg and $L/H_1 \sim 18$, both the maximum achievable C_P and a near-maximum diffusion efficiency η_D are realized. This optimal value of diffusion efficiency can be

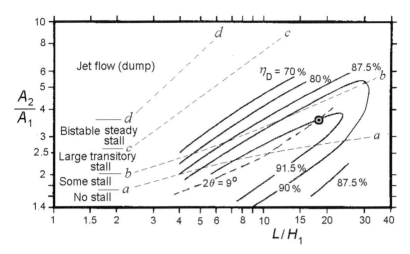

Fig. 9.22 **Contours of diffuser effectiveness on performance map of flat-wall diffuser without tailpipe and with thin inlet boundary layers, $B_t \sim 0.018$.**

represented approximately by an empirical relation,[20]

$$\eta_{D9°} \cong 0.965 - 2.72 B_t \qquad 0.01 < B_t < 0.12 \quad (9.68)$$

where B_t is the thickness of the turbulent boundary layer at diffuser entry. Note on Fig. 9.22 that the diffuser efficiency η_D is very nearly constant with varying L/H_1 for a constant wall angle $2\theta = 9$ deg for values of L/H_1 between ~ 4 and ~ 20. The corresponding range of area ratios, determined from the geometrical relations of Eq. (9.61) and shown on Fig. 9.20, is $1.5 < AR < 4$.

Combining Eqs. (9.63), (9.66), and (9.68), the total pressure loss coefficient for a flat-wall diffuser with divergence angle $2\theta = 9$ deg can be shown to be

$$\left(\frac{\Delta P_t}{q_1}\right)_{D9°} = C_{Pid}(1 - \eta_{D9°}) = \left(1 - \frac{1}{AR^2}\right)(1 - \eta_{D9°}), \quad 1.5 < AR < 4 \quad (9.69)$$

However, there are problems. The "sweet spot" diffuser length $L/H_1 \sim 18$ is unacceptable because it excessively increases the length of the engine core. In addition, the sweet spot area ratio $AR = 3.83$ is not likely to fit any specific engine design requirement, and area ratios AR greater than about four push the operating point into the region of large transitory stall, between b-b and c-c on Figs. 9.21 and 9.22. Finally, because the flow exiting the high-pressure compressor has been "sliced and diced" by the last row of rotor blades and straightening vanes, the boundary layers entering the diffuser are very thick, so that the optimal diffusion efficiency given by Eq. (9.68) may be as low as ~ 0.64. This is so low that consideration must be given to the alternative of abandoning the 9-deg angle, straight-wall diffuser design entirely, and simply "dumping" the flow into the required area at combustor entry, station 3.2.

9.1.5.2 Dump diffuser.

At first glance, it may seem that the dump diffuser, operating in the "jet flow" region above line d-d in Figs. 9.21 and 9.22, is the worst possible case for flow diffusion, but, in fact, the bistable stall and large transitory stall regions bounded by b-b and d-d in Figs. 9.21 and 9.22 are *much* worse.[20,21] Worst of all, in the large transitory stall region the flow separates and then momentarily reattaches to only one of the downstream walls. This in turn causes another, subsequent sudden expansion as the bifurcated flow tries to reattach and fill the duct. The separated flow acts as a bistable oscillator, jumping from wall to wall in a periodic Coanda effect, presenting randomly varying, nonuniform velocity profiles to downstream components and causing an excessive loss of total pressure, which can be 10–40% greater than a dump diffuser! Thus, a dump diffuser is the "best worst" case for a flat-wall diffuser.

Consider the classic case of head loss or total pressure loss caused by a sudden expansion in a duct.[21] Figure 9.20, with $2\theta = 180$ deg and $L_d \sim H_2$, is the control volume for this analysis. (The tailpipe length L_d has to be sufficiently long for the jet core flow at entry to reattach to both walls.) By applying the equations of conservation of mass and linear momentum to this control volume, together with the assumptions listed in the introduction to this section, the reader may (and should) verify that the pressure recovery coefficient, total pressure loss coefficient, and diffuser efficiency for the dump diffuser are given by

$$\left[C_P\right]_{dump} = 2\left(\frac{AR-1}{AR^2}\right), \quad \left[\frac{\Delta P_t}{q_1}\right]_{dump} = \left(1 - \frac{1}{AR}\right)^2, \quad \text{and}$$

$$\left[\eta_D\right]_{dump} = \frac{2}{1+AR} \tag{9.70}$$

For the "sweet spot" diffuser area ratio $AR = 3.83$, Eq. (9.70c) predicts a dump diffuser efficiency of only 0.414, which is considerably less than the absolutely best value of $\eta_D = 0.91$ obtainable by a thin-boundary layer, $2\theta = 9$ deg flat-wall diffuser of area ratio $AR = 3.83$ and length-to-entry height ratio $L/H_1 = 18$. Ways to overcome this perplexing problem will be presented in Sec. 9.2.3.

9.1.5.3 Main burner.

In the early day of turbojet engine development, the total pressure loss of the combustor was regarded as just another parasitic loss, in addition to those of the diffuser, compressor and turbine, all of which reduced the marginal engine performance achievable at the time. Consequently, main burner designers were under great pressure to minimize total pressure loss, or at least to justify the excessive amounts they claimed were necessary to achieve adequate combustion stability and efficiency. As engine designs evolved, increasing compression ratios and turbine inlet temperatures created a demand for increased compressor bleed airflow for turbine blade cooling. Moreover, because the bleed air itself was becoming increasingly hot, even greater flow rates were needed to adequately protect the turbine blades. Consequently, the main burner is today viewed not only as the source of thermal energy required by the propulsion cycle, but also as a necessary flow constriction or circuit resistance, which must provide adequate flow area blockage to maintain the required static pressure drop between compressor bleed outlet and turbine inlet. This is especially critical if the turbine first stage stator vanes depend on film cooling to protect their leading edges. If the total pressure of the cooling airflow, which will be less than P_{t3} as a result of losses in the cooling air delivery flow passages, does not exceed that of the main combustor exit stream P_{t4}, this method will not work.

But the question remains, how much pressure drop is actually needed to ensure adequate stirring and mixing in the main burner? As mentioned in Sec. 9.1, the primary zone is indeed "where the action is." The most important utilization of total pressure loss in the main burner is the dissipation of kinetic energy from the primary zone swirler jet, which is required for stirring and mixing the airblast-vaporized fuel with both the incoming primary air and with the hot, partially burned gases flowing upstream in the recirculation bubble.

The analysis of total pressure loss in the main burner is complicated by the lack of an appropriate single control volume. By inspection of Fig. 9.1, it can be seen that the perforated liner is effectively a "colander," which provides a blockage or impedance to the main burner airflow. An outer control volume having its radial boundaries inside the inner casing wall and outside the liner wall is effectively a plenum of constant total pressure. The various jets—primary swirler, secondary, and dilution round jets—all dynamically support a difference in both static and total pressure across the liner, as the jets flow into a second control volume having a single radial boundary inside the liner wall. The viscous dissipation of kinetic energy in all of the jets leads to an approximately uniform level of total pressure within the liner. As with the infinite wall between the idealized jets illustrated in Figs. 9.12 and 9.13, the purpose and effect of the perforated colander liner is to maintain a fixed (by design) level of total pressure between the upstream and downstream plenums.

Because the Mach numbers are low everywhere within the main burner except within the jet cores, the difference between static and total pressure is slight, and so it is convenient to also consider the static pressure to be approximately constant within the liner—except, again, within the structure of the jets themselves.

Flow enters the primary zone as a radial, swirling jet inside the liner dome, as shown in Fig. 9.1. Partial or incomplete combustion in the primary zone causes a temperature-rise ratio τ_{PZ} at the primary zone exit, as shown in Fig. 9.1a.

Assuming isentropic flow from the upstream reference state (station 3.2 in Fig. 9.1) to the vena contracta of the radial swirler jet, the total pressure is conserved, so that $P_{tr} = P_r + q_r = P_j + q_j$. Assuming uniform static pressure P_L inside the combustor liner, then $P_j = P_L$, and the total pressure loss caused by the swirling jet is given by

$$\Delta P_t = (P_L + q_j) - (P_L + q_{PZ}) = q_j - q_{PZ}$$

Employing the equation of mass conservation and nondimensionalizing by the reference dynamic pressure q_r, the total pressure loss coefficient becomes

$$\left(\frac{\Delta P_t}{q_r} \right)_{MB} = \frac{q_j}{q_r} - \frac{q_{PZ}}{q_r} = \left(\frac{\dot{m}_{PZ}}{\dot{m}_r} \right)^2 \left[\left(\frac{A_r}{A_j} \right)^2 - \frac{\rho_r}{\rho_{PZ}} \left(\frac{A_r}{A_L} \right)^2 \right] \quad (9.71)$$

where A_j is the vena contracta area of the swirling air jet.

Assuming as before that the mass density ratio depends only on the temperature-rise ratio and multiplying and dividing the first term in brackets by the liner cross-sectional area A_L, Eq. (9.71) becomes

$$\left(\frac{\Delta P_t}{q_r}\right)_{MB} = \left(\frac{\dot{m}_{PZ}}{\dot{m}_r}\right)^2 \left(\frac{A_r}{A_L}\right)^2 \left[\left(\frac{A_L}{A_j}\right)^2 - \tau_{PZ}\right] \tag{9.72}$$

Typical values for the primary zone of a 1950s turbojet engine are $\tau_{PZ} \sim 4$, $A_j/A_L = 0.12$, $A_L/A_r = 0.65$, and $\dot{m}_{PZ}/\dot{m}_r = 0.3$ (Ref. 10), for which Eq. (9.72) gives a total pressure loss coefficient of about 14.

All of the terms in Eq. (9.72) are fixed by various engine design criteria that will be presented in Sec. 9.2, except for (A_r/A_j), the ratio of liner cross-sectional area to swirler jet (vena contracta) area. It is this parameter that determines the amount of constriction or blockage required to obtain any given level of primary zone inlet swirler jet velocity. Therefore, the next task is to determine how great this swirler jet velocity has to be to achieve the degree of micromixing required for effective flameholding in the primary zone.

To do this, it is necessary to first estimate the time required for micromixing to occur, then ensure that the residence time or "stay time" in the primary zone is equal to or greater than the micromixing time.

The micromixing time t_m is estimated by assuming that the characteristic time for decay of a turbulent eddy is approximately the same as that required for reduction of a temperature or concentration fluctuation,[23]

$$t_m \cong \left(\frac{H^2}{\varepsilon_T}\right)^{\frac{1}{3}}, \tag{9.73}$$

where H is a characteristic linear dimension of the primary zone, which we take to be the liner height or "dome height" H_L and ε_T is the rate of dissipation of turbulence kinetic energy, which is equal to the mixing power of the stirring jets per unit mass in the primary zone,

$$\varepsilon_T \cong \frac{\rho_j A_j V_j \left(V_j^2/2\right)}{\rho_{PZ} H_L^3} = \frac{\tau_{PZ} A_j V_j^3}{2 H_L^3} \tag{9.74}$$

Substituting Eq. (9.74) into Eq. (9.73), the micromixing time estimate is

$$t_m \cong \left(\frac{2 H_L^2}{\tau_{PZ} A_j}\right)^{\frac{1}{3}} \frac{H_L}{V_j} \tag{9.75}$$

The residence time or stay time in the primary zone is defined as the mass of working substance in the primary zone divided by the mass flow rate of fuel and air into the primary zone:

$$t_s = \frac{\rho_{PZ} H_L^3}{\dot{m}_f + \dot{m}_{PZ}} \cong \frac{\rho_{PZ} H_L^3}{\dot{m}_{PZ}} = \frac{\rho_{PZ} H_L^3}{\rho_j A_j V_j} = \frac{H^3}{\tau_{PZ} A_j V_j} \tag{9.76}$$

where the fuel flow rate has been neglected compared to the primary zone air flow rate.

Dividing the stay time Eq. (9.76) by the micromixing time Eq. (9.75), there results the ratio

$$\frac{t_s}{t_m} = \left(\frac{H_L^3}{\tau_{PZ} A_j V_j}\right) \cdot \frac{V_j}{H_L} \left(\frac{\tau_{PZ} A_j}{2 H_L^2}\right)^{\frac{1}{3}} = \left(\frac{H_L^2}{\sqrt{2}\,\tau_{PZ} A_j}\right)^{\frac{2}{3}}, \quad > 1 \text{ required} \quad (9.77)$$

Equation (9.77) shows that all that is necessary to ensure that the stay time is greater than the micromixing time is to size the primary zone volume and swirler so that the ratio of the liner cross-sectional area, $A_L \sim H_L^2$, to the vena contracta area of the primary zone jets A_j is about square-root-two times the temperature rise ratio τ_{PZ}:

$$\frac{H_L^2}{A_j} = \frac{A_L}{A_j} \qquad > \sqrt{2}\,\tau_{PZ} \text{ required} \qquad (9.78)$$

With the inequality Eq. (9.78) substituted into Eq. (9.72), there follows

$$\left(\frac{\Delta P_t}{q_r}\right)_{MB} > \left(\frac{\dot{m}_{PZ}}{\dot{m}_r}\right)^2 \left(\frac{A_r}{A_L}\right)^2 \tau_{PZ}(2\tau_{PZ} - 1) \qquad \text{required} \quad (9.79)$$

Equation (9.79) is the desired estimate for how much total pressure loss is required to ensure adequate primary zone stirring and mixing, and Eq. (9.78) gives the minimum constriction or blockage required to achieve it. Using input values for the 1950s burner listed after Eq. (9.72), Eq. (9.79) gives a minimum required total pressure loss coefficient of about six, and so by this measure the 1950s burner appears to have had adequate primary zone stirring. Using a similar but somewhat more simplified analysis, Swithenbank asserts that primary zone mixing is adequate for flameholding if the total pressure loss coefficient is greater than ∼3 (Ref. 24).

Finally, note that the primary zone temperature rise ratio τ_{PZ} is linear in Eq. (9.78) and quadratic in Eq. (9.79), so that it has a very strong effect on the required total pressure loss for adequate mixing.

What about the secondary and dilution zones? From inspection of Fig. 9.1, it is apparent that there can be *only one value* of total pressure loss for the entire main burner, and it must be that determined for the primary zone and given by Eq. (9.72). The round jet holes in both the secondary and dilution zones must be sized to provide the correct blockage to not only support the required total pressure loss, but also to divide or "partition" the airflow into the appropriate mass flow rates into the primary, secondary, and dilution zones. How this is to be accomplished will be covered in Sec. 9.2.2.

9.1.5.4 *Afterburner.*

The total pressure loss of the afterburner is mainly composed of that caused by the diffuser, the drag of the flameholders, and the combustion process. The total pressure loss of the diffuser can be estimated using the methods presented earlier in this section.

To estimate the total pressure loss in the afterburner, a control volume must be defined for analysis. Reference will be made to the afterburner schematic Fig. 9.2b. The flow enters the control volume at station 2, which is at the maximum width W of the recirculation zone, where the streamlines of bypassing flow are essentially parallel. Flow exits the control volume at station 3, which is assumed to be sufficiently far downstream so that the flame front has reached the walls. The upper and lower walls are the confining boundaries of the control volume.

The gas is assumed to behave as a Boussinesq fluid, that is, flow is at low Mach number, and the mass density varies only with temperature.[11] Consequently, $\rho_2 = \tau_{AB}\rho_3$, where τ_{AB} is the ratio of total temperature rise across the afterburner.

The cross-sectional areas of the flow are $(H - W)$ at entry station 2 and H at exit station 3. Mass conservation requires that $\rho_2 A_2 U_2 = \rho_3 A_3 U_3$. Note that the static pressure at station 2 acts across the entire area, but flow enters only between the wall and the outer edge of the recirculation bubble. Conservation of linear momentum across the control volume gives

$$P_2 H + \rho_2 U_2^2 (H - W) = P_3 H + \rho_3 U_3^2 H \tag{9.80}$$

The total pressure drop across the control volume is, by definition,

$$\Delta P_t \doteq P_{t2} - P_{t3} = (P_2 + q_2) - (P_3 + q_3) = (P_2 - P_3) + (q_2 - q_3) \tag{9.81}$$

Noting that $\rho U^2 = 2q$, and substituting for $(P_3 - P_2)$ from Eq. (9.80), Eq. (9.81) may be rewritten as

$$\Delta P_t = \left[2q_3 - 2q_2 \left(1 - \frac{W}{H} \right) \right] + (q_2 - q_3) = q_3 - q_2 \left(1 - \frac{2W}{H} \right) \tag{9.82}$$

Nondimensionalizing by the upstream dynamic pressure q_1 and simplifying, there follows an expression for the afterburner total pressure loss coefficient,

$$\left(\frac{\Delta P_t}{q_1} \right)_{AB} = \frac{\rho_1}{\rho_3} - \left(\frac{H}{H - W} \right)^2 \left(1 - \frac{2W}{H} \right) = (\tau_{AB} - 1) + \frac{W^2}{(H - W)^2} \tag{9.83}$$

A similar linear momentum conservation control volume analysis between stations 1 and 2 on Fig. 9.2b can be used to find an expression for the drag coefficient C_D of the vee-gutter flameholder,

$$C_D \doteq \frac{F_{drag}}{q_1 D} = \frac{H}{D} \frac{W^2}{(H - W)^2} \tag{9.84}$$

where F_{drag} is the aerodynamic drag force on the vee-gutter, H is the channel height, and D is the height or lateral dimension of the gutter, as shown on Fig. 9.2b.

With Eq. (9.84) substituted into Eq. (9.83), the total pressure loss coefficient can be expressed as

$$\left(\frac{\Delta P_t}{q_1} \right)_{AB} = (\tau_{AB} - 1) + C_D B \tag{9.85}$$

where B is the "blockage," $B = D/H$.

Note that when the afterburner is not turned on, so that $\tau_{AB} = 1$, Eq. (9.85) gives the "cold" or "dry" loss of the afterburner caused solely by the aerodynamic drag of the vee-gutters.

The total pressure ratio is related to the total pressure loss coefficient by

$$\pi_{AB} \doteq \frac{P_{t3}}{P_{t1}} = 1 - \left(\frac{\Delta P_t}{q_1}\right)_{AB} \left(1 + \frac{2}{\gamma M_1^2}\right)^{-1} = 1 - \frac{(\tau_{AB} - 1) + C_D B}{1 + 2/\gamma M_1^2} \qquad (9.86)$$

All that remains to be done is to establish a relationship between the maximum wake width W, channel height H, and the vee-gutter dimensions D and half-angle θ. Citing a potential flow solution to this geometry published by von Mises in 1917, Cornell presents a graph of the variation of W/H as a function of blockage $B = D/H$ for values of half-angle θ between 0 and 180 deg (Ref. 25). Cornell's graphical solution can be represented to good approximation by a curve-fit,

$$\frac{W}{H} \cong B + (1 - \sqrt{B})\sqrt{B \sin(\theta/2)} \qquad (9.87)$$

Equations (9.83–9.87) constitute the desired estimate of total pressure loss for the afterburner, neglecting wall friction. By inspection of Eq. (9.83), it is apparent that the total pressure loss is at its least value when $W = 0$, that is, when there is no vee-gutter at all. At the other limit the total pressure loss increases without bound as W approaches H, that is, as the vee-gutter wake fills the entire channel. Because there is no optimal set of parameters that minimize the afterburner total pressure loss, the vee-gutters will just be made as small as possible while still able to function as flameholders. The choice of afterburner channel height H, vee-gutter dimensions D, and half-angle θ to ensure adequate flameholding will be dealt with in Sec. 9.3.

9.1.6 Fuels

In the early development of the gas turbine engine, it was commonly believed that the engine could use any fuel that would burn. While this is true in theory, it is not so in practice. The modern turbojet engine is quite particular about the fuel used, due to the high rate of fuel flow and wide temperature and pressure variations.

Jet fuel is refined from crude oil petroleum. A typical pound of jet fuel might be composed of 16% hydrogen atoms, 84% carbon atoms, and small amounts of impurities such as sulfur, nitrogen, water, and sediment. Various grades of jet fuel have evolved during the development of the jet engines in an effort to ensure both satisfactory performance and adequate supply. Historically, JP-4 was the most commonly used fuel for U.S. Air Force jet engines, while the U.S. Navy used JP-5, a denser, less volatile fuel than JP-4 that offered less explosion hazard when stored in the skin tanks of ships than did JP-4. At the present time, the most common fuels in both military and commercial aircraft are Jet A and JP-8 (Jet A-1). They are much alike, except that Jet A has a freezing point below $-40°F$ while JP-8/Jet A-1 has a freezing point below $-58°F$. Table 9.4 gives specifications for the most commonly used jet fuels.

Many aircraft engines are built to operate on any of these fuels. To do so, they must have a special switch on the fuel control to compensate for differences in the specific gravity which is used in fuel metering calculations.

Table 9.4   Jet engine fuels[a]

Property	JP-4 Specific requirement	JP-4 Typical	JP-5 Specific requirement	JP-5 Typical	JP-8 (Jet A-1) Specific requirement	JP-8 (Jet A-1) Typical
Vapor pressure, atm @ 38°C (100°F)	0.13–0.2	0.18	——	0.003	——	0.007
Initial boiling point, °F	——	140	——	360	——	336
Endpoint, °F	——	475	550	500	550	509
Flash point, °F	——	−13	>145	149	>120	126
Aromatic content (% vol.)	<25	12	<25	16	<20	16
Olefinic content (% vol.)	<5	1	——	1	——	1
Saturates content (% vol.)	——	87	——	83	——	83
Net heat of combustion, BTU/lbm	>18,400	18,700	>18,300	18,500	>18,400	18,600
Specific gravity	0.751–0.802	0.758	0.788–0.845	0.818	0.733–0.830	0.810

[a]H. R. Lander, private communication, Cleveland, OH, May 2001.

9.1.7   Ignition

In the main burner an ignition source is required for initial startup, as well as for relight following flameout or blowout. An ignition source is also required to ignite the afterburner. Usually, an electrical spark igniter is used for both applications (Appendix O).

In the main burner the spark igniter must be located in the primary zone in a location where the air/fuel mixture passes over the electrodes. However, because the spark igniter does not function during steady-state operation of the engine, it must also be located far enough away from the hottest part of the primary zone recirculation bubble so that the electrodes are not eroded or burned away. Because an ignited primary zone can propagate a flame laterally to ignite neighboring primary zones, not every primary zone has to have its own spark igniter. Determining the optimal location and number, as well as the level of electrical power that must be provided for the spark to be effective, is based on experience and trial and error.

In the afterburner the ignition source must be located somewhat upstream of one or more of the vee-gutters, but of course far enough downstream from the fuel injectors for adequate fuel/gas mixing to be achieved. Although more than one igniter is required, the number of igniters and their location is again largely a matter of experience and trial and error.

Preliminary design of the ignition subsystems of both the main burner and afterburner is considered to be too complex and specialized to be considered here.

9.2   Design Tools—Main Burner

Procedures for preliminary design of the main burner are the subject of the present section. Extensive use will of course be made of concepts and equations from the preceding Sec. 9.1. A complete example calculation illustrating the use of the AEDsys computational tools, primarily programs EQL, MAINBRN, and KINETX, can be found in Sec. 9.4.1.

In the spirit of the quote from Sir William Hawthorne that begins this chapter, the design of the main burner will be approached in the same manner as the design of blades and flow passages for the compressor and turbine. This philosophy and approach may be summarized in three steps:

1) From the preliminary design requirements of the engine, identify the mass flow rates, pressures, and temperatures that the main burner must produce, as illustrated in Table 7.E4.

2) Utilize aerodynamics, chemical reactor theory, equilibrium chemical thermodynamics, and chemical kinetics to design the processes the working substance must follow to meet the requirements of Step 1.

3) "Cut the tin," that is to say, lay out the geometry of walls and passages in such a way as to cause the working substance to follow the processes designed in Step 2.

9.2.1 Main Burner Design Parameters

Overall engine design considerations have already fixed the flow rates of fuel and air that must enter the main burner at station 3.1 in Fig. 9.1a. When using the AEDsys software for preliminary design, these values are displayed on the Engine Station Test Results sheet for the main burner design point conditions selected (see Table 7.E4). The required thermodynamic state of the entering air and of the combustion product gases exiting the burner are also fixed—the latter actually being prescribed at station 4, the first stage turbine nozzle entry throat, rather than at combustor exit station 3.9.

Although the Engine Station Test Results values listed for stations 3.1 (including the main burner fuel flow rate) and station 4 are fixed requirements, the values listed for station 3.2 are just "first cut" or "bogey" values, which may have to be adjusted in order to optimize the performance of both the diffuser and combustor. However, the radial location of the main burner assembly in the engine framework will be determined by matching the layout of the compressor and turbine sections determined from their respective preliminary designs.

9.2.2 Air Partitioning

The term "air partitioning" has been used since the beginning of gas turbine engine development to describe the design procedure of dividing or partitioning the main burner airflow into discrete streams, for delivering the appropriate amounts of air for liner cooling, primary zone, secondary/intermediate zone, and dilution zone processes, as illustrated in Fig. 9.23.

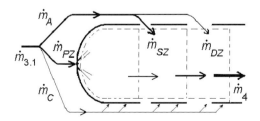

Fig. 9.23   Schematic and nomenclature for air partitioning.

The objective of air partitioning is to control the temperatures that the combustion product gases must either achieve, or be limited to, in order to fulfill cycle requirements, ensure the integrity of liner and casing materials, and protect the first-stage stators (nozzles) in the high-pressure turbine immediately downstream of the combustor. By design, only the primary and secondary airflows participate in the combustion process. The liner cooling and dilution airflows are provided only for thermal protection of the liner and of the high-pressure turbine, respectively.

In the early days of gas turbine engine development, pressures and temperatures at combustor entry were so low that it was necessary to design main burners with near-stoichiometric primary zones to ensure combustion stability. Copious amounts of cooling air were therefore required to protect the liner from the very high liner gas temperatures, and finally, an additional 300% or more additional air had to be dumped into the hot gas stream near combustor exit in order to dilute the hot gas stream for thermal protection of the first-stage high-pressure turbine. Combustion efficiency and pattern factor [defined by Eq. (9.120)] were the driving considerations in combustor development.

In the period 1950–1980 new high-temperature materials were developed for the combustor liner and high-pressure turbine nozzle materials, together with increased use of bypass air for cooling of the high-pressure turbine blades. These improvements led to increased combustor entry and exit temperatures and pressures, which in turn permitted wide combustion stability to be achieved with lower (leaner) primary zone equivalence ratios, typically with $\phi_{PZ} \sim 0.8$. These changes had little effect on liner cooling airflow requirements, as the available cooling air temperature was increasing as well as other temperatures, but both high combustion efficiency and satisfactory pattern factors became easier to achieve.

Since the mid-1970s, a new requirement has been added, namely, the regulation of liner gas temperatures in order to satisfy air pollutant emissions limits.

The present state of design constraints on liner gas temperatures may be summarized as follows:

1) If liner gas temperatures are too low, flame stability will be adversely affected, and combustion will not be complete at burner exit. Not only will combustion efficiency be reduced, but also the products of incomplete combustion will include excessive amounts of the pollutants carbon monoxide (CO) and unburned hydrocarbons (UHC).

2) If liner gas temperatures are too high, the structural integrity of the liner will be jeopardized, and the emitted air pollutants nitrogen oxide (NO) and nitrogen dioxide (NO_2), collectively termed "NO_x", may exceed prescribed limits.

Happily, *all* of the constraints just listed can be satisfied if the gas temperatures within the liner can be controlled to stay in the fairly narrow range 3000°R to 3420°R (Ref. 2), as illustrated in Fig. 9.24. Consequently, a good design target for liner gas temperatures, when suppression of air pollutant emissions is important, is $T_g \sim 3200$°R. This does, however, require a very lean primary zone, with ϕ_{PZ} as low as 0.5 or 0.6. Caution is in order, as this is approaching the absolute lean blowout limit, as can be seen from stability maps such as Fig. 9.9.

The approximate energy equation Eq. (9.25) will be utilized to guide the design choices:

$$T = T_i + \varepsilon \phi \Delta T_{\max} \qquad (9.88)$$

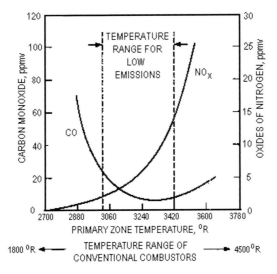

Fig. 9.24   Influence of primary zone temperatures on CO and NO$_x$ (Ref. 2).

The term ΔT_{max} in Eq. (9.88) can be evaluated by substituting Engine Station Test Results sheet values at main burner exit station 4. Because combustion is complete at station 4 ($\varepsilon_4 = 1$), then Eq. (9.88) can be solved for ΔT_{max}:

$$\Delta T_{max} = \frac{(T_{t4} - T_{t3.1})}{\phi_4} \tag{9.89}$$

Both temperatures in Eq. (9.89) are listed on the Engine Station Test Results sheet, and the equivalence ratio at combustor exit ϕ_4 can be evaluated (by definition) as

$$\phi_4 = \frac{\dot{m}_{fMB}}{f_{st}\dot{m}_{3.1}} \tag{9.90}$$

where both mass flow rates are also listed on the Engine Station Test Results sheet and f_{st} can be evaluated for any fuel from Eq. (9.2). For the representative jet fuel $C_{12}H_{23}$, $f_{st} = 0.0685$ lbm F/lbm A.

Rearranging Eq. (9.88) with Eq. (9.89) substituted and solving for the design value of the product $\varepsilon\phi$,

$$(\varepsilon\phi)_g = \frac{\left(T_g - T_{3.1}\right)}{\Delta T_{max}} \tag{9.91}$$

where T_g is the design value for both primary and secondary zones, which has been assumed to be $\sim 3200°$R for the moment, in consideration of the information in Fig. 9.24.

A word of caution follows: because both the combustion reaction progress variable ε and the equivalence ratio ϕ are nondimensional and vary between zero and one, these two variables are often confused. (Actually, ϕ can be greater than one, but in gas turbine practice, by design, it will always be less than one.) Recall that

ϕ is a measure of the fuel/air ratio, which has the same value whether all, some, or none of the fuel is burned locally, whereas ε is a measure of what fraction of any fuel-air mixture has actually burned at a particular location and/or time.

9.2.2.1 Primary zone.
The governing design principle for partitioning air for the primary zone is the Bragg Criterion, stated in Sec. 9.1.3: *The maximum overall combustor efficiency occurs when the primary zone is operating at incipient blowout.* Because today's gas turbines today can operate at much higher temperature levels than in the past, lower values of the local combustion efficiency at blowout ε_{BO} are possible. Whereas other trial values of $\varepsilon > \varepsilon_{BO}$ can be explored by means of the AEDsys software program KINETX, it is safe to assume, for the present, a design target value of $\varepsilon_{PZ} \sim 0.70$.

With this choice in hand, Eq. (9.91) can be solved for the primary zone equivalence ratio

$$\phi_{PZ} = \frac{(T_g - T_{t3.1})}{\varepsilon_{PZ} \Delta T_{\max}} \tag{9.92}$$

and the corresponding primary zone air flow rate $\dot{m}_{PZ}$ and flow fraction μ_{PZ} are

$$\dot{m}_{PZ} = \frac{\dot{m}_{fMB}}{f_{st}\phi_{PZ}} \quad \text{and} \quad \mu_{PZ} \doteq \frac{\dot{m}_{PZ}}{\dot{m}_{3.1}} = \frac{\phi_4}{\phi_{PZ}} \tag{9.93}$$

9.2.2.2 Liner cooling.
After the primary zone the next priority of air partitioning must be liner cooling, as sufficient cooling air must be allocated to protect the burner liner and dome from the high radiative and convective heat loads produced within the burner. The coolant air is normally introduced through the liner in such a way that a protective blanket or film of air is formed between the combustion gases and the liner hardware. The technology to accomplish this follows closely that of turbine blade cooling, which is described more fully in Sec. 8.2.2. Some techniques used for liner cooling are illustrated in Fig. 9.25.

The effectiveness of whatever cooling technique may be employed is quantified by the cooling effectiveness, defined by

$$\Phi \doteq \frac{T_g - T_m}{T_g - T_c} \tag{9.94}$$

where T_g, T_m, and T_c are the static temperatures of the mainstream gas, average wall material, and cooling air, respectively. Note that $T_c = T_{t3.0}$, the total temperature at station 3.0 listed on the Engine Station Test Results sheet.

Cooling air mass flow rates for varying values of cooling effectiveness are presented in Fig. 9.26 (Ref. 26).

Equations (9.95) and (9.96) are approximate curve fits to Fig. 9.26 and provide approximate design data for the fraction of main burner airflow required to achieve any desired cooling effectiveness, as illustrated in Fig. 9.26:

$$\mu_c \doteq \frac{\dot{m}_c}{\dot{m}_{3.1}} \cong \frac{\Phi}{6(1 - \Phi)} = \frac{1}{6}\left(\frac{T_g - T_m}{T_m - T_c}\right) \qquad \text{film cooling} \quad (9.95)$$

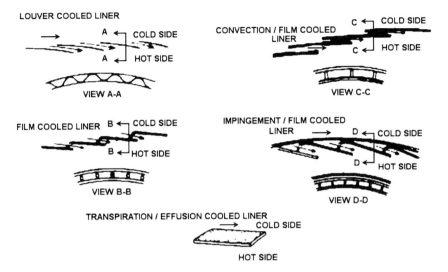

Fig. 9.25   Liner cooling techniques.

and

$$\mu_c \cong \frac{\Phi}{25(1-\Phi)} = \frac{1}{25}\left(\frac{T_g - T_m}{T_m - T_c}\right) \qquad \text{transpiration or effusion cooling} \quad (9.96)$$

Hastelloy X (see Appendix M) and similar metals generally used for the main burner liner have a useful upper materials temperature limit of $T_m \sim 2010°R$. If film cooling is to be considered with a design target $T_g = 3200°R$ and, say, $T_c = 1500°R$, and materials temperature limit $T_m = 2010°R$, then Eq. (94) shows that the cooling effectiveness must be at least $\Phi = 0.70$, and Eq. (9.95) shows the required coolant flow to be about 39% of the entering combustor airflow.

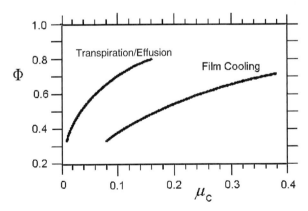

Fig. 9.26   Air flow fraction μ_c required for given cooling effectiveness Φ[26].

The materials limit temperature of metal liners can be increased by about $100°F$ by coating the liner with a ceramic thermal barrier coating. In the present example, Eq. (9.95) shows that this would reduce the required film-cooled effectiveness to 0.64, thereby reducing the required airflow fraction to 0.30, which is still a substantial fraction of the total airflow.

Alternatively, and fortunately, transpiration/effusion cooling, which uses advanced liner construction materials can obtain the same cooling effectiveness with only $>7\%$ cooling air fraction, according to Eq. (9.96).

As combustor inlet temperatures and allowed exit temperatures continue to increase, the percent of combustor air available for liner cooling will decrease accordingly, and new ways will have to be found to further increase the materials limit temperature T_m and/or the cooling effectiveness Φ.

9.2.2.3 Secondary zone.
As mentioned in Sec. 9.1.1, it is desired to have combustion essentially complete by the secondary zone exit. With $\varepsilon = 1$ substituted into Eq. (9.91), the desired equivalence ratio at secondary zone exit ϕ_{SZ} is determined to be

$$\phi_{SZ} = \frac{(T_g - T_{3.1})}{\Delta T_{max}} \tag{9.97}$$

However, because the airflows in the liner are cumulative,

$$\phi_{SZ} = \frac{\dot{m}_{fMB}}{f_{st}(\dot{m}_{PZ} + \dot{m}_{SZ})} \tag{9.98}$$

from which the secondary zone mass flow fraction is determined to be

$$\mu_{SZ} \doteq \frac{\dot{m}_{SZ}}{\dot{m}_{3.1}} = \frac{\dot{m}_{fMB}}{\phi_{SZ} f_{st} \dot{m}_{3.1}} - \frac{\dot{m}_{PZ}}{\dot{m}_{3.1}} = \frac{\phi_4}{\phi_{SZ}} - \frac{\phi_4}{\phi_{PZ}} \tag{9.99}$$

The very difficult design challenge for the secondary zone is to size and locate the secondary zone jet holes in the liner in such a way that, as the primary zone efflux mixes axially with the inflowing secondary air, the axial variation of mixture equivalence ratio $\phi(x)$ offsets the axial rise in combustion efficiency $\varepsilon(x)$ as the mixture continues to burn toward completion, thereby maintaining an approximately constant design temperature T_g. From Eq. (9.91) this design requirement can be expressed as

$$\phi(x) \approx \frac{(T_g - T_{3.1})}{\varepsilon(x) \Delta T_{max}} \tag{9.100}$$

9.2.2.4 Dilution zone.
This one is easy—if there is any air left over, it is simply dumped into the dilution zone:

$$\mu_{DZ} \doteq \frac{\dot{m}_{DZ}}{\dot{m}_{3.1}} = 1 - (\mu_{PZ} + \mu_{SZ} + \mu_c) \tag{9.101}$$

If Eq. (9.101) yields a negative value for dilution zone airflow fraction, then there is not enough airflow available to meet all of the demands. First, try to reduce the cooling flow fraction by increasing the cooling effectiveness. Next, adjust the design temperature T_g within the narrow temperature design window shown in Fig. 9.24. If in the end no dilution air is required, that's all right, because the micromixing in the secondary zone ensures that the "pattern factor" [defined by Eq. (9.120)] will be zero.

9.2.3 Main Burner Components

9.2.3.1 Diffuser. A design goal for the main burner diffuser is to reduce the velocity of the air exiting the compressor as much as necessary to enable optimal performance of the combustor, with the least loss of total pressure consistent with that goal. The total pressure loss from station 3.1 to 3.2 listed on the Engine Station Test Results sheet, as pointed out in Sec. 9.2.1, should be regarded as an upper bound, not as a design target. Any savings in total pressure loss achieved in the diffuser can be "spent" in the main burner to improve the mixing processes.

As pointed out in Sec. 9.1.5, an annular flat-wall diffuser has an extremely limited range of design and performance parameters. The best possible flat-wall diffuser has an included angle $2\theta = 9$ deg, length ratio $4 < r_{m2}L/r_{m1}H_1 < 20$, and corresponding area ratio $AR = H_2 r_{m2}/H_1 r_{m1}$ in the range $1.5 < AR < 4$. Within this limited range the diffusion efficiency is essentially constant at the value $\eta_{D9°}$ given by Eq. (9.68).

Whenever the required area ratio AR is less than four, the excessive length of the diffuser can be reduced by subdividing the flow into adjacent streams, each having an included angle $2\theta = 9$ deg, as illustrated in Fig. 9.27. By the introduction of equally spaced splitter plates, the required length for any $AR < 4$ is reduced by a dividing factor equal to the number of parallel streams, for example three for the case of two splitter plates as illustrated in Fig. 9.27. In principle, the number of splitter plates could be increased to three, four, five, or more, and a correspondingly shorter diffuser would result. However, geometric complexity and difficulty of manufacturing puts a practical limit on this approach, so that two splitter vanes seems to be optimal. No tailpipe is required, and so $L_d = 0$ when $AR < 4$.

If the design area ratio AR is greater than four, a dump diffuser can simply be added onto a three-stream, $2\theta = 9$ deg optimal flat-wall diffuser of length

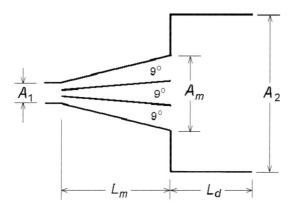

Fig. 9.27   Combined diffuser: three-stream optimized flat-wall diffuser discharging into a dump diffuser, approximately to scale.

$(L/H_1)(r_{m2}/r_{m1}) = 18/3 = 6$, and $A_m/A_1 = 4$, as shown in Fig. 9.27. The attached dump diffuser requires a tailpipe of length $L_d \sim (H_2 - H_m)$ so that the separated flow at dump diffuser entry (station m in Fig. 9.27) has sufficient axial distance to reattach to the upper and lower walls. The diffusion efficiency of the combined flat-wall + dump diffuser shown in Fig. 9.27 can be shown to be

$$\eta_D = \frac{\eta_{Dm}AR^2(1 - [A_1/A_m]^2) + 2(AR[A_1/A_m] - 1)}{(AR^2 - 1)} \qquad (9.102)$$

where η_{Dm} is the diffusion efficiency of the flat-wall diffuser. A derivation of Eq. (9.102) is given in an appendix included in the AEDsys software CD-ROM.

Even when AR is less than four, a combined flat-wall + dump diffuser can give somewhat better performance than an optimal or "sweet-spot" flat-wall diffuser alone, especially when the diffuser entry boundary layers are very thick. By taking the derivative of η_D in Eq. (9.102) with respect to $[A_m/A_1]$ and setting it equal to zero, there results an optimal area ratio that gives the greatest value of diffusion efficiency for the combined diffuser

$$\left[\frac{A_m}{A_1}\right]_{opt} = \eta_{Dm}AR, \qquad 1.5 < AR < 4 \quad (9.103)$$

and a corresponding optimum diffusion efficiency

$$\eta_{Dopt} = \frac{1 - 2\eta_{Dm} + (\eta_{Dm}AR)^2}{\eta_{Dm}(AR^2 - 1)} \quad \text{for} \quad \left[\frac{A_m}{A_1}\right]_{opt} = \eta_{Dm}AR, \quad 1.5 < AR < 4 \qquad (9.104)$$

where η_{Dm} should of course be $\eta_{D9°}$ of Eq. (9.68).

For example, consider a case with $AR = 3.5$ with very thick boundary layers, so that $\eta_{D9°} \sim 0.64$ from Eq. (9.68). From the geometry of Fig. 9.20 and Eq. (9.61), the three-stream diffuser alone would have a length $r_{m2}L/r_{m1}H_1 = 15.88/3 = 5.29$. For a combined diffuser Eq. (9.103) gives an optimal flat-wall diffuser area ratio $[A_m/A_1]_{opt} = 2.24$, and Eq. (9.104) gives the corresponding optimal diffusion efficiency $\eta_{Dopt} = 0.658$. The length of the shortened flat-wall diffuser is $r_{m2}L_m/r_{m1}H_1 = 7.88/3 = 2.63$, and the tailpipe length is $L_d/H_1 = (H_2 - H_m)/H_1 = (3.5 - 2.24) = 1.26$, for a combined diffuser length $(L_m + L_d)/H_1 = 1.26 + 2.63 = 3.79$. Although the combined diffuser efficiency is only a modest 2.8% better than the flat-wall diffuser alone, the combined diffuser length is 28% shorter, which is a significant improvement.

Figure 9.28 shows a combined flat-wall + dump diffuser used in practice. Note that the inlet airflow in Fig. 9.28 is split into two streams, each of which appears to have an area ratio of about 1.8 and length to inlet height ratio of about 6. From Fig. 9.22, with $A_m/A_1 \sim 1.8$ and $L_m/H_1 \sim 5$, it appears that the curved-wall diffuser is very conservatively designed, well within the "no stall" region of Fig. 9.22, and as a single diffuser would have a diffuser efficiency $\eta_D \sim 0.80-0.90$. (The boundary layer thickness is of course not known.) Again from inspection of Fig. 9.28, the dump area ratio appears to be $A_2/A_m \sim 4.7$, and the overall area ratio $AR = H_2/H_1 \sim 8.5$. With these values substituted into Eq. (9.102), the combined diffuser efficiency is about 0.66-0.73, which seems to be rather low.

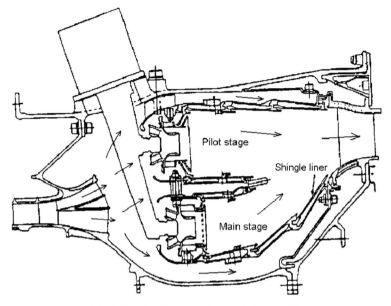

Fig. 9.28   Double-annular main burner.[27]

However, if an all-dump diffuser were used instead, the diffuser efficiency from Eq. (9.70) would be a disappointingly low 0.21. The geometric and manufacturing complexity of the curved, two-stream flat-wall diffuser in Fig. 9.28 is clearly well worth the cost.

9.2.3.2 Burner types.   A wide variety of liner and casing configurations have been used in various gas turbine engines. Three of the most widely used configurations are illustrated in Fig. 9.29.

In early turbojet engines, and still used today in some auxiliary power units, is the "can" configuration, in which the liner and casing are wrapped concentrically around the symmetry axis of a single fuel nozzle. This burner type was and is easy to fabricate and to modify for experimental development.

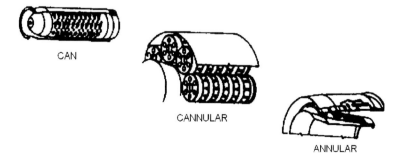

Fig. 9.29   Basic configurations of main burner liners and casings.

As engines became bigger, it was recognized that because the combustion process does not scale up, but rather remains optimized for one size scale, it is logical to simply replicate the entire burner can whenever more mass flow was required. As the geometric layout of a turbojet engine is dictated by the axial symmetry of the rotating components, the additional cans were arranged side by side in an annular ring. Two major problems of this "can-annular" configuration (not illustrated) are 1) that each burner is a stand-alone pressure vessel and 2) that each burner has to have its own igniter. Consequently, the next developmental step was to retain the cylindrical liners in annular array, but to encase them in a common, single annular casing. This configuration was termed "cannular." Next, it was found that also fabricating the liners as concentric annuli led to further performance improvements, and so the modern "annular" burner evolved.

Attention will be focused on the design of an annular burner. For simplicity, it will be assumed that the liner and casing walls are parallel, as shown in the schematic Fig. 9.1, even though there are good reasons to have divergent walls, as shown in Fig. 9.29.

9.2.3.3　Inner and outer casing.

The first step is to establish inner and outer radii at reference station 3.2 and at station 3.9, as illustrated in Fig. 9.30. These radii depend on the reference area $A_{3.2}$, which is listed on the Engine Station Test Results sheet (but which may be altered in the course of design iteration), and design choices for the engine envelope, such as whether the outer casing wall is to be in line with the tip of the last-stage high-pressure compressor stage or high-pressure turbine first-stage nozzle, or the inner wall is to be an extension of the root radius of either the high-pressure compressor or turbine, or someplace in between. The required radii are not listed on the Engine Station Test Results sheet, but must have been determined previously from the design of the high-pressure compressor and turbine. After these radii have been determined, the radial "heights" $H_r = (r_o - r_i)_{3.2}$ and $H_4 = (r_o - r_i)_4$ may be calculated, as shown in Fig. 9.30.

The liner and casing have widely different structural and thermal requirements. The inner and outer casings have negligible thermal loads, as they are convectively cooled by the annulus air. However, they are the walls of a pressure vessel that must withstand the full pressure difference between the interior total pressure $P_{t3.2}$ and the ambient static pressure. In marked contrast to the casing, the liner has a negligible mechanical load, as it has to support only the small total pressure difference $\Delta P_t = P_{t3.2} - P_{t4}$, but it is subject to a severe thermal load resulting from combustion, and therefore requires a rather elaborate system of slots and bleed

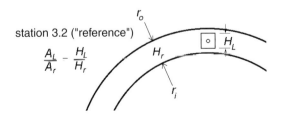

Fig. 9.30　Annular geometry of liner and casing radii and heights.

holes for the flow of cooling air to protect it. Determining the largest mechanical and thermal loads and designing for them separately is a critical step in the successful design of jet engines.

9.2.3.4 Fuel nozzles.

Historically, a great number of different ways have been tried to atomize and vaporize the kerosene-type liquid fuels pumped under pressure into fuel nozzles. Until the 1970s, the simplex spray nozzle was most commonly used. In this nozzle the liquid fuel is pumped tangentially into a small swirl chamber, then flows out into the primary zone through a constriction or throat, which concentrates the vorticity in the swirling fuel so that when the fuel emerges it is as a radial sheet, which then stretches and breaks up into a widely size-distributed spray of small droplets.[30] These droplets are then entrained and vaporized by the hot recirculating gases in the primary zone. Because of the distribution of droplet sizes, many of the large droplets support heterogeneous or two-phase combustion, with resulting smoke caused by incomplete vaporization and combustion, and correspondingly high concentrations of all of the air pollutants already mentioned.

The concern with pollutants starting in the late 1960s led to the development of the "airblast" atomizer, shown in Fig. 9.31, in which a sheet of air driven by the same pressure drop as all of the liner airflows are "blasted" into the liquid fuel sheet emerging from a simplex nozzle, further shattering the fuel sheet and droplets. This development effectively eliminated the problem of heterogeneous combustion around individual fuel droplets and enabled the development of the first "smokeless" (low unburned hydrocarbons) combustors of the 1970s, and in the 1980s and 1990s the "prevaporized, premixed" combustor of the type in universal use today.

An airblast atomizer typically requires about 3 lbm of primary air per lbm of fuel.[2] Note that this is not a separate demand on air partitioning. The airblast atomizer airflow is just a part of the primary airflow, which passes through the nozzle/atomizer rather than through the primary air swirler, as shown in Fig. 9.16.

If the reference radial height H_r in Fig. 9.30 is relatively small, the fuel nozzles and their associated air swirlers can be distributed in a "single-annular" array, as illustrated in Fig. 9.32. For a single array the number of fuel nozzles required can be calculated by dividing the annular flow passage into square segments (in rotating machinery terminology, a "solidity" of one), so that

$$N_{noz} \approx \frac{\pi \, (r_o + r_i)_{3.2}}{H_r} = \frac{A_{3.2}}{H_r^2} = \left(\frac{4\pi^2}{A_{3.2}}\right) r_{m3.2}^2 \qquad \text{rounded off} \quad (9.105)$$

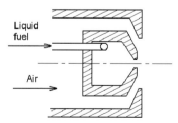

Liquid fuel

Air

Fig. 9.31 Schematic of a generic airblast atomizer. The radial sheet of fuel emerging from the on-axis, simplex swirl-spray nozzle is blasted by a circular jet of air flowing into it.

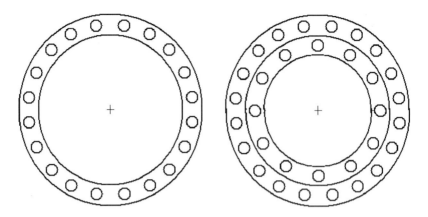

Fig. 9.32   Single- and double-annular arrays of fuel nozzles and air swirlers.

If the reference radial height H_r is very great, the fuel nozzles and swirlers can be distributed in a "double-annular" array, as shown in Figs. 9.28 and 9.32.

9.2.3.5   Dome and liner.   The next step is to determine the optimal dome and liner height H_L, or equivalently the liner-to-casing area ratio $\alpha = A_L/A_r = H_L/H_r$. For clarity, only the single-annular burner will be considered.

It is not immediately apparent what criteria should be used for finding the optimal area ratio α. Clearly, small α would cause reduced residence times in all three liner zones, and large α would cause high annular velocities, with correspondingly increased viscous shear on the casing and high axial momentum flux entering through the secondary and dilution holes, which would in turn reduce jet penetration.

Figure 9.15 illustrates annulus-to-liner jet flow, when both annulus and liner flows have finite axial velocities. Equation (9.44) estimates the maximum jet penetration for the jet shown in Fig. 9.15:

$$\frac{Y_{\max}}{d_j} = 1.15 \sqrt{\frac{q_j}{q_L}\left(1 - \frac{q_A}{q_j}\right)} \tag{9.106}$$

In Eq. (9.106) the jet dynamic pressure q_j is fixed by the prescribed total pressure loss, as determined by Eq. (9.36), but the annulus and liner dynamic pressures q_A and q_L may vary, depending on the choice for areas A_A and A_L. Inspection of Eq. (9.106) reveals that independently increasing either q_L or q_A will cause a decrease in jet penetration, and so it appears that there may be an optimal liner-to-reference area ratio $\alpha = A_L/A_r$ that will maximize the jet penetration $Y_{\max}$. However, as air flows from the annulus into the liner, q_A decreases in the axial direction as a result of mass outflow, while q_L increases correspondingly because of the same air mass inflow, so that a choice must be made as to the axial location at which the jet penetration will be maximized.

Because of the importance of the secondary zone process, it is logical to maximize the jet penetration for the secondary jets. Thus q_A in Eq. (9.106) will be taken

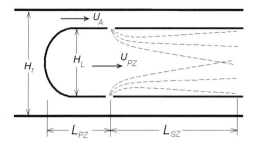

Fig. 9.33 Secondary zone air jet trajectories and nomenclature.

to be the airflow at annulus entry, and q_L will be taken to be q_{PZ} for the liner flow at primary zone exit, as shown in Fig. 9.33.

Multiplying and dividing by q_r in Eq. (9.106) and relabeling q_L as q_{PZ},

$$\frac{Y_{max}}{d_j} = 1.15 \sqrt{\frac{q_j}{q_r}\frac{q_r}{q_{PZ}}\left(1 - \frac{q_A}{q_r}\frac{q_r}{q_j}\right)} \tag{9.107}$$

From Eq. (9.36), $q_j/q_r = (\Delta P_t/q_r)_{MB}$, the main burner total pressure loss coefficient of Eq. (9.79). This is true for all jets, including the secondary zone jets. Also making use of Eq. (9.61), together with the Boussinesq assumption introduced in Sec. 9.1.5, Eq. (9.107) can be rewritten

$$\frac{Y_{max}}{d_j} = 1.15 \left(\frac{\dot{m}_r}{\dot{m}_{PZ}}\right)\sqrt{\tau_{PZ}^{-1}\left(\frac{\Delta P_t}{q_r}\right)_{MB}}\sqrt{\alpha^2\left[1 - \left(\frac{\dot{m}_A}{\dot{m}_r}\right)^2\left(\frac{\Delta P_t}{q_r}\right)_{MB}^{-1}\left(\frac{1}{1-\alpha}\right)^2\right]} \tag{9.108}$$

where $\alpha = A_L/A_r$, $(1 - \alpha) = A_A/A_r$, and τ_{PZ} is the design value of temperature rise ratio in both primary and secondary zones and where fixed-value parameters have been factored out of the square root term where possible.

By taking the derivative of the right-hand side of Eq. (9.108) with respect to α, setting it equal to zero and solving for α there results

$$\alpha_{opt} = 1 - \left(\frac{\dot{m}_A}{\dot{m}_r}\right)^{2/3}\left(\frac{\Delta P_t}{q_r}\right)_{MB}^{-1/3} \tag{9.109}$$

Substituting values cited for the 1950s burner following Eq. (9.73) into Eq. (9.109) gives an optimum area ratio of 0.67, compared with the stated area ratio of 0.65, which is more than adequate agreement.

9.2.3.6 Primary zone swirler.
With the casing, dome, and liner sized, and the number and type of fuel nozzles determined, one of the N_{noz} inlet air swirlers can now be designed.

From the Engine Station Test Results sheet, the prescribed total pressure loss across the main burner assembly $\Delta P_t = P_{t4} - P_{t3.1}$ can be obtained. Recall that this is the specified ΔP_t necessary to provide adequate turbine blade cooling and is not necessarily enough to satisfy both diffuser total pressure loss and that required for combustor stirring. Therefore, it is essential to verify from Eq. (9.81) that sufficient ΔP_t has been allocated for main burner stirring. If not, it may be necessary to redesign the diffuser, or to negotiate for a greater ΔP_t allocation.

Assuming that sufficient $\Delta P_t = P_{t4} - P_{t3.2}$ is available, then the jet velocity for all stirring jet flows into the liner—film cooling slots, primary air swirler, air for the airblast atomizer, and secondary and dilution jet holes—is determined from Eq. (9.36):

$$V_j = \sqrt{\frac{2\Delta P_t}{\rho_r}} = U_r \sqrt{\left(\frac{\Delta P_t}{q_r}\right)_{MB}} \quad \text{or} \quad \frac{q_j}{q_r} = \left(\frac{\Delta P_t}{q_r}\right)_{MB} \tag{9.110}$$

The annular area of a single air swirler is given by $A_{sw} = \pi \, (r_t^2 - r_h^2)$. The maximum area possible is limited by the envelope of dome/liner and fuel nozzle dimensions. Specifically, the swirl vane tip radius r_t cannot exceed half the dome height H_L, and the hub radius r_h must be at least $1/2$ in. in order to accommodate (that is, wrap around) the airblast atomizer assembly. As a rough guideline, the recirculation bubble should be about the size of a golf ball.

The mass flow that must pass through all N_{noz} swirlers is given by $(\dot{m}_{PZ} - 3\dot{m}_{fMB})$ because 3 lbm air per lbm fuel must be directed through each airblast atomizer, which is of course located concentrically within each swirler assembly.

Taking into account the necessary discharge coefficient (assuming flat blades for vanes) and swirler vane blade angle, the inner and out vane radii must be adjusted to satisfy mass conservation through all N_{noz} swirlers, so that mass conservation requires

$$\frac{(\dot{m}_{PZ} - 3\dot{m}_{fMB})}{N_{noz}} = A_j(\rho_r V_j) = \pi \, (r_t^2 - r_h^2) \, C_{D90°} \cos\alpha_{sw} \left[\frac{\dot{m}_r}{A_r} \sqrt{\left(\frac{\Delta P_t}{q_r}\right)_{MB}}\right]$$

$$\tag{9.111}$$

where the discharge coefficient is obtained from Eq. (9.33) and the swirler blade angle is determined from Eq. (9.48) for the selected design swirl number S'. An assumed swirler blade angle $\alpha_{sw} \sim 45$ deg can be used to start the iteration.

The axial length of the primary zone, measured from the "nose" of the dome, can be laid out according to the estimate Eq. (9.50), $L_{PZ} \sim 2S'r_t$.

9.2.3.7 Secondary air holes.
Equations (9.42–9.44) can be used to lay out trajectories of the secondary air jets, immediately downstream of the primary zone, as shown in Fig. 9.33.

A good target penetration depth of the secondary air jet trajectory is about $\frac{1}{4}$ of the dome/liner height H_L. As Y_{max}/d_j is available from Eq. (9.108), the required diameter of a single secondary jet is given by

$$d_j = \frac{1}{4} H_L \left(\frac{Y_{max}}{d_j}\right)^{-1} \tag{9.112}$$

Because all of the secondary air must pass through round holes with jet vena contractas of diameter d_j given by Eq. (9.112), the number of secondary holes is

$$N_{hSZ} = \frac{4\dot{m}_{SZ}}{\rho_r \pi d_j^2 V_j} = \mu_{SZ} \left(\frac{4A_r}{\pi d_j^2} \right) \frac{U_r}{V_j} \qquad (9.113)$$

and the diameter of each secondary air hole, from Eq. (9.43), is

$$d_h^2 = \frac{d_j^2}{C_{D90°} \sin^2 \theta} \qquad (9.114)$$

where

$$\sin^2 \theta = 1 - \frac{q_A}{q_r} \frac{q_r}{q_j} = 1 - \left(\frac{\dot{m}_A}{\dot{m}_r} \right)^2 \left(\frac{1}{1-\alpha} \right)^2 \left(\frac{\Delta P_t}{q_r} \right)_{MB}^{-1} \qquad (9.115)$$

The N_{hSZ} secondary air holes should be spaced evenly in a single lateral line (at right angles to the engine axis), with one-half located on the upper liner wall and the other half, staggered and opposed, on the lower wall. The axes of the secondary holes should be located immediately at the downstream end of the primary zone, or, in other words, at an axial distance L_{PZ} from the inside nose of the liner dome.

The axial length of the secondary zone should be long enough for the inflowing jets to mix out with the crossflowing primary zone effluent gases. For preliminary design purposes it can be assumed that the distance to mix out is that distance for the micromixed cores of the opposing secondary air jets to meet. This can be estimated from Eq. (9.37), in which the distance y is now interpreted as distance along the jet trajectory. However, the horseshoe vortex mixing system shown in Fig. 9.14 probably doubles the mixing and growth rate given by Eq. (9.37). Setting δ_m equal to $H_L/2$ in Eq. (9.37) (see Fig. 9.33) and doubling the growth rate from 0.123 to 0.246, the resulting distance along the jet trajectory becomes the estimated required length of the secondary zone

$$L_{SZ} \simeq \frac{H_L}{2(0.246)} \simeq 2H_L \qquad (9.116)$$

9.2.3.8 Dilution holes.

The same procedure will be followed as for the secondary zone, except that the dilution jet centerlines must be designed to penetrate $\frac{1}{3}$ of the distance to the opposite liner wall.[2] That is, the design goal is for dilution jets is $Y_{max} = H_L/3$, rather than $H_L/4$ for the secondary jets. This will require somewhat larger diameter jets,

$$d_j \simeq \frac{1}{3} H_L \left(\frac{Y_{max}}{d_j} \right)^{-1} \qquad (9.117)$$

and the required number of dilution holes is given by

$$N_{hDZ} = \frac{4\dot{m}_{DZ}}{\rho_r \pi d_j^2 V_j} = \mu_{DZ} \left(\frac{4A_r}{\pi d_j^2} \right) \frac{U_r}{V_j} \qquad (9.118)$$

The actual diameter of the dilution air holes is given by Eq. (9.114). However, the $\sin^2 \theta$ term is different from the secondary zone value because the annulus

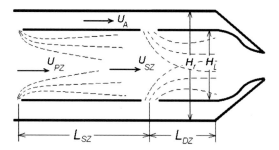

Fig. 9.34 Dilution zone air jet trajectories and nomenclature and layout of dilution zone and transition duct.

airflow has been reduced by the outflow of secondary air. This term is now

$$\sin^2 \theta = 1 - \frac{q_A}{q_r}\frac{q_r}{q_j} = 1 - \left(\frac{\dot{m}_{DZ}}{\dot{m}_r}\right)^2 \left(\frac{1}{1-\alpha}\right)^2 \left(\frac{\Delta P_t}{q_r}\right)_{MB}^{-1} \qquad (9.119)$$

Since, by design, combustion is complete by the time the secondary zone effluent reaches the plane of the dilution zone, micromixing is not required; only sufficiently good stirring or macromixing to ensure that the "hot spots" or incompletely mixed turbulent eddies with above-average temperatures are within some specified range. This requirement is couched in terms of the pattern factor, defined by

$$\text{Pattern factor} \doteq \frac{T_{max} - T_{t4}}{T_{t4} - T_{t3}} \qquad (9.120)$$

A rough guideline for an adequate length of the dilution zone in order to provide a satisfactory pattern factor is $L_{DZ} \sim 1.5 H_L$.[2]

The layout of the dilution zone, together with a sketch of the transition duct between stations 3.9 and 4, is shown in Fig. 9.34.

9.2.3.9 Transition duct. The shape of the transition duct is not a critical feature of the engine design. Accelerating subsonic flow creates a favorable (decreasing) axial pressure gradient, so all that is required is to reduce the height of the flow passage smoothly from H_L to $(r_o - r_i)_4$ within an axial length $\sim H_r$, as shown in Fig. 9.34. Note that the casing walls have been extended to allow cooling air to protect the transition duct.

9.3 Design Tools—Afterburners

Procedures for preliminary design of the afterburner are the subject of the present section. As with the design of the main burner, extensive use will be made of concepts and equations from Sec. 9.1, and the same design philosophy will be employed as that given in the introductory paragraph of Sec. 9.2. An example design of an afterburner, including the use of the AEDsys computational tools, principally subprograms EQL, AFTRBRN, and KINETX, can be found in Sec. 9.4.2.

Afterburning or reheating is a method of augmenting the basic thrust of the turbojet engine or the turbofan engine, on demand, without having to use a larger engine with increased frontal area and weight. The afterburner increases thrust by adding thermal energy to the entering gas stream. For a turbojet engine this gas stream corresponds to the exhaust gases of the turbine. However, for the augmented turbofan engine, this gas stream may be a mixture of the bypass air and the turbine exhaust gases. At the afterburner inlet there is still much unburned oxygen in the gas stream. The higher inlet temperatures and near-stoichiometric fuel-air ratio of the afterburners enable them to operate with a simpler configuration (see Fig. 9.2) than the main burner. The resultant increase in temperature raises the exhaust velocity of the exiting gases and therefore boosts engine thrust. Most afterburners will produce about 50% increase in thrust—but at a cost of a 300% increase in fuel flow rate!

Because the engine's specific and actual fuel consumption is considerably higher during afterburning ("hot" or "wet") operation, as compared to the nonafterburning ("cold" or "dry") mode, afterburning is used typically where large thrust is required for a short period of time, such as takeoff, climb, transonic acceleration, and combat maneuvers.

For a turbofan engine augmentation can be used in both fan and core streams. Afterburning in a separate fan stream is normally referred to as "duct burning," and this alone or in combination with afterburning in the core stream may be advantageous for certain flight conditions.

The major components of an afterburner are shown in Fig. 9.2. Gas leaving the turbine is deswirled and diffused, fuel is added by fuel spray bars (tubes) or rings, combustion is initiated by an igniter or pilot burner and in the wake of a number of flame stabilizing devices (flameholders), and the thermal energy of combustion is mixed along flame surfaces spreading outward and downstream from the flameholders. Also, a liner is used in afterburners as both a cooling liner and a screech or antihowl liner. (Screech and howl are acoustic-combustion instabilities.) This liner can also serve as an annular passage for the cooling air required by the exhaust nozzle. All engines incorporating an afterburner must also be equipped with a variable area throat exhaust nozzle, in order to provide for proper operation in both afterburning and nonafterburning modes (see Chapter 5).

Specific design requirements and/or desiderata for an afterburner are as follows: 1) large temperature rise (The afterburner is not subject to the physical and temperature limits of the turbine. The temperature rise is limited by the amount of oxygen that is available for combustion and by the liner and nozzle cooling air requirements.); 2) low dry loss (The engine suffers a very slight penalty in thrust during cold operation as a result of the drag caused by the flameholders, fuel spray bars, and the walls of the afterburner.); 3) wide temperature modulation [The ability to obtain "degrees" ("zones" or "stages) of afterburning permits more precise control of thrust.]; 4) high combustion efficiency; 5) short length and light weight; 6) altitude light-off capability; 7) no acoustic-combustion instabilities; 8) long life, low cost, easy repair; and 9) stealth—hiding hot elements of the engine (turbine exit).[28,29]

9.3.1 Afterburner Design Parameters

Overall engine cycle considerations have already fixed the molecular composition, thermodynamic state, and mass flow rates of core gas and bypass air that enter the afterburner at stations 6 and 16, respectively, in Fig. 9.2a. In addition, the afterburner fuel flow rate that enters between stations 6A and 6.1 is also specified. When using the AEDsys software for preliminary design, these values are displayed on the Engine Station Test Results sheet for the particular operating point chosen for design (see Table 7.E5). The required thermodynamic state of the combustion product gases exiting the afterburner at station 7 is also fixed. The radial and axial location of all components of the afterburner assembly in the engine framework will be determined by matching the layout of the fan, turbine, and variable area nozzles from their respective preliminary designs.

Although the afterburner fuel flow rate and Engine Station Test Results values listed for stations 6, 16, and 6A are fixed requirements, those values listed for station 7 are just "first cut" or "bogey" values, which may have to be adjusted in order to optimize performance. The Engine Station Test Results does not list any properties whatever for station 6.1. However, a value of total pressure loss from station 6A to station 7 is obtainable from the Engine Station Test Results sheet, and this should be regarded as a design target value. This design quantity can be represented as

$$\pi_{6A-7} \doteq \frac{P_{t7}}{P_{t6A}} = \frac{P_{t6.1}}{P_{t6A}} \frac{P_{t7}}{P_{t6.1}} = \pi_{ABD}\,\pi_{AB} \qquad (9.121)$$

which is the product of the total pressure ratios across the afterburner diffuser (stations 6A to 6.1) and the afterburner (stations 6.1 to 7).

9.3.2　Afterburner Components

9.3.2.1　Mixer. The hot core gas exiting from the low pressure turbine at station 6 must be mixed with the cooler, comparatively oxygen-rich bypass air at station 16, in order to provide a gas mixture with sufficiently high temperature to vaporize the liquid fuel injected and atomized by the spray bars downstream, and also with sufficiently high temperature and oxygen mol fraction to sustain combustion in the wake of the vee-gutter flameholders located still further downstream. A schematic representation of the near-constant-area mixer is presented in Fig. 9.35.

A control volume analysis for conservation of mass, momentum, and energy, presented in Appendix G, determines the state of the mixed gases at station 6A. This calculation is performed by the AEDsys cycle analysis software, with the results given on the Engine Station Test Results sheet. However, this control volume

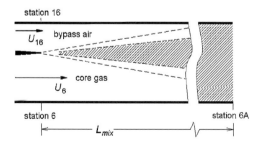

Fig. 9.35　Schematic of afterburner mixer: - - - -, micromixed region (see Sec. 9.1.4).

analysis is based on the assumption that mixing is complete at exit and does not address the question of how long the mixer must be to accomplish this mixing.

The length required for complete mixing of the core gas and bypass airstreams, as denoted by L_{mix} in Fig. 9.35, can be estimated by using the shear/mixing layer equations [Eqs. (9.52–9.60) from Sec. 9.1.4 (see also Figs. 9.18 and 9.19)]. However, as Fig. 9.35 suggests, the distance required may be excessively long, as one stream may "mix out" while the other stream still contains unmixed gas. One way to reduce the length required to mix out is to reduce the annular height of both passages at mixer inlet, which reduces the initial scale of segregation of the two mixant streams.[13] This can be done by constant-area ducting (that is, by keeping the product of cross-sectional radial height H and mean radius r_m constant as r_m is increased) both streams to the greatest permissible outer radius prior to mixing. Some other ways are to 1) increase the velocity ratio of the two streams [see Eqs. (9.52–9.54)], 2) purposely imbalance or "un-match" the static pressures in the two streams so that the higher-pressure stream is pushed laterally into the lower-pressure stream, and 3) replace the flat-edge splitter plate illustrated in Fig. 9.35 with a "fluted" plate, which can be visualized as a flat plate trailing edge that is smoothly crimped laterally, similar to hand-crimping the top and bottom layers of a pie crust. The fluted splitter plate induces vertical velocity components, spatially alternating upward and downward from both mixant streams, which reduces the scale of segregation between the two mixants to the pitch of the corrugations in the fluted splitter plate. Of course, all of the suggested ways to shorten L_{mix} cause further increases in total pressure loss.

In any case the rational design of the mixer is far too complicated for treatment at our level of description,[13] and so the properties at stations 6, 16, and 6A listed on the Engine Station Test Results sheet will simply be taken as given for preliminary design purposes, and the required length can only be guessed or based on observation of similar designs.

An alternative approach is to not mix the two streams at all. By keeping the two streams separate until just upstream of the hot section, temperature modulation for the afterburner can be achieved by having two separately fueled afterburner systems, one located in the core stream and the other in the unmixed bypass fan airstream. Stage 1 would be the inner, core stream afterburner, and after the first stage is lit off, the separately fueled, outer, bypass fan airstream afterburner could be ignited for stage 2. This in turn leads to flameholding difficulties in both streams because although the hot core stream is oxygen poor, compared to the bypass stream, the oxygen-rich bypass stream (air) is cold in comparison with the core stream.

9.3.2.2 *Diffuser.*

The flow entering the afterburner at station 6A (Fig. 9.2a) must be slowed to a Mach number that provides a balance between total pressure loss and afterburner cross-sectional area. The minimum Mach number entering the combustion zone of the afterburner at station 6.1 is usually fixed by a requirement that the diameter of the afterburner section not exceed that of the engine components located upstream, specifically the fan casing, for case of installation and removal. A short diffuser length is desired, of course without producing flow separation, in order to reduce engine weight and length. In augmented turbofan engines, the diffuser may be combined with a mixer so that a mixed stream enters

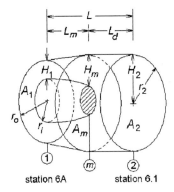

Fig. 9.36   Geometry of afterburner annular flat-wall + dump diffuser.

the combustion section, but the mixer and diffuser will be treated as separate components for present purposes.

Figure 9.36 shows the geometry and layout of the afterburner diffuser to be designed. Note that the dump diffuser is defined by truncating the tailcone of the low-pressure turbine. Extensive use will be made of the concepts and design equations and principles developed in Secs. 9.1.5 and 9.2.3.

The flow areas and linear dimensions of the annular geometry diffuser shown in Fig. 9.36 are

$$A = \pi\left(r_o^2 - r_i^2\right) = \pi(r_o - r_i)(r_o + r_i) = 2\pi(r_o - r_i)\frac{(r_o + r_i)}{2} = 2\pi\, H\, r_m \tag{9.122}$$

where $H = (r_o - r_i)$ and $r_m = (r_o + r_i)/2$, and for each of the three stations shown,

$$A_1 = \pi\left(r_o^2 - r_i^2\right)_1, \quad A_m = \pi\left(r_2^2 - r_{im}^2\right) \quad A_2 = \pi r_2^2$$

$$H_1 = (r_o - r_i)_1 \quad H_m = (r_2 - r_{im}) \quad H_2 = r_2$$

$$L = x_2 - x_1 \quad L_m = x_m - x_1 \quad L_d = x_2 - x_m \tag{9.123}$$

The flow area between stations 1 and m is to be designed to vary linearly with x according to the flat-wall diffuser geometry of Fig. 9.20 and Eq. (9.61),

$$\frac{A(x)}{A_1} = \frac{\left[r_o^2(x) - r_i^2(x)\right]}{\left[r_{o1}^2 - r_{i1}^2\right]} = \frac{H(x)\,r_m(x)}{H_1\,r_{m1}} = 1 + \frac{r_{mm}}{r_{m1}}\frac{(x - x_1)}{H_1}2\tan\theta \tag{9.124}$$

where θ will be always set equal to the "sweet spot" value of Fig. 9.22, $\theta = 4.5\,\text{deg}$.

By design, the outer radius will also vary linearly between stations 1 and m,

$$r_o(x) = r_{o1} + \left(\frac{r_2 - r_{o1}}{L_m}\right)(x - x_1) \qquad x_1 < x < x_m \tag{9.125}$$

so that the shape of the diffuser centerbody between x_1 and x_m is defined by the variation of inner radius of the flow area with x between 1 and m, from Eq. (9.124), as

$$r_i(x) = \sqrt{r_o^2(x) - \frac{A_1}{\pi}\left(1 + \frac{r_{mm}}{r_{m1}}\frac{(x - x_1)}{H_1}2 \tan 4.5 \deg\right)} \quad x_1 < x < x_m \quad (9.126)$$

Note that the axial variation of the inner radius $r_i(x)$ is *quasi-linear* in x, not quadratic, because it varies as the square root of a quadratic function.

If the overall area ratio $AR = A_2/A_1$ is greater than four, the length of the diffuser centerbody will be the "sweet spot" value $L_m/H_1 = 20$. If AR is less than four, then from Eqs. (9.103) and (9.124)

$$L_m = \frac{r_{m1}H_1}{r_{mm} \, 2 \tan 4.5 \deg}\left(\left[\frac{A_m}{A_1}\right]_{opt} - 1\right) \quad \text{where} \quad \left[\frac{A_m}{A_1}\right]_{opt} = \eta_{Dm}AR$$

$$(9.127)$$

Finally, the diffusion efficiency of the combined diffuser is given by Eq. (9.102),

$$\eta_D = \frac{\eta_{Dm}AR^2(1 - [A_1/A_m]^2) + 2(AR[A_1/A_m] - 1)}{(AR^2 - 1)} \quad (9.128)$$

where, as before, AR denotes the overall area ratio $AR = A_2/A_1$. η_{D9° from Eq. (9.68) should be used for η_{Dm} in Eq. (9.128), the total pressure loss can be calculated from Eq. (9.67), and the tailpipe length L_d of the combined diffuser will be $L_d = H_2 - H_m$.

9.3.2.3 Fuel injection, atomization, and vaporization.
This subject area is best summarized by Zukoski[3] and is quoted here:

> The goal of the fuel injection system is to produce a specified distribution of fuel vapor in the gas stream entering the afterburner. In most engines, fuel is introduced in a staged manner so that heat addition rate can be increased gradually from zero to the desired value. Because ignition, flame stabilization, and flame spreading are easiest to achieve when the fuel-air ratio is close to the stoichiometric value, staging is usually produced by adding fuel to successive annular stream tubes so that the mixture ratio in each tube is nearly stoichiometric. Each stream tube has its own set of fuel injectors and control system which can be activated independently.
>
> The most remarkable fact concerning the fuel system for afterburners is their simplicity. In many engine systems, fuel is supplied to a circular tube which lies with its axis perpendicular to the gas stream. Fuel is injected into the gas through small diameter holes located in the sides of the tubes such that the liquid jet enters the gas stream in a direction perpendicular to the undisturbed flow direction. The liquid jet penetrates some distance into the gas stream before its momentum is dissipated. During this penetration process, the air stream tears the jet apart and produces droplets with diameters of micron size. Heat transfer from the hot gas stream then vaporizes the droplets.
>
> Given the wide range of values of mass flows of fuel required, it is remarkable that reasonably thorough mixing of the fuel with the air can be achieved with

this simple injection system. In some recent engines efforts are being made to use simple variable area injection ports which may possibly give better preparation of the fuel-air mixture.

The whole area of fuel penetration, atomization, and vaporization is not well understood from first principles and one of the time consuming parts of an afterburner development program is to determine the optimum distribution of locations for injector tubes, injector ports, and port diameters.

A good source of information concerning fuel spray injection, atomization, and vaporization is given by Chigier.[30]

9.3.2.4   Ignition.

Ignition of the fuel-air mixture in the afterburner is usually accomplished using a spark or arc igniter or a pilot burner. Once initiated in the primary stream tube, combustion continues in the wake of the flame stabilizer, and the process will spread to the rest of the flame stabilizers.

The spark or arc igniter uses a high-energy electric arc to initiate combustion of the primary stream tube. The igniter is usually placed in the wake of a sheltered flame stabilizer having its own fuel supply. A stable flame results, and combustion is initiated behind other flame stabilizers by the mechanism just mentioned.

The pilot burner consists of a pilot zone where a small portion of the inlet air (usually 10% or less) is burned to stoichiometric temperatures in an enclosed protected region. The hot gases generated by the pilot are used as an ignition and stabilizing source for the main fuel injection system.

Afterburning for some turbofan engines is accomplished by adding fuel first to the core flow near the interface between the core and fan streams, then to the fan stream, and finally to the rest of the core flow. Afterburning in the fan stream produces the largest performance gain because of the low temperature of this stream. However, the fan stream's low temperature makes fuel vaporization and afterburning very difficult. By adding fuel first to the core flow near its interface with the fan stream, the resulting afterburning stream can act as a pilot for the combustion process in the fan stream.

9.3.2.5   Flame stabilization.

Two general types of flame stabilizing devices that have been used in afterburners are shown in Fig. 9.37. These are bluff body flameholder vee-gutters and piloted burners, where a small piloting heat source is used to ignite the main fuel flow.

The vee-gutter flameholders have the advantage of low flow blockage and low total pressure loss. They are simple and lightweight and have a good development history. The wake of a vee-gutter flameholder is divided into two regions: a recirculation zone or bubble and a shear-driven mixing layer, as shown in Fig. 9.2b. The recirculation zone is characterized by a strong reverse flow and very low chemical reaction rates. As combustion is essentially complete in the recirculation zone, the temperature is nearly equal to the adiabatic flame temperature corresponding to the fuel-air ratio of the approaching stream. The mixing layer is characterized by very strong shear, steep temperature gradients, and vigorous chemical reaction in the micromixed reaction zone behind the flame front, which is propagating upstream against the mean velocity within the mixing layer, as shown in Fig. 9.38. Following the termination of the mixing layer by disentrainment of the recirculating gases, the flame front continues to propagate outward towards the walls.

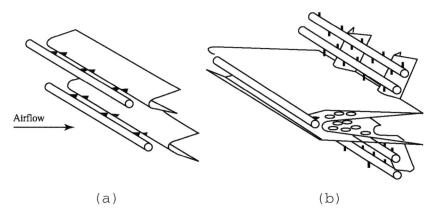

Fig. 9.37   Two types of flameholders: a) vee-gutter; and b) piloted burner.

The design goal is to select parameters that will cause the flame region to stand at a location between x_m, the mixing transition point shown in Fig. 9.19 and defined by Eqs. (9.55) and (9.54), and $x = L/2$, where L is the length of the recirculation bubble, also as shown in Fig. 9.2b. At about $x = L/2$ the mixing layer begins to break down as a result of disentrainment of gases from the mixing layer into the recirculation bubble. This is an interesting balancing act because the flame front must not be permitted to propagate so freely upstream that it "flashes back" to the spray bars, nor must it be allowed to "blow off" downstream because the mixing layer and recirculation zone are not long enough.

To find the values of parameters that will provide the needed range for flame stabilization, the mixing zone will be modeled as a single micromixed well-stirred reactor (WSR) of lateral thickness equal to the average shear layer thickness δ_m and of axial length equal to one-half the length of the recirculation bubble. The mean residence time or stay time in this WSR can be estimated by

$$t_s \approx \frac{m}{\dot{m}} = \frac{\rho \delta_m (L/2)}{\rho \delta_m U_c} = \frac{L}{2U_c} \qquad (9.129)$$

where U_c is the convective velocity within the mixing layer, as defined by Eq. (9.55), and where the mass density ρ has been assumed to be approximately constant. Further, neglecting the density difference between the two mixing streams,

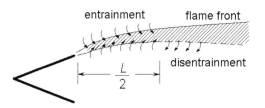

Fig. 9.38   Entrainment of reactant gases into, and disentrainment out of, the shear-driven mixing layer, which is responsible for flameholding in a vee-gutter flameholder.

then $U_c \sim U_2/2$, and Eq. (9.129) may be rewritten as

$$t_s \approx \frac{(L/2)}{(U_2/2)} = \frac{L}{U_2} \qquad (9.130)$$

The requirement for the flame front to stabilize is therefore that the residence time or stay time t_s of the gases flowing through the mixing layer must be greater than, or equal to, the WSR residence time at blowout t_{BO} as defined and discussed in Sec. 9.1.3.

Because $t_s > t_{BO}$ in the mixing layer is required, then the design requirement for flame stabilization can be stated as

$$t_s \approx \frac{L}{U_2} > t_{BO} \quad \text{required} \qquad (9.131)$$

Substituting the estimate $L \sim 4W$ (Ref. 3) into Eq. (9.131), the stabilization requirement becomes

$$t_s \approx \frac{4W}{U_2} > t_{BO} \quad \text{required} \qquad (9.132)$$

Because both U_2 and W depend on the blockage B, approach velocity U_1, and vee-gutter half-angle θ, the requirement Eq. (9.132) must be rewritten in terms of the controllable design parameters H, D, θ, and U_1. Conservation of mass requires that

$$U_1 H = U_2(H - W), \quad \text{so that } U_2 = U_1\left(\frac{H}{H-W}\right) = \frac{U_1}{(1 - W/H)} \qquad (9.133)$$

which enables Eq. (9.132) to be rewritten as

$$t_s \approx \frac{H}{U_1}\frac{4W}{H}\left(1 - \frac{W}{H}\right) > t_{BO} \quad \text{required} \qquad (9.134)$$

By inspection of Eq. (9.134), it can be seen that for any given values of channel height H and approach velocity U_1, the residence time in the mixing layer is maximized when $W/H = 1/2$, so that for optimal flameholding

$$\frac{H}{U_1} > t_{BO} \quad \text{required}, \quad \text{when} \left(\frac{W}{H}\right) = 0.5 \qquad (9.135)$$

Note, however, that the optimum is fairly flat. For example, if $W/H = 0.4$ is substituted into Eq. (9.134) instead of the optimal $W/H = 0.5$, then the required ratio H/U_1 is increased by only 4%, so that variations in practice can be expected.

The WSR blowout residence time t_{BO} must be obtained either from experiment or from chemical–kinetic WSR modeling, for example, from the AEDsys software program KINETX. Required inputs to KINETX for calculating t_{BO} are the pressure, temperature, and composition of the approach gas stream and the ratio of afterburner fuel flow rate to main gas stream flow rate. All of these parameters except the gas composition are available from the Engine Station Test Results sheet. The composition of the main gas stream can be obtained from the AEDsys program EQL.

With U_1 given from the Engine Station Test Results sheet, t_{BO} determined from the AEDsys program KINETX, and the minimum H determined from Eq. (9.134) for a single vee-gutter, design choices still have to be made for the vee-gutter lateral dimension D and half-angle θ, and how many rows (rings) of vee-gutters and associated spray bars will be required.

Equation (9.87) gives W/H as a function of the blockage $B = D/H$ and half-angle θ:

$$\frac{W}{H} \cong B + (1 - \sqrt{B})\sqrt{B}\sin(\theta/2) \qquad (9.136)$$

For any value of W/H, B and θ are related by Eq. (9.136), but neither value is specified. Because a half-angle of $\theta = 15$ deg has been widely utilized for vee-gutter flameholders, that value will be used here. For $\theta = 15$ deg, and over the useful range $0.3 < W/H < 0.5$, Eqs. (9.87) and (9.136) can be represented to good approximation by

$$B \cong 1.034\left(\frac{W}{H}\right) - 0.1 \quad \text{for} \quad \theta = 15 \text{ deg}, \quad 0.3 < \frac{W}{H} < 0.5 \quad (9.137)$$

With the optimal $W/H = 0.5$ as input, Eq. (9.137) gives the corresponding value of blockage $B = 0.417$, and the gutter lateral width $D = BH = 0.417H$. The corresponding vee-gutter drag coefficient $C_D = 2.4$ is obtained from Eq. (9.84). These values are typical of currently operational afterburners.

However, for $W/H = 0.4$, Eq. (9.137) gives $B = 0.314$, and Eq. (9.84) gives the corresponding $C_D = 1.4$. From Eq. (9.85) it can be seen that reducing the design value of W/H from 0.5 to 0.4 reduces the "dry" total pressure loss coefficient from 1.0 to 0.444. This reduction of dry total pressure loss by 55%, at a cost of only 4% reduction in flameholding stability, is significant and should be considered during design of the afterburner.

9.3.2.6 Flame spread and afterburner length.

Figure 9.39 illustrates how the channel height H and flame spread angle determine the length of the afterburner between stations 6.1 and 7 required for the flame front to consume all of the reactant gases. Regrettably, there does not appear to be a reliable method to determine the flame spread angle based on first principles,[3] and so a standard design value of 17 deg total included angle will be assumed.

Assuming that afterburner a) of Fig. 9.39 has a channel height H that is equal to or slightly greater than the minimum value required by Eq. (9.135), the single-gutter afterburner b) has an unnecessarily wide stability margin for flameholding, and the twice-as-long flame spreading region results in a much longer afterburner. Why not make the afterburner even shorter by further reducing the channel height, so that there would be three or four rows (rings) of flameholders? Because the vee-gutters would then be too small to stabilize the flame!

In summary, two design guidelines have been established for optimizing both afterburner flameholding and flame spread: 1) H should be as small as possible in order to minimize the length of the afterburner (flame spread), and 2) U_1 should be small as possible to maximize residence time in the mixing layer (flameholding.)

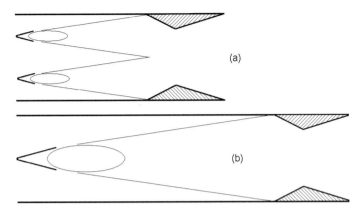

Fig. 9.39   Effect of channel height H and flame spread angle on afterburner length. Both afterburners have the same area and approach velocity U_1, but the channel height H of b) is twice that of a). Both have the same, optimum flameholding values $W/H =$ 0.5, blockage $B = 0.417$, gutter half-angle $\theta = 15$ deg, and assumed included angle of 17 deg for flame spread (approximately to scale).

Finally, stealth requirements of modern fighter aircraft may require the flame-holders be located to hide the high temperature of the turbine exit and thus reduce the infrared signature. Cool bypass air can be ducted and mixed in such a way as to cool these flameholders.

9.3.2.7   Afterburner liner.   The afterburner liner is used as a cooling liner and to improve combustion stability. As a cooling liner, it isolates the very high temperatures from the outer casing, similar to the liner of the main burner. A film of cooler air is distributed along the length of the cooling liner that reduces the metal temperature of this liner and subjects the outer casing of the afterburner to the afterburner pressure and the temperature of the cooling flow.

The liner is also used as a screech or antihowl liner to prevent extreme high frequency and amplitude pressure fluctuations resulting from combustion insta-bility or the unsteady release of thermal energy. This is accomplished by use of multiple holes along the initial length of the liner. Selective acoustic frequencies can be dampened by the selection of the proper hole size and distribution and the geometry of the cavity behind the holes.

9.4   Example Engine Component Design: Combustion Systems

9.4.1   AAF Engine Main Burner Design

Strictly speaking, the main burner should be designed for more than a single operating point. Specifically, 1) the liner dome should be designed for high-altitude relight, 2) the primary zone should be sized for idle conditions, 3) the liner air cooling should be designed for the maximum liner gas temperature, and 4) the combustor length should be designed for the maximum throughput mass flow rate condition.[*]

---

[*]Sturgess, G. R., private communication, Dayton, OH, July 2002.

As pointed out in Sec. 9.1.7, design of the ignition subsystem is regarded as too complex for inclusion in this textbook, and so design for high-altitude relight will not be considered. Of the remaining three considerations, it can be seen from inspection of Table 7.E4, AAF Engine Main Burner Operation, that the maximum dynamic pressure condition (sea level, flight Mach number $M_0 = 1.2$) establishes both the maximum gas temperature and maximum throughput condition. In the interest of clarity and simplicity, therefore, that condition will be chosen as the single design point for both the main burner and the afterburner. The corresponding design interface quantities are presented on the Engine Stations Test Results sheet (see Table 9.E1).

As explained in Sec. 9.2.1, the values listed for station 3.2 are to be regarded as "first-cut" or "bogey" values, and will have to be checked and/or iterated to ensure adequate jet penetration and mixing, and to accommodate the swirler.

From the component design of the compressor and turbine, the mean radii at stations 3.1 and 4 have been established as 9 in. and 7 in., respectively. Using the

Table 9.E1   AAF engine stations test results at design point (maximum dynamic pressure)

Results at Engine Stations (AEDsys Ver 3.00)   Date:10/1/2002 6:00:00 AM
Filename: C:\Programs\AEDsys\AAF Data\AAF Final Engine.AED
Engine File Name: C:\Programs\AEDsys\AAF Data\AAF Final Engine.ref
Thrust Scale Factor = 1.0000   Percent Thrust = 100
Altitude = 0 ft

Station	m dot (lbm/s)	gamma	Pt (psia)	Tt (R)	Press (psia)	Mach	Velocity (ft/s)	Area (ft²)	Area* (ft²)	I (lbf)
0	227.10	1.4000	35.637	668.07	14.696	1.2000	1339.68	2.216	2.151	14145.9
1	227.10	1.4000	35.333	668.07	31.808	0.3904	487.28	3.519	2.169	19557.7
2	227.10	1.4000	33.920	668.07	31.170	0.3496	437.67	4.022	2.260	21140.0
13	227.10	1.4000	83.391	893.29	74.176	0.4125	594.28	1.649	1.063	21805.8
core	117.12	1.4000	83.391	893.29	74.176	0.4125	594.28	0.850	0.548	11245.9
bypass	109.98	1.4000	83.391	893.29	74.176	0.4125	594.28	0.798	0.515	10559.9
2.5	117.12	1.4000	83.391	893.29	76.022	0.3660	529.14	0.938	0.548	12198.7
3	117.12	1.4000	585.114	1659.99	550.205	0.2978	589.47	0.218	0.106	19433.6
3.1	104.24	1.4000	585.114	1659.99	550.205	0.2978	589.47	0.194	0.095	17295.9
3.2	104.24	1.4000	579.263	1659.99	576.537	0.0821	163.90	0.677	0.096	56771.8
MB fuel	2.7017									
4	106.94	1.3000	555.859	3138.80	303.347	1.0000	2467.65	0.144	0.144	14494.6
4.1	112.80	1.3000		3042.54						
4.4	112.80	1.3000		2389.37						
4.5	118.65	1.3000	171.378	2334.78	93.526	1.0000	2128.26	0.448	0.448	13867.4
5	118.65	1.3000	78.129	1983.04	64.783	0.5427	1117.06	1.153	0.906	14878.7
6	118.65	1.3000	78.129	1983.04	71.533	0.3702	770.87	1.549	0.906	18796.4
16	109.98	1.4000	83.391	893.29	71.570	0.4725	677.21	0.719	0.515	7407.6
6A	228.63	1.3360	76.859	1513.71	68.248	0.4249	779.89	2.338	1.536	28516.0
AB fuel	8.7033									
7	237.33	1.3000	73.016	3600.00	61.806	0.5113	1421.42	3.466	2.613	41335.2
8	237.33	1.3000	73.016	3600.00	39.847	1.0000	2642.73	2.613	2.613	34489.9
9	237.33	1.3000	70.826	3600.00	14.696	1.7079	4036.90	3.711	2.694	37631.8

**Table 9.E2   Annular geometry of AAF
engine at stations 3.1 and 4**

	Station 3.1	Station 4
A (ft^2)	0.194	0.144
r_m (in.)	9.0	7.0
r_i (in.)	8.753	6.764
r_o (in.)	9.247	7.235
H (in.)	0.494	0.472

annular geometry relations and definitions given in Fig. 9.36 and Eq. (9.122),

$$r_m \doteq \frac{1}{2}(r_i + r_o), \quad H \doteq (r_o - r_i), \quad \text{and}$$

$$A = \pi \left(r_o^2 - r_i^2 \right) = \pi (r_o - r_i)(r_o + r_i) = 2\pi \, r_m H$$

the inner and outer radii and the radial heights H at stations 3.1 and 4 can be calculated and are summarized in Table 9.E2.

9.4.1.1 Layout.   Some obvious ways to lay out the combustor are to match the radius of the outer casing either to the outer radius at station 3.1 (Design A), or to the outer radius at station 4 (Design B), or somewhere in between. Annular geometry has been calculated for the two layouts A and B, and the number of fuel nozzle assemblies calculated from Eq. (9.105). The results are summarized in Table 9.E3, and the layouts of designs A and B are sketched in Fig. 9.E1.

Chiefly because it has fewer fuel nozzles, design B will be selected. However, because design A has the smaller radial height H, mixing in the secondary and dilution zones will be somewhat more effective than in design B [see Eq. (9.116)].

9.4.1.2 Diffuser.   The required diffuser area ratio is $AR = A_{3.2}/A_{3.1} = 0.677/0.194 = 3.490$, which is less than the maximum "sweet spot" $AR = 4$ of Figs. 9.21 and 9.22. For this area ratio Eqs. (9.66) and (9.67) give the total pressure loss coefficient $(\Delta P_t/q_r)_D$ and total pressure ratio π_D, respectively, for any assumed diffusion efficiency. Using these equations, it is found that a value of η_D as

**Table 9.E3   Annular geometry of station 3.2 for
two possible combustor layouts**

	Design A $r_{o3.2} = r_{o3.1}$	Design B $r_{o3.2} = r_{o4}$
r_o (in.)	9.247	7.235
r_i (in.)	7.381	4.617
r_m (in.)	8.314	5.926
H (in.)	1.866	2.618
N_{noz}	28	14

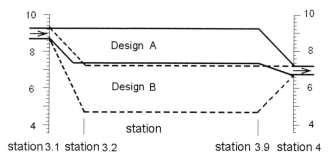

Fig. 9.E1   Layouts of designs A and B of Table 9.E3 (radial dimensions to scale).

low as $\eta_D = 0.83$ will satisfy the allocated total pressure loss, $\Delta P_t = P_{t3.1} - P_{t3.2}$. If a higher diffusion efficiency is assumed, the "savings" in total pressure loss can be allocated to the main burner, if required, to improve mixing.

All of the design relations for an annular flat-wall + dump diffuser were presented in Sec. 9.2.3, in Eqs. (9.102–9.104). Assuming a diffusion efficiency $\eta_{Dm} = \eta_{D9°} = 0.9$, and the given overall area ratio $AR = 3.490$, Eq. (9.103) gives the optimal area ratio for transition from flat-wall to dump diffuser as $A_m = (0.194)(0.9)(3.490) = 0.609$ ft^2. However, because the AR is less than the "sweet spot" value of four, a simple (no dump) flat-wall diffuser will be chosen.

For a one-stream diffuser (no splitter plates), the slant-height distance along the diffuser mean line can be calculated from Eq. (9.61),

$$L = H_1 \left(\frac{r_{m1}}{r_{m2}} \right) \frac{AR - 1}{2 \tan 4.5 \deg} = 0.494 \left(\frac{9}{5.926} \right) \frac{3.490 - 1}{2(0.0787)} = 11.868 \text{ in.}$$

Because the main burner should be as short as possible, L can be reduced by a factor of two or three, by employing one or two splitter plates. Although two splitters plates could perhaps be mounted on the liner dome as a "snout" (see Fig. 9.1), that may be too complex for this geometry, and so a two-stream (one splitter plate) flat-wall annular diffuser might be a good compromise. For the two-stream design the slant-height distance L is now $L = 11.868/2 = 5.934$ in., and the corresponding axial distance is

$$\Delta x = \sqrt{L^2 - (r_{3.1} - r_{3.2})^2} = \sqrt{(5.934)^2 - (9 - 5.926)^2} = 5.076 \text{ in.}$$

The layout for the two diffuser designs is shown in Fig. 9.E2.

9.4.1.3   Air partitioning.

From Table 9.E1 and Eq. (9.90), the equivalence ratio at station 4 is calculated to be $\phi_4 = \dot{m}_{fMB}/f_{st}\dot{m}_{3.1} = 2.7017/(0.0685 \times 104.24) = 0.3784$.

The liner material will be assumed to be capable of withstanding a temperature $T_m = 2110°$R, by using thermal barrier coatings. The cooling gas temperature is $T_c = T_{t3.1} = 1660°$R, and a decision to use film cooling or transpiration/effusion cooling is deferred for the moment.

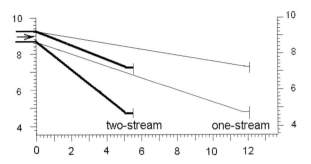

Fig. 9.E2 Annular flat-wall diffusers for none or one splitter plate (to scale).

Using Eqs. (9.88) through (9.101), the air mass fractions μ for primary and secondary zones can be calculated, as well as the cooling mass fraction μ_c for any assumed liner gas temperature T_g. For example, for assumed $T_g = 3200°$R, from Eq. (9.89), $\Delta T_{max} = (T_{t4} - T_{3.1})/\phi_4 = (3138.8 - 1660.0)/0.3784 = 3909°$R. From Eq. (9.97), $\phi_{SZ} = (3200 - 1660)/3909 = 0.394$, and for assumed $\varepsilon_{PZ} = 0.7$, Eq. (9.92) gives $\phi_{PZ} = \phi_{SZ}/0.7 = 0.563$. The resulting mass flow fractions are given by Eq. (9.93), $\mu_{PZ} = \phi_4/\phi_{PZ} = 0.3784/0.563 = 0.672$, and from Eq. (9.99), $\mu_{SZ} = (\phi_4/\phi_{SZ}) - (\phi_4/\phi_{PZ}) = (0.3784/0.394) - (0.3784/0.563) = 0.288$.

The primary and secondary air flow fractions added together equal 96% of the total airflow, leaving only 4% available for cooling and dilution. Even without dilution, there is not enough air available for liner cooling.

To understand and find a solution to this problem, the preceding calculations were repeated for assumed liner gas temperatures T_g ranging from 3000 to 4000°R, and assumed primary zone combustion efficiency $\varepsilon_{PZ} = 0.7$. The results of these calculations, together with the corresponding cooling mass fractions from Eqs. (9.95) and (9.96), are presented in Fig. 9.E3.

The lack of cooling air available stems from the fact that $T_{t4} = 3138.8°$R happens to be right in the mid-range of target liner gas temperatures that minimize

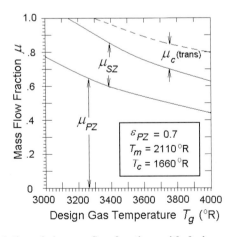

Fig. 9.E3 Variation of air mass flow fractions with design gas temperature.

the production of pollutant species CO and NO_x, as shown in Fig. 9.24. If $T_g = T_{t4} = 3138.8°R$ were assumed, exactly *all* of the air would be required for primary and secondary air combustion, and there would be not only no dilution air required, but also none available for liner cooling. However, if transpiration/effusion cooling were employed, the required air fraction is so modest that $T_g \sim 3500°R$ would probably work. If for some reason (probably manufacturing cost), film cooling were to be specified, T_g would have to be raised to well beyond $4000°R$, and there still would be no requirement for dilution air.

Because the AAF engine being designed is a warplane, and not a global range airlifter, commercial passenger, or transport jet, minimizing pollutant emissions is not a principal design objective. Rather, what is required is a very wide turndown ratio, or in other words, a very wide range of flame stability and thus freedom from flameout from maneuvers or high altitude. It is therefore desirable to have a primary zone equivalence ratio above 0.8, well above the lean blowout limit $\phi_{BO} \sim 0.4 - 0.5$.

Using these assumptions, a good choice for target liner gas temperature can be obtained by solving Eq. (9.92) for $T_g = T_{t3.1} + \phi_{PZ}\varepsilon_{PZ}\Delta T_{max} = 1660 + 0.8(0.7)(3909) = 3849°R$.

With $T_g = 3849°R$ as the design target gas temperature, and still assuming $\varepsilon_{PZ} = 0.7$ and $\phi_{PZ} = 0.80$, Eq. (9.93) gives the primary zone air mass fraction as $\mu_{PZ} = \phi_4/\phi_{PZ} = 0.3784/0.80 = 0.473$. From Eq. (9.97), $\phi_{SZ} = (3849 - 1660)/3909 = 0.560$, and Eq. (9.99) gives the secondary zone air mass fraction, $\mu_{SZ} = (\phi_4/\phi_{SZ}) - (\phi_4/\phi_{PZ}) = (0.3784/0.560) - (0.3784/0.80) = 0.203$. The remaining mass flow fraction $(1 - \mu_{PZ} - \mu_{SZ}) = 1 - 0.473 - 0.203 = 0.324$ is available for film cooling, or for transpiration/effusion cooling and dilution.

For $T_g = 3849°R$ the required cooling effectiveness is, from Eq. (9.94), $\Phi = (T_g - T_m)/(T_g - T_c) = (3849 - 2110)/(3849 - 1660) = 0.794$. From Eqs. (9.95) and (9.96), the corresponding requirements for cooling air mass fraction are $\mu_c = 0.644$ for film cooling, and $\mu_c = 0.155$ for transpiration/effusion cooling. Because there is not enough air available for film cooling, transpiration/effusion cooling must be selected. With transpiration/effusion chosen for liner cooling, the required dilution air fraction from Eq. (9.101) is $\mu_{DZ} = 1 - (\mu_{PZ} + \mu_{SZ} + \mu_c) = 1 - (0.473 + 0.203 + 0.155) = 0.169$. The results of the air partitioning are summarized in Table 9.E4.

9.4.1.4 Dome and liner.
With the radial height of the outer casing H_r fixed, and air partitioning determined, it is now possible to determine the liner height H_L and corresponding dome diameter. From Eq. (9.109), the optimal

Table 9.E4   Air partitioning for AAF engine main burner, for assumed $T_g = 3849°R$ and $\varepsilon_{PZ} = 0.7$

	Total	Primary zone	Secondary zone	Transpiration cooling	Dilution zone
Air flow (lbm/s)	104.24	49.306	21.161	16.157	17.616
Mass fractions	1.00	0.473	0.203	0.155	0.169

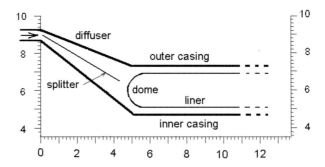

Fig. 9.E4 Layout of AAF engine combustor dome, liner, inner and outer casing (to scale).

liner-to-reference height ratio for maximum secondary jet penetration is

$$\alpha_{opt} = 1 - \left(\frac{\dot{m}_A}{\dot{m}_r}\right)^{2/3} \left(\frac{\Delta P_t}{q_r}\right)^{-1/3}_{MB}$$

From Table 9.E1, $\Delta P_t/q_r = (P_{t3.2} - P_{t4})/(P_{t3.2} - P_{3.2}) = (579.263 - 555.859)/(579.263 - 576.537) = 8.585$, and the ratio of annulus to reference flow rate $\dot{m}_A/\dot{m}_r = \mu_{SZ} + \mu_{DZ} = 0.203 + 0.169 = 0.372$. With these values, $\alpha_{opt} = 1 - (0.372)^{2/3}/(8.585)^{1/3} = 0.747$, and $H_L = \alpha_{opt}H_r = 0.747(2.618) = 1.957$ in. The current state of the main burner layout is shown in Fig. 9.E4.

9.4.1.5 Total pressure loss. With the liner-to-reference area determined, Eq. (9.79) can be used to see whether or not the allocated total pressure loss is sufficient for adequate stirring by the primary zone swirler. For $\tau_{PZ} = T_g/T_{t3.2} = 3849/1660 = 2.319$, this minimum required total pressure loss coefficient is

$$\left(\frac{\Delta P_t}{q_r}\right)_{min} = \left(\frac{\dot{m}_{PZ}}{\dot{m}_r}\right)^2 \left(\frac{A_r}{A_L}\right)^2 \tau_{PZ}(2\tau_{PZ} - 1)$$

$$= \left(\frac{0.473}{0.747}\right)^2 (2.319)[2(2.319) - 1] = 3.383$$

which is less than 40% of the allocated value of $(\Delta P_t/q_r)_{MB} = 8.585$, a comfortable margin.

9.4.1.6 Primary zone. With the reference velocity $U_r = 163.90$ ft/s from Table. 9.E1, the velocity for all jets is determined from Eq. (9.110),

$$V_j = U_r \sqrt{\left(\frac{\Delta P_t}{q_r}\right)_{MB}} = 163.90\sqrt{8.585} = 480.23 \text{ ft/s},$$

The air swirler annular area is determined by first assuming a hub radius of $r_h = 0.5$ in. to accommodate the airblast atomizer, a sharp-edge hole discharge coefficient of $C_D = 0.64$ from Eq. (9.33), and a swirl blade angle of $\alpha_{sw} = 45$ deg.

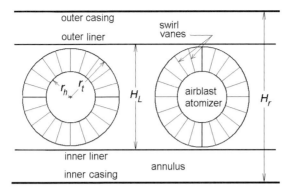

Fig. 9.E5   Layout of primary air swirlers and atomizers (to scale).

With these values as inputs, Eq. (9.111) can be solved for the swirler blade tip radius,

$$
r_t = \sqrt{r_h^2 + \frac{(\dot{m}_{PZ} - 3\dot{m}_{fMB})}{N_{noz}\pi \, C_{D90^\circ} \cos \alpha_{sw}} \left(\frac{A_r}{\dot{m}_r}\right) \left(\frac{\Delta P_t}{q_r}\right)_{MB}^{-1/2}}
$$

$$
= \sqrt{(0.5)^2 + \frac{49.306 - 3(2.7017)}{14\pi \, (0.64) \cos 45 \deg} \left(\frac{0.677(144)}{104.24}\right) \left(\frac{1}{\sqrt{8.585}}\right)} = 0.954 \text{ in.}
$$

Fortunately, this swirler tip radius is less than $H_L/2 = 0.9595$, so the swirler just fits within the envelope of the liner. The pitch of the $N_{noz} = 14$ swirler + atomizer assemblies at mean radius is $2\pi r_m/N_{noz} = 2\pi(5.926)/14 = 2.66$ in. The layout of the swirler + atomizer assembly is shown in Fig. 9.E5.

The swirl number for this design is obtained from Eq. (9.48),

$$
S' = \frac{2}{3} \tan \alpha_{sw} \left[\frac{1 - (r_h/r_t)^3}{1 - (r_h/r_t)^2}\right] = \frac{2}{3} \tan 45 \deg \left[\frac{1 - (0.5/0.954)^3}{1 - (0.5/0.954)^2}\right] = 0.787,
$$

which is satisfactory. The swirler area is $A_{SW} = \pi(r_t^2 - r_h^2) = \pi[(0.954)^2 - (0.5)^2] = 2.073$ in.^{2} per nozzle.

The axial length of the primary zone, measured from the "nose" of the dome, can be laid out according to the estimate Eq. (9.50), $L_{PZ} \sim 2S'r_t = 2(0.787)(0.954) = 1.501$ in. ~ 1.5 in.

If the calculated swirler tip radius had been greater than $H_L/2$, some adjustments would have been necessary. These could have been any or all of the following: a) smooth the edges of the flow passage at entry to the swirler annulus and/or make the swirler blades airfoils instead of flat plates or slats, which would increase C_D to perhaps 0.8, even though experience shows that flat-plate blades provide slightly better mixing than airfoils; b) reduce the swirler blade angle to 40°—but that would reduce the swirl number S' too close to the minimum value of 0.6; c) decrease the reference Mach number M_r by slightly increasing the reference area A_r, and recalculate everything; or d) increase N_{noz} from 14 to 16, 18 or 20—although this would have necessarily reduced the spacing or pitch between adjacent fuel nozzle/air swirler assemblies.

The design of the primary zone can be validated by using the AEDsys program KINETX to model the primary zone as a single WSR. For a single nozzle/swirler, the inputs to KINETX are as follows: $T_A = 1660°R$; $T_F = 540°R$; $P = 579.263$ psia; $\dot{m}_A = \dot{m}_{PZ}/N_{noz} = 49.306/14 = 3.522$ lbm/s; $\dot{m}_F = 2.7017/14 = 0.1930$ lbm/s; $L_{PZ} = 1.5$ in.; $A_{PZ} = \pi r_t^2/8 = \pi(0.954)^2/8 = 0.357$ in.^{2} (Note that, as explained at the end of Sec. 9.1.4.4, the micromixed portion of the primary zone volume is approximately one-eighth of the volume of the recirculation bubble.) With these inputs, and with an assumed lower heating value of 18,400 BTU/lbm for the fuel, KINETX gives a residence time $t_s = 3.376 \times 10^{-5}$ s, which is an order-of-magnitude greater than the blowout residence time $t_{BO} = 4.403 \times 10^{-6}$ s. The predicted primary zone combustion efficiency $\varepsilon_{PZ} = 78.32\%$ and gas temperature $T_{PZ} = 3822°R$ compare favorably with the assumed design values $\varepsilon_{PZ} = 0.7$ and $T_{PZ} = 3849°R$ that were based on a linear approximation to the thermochemistry [Eq. (9.23)].

9.4.1.7 Secondary zone.

To design the number and location of the secondary zone air holes, it is necessary to first calculate the various dynamic pressure ratios,

$$\frac{q_j}{q_r} = \frac{\Delta P_t}{q_r} = 8.585,$$

$$\frac{q_A}{q_r} = \left(\frac{\dot{m}_A}{\dot{m}_r}\frac{A_r}{A_A}\right)^2 = \left(\frac{\mu_{SZ} + \mu_{DZ}}{1 - \alpha}\right)^2 = \left(\frac{0.203 + 0.169}{1 - 0.747}\right)^2 = 2.162,$$

and

$$\frac{q_L}{q_r} = \frac{q_{PZ}}{q_r} = \tau_{PZ}\left(\frac{\dot{m}_{PZ}}{\dot{m}_r}\frac{A_r}{A_L}\right)^2 = \tau_{PZ}\left(\frac{\mu_{PZ}}{\alpha_{opt}}\right)^2 = 2.319\left(\frac{0.473}{0.747}\right)^2 = 0.930$$

The maximum penetration of the jet centerline is obtained from Eq. (9.107),

$$\frac{Y_{max}}{d_j} = 1.15\sqrt{\frac{q_j}{q_r}\frac{q_r}{q_L}\left(1 - \frac{q_A}{q_r}\frac{q_r}{q_j}\right)} = 1.15\sqrt{\frac{8.585}{0.930}\left(1 - \frac{2.162}{8.585}\right)} = 3.022$$

The required single jet vena contracta area is obtained from Eq. (9.112),

$$d_j = \frac{1}{4}H_L\left(\frac{Y_{max}}{d_j}\right)^{-1} = \frac{1.957}{4(3.022)} = 0.162 \text{ in.}$$

The total number of secondary holes is obtained from Eq. (9.113),

$$N_{hSZ} = \frac{4\dot{m}_{SZ}}{\rho_r \pi d_j^2 V_j} = \mu_{SZ}\left(\frac{4A_r}{\pi d_j^2}\right)\frac{U_r}{V_j} = 0.203\left[\frac{4(0.677)144}{\pi(0.162)^2}\right]\left(\frac{163.90}{480.23}\right) \approx 328$$

or $328/14 \sim 23$ secondary holes per nozzle/swirler assembly.

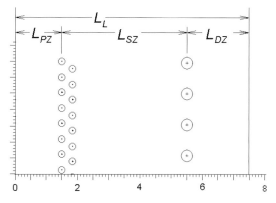

Fig. 9.E6 Layout of secondary and dilution air holes in inner and outer liner (to scale).

The secondary jets enter the liner at an angle θ, as shown in Fig. 9.15, obtained from Eq. (9.115),

$$\sin\theta = \sqrt{1 - \frac{q_A\, q_r}{q_r\, q_j}} = \sqrt{1 - \frac{2.162}{8.585}} = 0.865, \quad \text{so } \theta = 59.9\,\text{deg}$$

and the diameter of each secondary air hole, from Eq. (9.43) or (9.114), is

$$d_h = \frac{dj}{\sqrt{C_{D90°}}\,\sin\theta} = \frac{0.162}{\sqrt{0.64}\,(0.865)} = 0.234\,\text{in.}$$

There are too many secondary air holes to arrange in a single lateral line, top and bottom of the liner, as recommended in Sec. 9.2.3, but they should be positioned as closely as possible to the end of the primary zone. Because there are 23 holes per nozzle/swirler, they should be divided into twelve on the outer liner, and eleven on the inner liner, arrayed as shown in Fig. 9.E6.

Following Eq. (9.116), the length of the secondary zone is calculated as $L_{SZ} \simeq 2H_L = 2(1.957) \approx 4$ in.

9.4.1.8 Dilution zone. The same procedure is followed as for the secondary zone, except that the design goal is $Y_{max} = H_L/3$, rather than $H_L/4$ for the secondary jets, so that somewhat larger diameter jets will be required. From Eq. (9.117),

$$d_j \simeq \frac{1}{3} H_L \left(\frac{Y_{max}}{d_j} \right)^{-1}$$

Because the secondary zone jets have reduced the annulus airflow, only the dilution air now flows in the annulus, so that the annulus flow dynamic pressure is reduced to

$$\frac{q_A}{q_r} = \left(\frac{\dot{m}_A\, A_r}{\dot{m}_r\, A_A} \right)^2 = \left(\frac{\mu_{DZ}}{1 - \alpha} \right)^2 = \left(\frac{0.169}{1 - 0.747} \right)^2 = 0.446$$

and because the liner flow has been increased by the inflow of the secondary air,

$$\frac{q_L}{q_r} = \frac{q_{SZ}}{q_r} = \tau_{PZ}\left(\frac{\dot{m}_{PZ} + \dot{m}_{SZ}}{\dot{m}_r}\frac{A_r}{A_L}\right)^2 = \tau_{PZ}\left(\frac{\mu_{PZ} + \mu_{SZ}}{\alpha}\right)^2$$

$$= 2.319\left(\frac{0.473 + 0.203}{0.747}\right)^2 = 1.899$$

The maximum penetration of the dilution jet centerline is obtained from Eq. (9.107),

$$\frac{Y_{max}}{d_j} = 1.15\sqrt{\frac{q_j}{q_r}\frac{q_r}{q_L}\left(1 - \frac{q_A}{q_r}\frac{q_r}{q_j}\right)} = 1.15\sqrt{\frac{8.585}{1.899}\left(1 - \frac{0.446}{8.585}\right)} = 2.381$$

so the dilution jet vena contract area of each jet is

$$d_j \simeq \frac{1}{3}H_L\left(\frac{Y_{max}}{d_j}\right)^{-1} = \frac{1.957}{3(2.381)} = 0.274 \text{ in.},$$

and the dilution jet entry angle is

$$\sin\theta = \sqrt{1 - \frac{q_A}{q_r}\frac{q_r}{q_j}} = \sqrt{1 - \frac{0.446}{8.585}} = 0.974, \quad \text{so } \theta = 76.8 \text{ deg}$$

The diameter of each dilution air hole, from Eq. (9.43) or (9.114), is

$$d_h = \frac{d_j}{\sqrt{C_{D90°}}\sin\theta} = \frac{0.274}{\sqrt{0.64}(0.974)} = 0.352 \text{ in.}$$

and the required number of dilution holes is given by Eq. (9.113),

$$N_{hDZ} = \frac{4\dot{m}_{DZ}}{\rho_r\pi d_j^2 V_j} = \mu_{DZ}\left(\frac{4A_r}{\pi d_j^2}\right)\frac{U_r}{V_j} = 0.169\left[\frac{4(0.677)\,144}{\pi(0.274)^2}\right]\left(\frac{163.90}{480.23}\right) \approx 95$$

or 95/14 ~ 7 dilution holes per nozzle/swirler. Because their lateral location is not essential, the total 95 holes can be spaced equally, 47 on the inner liner wall and 48 on the outer wall, around the periphery at the end of the secondary zone, as shown in Fig. 9.E6.

The estimate of Sec. 9.3.2 can be used for the length of the dilution zone, $L_{DZ} \sim 1.5H_L \sim 3$ in.

The total length of the main burner liner can now be summed,

$$L_L = L_{PZ} + L_{SZ} + L_{DZ} = 1.5 + 4 + 3 = 8.5 \text{ in.}$$

A side view of the main burner layout is presented in Fig. 9.E7.

9.4.2 AAF Engine Afterburner Design

In Sec. 9.3.2, it was shown that the axial length of both the mixer and the afterburner hot section can be minimized by making the outer radii as large as possible. Happily, there are no tradeoffs to consider with this issue, and so the afterburner will be sized with its outer diameter equal to the maximum diameter

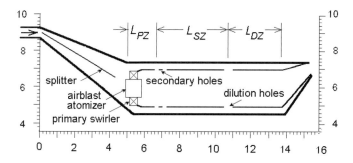

Fig. 9.E7   Side view of AAF engine main burner layout (to scale).

of all of the upstream components, namely, the outer diameter at fan inlet, $r_o = 15.7$ in.

Ducting will be required to direct the core flow and fan bypass air outward from their respective outlets to their pressure-matched entries to the mixer. For the core flow, the ducting will be from station 5 to station 6, and for the bypass air flow, the ducting will be from station 13 (bypass) to station 16.

Because station 16 is radially outboard of station 6 (see Fig. 9.2), its outer radius will be set to the maximum afterburner design radius, $r_o = 15.7$ in, and the station 16 inner radius determined from r_o and the area given in Table 9.E1, using the geometric relations for annuli given by Fig. 9.36 and Eq. (9.122).

The outer radius at station 6 will be set equal to the inner radius at station 16, and the station 6 inner radius determined from the outer radius and area from Table 9.E1, in the same manner as for station 16. After exiting the mixer, the gas stream must then be diffused from station 6A to the afterburner hot section entry at station 6.1. The given areas and both given and calculated radii are summarized in Table 9.E5, and the ducting is shown in Fig. 9.E8.

Note that, because $r_{i6} > r_{o5}$, the duct from station 5 to station 6 hides from downstream view the motion of the last stage low-pressure turbine rotor blades, a good stealth feature of this design.

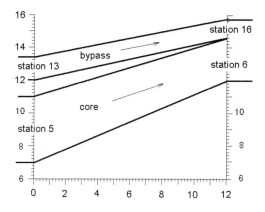

Fig. 9.E8   Ducting from station 5 to 6 and from station 13 to 16 (to scale).

Table 9.E5   AAF engine afterburner core and bypass flow areas and radii

	Station 5 (core)	Station 6 (core)	Station 13 (bypass)	Station 16 (bypass)	Station 6A (mixed)	Stations 6.1 and 7 (mixed)
r_o (in.)	11.0	14.6	13.4	15.7	15.7	15.7
r_i (in.)	7.0	11.9	12.0	14.6	11.8	0.0
A (ft^2)	1.571[a]	1.549	0.798	0.719	2.338	5.378

[a]Area at station 5 from low-pressure turbine design (see Sec. 8.3.4).

9.4.2.1 Mixer. As shown in Sec. 9.3.2, it is not feasible to design the mixer from first principles. However, some calculations can be performed that illustrate the magnitude of the mixing problem, and some possible solutions can be suggested. From Table 9.E1, the areas, mass flow rates and thermodynamic properties of the mixer inlet flows at stations 6 and 16 are available. Substituting these numbers into the mixing layer Eqs. (9.52–9.58), the velocity ratio r and density ratio s for the shear/mixing layer can be calculated,

$$r = \frac{U_{16}}{U_6} = \frac{677.21}{770.87} = 0.8785 \quad \text{and} \quad s = \frac{\rho_{16}}{\rho_6} \approx \frac{T_{t6}}{T_{t16}} = \frac{1983.04}{893.29} = 2.220$$

from which the maximum possible rate of growth of the mixing layer (imbedded in the shear layer) is

$$\frac{\delta_m}{x} = C_\delta (0.0332) = 0.0150, \quad \text{for } (C_\delta)_{max} = 0.45$$

From the geometry of Fig. 9.35 in Sec. 9.3.2, L_m would have to be over 12 ft, for just the bypass stream to mix out! This is obviously not acceptable. What is wrong, and what is to be done about it?

The problem is that in order to pressure-match the two streams prior to mixer entry the bypass stream is slightly accelerated from station 13 to 16, while the core stream remains at essentially constant area and velocity from station 5 to 6 (see Sec. 8.3.4.) This results in a velocity difference between the two streams at mixer entry $\Delta U = (U_6 - U_{16}) = (770.87 - 677.21) = 93.66$ ft/s, which appears to be large enough to strongly drive the shear layer. However, as can be seen by inspection of Eq. (9.54), it is the velocity *ratio*, not the difference, that determines the axial rate of growth of the shear layer, and the ratio of two large velocities, $r = 0.8785$, is too close to 1.0 for the shear/mixing layer to grow at an adequate rate. Even though a ~94 ft/s velocity difference produces a strongly driven shear/mixing layer, the mean convective velocity of 724 ft/s convects the developing shear/mixing layer downstream so rapidly that the axial growth rate is small.

What is to be done about it? Noting that the component immediately downstream of the mixer is the diffuser, it will be recalled from Secs. 9.1.5 and 9.2.3 that the best, "sweet spot" diffuser design operates within the mild transitory stall regime, labeled "some stall" in Figs. 9.21 and 9.22. The flow in this regime periodically

Table 9.E6 Dimensions of AAF engine afterburner mixer + diffuser shown in Fig. 9.E9[a]

	Station 1 (6A)	Station m	Station 2 (6.1)
r_o (in.)	15.7	15.7	15.7
r_i (in.)	11.8	5.0	0.0
r_m (in.)	13.75	10.35	7.85
H (in.)	3.9	10.7	15.7
A (ft^2)	2.338	4.840	5.378

[a] $L_m = 35.2$ in. $L_d = 5.0$ in.

separates from both walls, which causes stirring, which in turn enhances the mixing of the co-flowing streams. This suggests that a combined mixer + diffuser might be a good idea. However, if design data for such a combined mixer + diffuser exists, it must be proprietary to the engine manufacturers, as no references could be found in the open literature.

Consequently, for preliminary design purposes, the total pressure losses caused by mixing and flow diffusion must be calculated individually, as if the processes of mixing and diffusion occurred in axially separate components, whereas in actual fact, the mixing and diffusion processes will be combined into a single component.

9.4.2.2 Diffuser.
All of the design relations for an annular flat-wall + dump diffuser were presented in Sec. 9.3.2, in Eqs. (9.122–9.128). Assuming a flat-wall diffusion efficiency $\eta_{Dm} = \eta_{D9°} = 0.90$ and an overall area ratio $AR = A_{6.1}/A_{6A} = 5.378/2.338 = 2.30$, Eq. (9.127) gives the optimal area ratio for transition from flat-wall to dump diffuser $A_{m\,opt} = (2.338)(0.90)(2.30) = 4.840$ ft^2.

From the annular geometry relations Eqs. (9.122) and (9.123), all of the dimensions for the diffuser can be calculated, and are summarized in Table 9.E6. The resulting combined mixer + diffuser is drawn to scale in Fig. 9.E9.

From Eq. (9.128), the combined or overall diffusion efficiency is $\eta_D = 0.903$, essentially equal to that assumed for the flat-wall section alone.

A few comments about this design are in order. First, it may seem optimistic to assume a diffusion efficiency as high as $\eta_D = 0.9$, but it must be borne in mind that the combined mixer + diffuser has already been assessed a total pressure loss

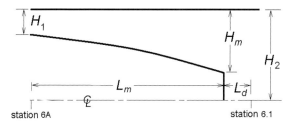

Fig. 9.E9 Combined mixer + diffuser with dimensions given in Table 9.E6 (to scale).

for mixing alone. Secondly, the centerbody length $L_m \sim 3$ ft may seem somewhat long, but one design goal is to provide adequate length for mixing of the core gas and bypass air streams, as well as efficient diffusion. Finally, if a worst-case diffusion efficiency of $\eta_D = 0.6$ were to be assumed, the centerbody length would be reduced to $L_m \sim 1$ ft, just one-third of the design value! It appears that there are some interesting trade-offs to be considered here.

All properties at station 6.1 can now be calculated, as follows:

1) At diffuser entry station 1, using values from Table 9.E1 for station 6A,

$$q_1 = P_{t1} - P_1 = 76.859 - 68.248 = 8.611 \text{ psia},$$

or

$$q_1 = \frac{1}{2}\gamma P_1 M_1^2 = 0.5\,(1.336)\,(68.248)\,(0.4249)^2 = 8.231 \text{ psia}$$

To be conservative, the larger value $q_1 = 8.611$ psia will be utilized.

2) The total pressure loss coefficient, from Eq. (9.66), is

$$\left(\frac{\Delta P_t}{q_1}\right)_D \doteq \frac{P_{t1} - P_{t2}}{q_1} = \left(1 - \frac{1}{AR^2}\right)(1 - \eta_D)$$

$$= \left(1 - \frac{1}{(2.30)^2}\right)(1 - 0.903) = 0.0787$$

from which the total pressure at station 6.1 is

$$P_{t2} = P_{t1} - \left(\frac{\Delta P_t}{q_1}\right)_D q_1 = 76.859 - 0.0787(8.611) = 76.181 \text{ psia},$$

and the static pressure, from Eqs. (9.62–9.64), is

$$P_2 = P_1 + \left(1 - \frac{1}{AR^2}\right)\eta_D q_1 = 68.248 + \left(1 - \frac{1}{(2.30)^2}\right)(0.903)(8.611)$$

$$= 74.538 \text{ psia}$$

and the dynamic pressure is $q_2 = P_{t2} - P_2 = 76.181 - 74.538 = 1.643$ psia.

3) The Mach number at station 6.1 is determined by

$$M_2 = \sqrt{\frac{2q_2}{\gamma P_2}} = \sqrt{\frac{2(1.643)}{1.336(74.538)}} = 0.1817,$$

for which the corresponding velocity is

$$U_2 = \frac{g_c P_2 A_2 M_2^2}{\dot{m}} = \frac{32.174(74.538)(5.378)(144)(0.1817)^2}{228.63} = 268.19 \text{ ft/s}$$

and the stream thrust function at station 6.1 is

$$I_2 = P_2 A_2 (1 + \gamma M_2^2) = 74.538(5.378)(144)[1 + 1.336(0.1817)^2] = 60{,}270.7 \text{ lbf}$$

All of these values are summarized on a new line to be added to the Engine Station Test Results sheet of Table 9.E1 for station 6.1, given in Table 9.E7.

Table 9.E7 Added line (bold text) in Table 9.E1 for station 6.1

Station	m dot (lbm/s)	gamma	Pt (psia)	Tt (R)	Press (psia)	Mach	Velocity (ft/s)	Area (ft²)	Area* (ft²)	I (lbf)
6A	228.63	1.3360	76.859	1513.71	68.248	0.4249	779.89	2.338	1.536	28516.0
6.1	**228.63**	**1.3360**	**76.181**	**1513.71**	**74.538**	**0.1817**	**268.19**	**5.378**	**1.645**	**60270.7**

With the fluid flow and thermodynamic properties and geometry for station 6.1 now determined, the next step is to design the hot section of the afterburner.

Before sizing the vee-gutters, however, because enough information has been collected to calculate the total pressure loss for the afterburner, a check should be made to see if the design goal of $P_{t7} = 73.016$ psia listed in Table 9.E1 has been met.

From Eq. (9.83) of Sec. 9.1.5, the total pressure loss coefficient for the afterburner between stations 6.1 and 7 is given by

$$\left(\frac{\Delta P_t}{q_1}\right)_{AB} \doteq \frac{P_{t2} - P_{t1}}{q_1} = (\tau_{AB} - 1) + \frac{W^2}{(H - W)^2}$$

In Sec. 9.3.2, it was shown that W/H, the ratio of vee-gutter wake width W to lateral spacing H, should be equal to one-half for optimal flameholding. With $W/H = 0.5$, and with total temperatures taken from Table 9.E1 for stations 6A and 7, the total pressure loss coefficient is

$$\left(\frac{\Delta P_t}{q_1}\right)_{AB} = (\tau_{AB} - 1) + \frac{W^2}{(H - W)^2} = \left(\frac{3600.0}{1513.71} - 1\right) + 1.0 = 2.378,$$

and the total pressure at station 7 is therefore

$$P_{t2} = P_{t1} - q_1\left(\frac{\Delta P_t}{q_1}\right)_{AB} = 76.178 - 1.643\,(2.378) = 72.271 \text{ psia}$$

which falls short of the design goal of $P_{t7} = 73.016$ psia given in Table 9.E1.

In Sec. 9.3.2, following Eq. (9.137), it was shown that by reducing W/H from its optimal value of 0.5 to 0.4, the total pressure loss could be significantly reduced with relatively little negative effect on flameholding. Subject to later verification that flameholding is not in fact seriously compromised, $W/H = 0.4$ will be assumed. From Eq. (9.137), with $\theta = 15$ deg and $W/H = 0.4$, a new design blockage $B = 0.314$ is calculated.

Again employing Eq. (9.83) with $W/H = 0.4$, the resulting total pressure loss coefficient is found to be

$$\left(\frac{\Delta P_t}{q_1}\right)_{AB} = (\tau_{AB} - 1) + \frac{W^2}{(H - W)^2} = \left(\frac{3600.0}{1513.71} - 1\right) + 0.444 = 1.822$$

and the corresponding total pressure at station 7 is

$$P_{t2} = P_{t1} - q_1 \left(\frac{\Delta P_t}{q_1}\right)_{AB} = 76.178 - 1.643\,(1.822) = 73.184 \text{ psia}$$

which is above the target value of $P_{t7} = 73.016$ psia.

Note that this value of P_{t7} is for "wet" operation. For "dry" operation, for which $\tau_{AB} = 1.0$, the total pressure at station 7 is $(P_{t7})_{dry} = 76.178 - 1.643(0.444) = 75.448$ psia.

Corrected Engine Station Test Results values for station 7 can now be calculated. Recall that only the mass flow rate, ratio of specific heats, and total temperature are fixed, and that all other values are "bogeys" which must now be re-calculated because of the larger area and slightly greater total pressure of the present design. This is easily done by calculating the mass flow parameter at station 7,

$$MFP \doteq \frac{\dot{m}\sqrt{T_t}}{A\,P_t} = \frac{237.33\sqrt{3600.0}}{5.378\,(144)\,(73.184)} = 0.2512 \ \frac{\text{lbm-}\sqrt{°R}}{\text{s-lbf}},$$

then, using the isentropic flow functions of the AEDsys program GASTAB, enter the values $\gamma = 1.300$, molecular weight ~ 28.8 lbm/lbmol, and the just-calculated value of MFP (watch the units!), select subsonic values, and obtain

$$M = 0.2986, \quad \frac{A}{A^*} = 2.0623, \quad \text{and} \quad \frac{P}{P_t} = 0.9441,$$

from which follows $P = 0.9441\,(73.184) = 69.093$ psia, $A^* = 5.378/2.0623 = 2.608 \text{ ft}^2$,

$$U = \frac{g_c \gamma\,PAM^2}{\dot{m}} = \frac{32.174\,(1.300)\,(69.093)\,(5.378)\,(144)\,(0.2986)^2}{237.33} = 821.13 \text{ ft/s}$$

and

$$I = PA(1 + \gamma M^2) = 69.093(5.378)(144)[1 + 1.300(0.2986)^2] = 59{,}710.0 \text{ lbf.}$$

For designing the thrust nozzle and determining the total thrust of the engine, the data for station 7 recorded in Table 9.E1 must be corrected, as shown by bold text in Table 9.E8.

9.4.2.3 Flameholders.
The next step is to determine how large the vee-gutters must be, and how many rows(rings) of vee-gutters there should be. As recommended in Sec. 9.3.2, the vee-gutters will be designed with included angle

Table 9.E8   Corrections to Table 9.E1 (bold text) for station 7

Station	m dot (lbm/s)	gamma	Pt (psia)	Tt (R)	Press (psia)	Mach	Velocity (ft/s)	Area (ft²)	Area* (ft²)	I (lbf)
6A	228.63	1.3360	76.859	1513.71	68.248	0.4249	779.89	2.338	1.536	28516.0
6.1	228.63	1.3360	76.181	1513.71	74.538	0.1817	268.19	5.378	1.645	60270.7
AB fuel	8.7033	——	——	——	——	——	——	——	——	——
7	237.33	1.3000	**73.193**	3600.00	**69.093**	**0.2986**	**821.29**	**5.378**	**2.608**	**59710.0**

$2\theta = 30$ deg. In the present design, in order to meet the goal value of total pressure loss, a sub-optimal $W/H = 0.4$ and corresponding blockage $B = D/H = 0.314$ will be utilized, where D is the lateral dimension or height of the vee-gutters and H is the channel height or "pitch" between vee-gutters.

Equation (9.134) states that, for $W/H = 0.4$, H must be greater than 1.042 times the product of approach velocity $U_{6.1}$ and t_{BO}, the residence time at blowout in the mixing layer at the edge of the recirculation bubble. Because $U_{6.1}$ has been determined from the design of the afterburner diffuser, the sole task remaining is to use the AEDsys chemical kinetics program KINETX to determine t_{BO}.

Establishing inputs for KINETX requires some rather tedious calculations to determine the composition of the mixture of core gas combustion products with turbine cooling air and fan bypass air. The required steps are:

1) Find the composition of combustion products entering the high pressure turbine at station 4. This can be done from stoichiometric "complete combustion" calculations, because minor or pollutant species have a negligible effect on this calculation, or more easily by using either of the two AEDsys programs EQL or KINETX. Either way, the mass-specific mol numbers of major combustion products at station 4 are found to be

$$n_{O2} = 4.354 \times 10^{-3} \text{ lbmols } O_2/\text{lbm mixture}$$
$$n_{N2} = 2.669 \times 10^{-2} \text{ lbmols } N_2/\text{lbm mixture}$$
$$n_{H2O} = 1.928 \times 10^{-3} \text{ lbmols } H_2O/\text{lbm mixture}$$
$$n_{CO2} = 1.780 \times 10^{-3} \text{ lbmols } CO_2/\text{lbm mixture}$$

The mass-specific mole numbers at station 16 are those for air alone,

$$n_{O2} = 7.098 \times 10^{-3} \text{ lbmols } O_2/\text{lbm air}$$
$$n_{N2} = 2.669 \times 10^{-2} \text{ lbmols } N_2/\text{lbm air}$$

2) From Table 9.E1, the mass flow of main burner combustion products at station 4 is 106.94 lbm/s, and the sum of the air mass flow rates for both turbine cooling and fan bypass is 121.69 lbm/s. The mole numbers in the combined streams at stations 6A and 6.1 are therefore calculated to be

$$n_{O2} = 5.815 \times 10^{-3} \text{ mols } O_2/\text{lbm mixture}$$
$$n_{N2} = 2.669 \times 10^{-2} \text{ mols } N_2/\text{lbm mixture}$$
$$n_{H2O} = 9.018 \times 10^{-4} \text{ mols } H_2O/\text{lbm mixture}$$
$$n_{CO2} = 8.326 \times 10^{-4} \text{ mols } CO_2/\text{lbm mixture}$$

This is the composition of the gas approaching the flameholders and being entrained into the mixing layer at the edge of the recirculation bubble.

3) Equations (9.59) and (9.60) show that the mixing layer entrains essentially equal amounts of cold gas and hot recirculation products, which corresponds to a recirculation ratio $RR = 0.5$ for input to KINETX.

4) With the mass flow rate, gas composition, temperature and pressure established at station 6.1, with recirculation ratio $RR = 0.5$, and the afterburner fuel mass flow rate as inputs to KINETX, there results $t_{BO} \sim 8.5 \times 10^{-5}$ s.

It is now possible to determine the minimum channel height H from Eq. (9.134):
$$H_{min} = 1.042 \, (U_{6.1} \, t_{BO}) = 1.042 \, (268.19) \, (8.5 \times 10^{-5}) = 0.0238 \text{ ft} \times 12 \sim 0.3 \text{ in.}$$

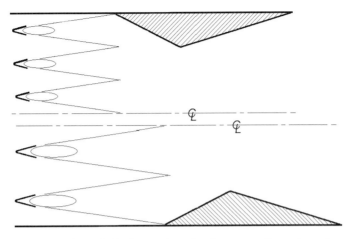

Fig. 9.E10   Comparison of afterburner length using two or three rings of vee-gutters (to scale).

For a design blockage of $B = 0.314$, the corresponding minimum value of vee-gutter height is $D_{min} = BH_{min} = 0.314(0.3) \sim 0.1$ in. In other words, a ~ 0.1 in. vee-gutter would be marginal, operating near extinction or blowout. To ensure stable flameholding, operating far away from blowout, both the vee-gutter size D and spacing H will have to be significantly larger than the minimum values, while maintaining the design ratio $B = D/H = 0.314$. Typically, using a factor of 10 to ensure a "significantly larger" margin, the vee-gutter dimension D should be greater than 1.0 in.

The maximum number of vee-gutter rings is determined by dividing the height of the total afterburner flow area, $H_{6.1} = 15.7$ in., by the minimum vee-gutter channel height H_{min}, and rounding down: $[N_{vee}]_{max} = 15.7/1.0 \sim 15$. As long as there are *fewer* than 15 rings of proportionately sized ($B = 0.314$) vee-gutters, they should perform their flameholding function satisfactorily. The choice of number of rings therefore depends on other design considerations such as afterburner length, stealth shielding, and structural and manufacturing complexity.

Figure 9.E10 shows graphically the effect on afterburner length of two versus three rings of afterburners. Note that, compared to the comparison of one versus two rings shown in Fig. 9.41, the effect of more rings of smaller vee-gutters is diminished as the number of rings increases. This is because the axial length scale reduction goes from 1:2 to 2:3. Bearing in mind the complexity of adding as many spray bars and manifolds as vee-gutter rings, there does not appear to be a compelling reason to increase the number of vee-gutter rings beyond three or four. For the present design, three rings will be satisfactory, for which $H = 15.7/3 = 5.25$ in, and $D = (0.314)(5.25) = 1.65$ in. For this design, the distance from the nose of the vee-gutter to where the flame strikes the wall, still assuming flame spread at 17 deg for lack of better information, is approximately 20 in. This dimension should probably be increased to 24 in or even 30 in, because of our imprecise knowledge of the flame spread angle, and of course while respecting constraints on axial length as a result of the "packaging" of the entire engine within the airframe.

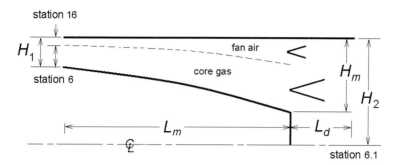

station 16

H_1

fan air

core gas

H_m

H_2

station 6

L_m

L_d

station 6.1

Fig. 9.E11 **"No-mix" diffuser for alternative example afterburner design.**

9.4.2.4 Spray bars. Lacking more information or better guidance, three rings of spray bars will also be chosen, each spray bar to be located directly upstream of each vee-gutter, and tucked back inside the diffuser tailpipe to conserve axial space.

9.4.2.5 Summary. The overall length of the afterburner can now be calculated, as the sum of the calculated or estimated lengths of 1) the ducting between stations 5 and 6 and between stations 13 and 16, [12 in.]; 2) the combined mixer + diffuser + spray bars, [45 in.]; 3) the flameholding and flame spread section, [24 in.]; for a total length $L_{AB} = 12 + 45 + 24 = 83$ in $\sim$7 ft.

9.4.2.6 Alternate "no-mix" afterburner design. The difficulty of mixing the core gas stream with the bypass fan air stream has been emphasized earlier in this section. An alternative approach, mentioned in Sec. 9.3.2, is to not try to mix the two streams at all, but simply allow them to co-flow through the diffuser, as shown in Fig. 9.E11.

In this "no-mix"approach, the vee-gutter flameholders would be located at the entrance to the "dump" portion of the diffuser, the intermediate station m in Fig. 9.E9. If the flameholder were to be located at the end of the tailpipe section, station 6.1, the flow dispersion in the dump section would result in unpredictable, large-scale stirring between the two streams, as described in Sec. 9.1.5, which would defeat the design premise of a two-stage, two-stream "no-mix" afterburner.

It will be assumed that the two streams are separated by a "slip surface" across which no mixing occurs. As can be seen from Fig. 9.35 and related estimates made earlier in this section, this is not a bad assumption. Because both co-flowing streams are subsonic, the static pressure is always matched in both streams, and so Eq. (9.64) can be used to find the areas of the two streams at station m in Fig. 9.E9, as follows:

$$\Delta P = \left\{ \eta_D q_1 \left(1 - \frac{1}{AR^2} \right) \right\}_{core} = \left\{ \eta_D q_1 \left(1 - \frac{1}{AR^2} \right) \right\}_{fan}$$

The area ratios of the two streams are $AR_{core} = \alpha A_m / A_6$ and $AR_{fan} = (1-\alpha) \times A_m / A_{16}$, where α is the area fraction of the core stream at station m, and where $A_m = 4.840$ ft^2 from Table 9.E6. The dynamic pressures in the two streams at entry can be found from the difference between static and total pressures in Table 9.E1, $q_{1\,core} = (P_t - P)_6 = 78.129 - 71.533 = 6.596$ psia, and $q_{1fan} = (P_t - P)_{16} = 83.391 - 71.570 = 11.821$ psia. Assuming the diffusion efficiencies in the two streams to also be equal, Eq. (9.64) can now be solved to find the core stream area fraction $\alpha = 0.7963$, and the corresponding two areas at station m as $A_{m\,core} = 0.7963\,(4.840) = 3.854$ ft^2, and $A_{mfan} = (1 - 0.7963)\,4.840 = 0.9859$ ft^2. From the annular geometry relations Eqs. (9.122), the radius of the slip surface dividing the two streams at station m is found to be $r_{slip} = 14.2$ in., so the radial heights of the two streams are $H_{mcore} = (14.2 - 5.0) = 9.2$ in., and $H_{mfan} = (15.7 - 14.2) = 1.5$ in.

Applying Eq. (9.64) to either stream, and assuming a diffusion efficiency $\eta_D = 0.9$, the station pressure at station m is found to be $P_m = 76.53$ psia.

From mass continuity the corresponding stream velocities at station m are

$$U_{m\,core} = U_6 \frac{A_6}{A_{m\,core}} = (770.87)\frac{1.549}{3.854} = 309.82 \text{ ft/s},$$

and

$$U_{m\,fan} = U_{16} \frac{A_{16}}{A_{m\,fan}} = (677.21)\frac{0.719}{0.9859} = 493.88 \text{ ft/s}$$

and the static temperatures in both streams are essentially equal to their respective total temperatures, listed in Table 9.E1 for stations 6 and 16.

The gas compositions of the two streams have already been determined earlier in this section. With all inputs to the AEDsys software program KINETX now fixed, including the design afterburner exit temperature of $T_t = 3600°$R, the blowout residence times in the two streams are found to be $t_{BO\,core} = 1.49 \times 10^{-4}$ s and $t_{BO\,fan} = 7.07 \times 10^{-5}$ s, and the required fuel mass flow rates in the two streams are $\dot{m}_{f\,core} = 3.331$ lbm/s and $\dot{m}_{f\,fan} = 5.795$ lbm/s.

Assuming the optimal wake width to channel height ratio $W/H = 0.5$, Eq. (9.135) gives the minimum channel widths for flameholding for the two streams, $H_{core} > U_6\,t_{BO\,core} = 309.82\,(12)\,(1.49 \times 10^{-4}) = 0.55$ in., and $H_{fan} > U_{16}\,t_{BOfan} = 493.88(12)(7.07 \times 10^{-5}) = 0.42$ in. The maximum number of vee-gutter rings in each stream is determined as before by dividing the radial passage height by a safety margin of 10 times the minimum height required for flameholding and rounding down, $[N_{vee}]_{core} = 9.2/10(0.55) \sim 1$, and $[N_{vee}]_{fan} = 1.5/10(0.42) \sim 0$.

For the core stream with a single vee-gutter ring, and with the optimal blockage $B = 0.417$ for a 30 deg included angle vee-gutter, as given by Eq. (9.137), the corresponding vee-gutter lateral dimensions are $D_{core} = 0.417(9.2) = 3.84$ in. This corresponds to a shear layer residence time $t_s = H_{core}/U_{m\,core} = 9.2/(12)\ 309.82 = 2.48 \times 10^{-3}$ s, which is a comfortable ~16 times the minimum residence time for flameholding, $t_{BOcore} = 1.49 \times 10^{-4}$ s. In the fan stream, a single vee-gutter with the same blockage would required a vee-gutter of dimension $D_{fan} = 0.417\,(1.5) = 0.62$ in. This gives a shear layer residence time $t_s = H_{fan}/U_{m\,fan} = 1.5/(12)\ 493.88 = 2.53 \times 10^{-4}$ s, which is less than ~3.6 times the minimum residence time for flameholding, $t_{BO\,fan} = 7.07 \times 10^{-5}$ s.

There are some problems with this alternative flame stabilization design: 1) The required fuel mass flows to achieve the design exit temperature of $T_t = 3600°$R

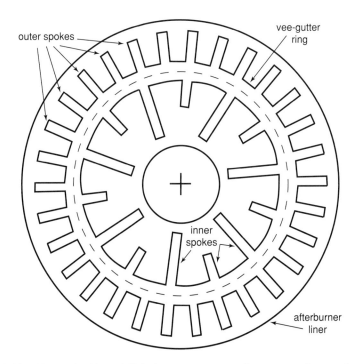

Fig. 9.E12   Alternative "no-mix" design arrangement of vee-gutter rings and spokes.

in both streams add up to $\dot{m}_f = 3.331 + 5.795 = 9.126$ lbm/s, nearly 5% greater than the fuel flow required for the mixed-stream design, and 2) The 9.2-in. height of the core stream is not quite large enough to accommodate two flameholders with good stability, so a single, $D = 3.8$ in. vee-gutter is required, whereas the 1.5-in. height of the fan stream can accommodate only a single $D = 0.625$ in. vee-gutter, for which the residence time is only a marginal 3.6 times greater than the minimum required for flameholding.

One workaround to the flameholder size problem, used on at least one currently operational engine and as illustrated in Fig. 9.E12, is to attach radial spokes of vee-gutter shape and lateral dimension great enough to give a residence time 10 times the blowout value, $D_{fan} = 1.76$ in. The spokes can be spaced circumferentially with appropriate solidity to maintain the desired blockage $B = 0.417$ in the fan stream.

However, because the root area of the spokes is in the core stream, the ring vee-gutter must be reduced in lateral dimension D_{core} to, say, 3 in., to offset the core gas blockage of the root area of the spokes. Further complicating this design solution, additional inward-protruding spokes must be provided to add back the needed blockage in the portion of the core gas stream inboard of the vee-gutter ring.

A stealth variation of this design is to locate the single vee-gutter ring in such a way as to hide the moving blades at low-pressure turbine exit, in case the turbine blades are not already hidden by ducting as in the present design.

References

[1]Hawthorne, W. R., "The Early History of the Aircraft Gas Turbine in Britain," Deutsche Gesellschaft für Luft- und Raumfarht Symposium, Munich, 1989.

[2]Lefebvre, A. H., *Gas Turbine Combustion*, 2nd ed., Taylor and Francis, Philadelphia, 1999.

[3]Zukoski, E. E., "Afterburners," *Aerothermodynamics of Aircraft Engine Components*, edited by G. C. Oates, AIAA Education Series, AIAA, Washington, DC, 1985.

[4]Pratt, D. T., "Calculation of Chemically Reacting Flows with Complex Chemistry," *Studies in Convention*, Vol. II, edited by B. E. Launder, Academic Press, 1977.

[5]Kollrack, R., "Model Calculations of the Combustion Product Distributions in the Primary Zone of a Gas Turbine Combustor," American Society of Mechanical Engineers, Paper 76-WA/GT-7, 1976.

[6]Radhakrishnan, K., and Pratt, D. T., "Fast Algorithm for Calculating Chemical Kinetics in Turbulent Reacting Flow," *Calculations of Turbulent Reactive Flows*, AMD-Vol. 81, edited by R. M. C. So, J. H. Whitelaw, and H. C. Mongia, American Society of Mechanical Engineers, New York, 1986.

[7]Spalding, D. B., *Combustion and Mass Transfer*, Pergamon, Oxford, England, U.K., 1979.

[8]Levenspiel, O., *Chemical Reaction Engineering*, Wiley, New York, 1962.

[9]Pratt, D. T., "Gas Phase Chemical Kinetics," *Pulverized-Coal Combustion and Gasification*, edited by L. D. Smoot and D. T. Pratt, Plenum, New York, 1979.

[10]Bragg, S. L., and Holliday, J. B., "The Influence of Altitude Operating Conditions on Combustion Chamber Design," *Selected Combustion Problems*, Vol. II, Butterworths, London, 1956.

[11]Kays, W. M., and Crawford, M. E., *Convective Heat and Mass Transfer*, 2nd ed., McGraw–Hill, New York, 1980.

[12]Dittrich, R. T., and Graves, C. C., "Discharge Coefficients for Combustor-Liner Air-Entry Holes, I-Circular Holes with Parallel Flow," NACA TN 3663, 1956.

[13]Brodkey, R. S. "Mixing in Turbulent Fields," *Turbulence in Mixing Operations*, edited by R. S. Brodkey, Academic Press, New York, 1975.

[14]Simpson, L. L., "Industrial Turbulent Mixing," *Turbulence in Mixing Operations*, edited by R. S. Brodkey, Academic Press, New York, 1975.

[15]Eroglu, A., "An Experimental Investigation of Entrainment and Mixing in Pulsed and Exponential Transverse Jets," Ph.D. Dissertation, Univ. of Washington, Seattle, 1991.

[16]Pratt, D. T., "An Analytical Investigation of the Pressure Loss in a Cylindrical Gas Turbine Combustor," M.S. Thesis, Univ. of California, Berkeley, 1962.

[17]Beer, J. M., and Chigier, N. A., *Combustion Aerodynamics*, Krieger, Malabar, FL, 1983.

[18]Dimotakis, P. E., "Turbulent Free Shear Layer Mixing and Combustion," *High-Speed Flight Propulsion Systems*, edited by S. N. B. Murthy and E. T. Curran, Vol. 137, Progress in Astronautics and Aeronautics Series, AIAA, Washington, DC, 1991.

[19]Schlichting, H., *Boundary Layer Theory*, 6th ed., McGraw–Hill, New York, 1968.

[20]Wilson, D. G., *The Design of High-Efficiency Turbomachinery and Gas Turbines*, MIT Press, Cambridge, MA, 1984.

[21]White, F. M., *Fluid Mechanics*, 2nd ed., McGraw–Hill, New York, 1986.

[22]Dixon, S. L., *Fluid Mechanics, Thermodynamics of Turbomachinery*, 3rd ed., Pergamon, Oxford, England, 1978.

[23]Evangelista, J. J., Shinnar, R., and Katz, S., "The Effect of Imperfect Mixing on Stirred Combustion Reactors," *Twelfth Symposium (International) on Combustion*, Combustion Inst., Pittsburgh, PA, 1969.

[24]Swithenbank, J., "Flame Stabilization in High Velocity Flow," *Combustion Technology: Some Modern Developments*, edited by H. B. Palmer and J. M. Beer, Academic Press, New York, 1974.

[25]Cornell, W. G., "The Flow in a Vee-Gutter Cascade," *Transactions of the ASME*, Vol. 78, Pt. 1, 1956, pp. 573–580.

[26]Mattingly, J. D., *Elements of Gas Turbine Propulsion*, McGraw–Hill, New York, 1996.

[27]Bahr, D. W., "Technology for the Design of High Temperature Rise Combustors," AIAA Paper 85-1292, 1985.

[28]Aronstein, D., and Picirillo, A., *Have Blue and the F-117A: Evolution of the Stealth Fighter*, AIAA, Reston, VA, 1997.

[29]"Stealth Engine Advances Revealed in JSF Designs," *Aviation Week and Space Technology*, 19 March 2001.

[30]Chigier, N. A., *Energy, Combustion, and Environment*, McGraw–Hill, New York, 1981.

Engine Component Design: Inlets and Exhaust Nozzles

10.1 Concept

The inlet and exhaust nozzles are the two engine components that directly interface both with the internal airflow and the flow about the aircraft. In fact, the integration of the engine and the airframe is one of the most complex and has a major impact on the performance of the aircraft system. Many technical books, reports, articles, etc., are available in open literature that concentrate on only small parts of this major design challenge. This chapter (see also Chapter 6) identifies the major design considerations of inlets and exhaust nozzles and presents basic design tools for their preliminary sizing and design.

The results of the preceding engine performance analysis provide a wealth of information about the required performance of both the inlet and the exhaust nozzle. For example, the inlet area vs both Mach number and altitude can be obtained from the engine performance (off-design) cycle analysis program of AEDsys (see Fig. 6.14). Likewise, the engine airflow at specific partial throttle conditions (corresponding to cruise, loiter, etc.) and the assumed inlet total pressure ratio vs Mach number can be obtained. This design information defines the requirements of the inlet in terms of total pressure ratio and mass flow rate and its preliminary design starts with this information.

The simplest and most powerful design tool available for preliminary design of these components is one-dimensional compressible flow. Both the inlet and the exhaust nozzle can be modeled as simple one-dimensional adiabatic flows or a series of these flows. The following sections of this chapter present the basic principles of operation for each component, the major design considerations, and the basic design tools. Starting at the front of the engine, the inlet is considered first.

10.2 Inlets

10.2.1 Introduction

The inlet interchanges the organized kinetic and random thermal energies of the gas in an essentially adiabatic process. The perfect (no loss) inlet would thus correspond to an isentropic process. The inlet works in concert with the compressor to give the overall pressure ratio of the engine cycle

$$\frac{P_{t3}}{P_0} = \frac{P_{t0}}{P_0} \frac{P_{t2}}{P_{t0}} \frac{P_{t3}}{P_{t2}} = \pi_r \pi_d \pi_c$$

where $\pi_r \pi_d$ represents the pressure ratio of the inlet ($\pi_i = \pi_r \pi_d$) and π_c is the pressure ratio of the compressor. The inlet may be thought of as a compressor with no moving parts. Thus, by analogy with Eq. (4.9a) or (4.9b), the adiabatic efficiency of the inlet (η_i) can be written as

$$\eta_i = \frac{\pi_i^{(\gamma-1)/\gamma} - 1}{\tau_i - 1} = \frac{\tau_i \pi_d^{(\gamma-1)/\gamma} - 1}{\tau_i - 1} \tag{10.1}$$

where $\tau_r = \tau_i$. This expression can be recast in terms of an inlet polytropic efficiency (e_i) by using $\tau_i = \pi_i^{(\gamma-1)/(\gamma e_i)}$. Thus

$$e_i = \frac{\ln\{1 + (\tau_i - 1)\eta_i\}}{\ln(\tau_i)} = \frac{\ln\{\tau_i \pi_d^{(\gamma-1)/\gamma}\}}{\ln(\tau_i)} = 1 + \frac{\gamma-1}{\gamma}\frac{\ln(\pi_d)}{\ln(\tau_r)} \tag{10.2}$$

where

$$\pi_d = \pi_{d\,max}\eta_{R\,spec} \tag{4.12a}$$

For supersonic flow below Mach five, military specification MIL-E-5008B gives

$$\eta_{R\,spec} = 1.0 - 0.075(M_0 - 1)^{1.35} \tag{4.12c}$$

Using the above equations, the variation of inlet adiabatic efficiency and equivalent polytropic efficiency versus flight Mach number are given in Fig. 10.1. The high inlet efficiencies show that the inlet is superior to the mechanical compressor in

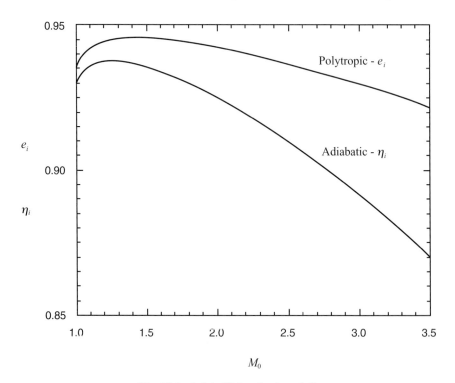

Fig. 10.1   Inlet efficiencies ($\gamma = 1.4$).

increasing pressure up to Mach 3.5 (see Table 4.4)—a surprising result, and an extremely useful one for supersonic applications.

The primary purpose of the inlet is to bring the air required by the engine from freestream conditions to the conditions required at the entrance of the fan or compressor with minimum total pressure loss and flow distortion. The fan or compressor work best with a uniform flow of air at a Mach number of about 0.5. Also, since the installed engine performance depends on the inlet's installation losses (additive drag, external forebody or cowl drag, bypass air, boundary layer bleed air, etc.), the design of the inlet should minimize these losses. The performance of an inlet is related to the following characteristics: high total pressure ratio (π_d), controllable flow matching, good uniformity of flow, low installation drag, good starting and stability, low signatures (acoustic, radar, and infrared), and minimum weight and cost while meeting life and reliability goals. An inlet's overall performance must be determined by simultaneously evaluating all of these characteristics since an improvement in one is often achieved at the expense of another.

The design and operation of subsonic and supersonic inlets differ considerably due to the characteristics of the flow. For the subsonic inlets, near-isentropic internal diffusion can easily be achieved and the inlet flow rate adjusts to the demand. The internal aerodynamic performance of a supersonic inlet is a major design challenge since efficient and stable supersonic diffusion over a wide range of Mach numbers is very difficult to achieve. In addition, the supersonic inlet must be able to capture its required mass flow rate, which may require variable geometry to minimize inlet loss and drag and provide stable operation. Because of these differences, the following sections will consider the subsonic and supersonic inlets separately, beginning with the subsonic inlet.

10.2.2 Design Tools—Subsonic Inlets

Most subsonic aircraft have their engines placed in nacelles and thus this section will not deal with the inlet alone, but will include the nacelle. The cross section of a typical subsonic inlet and its geometric parameters are shown in Fig. 10.2. The

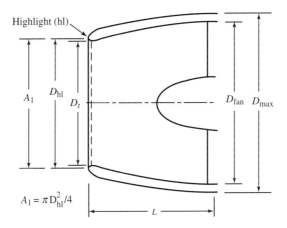

Fig. 10.2   Subsonic inlet nomenclature.

inlet area, A_1, is based on the flow cross section at the most upstream opening of the inlet, known as the inlet highlight. Because the subsonic inlet can draw in airflow whose freestream area (A_0) is larger than the inlet area (A_1), variable inlet geometry is not required (except that blow-in doors are often used to reduce installation drag during takeoff). The material in this section on subsonic inlets is based on a fixed geometry inlet.

A list of the major design variables for the inlet/nacelle would include the following:

1) Inlet total pressure ratio and drag at cruise.

2) Engine location on wing or fuselage (avoidance of foreign object damage, inlet flow upwash and downwash, exhaust gas reingestion, ground clearance).

3) Aircraft attitude envelope (angle of attack, yaw angle, crosswind takeoff).

4) Inlet total pressure ratio and distortion levels required for engine operation.

5) Engine-out windmilling airflow and drag (nacelle and engine).

6) Integration of diffuser and fan flow path contour.

7) Integration of external nacelle contour with thrust reverser and accessories.

8) Flowfield interaction between nacelle, pylon, and wing.

9) Community and/or stealth noise suppression requirements.

10) Stealth electromagnetic signal suppression requirements {low Radar Cross-Section (RCS)}.

Basic design tools for many of these items will be identified in this section. The reader is encouraged to research open literature for a more in-depth analysis of any single item. Special attention is drawn to Ref. 1, which is a recently updated textbook on the aerodynamics of inlets. The recent developments in stealth have impacted inlet design as seen in the application of this technology to new subsonic military aircraft (e.g., F-117A Nighthawk stealth fighter and B-2 Spirit stealth bomber).

10.2.2.1 Inlet total pressure ratio (π_d).

In the cycle analysis used in the preceding chapters, the inlet total pressure ratio (π_d) was assumed to be constant for subsonic inlets and equal to $\pi_{d\,\mathrm{max}}$ (the total pressure ratio due to friction). Due to the complexity of the flow, a method will not be presented for calculating the inlet total pressure ratio. However, Fig. 10.3 presents attainable π_d and its variation with flight Mach number and corrected engine mass flow. If desired, the impact of the varying π_d on engine performance can be estimated using this figure in concert with the off-design cycle deck and mission profile.

10.2.2.2 Inlet sizing—throat diameter (D_{th}).

The diameter at the throat of the subsonic inlet is sized such that the Mach number at this location (based on one-dimensional flow) does not exceed 0.8. This will provide some margin for growth or error since the one-dimensional Mach number at the throat corresponding to actual inlet choke is about 0.9. The maximum corrected engine mass flow that the throat must pass will then correspond to this limiting Mach number and the diameter is easily calculated using

$$D_{th} = \sqrt{\frac{4}{\pi} A_{th\,\mathrm{max}}} = \sqrt{\frac{4}{\pi} \left(\frac{\dot{m}_0 \sqrt{T_{t0}}}{P_{t0}} \right)_{\mathrm{max}} \frac{1}{MFP@M = 0.8}}$$

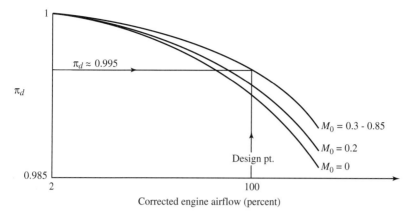

Fig. 10.3   Typical subsonic inlet total pressure ratio.[2]

which can be expressed in terms of the corrected mass flow as

$$D_{th} = \sqrt{\frac{4}{\pi} \frac{\sqrt{518.7}}{2116} \frac{\dot{m}_{c0\,max}}{MFP@M = 0.8}}$$

and reduces to

$$D_{th} = 0.1636\sqrt{\dot{m}_{c0\,max}} \quad \text{or} \quad D_{th} = 1.150\sqrt{A^*_{0\,max}} \qquad (10.3)$$

where $\dot{m}_{c0\,max}$ has units of lbm/s, D_{th} has units of ft, and $A^*_{0\,max}$ has units of ft^2.
Figure 10.4 is a representative output from the engine performance (off-design)
portion of the AEDsys computer program showing the corrected mass flow for a
high-bypass ratio turbofan engine with the engine's cruise envelope superimposed.
A figure like this can be used for selecting the point of maximum corrected mass
flow that determines the throat diameter (D_{th}).

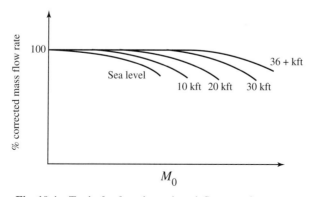

Fig. 10.4   Typical subsonic engine airflow requirements.

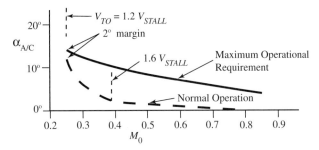

Fig. 10.5   Variation in angle of attack.[2]

10.2.2.3   Effect of aircraft attitude and crosswind.   During an aircraft's flight, the angle of attack of the aircraft can vary substantially, which will change the angle of the airflow with respect to the centerline of the engine. The largest variations normally occur during the takeoff rotation and landing phases of flight. Figure 10.5 shows the variation in angle of attack for a typical subsonic passenger aircraft. Note that, during normal operation, the major changes in angle of attack occur between 1.2 V_{STALL} and 1.6 V_{STALL}. The design of the inlet can compensate for this variation in aircraft angle of attack by inclining the face of the nacelle and changing the shape of the inlet as shown in Fig. 10.6. Note the difference in shape of the inside inlet contour of top and bottom that is required for high angle of attack and cruise operation. The incidence of the nacelle face can be estimated[2] using

$$\alpha_{nac} = 0.5 \deg + 1.4 \deg \, \alpha_{A/C} \text{(low speed aircraft)} \qquad (10.4a)$$

$$\alpha_{nac} = 0.5 \deg + 1.1 \deg \, \alpha_{A/C} \quad \text{(high subsonic speed aircraft)} \quad (10.4b)$$

where $\alpha_{A/C}$ is the cruise angle of attack for the aircraft.

The major effect of crosswind is flow separation inside the inlet with the resulting flow distortion and possible fan stall. This effect can be reduced by making the leading edges on the side of the inlet thicker to minimize flow separation with crosswinds.

The ratio of D_{hl}/D_{th} for the top, sides, and bottom of the inlet are influenced by takeoff performance, angle of attack capability, and crosswind capability. Design values for D_{hl}/D_{th} range between 1.10 and 1.16 for conventional takeoff and landing subsonic aircraft.[2]

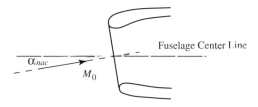

Fig. 10.6   Inclined nacelle face.

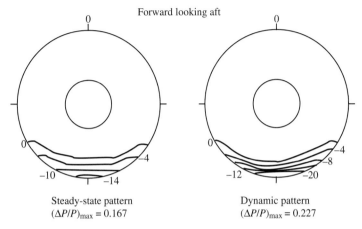

Run -470
Mach No. = 0.30
α nacelle = 28.0
Corrected engine flow = 1627 lbm/sec

Forward looking aft

Steady-state pattern
$(\Delta P/P)_{max} = 0.167$

Dynamic pattern
$(\Delta P/P)_{max} = 0.227$

Fig. 10.7   Typical steady-state and dynamic total pressure distortion patterns.[2]

10.2.2.4   Inlet flow distortion.   Inlets operated at high angles of flow incidence are susceptible to flow separation from the inside contour of the inlet. This flow separation causes large regions of low total pressure as shown in Fig.10.7. The magnitude of this distortion from the desired uniform flow is measured by the term called "inlet distortion" and calculated by

$$\text{Inlet Distortion} = (P_{t\,max} - P_{t\,min})/P_{t\,avg} \qquad (10.5)$$

Both the instantaneous (dynamic) and time-averaged (steady-state) distortion levels are used to measure the quality of an inlet's flow. When using Eq. (10.5) for calculation of dynamic inlet distortion, the average total pressure in the denominator is the spatial average at an instant in time and the maximum and minimum total pressures are for that same instant in time. Determination of the steady-state inlet distortion requires time averaging of the total pressures in the inlet. The average total pressure $(P_{t\,avg})$ of Eq. (10.5) is the spatial average of the time averaged total pressures.

The magnitude of the inlet distortion is a function of the inlet's geometry, mass flow rate, flight Mach number, and flow incidence angle. The importance of each of these variables on inlet distortion is shown in Figs. 10.8 and 10.9. The effect of high distortion is to shift the fan or compressor surge line to values of lower pressure ratio and/or higher mass flow rate as shown in Fig. 10.10 (see Sec. 5.3.2).

10.2.2.5   Inlet drag and engine-out drag.   Detailed design of the nacelle geometry is beyond the scope of this textbook and this material is included only to give a qualitative understanding of several nacelle design issues. The size of the nacelle forebody (D_{hl}/D_{max} and L/D_{max}) is a design compromise between the requirement of low cruise drag and avoiding catastrophes when one or more

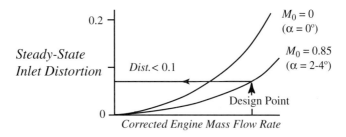

Fig. 10.8   Typical variation in inlet distortion with Mach number.[2]

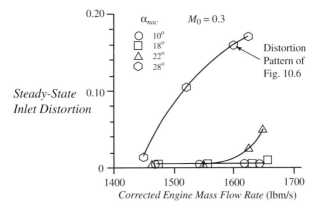

Fig. 10.9   Typical variation in inlet distortion with angle of attack.[2]

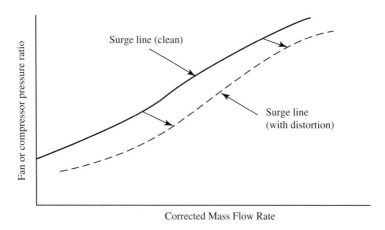

Fig. 10.10   Effect of inlet distortion on the fan or compressor surge line.

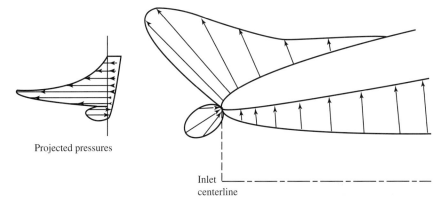

Projected pressures

Inlet
centerline

Fig. 10.11   Pressure distribution around a subsonic inlet lip.

engines are out. The nacelle forebody size that gives minimum drag at cruise may
not give satisfactory engine-out drag. In Chapter 6, the additive drag given by
Eq. (6.6) was used as a conservative estimate of the inlet drag for engine sizing.
A portion of the additive drag can be recovered along the forebody portion of the engine nacelle if the flow does not separate. This is indicated by the suction pressures
near the lip of the nacelle in Fig. 10.11. The resulting pressure force on the outside of
the nacelle forebody is called the forebody drag. The sum of the additive drag and
the forebody drag is called the inlet drag.

The length ratio of the nacelle forebody $(L/D_{\max})$, diameter ratio $(D_{hl}/D_{\max})$,
and contour influence the freestream Mach number at which the nacelle drag
increases dramatically due to local areas of supersonic flow (normally called the
"drag divergence" Mach number, M_{dd}). These effects are shown by the curves in
Fig. 10.12. For a fixed ratio of engine mass flow freestream area (A_0) to nacelle
maximum area $(A_{\max})$, an increase in nacelle forebody length $(L/D_{\max})$ will increase the drag divergence Mach number and decrease the required highlight
diameter of the nacelle (D_{hl}). Typically, the ratio of $D_{hl}/D_{\max}$ is selected to obtain
a specific drag divergence Mach number for the nacelle forebody while maintaining a reasonable engine-out (windmilling) drag (this is crucial for twin-engine
aircraft).

The inlet spillage drag versus inlet mass flow ratio is shown in Fig. 10.13 for a
flight Mach number of 0.4. This figure shows the effect of $D_{hl}/D_{\max}$ on the coefficient of spillage drag, $C_{D\,sp} = Drag_{sp}/q_0 A_1$, for typical engine-out operation.[2]
A good estimate of the inlet mass flow ratio (A_0/A_1) for engine-out operation
(windmilling) is 0.3.

As an example, consider an engine whose cruise Mach number is desired to be
0.85 using a NACA 1-series contour nacelle with $L/D_{\max} = 1.0$. If the designer
selects $D_{hl}/D_{\max} = 0.80$, then the inlet will have $M_{dd} > 0.94$ and $A_0/A_{\max} = 0.4$
at cruise (see Fig. 10.12) and $C_{D\,sp} < 0.08$ at $M_0 = 0.4$ (see Fig. 10.13).

The influence of engine mass flow, flight Mach number, and nacelle size
$(D_{hl}/D_{\max})$ on inlet drag at cruise is shown in Fig. 10.14. These curves are typical of high bypass turbofan engines and based on the correlation of analytical and
experimental results.

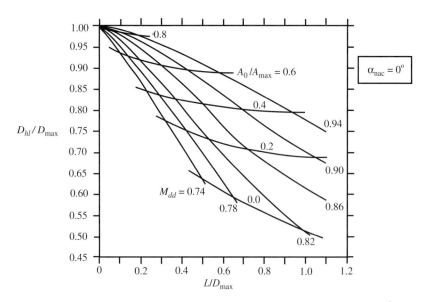

Fig. 10.12   Drag divergence Mach number for NACA 1-series contour.[2]

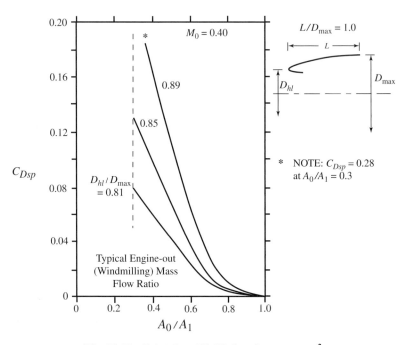

Fig. 10.13   Inlet drag NACA 1-series contours.[2]

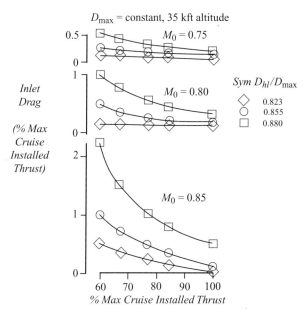

Fig. 10.14   Variation of inlet drag.[2]

10.2.2.6   Nacelle and interference drag.   The minimum drag for a nacelle does not necessarily occur when the inlet is designed for minimum inlet drag at cruise. The influence of the afterbody drag, interference drag, and aircraft trim drag need to be included in the integration and design of an engine nacelle. The inlet and afterbody drag of a typical nacelle is shown in Fig. 10.15 as a function of forebody diameter (D_{hl}/D_{max}) and flight Mach number. Note that the design value of D_{hl}/D_{max} corresponding to minimum inlet drag does not correspond to minimum inlet plus afterbody drag. Also note that the design value of D_{hl}/D_{max} corresponding to minimum inlet plus afterbody drag changes with flight Mach number. Thus, the selection of D_{hl}/D_{max} for an inlet will depend on the design flight Mach Number and may require the compromise of an individual component design goal to achieve the best overall system performance.

The engine location on the wing that provides the best integration of engine and airframe depends on the nacelle design, wing design, and resulting interference drag. Considerable analytical and experimental work is needed in the design of each installation. The resulting difference in best engine location on three aircraft is shown in Fig. 10.16.

10.2.2.7   Diffuser.   Before increased stealth requirements became important, the diffuser curvature and length were based mainly on maintaining the flow attached to the inside walls of the inlet and matching the inlet diameter of the engine while making allowance for the engine spinner. Figure 9.9 shows the performance of typical two-dimensional diffusers. The flow in the three-dimensional diffuser of the engine inlet is more complex than that in a two-dimensional diffuser, however,

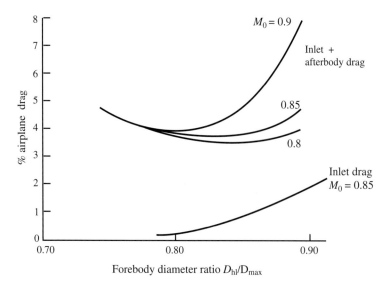

Fig. 10.15   Typical inlet and inlet plus afterbody drag.[2]

this figure can be used for preliminary conceptual design similar to that of the example problem of this textbook.

In the presence of the adverse pressure gradient existing in diffusers, boundary layers tend to separate when they are not re-energized rapidly enough by turbulent mixing. Vortex generators can be and are used as mechanical mixing devices to supplement the turbulent mixing as shown in Fig. 10.17. By using vortex generators together with a short, wide-angle diffuser, it may be possible to have a lower total pressure loss than with a long diffuser without vortex generators. Here the reduced skin friction losses associated with flow separation are traded against vortex generator drag losses. The use of shorter diffusers may also reduce aircraft system weight and facilitate engine installation.

The rotating blades of an engine are a large source of an easily detected reflected radar signature. In order to reduce this signature, every effort is used to hide the

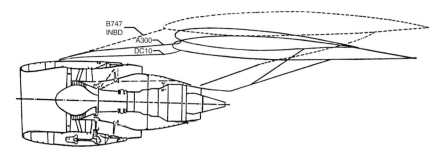

Fig. 10.16   CF6-50 installation on three aircraft (reproduced with permission of the General Electric Co.).

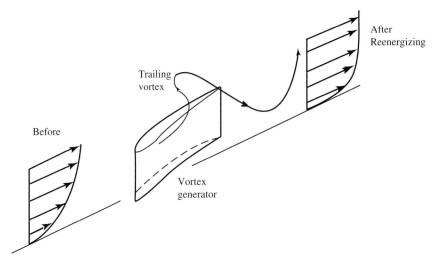

Fig. 10.17 Vortex generators reenergize a boundary layer.

engine face from direct (line-of-sight) view and thus reduce reflected radar. A serpentine shaped diffuser with radar-absorbing material (RAM) can reduce the inlet's signature. Figure 10.18 shows some of the challenges facing designers—the energy transmission is at least a function of the shape of the duct (e.g., the number of reflections) and the wavelength to duct width ratio. The F-117A stealth fighter also uses a gridded inlet with 1.5 cm pitch between elements to keep out X-band and below radiation (Ref. 3).

10.2.2.8 Zero flight speed.   For an inlet at zero flight speed (see Fig. 10.19 and Sec. 6.2.1), the very sharp curvature of the streamlines around the lip leads to flow separation and high internal inlet total pressure losses. The magnitude of the total pressure ratio (π_d) is directly related to the Mach number in the throat (M_{th}) and the ratio of the area of the throat (A_{th}) to the area of the lip bellmouth (A_b). This ratio is plotted in Fig. 10.20 and expressed as[4]

$$\pi_d = \left(1 + \frac{\gamma - 1}{2} M_{th}^2\right)^{\gamma/(\gamma-1)} \Big/ \left(1 + \gamma M_{th}^2\right)$$

$$+ \left\{1 - \left(1 + \frac{\gamma - 1}{2} M_{th}^2\right)^{\gamma/(\gamma-1)} \Big/ \left(1 + \gamma M_{th}^2\right)\right\} \exp\left(\frac{-A_{th}}{7 A_b}\right) \quad (10.6)$$

Auxiliary air inlets are used to keep $\pi_d \geq 0.95$. Thus a sharp lip inlet will require that $M_{th} = 0.285$ for $\pi_d = 0.95$.

10.2.3 Design Tools—Supersonic Inlets

The supersonic inlet is required to provide the proper quantity and uniformity of air to the engine over a wider range of flight conditions than does the subsonic inlet. In addition, the nature of supersonic flow makes this inlet more difficult to

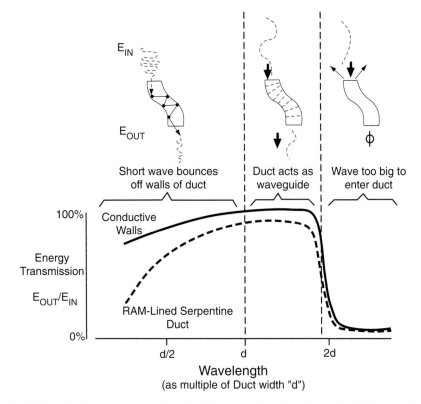

Fig. 10.18   Radar attenuation of engine inlet duct (Reprinted from Ref. 3. Copyright © 2001 McGraw–Hill Companies, Inc. Reproduced with permission).

design and integrate into the airframe. In the material that follows, the major design variables of the supersonic inlet are described and preliminary design information is provided. A list of the design variables for this inlet would include the following:

1) Inlet total pressure ratio and installed drag at cruise.

2) Engine inlet location on wing or fuselage (avoidance of foreign object damage, inlet flow upwash and downwash, exhaust gas re-ingestion, ground clearance).

3) Aircraft attitude envelope (angle of attack, yaw angle, crosswind takeoff).

4) Inlet total pressure ratio and distortion levels required for engine operation.

5) Integration of inlet exterior contour to that of the adjacent aircraft surface.

6) Integration of inlet interior contour with that of the fan or compressor.

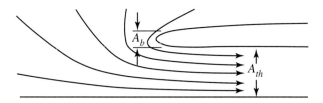

Fig. 10.19   Rounded lip inlet at zero flight speed.

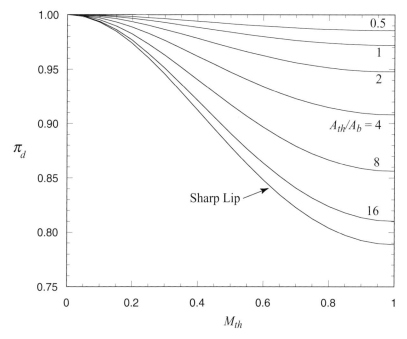

Fig. 10.20   Inlet total pressure ratio at zero flight speed.[4]

7) Boundary layer bleed air.

8) Bypass of excess inlet air.

9) Community and/or stealth noise suppression requirements.

10) Stealth electromagnetic signal suppression requirements {low Radar Cross-Section (RCS)}.

The study of supersonic inlets is not new and many excellent books and reports have been written for the benefit of students and practicing professionals (see Refs. 1–16). Special attention is drawn to Ref. 1, a recently updated textbook that covers the aerodynamics of inlets. The recent developments in stealth have impacted inlet design as seen in the application of this technology to new supersonic military aircraft (e.g., F/A-18E/F Super Hornet, F-22 Raptor, and F-35 Joint Strike Fighter).

The GASTAB program included with this text can calculate the change in properties across the shocks (normal, oblique, and multiple oblique) that may be present in any of these inlets.

10.2.3.1   Inlet types.   As discussed in Sec. 6.2.2, supersonic inlets are classified into three basic types, characterized by the location of the supersonic compression wave system. These three types are internal compression, external compression, and mixed compression.

Internal compression inlet.   The internal compression inlet shown in Fig. 10.21a achieves compression through a series of internal oblique shock waves followed by a terminal normal shock positioned downstream of the throat (its stable location). This type of inlet requires variable throat area to allow the inlet to swallow

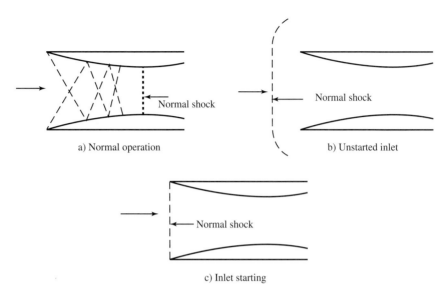

a) Normal operation

b) Unstarted inlet

c) Inlet starting

Fig. 10.21   Internal compression inlet: a) normal operation; b) unstarted inlet; c) inlet starting.

the normal shock (during starting). Fast reaction bypass doors are also required downstream of the throat to permit proper positioning of the normal shock under varying flight and engine conditions.

Figure 10.21a shows an internal compression inlet with an area contraction ratio (A_1/A_{th}) of 2.56 (corresponding to $M_1 = 2.5$ and $M_{th} = 1.2$) operating at design. With the terminal normal shock positioned downstream of the throat for stable operation, where the Mach number is 1.3, this inlet's ideal (ignoring oblique shock wave and friction) total pressure ratio (total pressure recovery, η_R) corresponds to that across a normal shock at a Mach number of 1.3 or $\eta_R = 0.9794$ when $\gamma = 1.4$. Reduction in the flight Mach number to 2.47 or movement of the terminal shock to the throat (which is an unstable location) will cause the total internal flow pattern to be completely disrupted (inlet unstarting), followed by formation of a normal shock ahead of the inlet and its associated low total pressure ratio (about 0.52), reduced mass flow through the inlet, high spillage drag, and possible engine flameout. The unstarted inlet is shown in Fig. 10.21b. This unstarted condition of the inlet can also be achieved by bringing the freestream Mach number from subsonic up to 2.5 without changing the throat area sufficiently to start the inlet (swallow the normal shock).

Starting of the inlet can be achieved when the area of the throat (flow is choked at the throat) is made large enough for the normal shock to move back and touch the inlet lip (critical operation), as shown in Fig. 10.21c. The ratio of the throat area required to start the inlet (A_{ths}) to the throat area required at normal operation $(A_{thr}$, corresponding to $M_{th} = 1.2$) is obtained from basic one-dimensional flow, is plotted in Fig. 10.22, and can be expressed as

$$\frac{A_{ths}}{A_{thr}} = \frac{1}{1.030(P_{ty}/P_{tx})_{M_0}} \qquad (10.7)$$

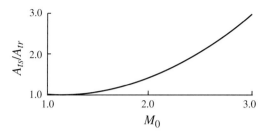

Fig. 10.22   Throat area variation required of an internal compression inlet.

where 1.030 is the value of A/A^* corresponding to $M_{th} = 1.2$ and $(P_{ty}/P_{tx})_{M_0}$ is the total pressure ratio across a normal shock with upstream Mach number of M_0. As can be seen in Fig. 10.22, the internal compression inlet has a large throat area variation required to start the inlet at Mach numbers greater than two. For example, the throat area required to start an inlet at a Mach number of 2.4 is about 1.8 times the throat area required for normal operation. This large area variation, the problem of inlet unstart, the poor performance at angles of attack, and many other issues have led to the demise of the internal compression inlet. Many experts do not include it as a useful type of inlet and leave its analysis to purely academic textbooks. It is included here to help bridge the gap between the practical and academic worlds.

External compression inlet.   The compression of the external compression inlet (Fig. 10.23) is achieved through either one or a series of oblique shocks followed by a normal shock or simply through one normal shock. As shown in Fig. 10.23, A_{0i}, A_0, A_{0bl}, and A_{0bp} are the freestream tube areas containing the inlet, engine, boundary layer bleed, and bypass airflows, respectively.

The external compression inlet that achieves compression through only a single normal shock is called a "pitot inlet" or "normal shock inlet" and is shown in Fig. 10.24. The pitot inlet is simple, short, lightweight, and inexpensive. The total pressure recovery (η_R) of this inlet corresponds to the total pressure ratio across a normal shock shown in Fig. 10.25 by the solid line. When compared with the MIL-E-5008B recovery ($\eta_{R\,spec}$) shown by the dashed line, the total pressure

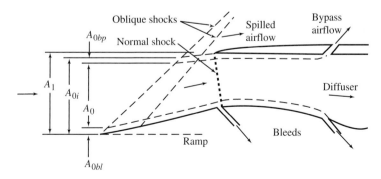

Fig. 10.23   External compression inlet and flow areas.

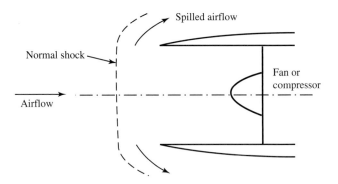

Fig. 10.24   Pitot or normal shock inlet.

recovery of this inlet is acceptable only for flight Mach numbers up to about 1.6. Above this Mach number, the total pressure recovery of the inlet is too low and another, more efficient inlet design must be used.

Ideal operation of the pitot inlet is at the critical state (shock touching lip of inlet). At this operating state, the drag of the inlet is associated mainly with the loss in momentum of the excess air captured by the inlet that must be bypassed as shown in Fig. 10.26. Equating the drag of the bypassed air to its loss in axial momentum as was done in Sec. 6.2.2 but now including the exit flow angularity yields

$$Drag_{bp} = \frac{\dot{m}_{bp}}{g_c}(V_0 - V_e \cos\phi) = \frac{\dot{m}_{bp} V_0}{g_c}\left[1 - \cos\phi \frac{M_e}{M_0}\sqrt{\frac{1 + (\gamma - 1)M_0^2/2}{1 + (\gamma - 1)M_e^2/2}}\right]$$

When this is written in terms of a drag coefficient based on the inlet capture area (A_1), the following expression is obtained:

$$C_{Dbp} = \frac{Drag_{bp}}{q_0 A_1} = 2\frac{A_{0bp}}{A_1}\left[1 - \cos\phi \frac{M_e}{M_0}\sqrt{\frac{1 + (\gamma - 1)M_0^2/2}{1 + (\gamma - 1)M_e^2/2}}\right] \qquad (10.8)$$

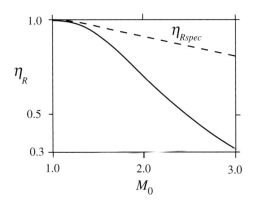

Fig. 10.25   Total pressure ratio of a pitot or normal shock inlet.

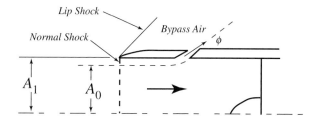

Fig. 10.26   Model pitot inlet.

where A_{0bp}/A_1 is equal to the mass flow ratio of bypassed air to total inlet airflow $(\dot{m}_{bp}/\dot{m}_1)$. Equation (10.8) is plotted in Fig. 10.27 vs M_0 for $M_e = 1$ and $\phi = 0$ deg, the same conditions assumed in the development of Eq. (6.8).

The external compression inlet with one or more oblique shocks (Fig. 10.23) has its inlet throat at or very near the cowl leading edge. Desired operation of this inlet is with the normal shock positioned at or very near the cowl lip (critical operation).

The total pressure recovery (η_R) across n oblique shocks of equal strength (same total pressure ratio) followed by a normal shock is shown by solid lines in Fig. 10.28 ($n = 0$ corresponds to a normal shock wave). The total pressure recovery of MIL-E-5008B is drawn as a dashed line. Increasing the number of oblique shocks increases η_R for any given freestream Mach number. However, the ramp of the external compression inlet turns the flow away from the axial direction and thus the subsonic diffuser duct must turn back the flow to the axial direction, which may add weight, length, and friction loss to the inlet. Figure 10.29 shows the total turning angle of an external compression shock system that attains the total pressure recovery of MIL-E-5008B ($\eta_{R spec}$ in Fig. 10.28) as a function of freestream Mach number. As the freestream Mach number increases, the total shock turning angle of the external ramp increases, resulting in increases in cowl angle and cowl drag (see Sec. 6.2.2). External compression inlets can maintain acceptable total pressure ratio and cowl drag up to a flight Mach number of about 2.5.

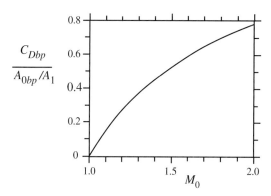

Fig. 10.27   Bypass drag of model pitot inlet (Fig. 10.24) with $M_e = 1$ and $\phi = 0$ deg.

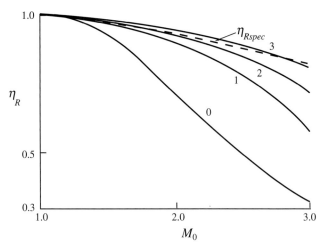

Fig. 10.28   Total pressure recovery of oblique shocks terminated by a normal shock.[5,6]

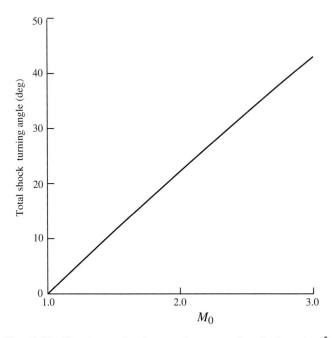

Fig. 10.29   Turning angle of external compression shock system.[5]

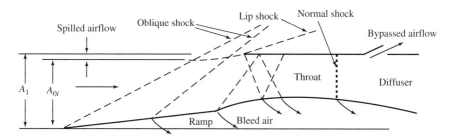

Fig. 10.30   Two-dimensional mixed compression inlet.

Mixed compression inlet.   At flight Mach numbers above 2.5, the mixed compression inlet is used to obtain an acceptable total pressure ratio (utilizing the required number of oblique shocks) while obtaining acceptable cowl drag. The mixed compression inlet is more complex, heavier, and costlier than the external compression inlet. The typical mixed compression inlet (Figs. 10.30 and 10.31) achieves compression through the external oblique shocks, the internal reflected oblique shocks, and the terminal normal shock. The ideal location of the normal shock is just downstream of the inlet throat to minimize total pressure loss while maintaining a stable operating location of this shock. Similar to the internal compression inlet, the mixed compression inlet requires both fast reacting bypass doors (to maintain the normal shock in a stable location) and variable throat area (to allow the inlet to start by swallowing the normal shock). However, the variation in inlet throat area of the mixed compression inlet is considerably less than that of the internal compression inlet because of the mixed compression inlet's external oblique shock system.

Supersonic inlets can also be classified further as two-dimensional (rectangular) and axisymmetric (circular or a portion of a circle). Figure 10.31 shows a typical axisymmetric mixed compression inlet, whereas Fig. 10.30 shows a typical two-dimensional mixed compression inlet. Axisymmetric inlets have a slight advantage over two-dimensional inlets with respect to weight and total pressure ratio. However, the two-dimensional inlets have an advantage in design simplicity and in providing a larger variation in inlet airflow. Furthermore, axisymmetric inlets have the added design problem of getting sufficient boundary layer bleed air out from the centerbody through the support struts.

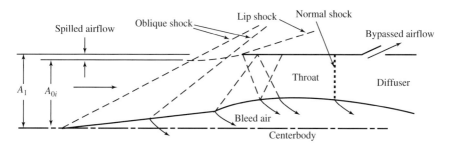

Fig. 10.31   Axisymmetric mixed compression inlet.

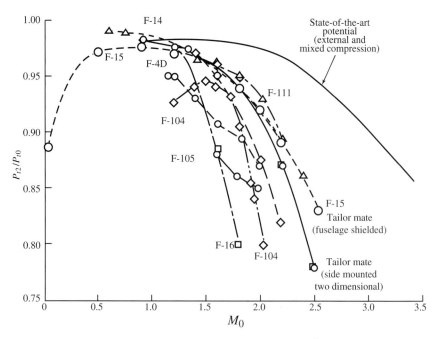

Fig. 10.32   Total pressure ratio survey.[7]

The improved performance of variable geometry mixed compression inlets and external compression inlets at high Mach numbers comes with some reduced performance at low supersonic Mach numbers due to the increased frictional losses. Figures 10.32 and 10.33 show the inlet total pressure ratios of past and current aircraft and the Supersonic Transport (SST) model. Note in Fig. 10.33, the reduced total pressure ratio of the complex SST mixed compression inlet at subsonic and low supersonic Mach numbers when compared to the simple pitot intake. The message of these two figures is that a supersonic inlet can be designed for good performance at supersonic or subsonic flight Mach numbers, but not at both.

10.2.3.2 Total pressure recovery (η_R).   In the engine cycle analysis of this textbook, the total pressure recovery of the shock system for the supersonic inlet was estimated by

$$\eta_{R\,spec} = 1 - 0.075\,(M_0 - 1)^{1.35} \qquad \text{for } 1 < M_0 < 5 \quad (4.12c)$$

$$\eta_{R\,spec} = \frac{800}{M_0^4 + 935} \qquad \text{for } 5 < M_0 \quad (4.12d)$$

the ram recovery of military specification MIL-E-5008B. This design inlet total pressure recovery has been added to Fig. 10.28 to give Fig. 10.34, a very useful design tool for selection of inlet type and preliminary number of oblique shocks required. As an example, consider an inlet for flight at a Mach number of 2.5. Equation (4.12c) or Fig. 10.34 gives an allowable total pressure recovery for the shock system of 0.87. Figure 10.34 shows that more than two oblique shocks of

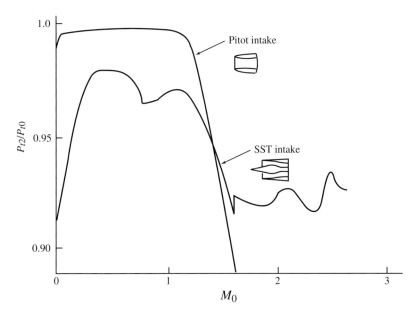

Fig. 10.33 Total pressure ratio—SST model.[7]

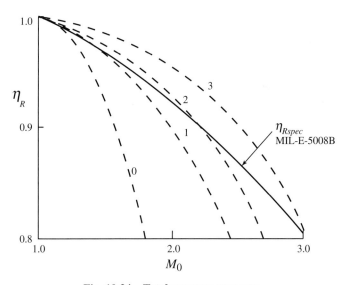

Fig. 10.34 Total pressure recovery.

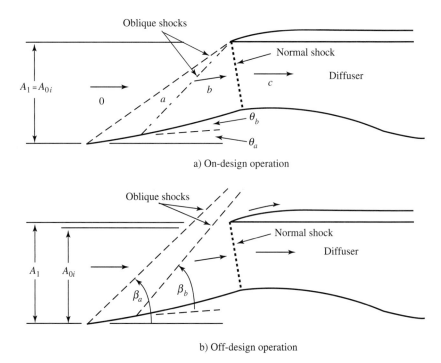

a) On-design operation

b) Off-design operation

Fig. 10.35   Example external compression inlet: a) on-design operation; b) off-design operation.

equal strength followed by a normal shock are required. The required total pressure recovery can be obtained by an external compression inlet with three oblique shocks or a mixed compression inlet.

The total pressure recovery of the general external compression inlet shown in Fig. 10.35 can be determined using the normal and oblique shock equations/tables[9]. The total pressure ratio across a normal shock can be calculated using

$$\frac{P_{ty}}{P_{tx}} = \left\{ \frac{\frac{\gamma+1}{2}M_x^2}{1 + \frac{\gamma-1}{2}M_x^2} \right\}^{\gamma/(\gamma-1)} \left\{ \frac{2\gamma}{\gamma+1}M_x^2 - \frac{\gamma-1}{\gamma+1} \right\}^{-1/(\gamma-1)} \quad (10.9)$$

where M_x is the upstream Mach number and the downstream Mach number (M_y) is calculated using

$$M_y = \sqrt{\frac{M_x^2 + \frac{2}{\gamma-1}}{\frac{2\gamma}{\gamma-1}M_x^2 - 1}} \quad (10.10)$$

For oblique shocks, the total pressure ratio is calculated using Eq. (10.9) with M_x replaced by $M_1 \sin \beta$, where M_1 is the upstream Mach number and β is the angle of the oblique shock with respect to the upstream velocity (see Fig. 10.35). The downstream Mach number (M_2) is calculated using Eq. (10.10) with M_y

replaced by $M_2 \sin(\beta - \theta)$, where θ is the ramp angle. The angles β and θ and upstream Mach number M_1 are related by

$$\tan(\beta - \theta) = \left\{ \frac{2}{\gamma + 1} + \frac{\gamma - 1}{\gamma + 1}(M_1 \sin \beta)^2 \right\} \bigg/ \left(M_1^2 \sin \beta \cos \beta \right)$$

which can be solved for the ramp angle (θ) to give

$$\tan \theta = \frac{2 \operatorname{ctn} \beta \left(M_1^2 \sin^2 \beta - 1 \right)}{2 + M_1^2(\gamma + 1 - 2 \sin^2 \beta)} \qquad (10.11)$$

Two limiting values of ramp angle occur[9]: the ramp angle (θ^*) leading to $M_2 = 1$ and the maximum ramp angle $(\theta_{\max})$ for which an oblique shock solution exists. The corresponding values of oblique shock angle (β) are given by

$$(\sin^2 \beta)_{\theta_{\max}} = \frac{(\gamma + 1)M_1^2 - 4\sqrt{(\gamma + 1)\{(\gamma + 1)M_1^4 + 8(\gamma - 1)M_1^2 + 16\}}}{4\gamma M_1^2}$$

$$(10.12\text{a})$$

$$(\sin^2 \beta)_{\theta^*} = \frac{(\gamma + 1)M_1^2 - (3 - \gamma)\sqrt{(\gamma + 1)\{(\gamma + 1)M_1^4 - 2(3 - \gamma)M_1^2 + \gamma + 9\}}}{4\gamma M_1^2}$$

$$(10.12\text{b})$$

and the ramp angle (θ) calculated using Eq. (10.11).

The GASTAB program included with this textbook as a part of the AEDsys software can perform these calculations for normal and oblique shocks plus many others (e.g., multiple oblique shocks and conical shocks).

Example 10.1   External Compression Inlet (Part I)

Applying the normal and oblique shock equations to the external compression inlet of Fig. 10.35 with $\theta_a = \theta_b = 5$ deg yields the results tabulated in Table 10.1 and plotted in Fig. 10.36. The total pressure recovery (η_R) of the inlet is the product of the total pressure ratio across every shock. This inlet's η_R exceeds the total pressure recovery of MIL-E-5008B $(\eta_{R\,spec})$ at 1.7M (0.9654 vs 0.9537) but not at 1.8M (0.9396 vs 0.9445). These results can also be obtained easily using the INLET computer program included with AEDsys.

Note that for M_0 between 1.26 and 1.42, the second oblique shock becomes the terminal normal shock because its ramp angle (θ_b) is larger than $\theta_{\max}$ for M_a between 1.238 and 1.023. Likewise, the first oblique shock becomes the terminal normal shock for M_0 between 1.23 and 1.0. Also note that the total pressure recovery goes through local maxima and minima as these oblique shocks become normal shocks.

10.2.3.3 Mass flow characteristics.

The inlet mass flow ratio is defined as the ratio of the actual mass flow rate of the inlet $(\dot{m}_i)$ to the mass flow rate that

Table 10.1   Example 10.1: External compression inlet of Fig. 10.35 with
$\theta_a = \theta_b = 5$ deg

M_0	β_a	P_{ta}/P_{t0}	M_a	β_b	P_{tb}/P_{ta}	M_b	P_{tc}/P_{tb}	η_R
2.00	34.30	0.9979	1.821	37.95	0.9982	1.649	0.8765	0.8731
1.95	35.23	0.9980	1.773	39.09	0.9983	1.602	0.8945	0.8912
1.90	36.23	0.9981	1.725	40.34	0.9983	1.554	0.9117	0.9084
1.85	37.30	0.9982	1.677	41.70	0.9984	1.506	0.9278	0.9246
1.80	38.44	0.9982	1.628	43.19	0.9984	1.457	0.9428	0.9396
1.75	39.68	0.9983	1.579	44.84	0.9985	1.407	0.9563	0.9533
1.70	41.03	0.9984	1.529	46.69	0.9985	1.356	0.9684	0.9654
1.65	42.50	0.9984	1.480	48.78	0.9985	1.303	0 9788	0.9758
1.60	44.11	0.9985	1.429	51.21	0.9985	1.248	0.9873	0.9842
1.55	45.89	0.9985	1.378	54.11	0.9984	1.190	0.9937	0.9906
1.50	47.89	0.9985	1.325	57.77	0.9982	1.125	0.9980	0.9947
1.45	50.16	0.9985	1.272	63.05	0 9976	1.045	0.9999	0.9960
1.44	50.65	0.9985	1.261	64.59	0.9973	1.024	1.0000	0.9958
1.43	51.16	0.9985	1.250	66.59	0.9969	0.9974	1.0000	0.9953
1.42	51.68	0.9984	1.238	90	0.9886	0.8223	1.0000	0.9870
1.41	52.22	0.9984	1.227	90	0.9899	0.8289	1.0000	0.9884
1.40	52.78	0.9984	1.216	90	0.9912	0.8357	1.0000	0.9896
1.35	55.93	0.9983	1.156	90	0.9963	0.8739	1.0000	0.9946
1.30	59.96	0.9980	1.090	90	0.9992	0.9230	1.0000	0.9972
1.29	60.95	0.9979	1.075	90	0.9995	0.9352	1.0000	0.9974
1.28	62.04	0.9977	1.059	90	0.9998	0.9486	1.0000	0.9975
1.27	63.26	0.9976	1.042	90	0.9999	0.9639	1.0000	0.9975
1.26	64.69	0.9973	1.023	90	1.0000	0.9819	1.0000	0.9973
1.25	66.50	0.9969	0.9986	0	1.0000	0.9986	1.0000	0.9969
1.24	69.90	0.9957	0.9553	0	1.0000	0.9553	1.0000	0.9957
1.23	90	0.9896	0.8272	0	1.0000	0.8272	1.0000	0.9896
1.22	90	0.9907	0.8332	0	1.0000	0.8332	1.0000	0.9907
1.21	90	0.9918	0.8392	0	1.0000	0.8392	1.0000	0.9918
1.20	90	0.9928	0.8454	0	1.0000	0.8454	1.0000	0.9928
1.15	90	0.9967	0.8784	0	1.0000	0.8784	1.0000	0.9967
1.10	90	0.9989	0.9153	0	1.0000	0.9153	1.0000	0.9989
1.05	90	0.9999	0.9568	0	1.0000	0.9568	1.0000	0.9999
1.00	——	1.0000	1.0000	0	1.0000	1.0000	1.0000	1.0000

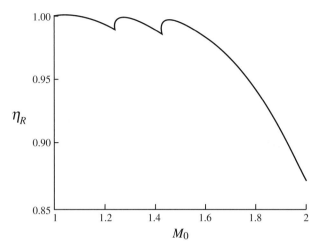

Fig. 10.36   Total pressure recovery of Example 10.1—external compression inlet of Fig. 10.35 with $\theta_a = \theta_b = 5$ deg.

could be captured ($\dot{m}_1$) by the geometrical opening A_1 of the inlet if the freestream flow were undisturbed (see Fig. 10.37). From the conservation of mass equation

$$\frac{\dot{m}_i}{\dot{m}_1} = \frac{\rho_0 V_0 A_{0i}}{\rho_0 V_0 A_1} = \frac{A_{0i}}{A_1} \tag{10.13}$$

which is the inlet area ratio. Thus the inlet mass flow ratio and the inlet area ratio are used interchangeably. The difference between $\dot{m}_1$ and $\dot{m}_i$ is the air that is spilled around the inlet. The engine mass flow ratio is defined, similarly to that of the inlet, as the ratio of the required engine mass flow rate ($\dot{m}_0$) to the mass flow rate that the inlet could capture ($\dot{m}_1$) or

$$\frac{\dot{m}_0}{\dot{m}_1} = \frac{\rho_0 V_0 A_0}{\rho_0 V_0 A_1} = \frac{A_0}{A_1} \tag{10.14}$$

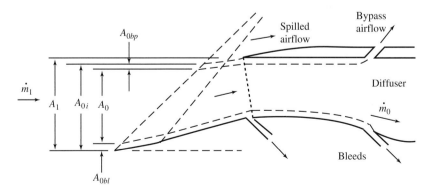

Fig. 10.37   External compression inlet operating at its critical condition.

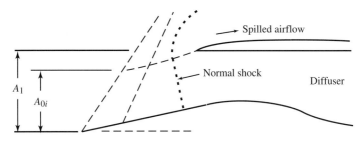

Fig. 10.38   Subcritical inlet operation.

The difference between $\dot{m}_i$ and $\dot{m}_0$ is the air that enters the inlet but is removed through boundary layer bleed, the bypass system, or the secondary air system.

When the inlet can accept the mass flow rate of air required to position the terminal shock just inside the cowl lip, as shown in Fig. 10.37 ("critical" operation), the fraction of air spilled around the inlet is a minimum and the inlet is said to be "matched" to the engine. When the inlet is not matched, as shown in Fig. 10.38, the normal shock moves upstream ("subcritical" operation) and the fraction of air spilled is increased. This increase in air spillage has associated with it an increase in "spillage drag," drag due to the change in momentum of the spilled air and the pressure forces on its streamtube.

When the inlet cannot capture the mass flow rate required by the engine and the other systems, the terminal normal shock is sucked down into the diffuser ("supercritical" operation), as shown in Fig. 10.39, which strengthens the shock and increases the *corrected* mass flow rate to the engine. At a specific operating point on the fan or compressor map, the engine operates as a constant corrected mass flow device. Thus, when the inlet cannot provide the required corrected mass flow rate at "critical" operation, the engine causes "supercritical" operation and attains the required corrected mass flow rate. Note that "supercritical" operation has a lower inlet total pressure recovery associated with it and thus a reduction in engine performance (lower thrust and higher specific fuel consumption). "Supercritical" operation of the inlet is to be avoided when possible because of the poor engine performance.

A common way of presenting the mass flow rate characteristics of an inlet is through a map of the total pressure recovery vs the inlet mass flow ratio as shown in Fig. 10.40. The performance of a typical external compression inlet is presented

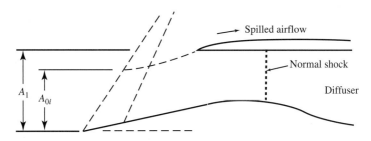

Fig. 10.39   Supercritical inlet operation.

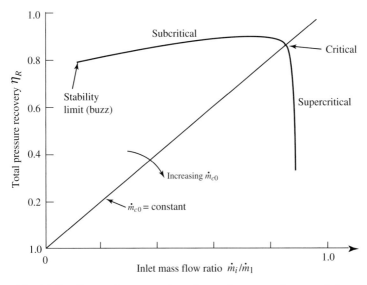

Fig. 10.40   External compression inlet performance characteristics.

in Fig. 10.40 for a specific freestream Mach number. The "critical" operation point and the "subcritical" and "supercritical" operating regimes are also shown on this figure.

The engine mass flow ratio ($\dot{m}_0/\dot{m}_1$) can be expressed in terms of corrected mass flow rates and the inlet recovery as

$$\frac{\dot{m}_0}{\dot{m}_1} = \frac{\dot{m}_{c0}}{\dot{m}_{c1}} \frac{P_{t1}}{P_{t0}} = \frac{\dot{m}_{c0}}{\dot{m}_{c1}} \eta_R \qquad (10.15)$$

where $\dot{m}_{c0}$ is the corrected mass flow rate of the engine and $\dot{m}_{c1}$ is the corrected mass flow rate based on the capture area, a constant for fixed capture area A_1 and flight condition. Variation in the engine corrected mass flow rate ($\dot{m}_{c0}$) due to a change in engine throttle can be presented on the inlet mass flow map of Fig 10.40 for the case where the boundary layer bleed and bypass flows are essentially constant. A line of constant $\dot{m}_{c0}$ is shown on Fig. 10.40 along with the direction of change of slope due to increasing $\dot{m}_{c0}$. When the engine's requirement for air decreases below that required for "critical" inlet operation, the inlet operating point moves into the "subcritical" region as the engine mass flow ratio decreases and the fraction of air spilled increases. When the engine's requirement for air increases above that required for "critical" operation, the inlet operating point moves into the "supercritical" region as the engine mass flow ratio remains constant and the total pressure recovery of the inlet decreases with the strengthening of the terminal normal shock in the diffuser.

Two supersonic flow phenomena associated with the stability of the shock structure in external and mixed compression inlets require consideration at this point. One is called inlet "buzz" and the other is associated with the location of the terminal normal shock.

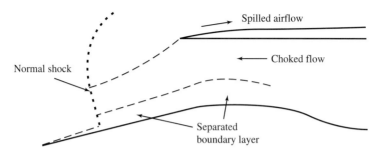

Fig. 10.41   Condition leading to inlet "buzz."

"Buzz" is a low-frequency, high-amplitude pressure oscillation that is linked to shock/boundary layer and/or shock/shock interaction at relatively low inlet mass flow ratio. As an example of a flow condition leading to inlet buzz, consider the external compression inlet of Fig. 10.41. When this inlet is operated in the "subcritical" regime, the terminal normal shock will impinge on the boundary layer formed along the wall of the ramp causing the boundary layer to separate. If the separated boundary layer produces a large enough low-velocity flow region, the inlet will choke, reducing the inlet mass flow rate and moving the normal shock forward along the ramp. The boundary layer at this forward location is thinner, its separated flow region does not choke the inlet, and thus the inlet mass flow increases, moving the normal shock back up the ramp toward its original location, to be repeated again and again—creating buzz. When "buzz" occurs on a mixed compression inlet, the inlet will unstart and engine flameout is possible.

The stability of the terminal normal shock in a mixed compression inlet is important when operating the inlet near its design point. Design for stability of the terminal normal shock requires that the need for higher total pressure recovery be compromised and the design throat Mach number be 1.2 with the normal shock positioned downstream where the Mach number is 1.3. Thus, the mixed compression inlet is designed to operate in the "supercritical" regime. When the engine needs less air than provided by this inlet, the excess air must bypass the engine to maintain the terminal normal shock at its stable location and prevent the inlet from "unstarting" (expelling the normal shock). When the engine wants more air than the inlet can provide, the terminal normal shock is drawn downstream into the diffuser, strengthening the shock and increasing corrected mass flow rate to the engine. When the normal shock is drawn downstream into the diffuser, flow separation and flow distortion become dominant design considerations. To limit this problem, the inlet needs to be designed to provide the required engine mass flow rate with the terminal normal shock positioned where the Mach number in the diffuser is 1.3.

The total pressure recovery vs mass flow ratio of a typical mixed compression inlet is shown in Fig. 10.42. Note that this inlet has a much smaller allowable variation in mass flow ratio before onset of buzz than does the external compression inlet of Fig. 10.40. This reduction in the range for inlet mass flow ratio ($\dot{m}_i/\dot{m}_1$) corresponds to a larger change in the amount of inlet air that is required to be bypassed ($\dot{m}_{bp}$) to prevent buzz (maintain $\dot{m}_i/\dot{m}_1$ above stability limit), with a corresponding smaller variation in the amount of air that is spilled (Ref. 1).

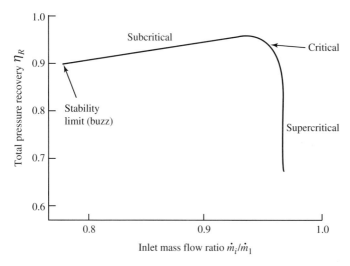

Fig. 10.42   Mixed compression inlet performance characteristics.

10.2.3.4   Boundary layer control.   Boundary layer control is a major design consideration in the design of supersonic inlets. The boundary layer will build up on the external compression surfaces of external and mixed compression inlets as well as on the internal duct surfaces. Since there is an adverse pressure gradient in a supersonic inlet (static pressure rises in the direction of flow), the boundary layer is susceptible to separation when this pressure gradient is too severe, as can be the case when the inlet is made very short or when a shock wave interacts with a boundary layer. Figure 10.43 shows normal shock/boundary layer interaction without and with wall suction. If the boundary layer is thick where the shock interacts, then separation of the boundary layer will occur with a resulting degradation in the uniformity of flow to the engine. For a mixed compression inlet, shock/boundary layer interaction can lead to inlet "unstarting." To prevent these problems, active boundary layer bleed systems are used to remove most of the boundary layer just prior to the region(s) where interaction(s) with shocks will occur. Both slot and porous plate bleed methods are used, as shown in Fig. 10.44. The porous plate method is used for regions where the interaction area can move about, as can be the case for the terminal normal shock for both external and mixed compression inlets and shock wave reflection in mixed compression inlets.

The boundary layer bleed air requirement is mainly a function of the type of inlet and its design Mach number. Figure 10.45 shows the typical bleed mass flow ratio ($\dot{m}_{bl}/\dot{m}_1 = A_{0bl}/A_1$) requirements. This figure is very useful in preliminary design of an inlet. Note that the mixed compression inlet requires about twice the bleed air as that needed for an external compression inlet due mainly to the increased number of bleeds required for the mixed compression inlet.

10.2.3.5   Inlet design and sizing.   The design and sizing of a supersonic inlet is considerably more difficult than that of the subsonic inlet (see Sec. 10.2.2) due mainly to the differences in the nature of supersonic and subsonic flows.

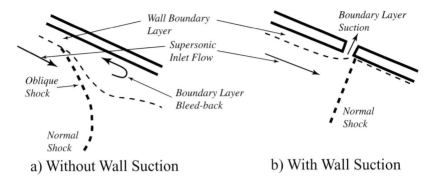

a) Without Wall Suction

b) With Wall Suction

Fig. 10.43 Shock/boundary layer interaction: a) without wall suction; b) with wall suction.

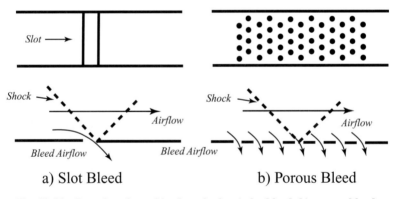

a) Slot Bleed

b) Porous Bleed

Fig. 10.44 Boundary layer bleed methods: a) slot bleed; b) porous bleed.

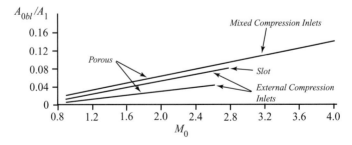

Fig. 10.45 Typical boundary layer bleed mass flow ratio.[6]

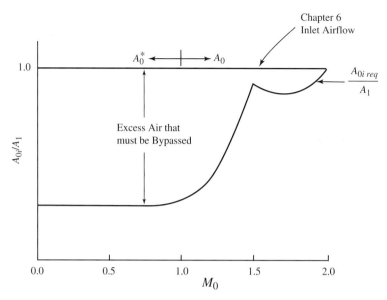

Fig. 10.46   Chapter 6 inlet airflow performance.

The supersonic inlet is designed to operate at both subsonic and supersonic flight Mach numbers. The capture and throat areas of the inlet must be large enough not to choke the airflow required by the engine, while providing for the bypass, boundary layer bleed, and auxiliary air systems. For supersonic flight conditions, the inlet's capture area (A_1) is sized to capture the required airflow. Since this airflow varies with both flight Mach number and engine throttle setting, variable geometry inlet design is sometimes needed to meet the total pressure recovery goal of military specification MIL-E-5008B and/or keep the installation losses low (spillage drag and/or bypass air drag).

10.2.3.6   Inlet performance model.   The model supersonic inlet of Fig. 6.4 consists of an external compression inlet with fixed capture area and variable geometry such that the inlet's shocks converge at the outer lip (see Fig. 10.35a). As a result the inlet mass flow ratio (A_{0i}/A_1) has a constant value of unity. The airflow performance of this variable inlet is shown in Fig. 10.46 along with the required inlet airflow. The difference between the inlet mass flow ratio and the inlet's required mass flow ratio is the "excess air" that enters the inlet and *must* bypass the engine. The drag associated with the change in momentum of this excess air was used in Chapter 6 to estimate the inlet installation loss (ϕ_{inlet}). This was a conservative estimate since the installation loss can be reduced by changing the inlet capture area and by operating with some spillage and its associated drag as shown in Fig. 10.47.

10.2.3.7   Required inlet airflow.   The required values of engine airflow ($\dot{m}_0$) and the corresponding values of freestream area (A_0) calculated by the parametric

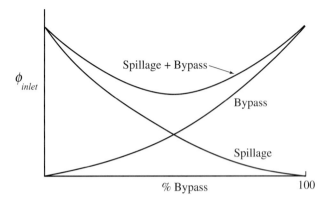

Fig. 10.47 Spillage and bypass drag.

(on-design) and performance (off-design) analyses of this textbook and the computer programs ONX and AEDsys are based on the total pressure recovery given by military specification MIL-E-5008B where

$$\eta_{R\,spec} = 1 \qquad\qquad \text{for } M_0 \le 1 \quad (4.12b)$$

$$\eta_{R\,spec} = 1 - 0.075(M_0 - 1)^{1.35} \quad \text{for } 1 < M_0 < 5 \quad (4.12c)$$

$$\eta_{R\,spec} = \frac{800}{M_0^4 + 935} \qquad \text{for } 5 < M_0 \quad (4.12d)$$

This same reference inlet total pressure recovery is used by many others.

Note: Since the total pressure recovery η_R of an inlet design may be different than $\eta_{R\,spec}$, the required values of engine airflow $\dot{m}_0$ and the corresponding values of freestream area A_0 will be different from those calculated in the engine performance analyses. Thus the values of $\dot{m}_0$ and A_0 determined by using the total pressure recovery of Eq. (4.14) will be referred to as $\dot{m}_{0\,spec}$ and $A_{0\,spec}$, respectively, from this point on.

Inlet design and sizing begins with an analysis of its airflow requirements. Figure 10.48 shows the variation in inlet airflow requirements from engine performance analyses $A_{0\,spec}$ with flight Mach number and altitude for a typical supersonic engine. Variable boundary layer bleed (see Fig. 10.45) and safety margin of 4% have been added to the maximum full-throttle engine airflow to obtain the required inlet airflow $A_{0i\,spec}$.

The engine airflow requirements ($\dot{m}_0$, A_0) for any arbitrary inlet design η_R can be estimated based on the engine airflow requirements ($\dot{m}_{0\,spec}$, $A_{0\,spec}$) obtained using the original inlet total pressure recovery $\eta_{R\,spec}$. Since the engine operates as essentially a constant corrected mass flow device ($\dot{m}_{c2}$ = constant) when throttle and flight conditions are constant, then the required engine airflow $\dot{m}_0$ for a specific inlet design η_R can be determined from required engine airflow data ($\dot{m}_{0\,spec}$, $A_{0\,spec}$) based on a reference inlet total pressure recovery $\eta_{R\,spec}$ using

$$\frac{\dot{m}_0}{\dot{m}_{0\,spec}} = \frac{A_0}{A_{0\,spec}} = \frac{\eta_R}{\eta_{R\,spec}} \qquad (10.16)$$

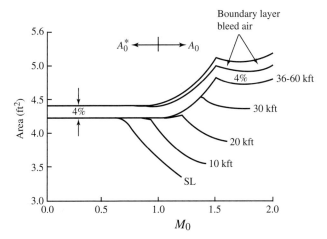

Fig. 10.48   Airflow requirements.

Likewise for the inlet airflow area

$$\frac{A_{0i}}{A_{0i\,spec}} = \frac{\eta_R}{\eta_{R\,spec}} \tag{10.17}$$

10.2.3.8   Inlet mass flow.   Preliminary inlet design and sizing requires the performance analysis of candidate designs. The previous material on total pressure recovery presented the tools for estimating the total pressure recovery of an inlet (η_R), and the tools for estimating the inlet mass flow ratio (A_{0i}/A_1) are presented below.

Consider the generalized external compression inlet of Fig. 10.49 with capture area A_1 and area A_s at location s. The inlet mass flow ratio can be written as

$$\frac{A_{0i}}{A_1} = \frac{A_{0i}}{A_s}\frac{A_s}{A_1} \tag{10.18a}$$

where A_s/A_1 is determined by the geometry of the inlet. The shock system determines the area ratio A_{0i}/A_s as follows. Conservation of mass gives

$$\dot{m}_i = \dot{m}_s \quad \text{or} \quad \rho_0 V_0 A_{0i} = \rho_s V_s A_s$$

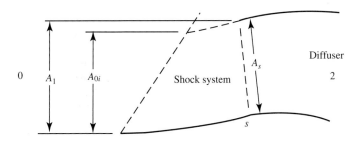

Fig. 10.49   External compression inlet.

thus

$$\frac{A_{0i}}{A_s} = \frac{\rho_s V_s}{\rho_0 V_0}$$

and, for adiabatic flow in the inlet, the ratio of density times velocity in the above equation can be written in terms of the total pressure ratio and the Mach numbers using the mass flow parameter [see Eq. (1.3)] as

$$\frac{A_{0i}}{A_s} = \frac{\rho_s V_s}{\rho_0 V_0} = \frac{P_{ts}}{P_{t0}} \frac{MFP(M_s)}{MFP(M_0)} = \frac{P_{ts}}{P_{t0}} \frac{[A/A^*]_{M_0}}{[A/A^*]_{M_s}} \qquad (10.18b)$$

where A/A^* is the isentropic area ratio defined for a calorically perfect gas as

$$\frac{A}{A^*} = \frac{1}{M} \left\{ \frac{2}{\gamma+1} \left(1 + \frac{\gamma-1}{2} M^2 \right) \right\}^{\frac{\gamma+1}{2(\gamma-1)}} \qquad (10.19)$$

A/A^* is tabulated in many gas dynamics textbooks and is available in the gas tables program (GASTAB) included within the AEDsys software package. Equations (10.18a) and (10.18b) provide the tools to estimate the inlet mass flow ratio (A_{0i}/A_1) of an inlet. The area ratio (A_s/A_1) is a geometric function of the inlet design, whereas the area ratio (A_{0i}/A_s) is a function of the flow properties at stations 0 and s. The previous section on total pressure recovery presented the analytical tools for determining both M_s and P_{ts}/P_{t0} of a general inlet as is shown in the following example. Reference 1 contains exact solutions for one and two oblique shock inlets designed for critical operation.

10.2.3.9 Inlet size.
The ratio of the inlet capture area A_1 to the engine's area at state 0^* (i.e., at $M = 1$) for the cycle reference point $A^*_{0\,ref}$ will be referred to as the *inlet size* $A_1/A^*_{0\,ref}$ since this ratio is the size of the inlet relative to the engine. The required inlet size $(A_1/A^*_{0\,ref})_{req}$ at a flight condition can be calculated from the required inlet airflow $(A_{0i}/A^*_{0\,ref})_{req}$ and the inlet mass flow ratio A_{0i}/A_1 using

$$\left(\frac{A_1}{A^*_{0\,ref}} \right)_{req} = \frac{(A_{0i}/A^*_{0\,ref})_{req}}{A_{0i}/A_1} \qquad (10.20)$$

For a fixed inlet capture area inlet, the flight condition requiring the largest inlet size $(A_1/A^*_{0\,ref})_{req}$ is used to size the inlet capture area A_1.

Care must be taken that the inlet does not choke the flow to the engine at subsonic flight conditions. As discussed in Chapter 6, this can be assured by having the inlet capture area (A_1) larger than the maximum required one-dimensional inlet area A^*_{0i} by about 4% ($A/A^* = 1.038$ at $M = 0.8$) and/or providing additional air inlet area for takeoff requirements.

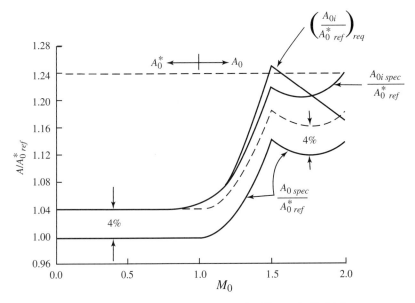

Fig. 10.50   Inlet airflow requirement for Example 10.2 inlet.

Example 10.2   External Compression Inlet (Part II)

As an example, consider the fixed geometry, double ramp, external compression inlet of Fig. 10.35 with $\theta_a = \theta_b = 5$ deg to be used with the engine whose required airflow is plotted as $A_0/A^*_{0\,ref}$ in Fig. 10.50. These data are based on the airflow requirements of Fig. 10.48 at 40 kft altitude and an $A^*_{0\,ref}$ of 4.22 ft^2 at sea-level static conditions. The inlet is to be capable of operating up to Mach 2 at 40 kft with efficient operation at Mach numbers less than 1.7. The inlet size and mass flow characteristics of inlet and engine are required.

Inlet airflow requirements.   From performance (off-design) cycle calculations based on the reference inlet recovery of military specification MIL-E-5008B, the required full throttle engine mass flow ratio is given as $A_{0\,spec}/A^*_{0\,ref}$ in Fig. 10.50. Inspection of Fig. 10.50 shows that the most demanding mass flow requirements of the inlet occur at altitudes above 36 kft. Increasing these values for boundary layer bleed (0% at 0.8M, 4% at 2.0M. and linearly in between) and for safety margin (4%) yields the required inlet mass flow ratio $A_{0\,spec}/A_1$ (based on the reference inlet recovery, $\eta_{R\,spec}$) times the inlet size $A_1/A^*_{0\,ref}$ or $A_{0i\,spec}/A^*_{0\,ref}$. Correcting these data for the total pressure recovery η_R of the inlet of interest (Table 10.1) yields the required inlet performance $(A_{0i}/A^*_{0\,ref})_{req}$.

Inlet performance.   The total pressure recovery of this inlet (η_R) is tabulated in Table 10.1, is plotted in Fig. 10.36, and was found to meet the requirement for efficient total pressure recovery at Mach numbers less than 1.7. Analysis of the mass flow characteristics of the inlet and engine are required before this inlet can be sized. As long as the normal shock between stations b and c touches the lip of the inlet, either station b or c of Fig. 10.35 can be equated to station s of Fig.10.49.

Thus

$$\frac{A_{0i}}{A_s} = \frac{P_{tb}}{P_{t0}} \frac{[A/A^*]_{M_0}}{[A/A^*]_{M_b}} = \frac{P_{tc}}{P_{t0}} \frac{[A/A^*]_{M_0}}{[A/A^*]_{M_c}}$$ (10.21a)

and

$$\frac{P_{tc}}{P_{t0}} = \eta_R; \qquad \frac{P_{tb}}{P_{t0}} = \frac{\eta_R}{P_{tc}/P_{tb}}$$ (10.21b)

The area ratio (A_{0i}/A_s) can be calculated using the results of Table 10.1 assuming that $M_s = M_b$ at subsonic values of M_b (no local flow acceleration or deceleration). For subsonic M_0, a reasonable approximation is for choked flow at station s and thus $A_{0i}^* = A_s$.

The results of the area ratio A_{0i}/A_s calculations for this example inlet are plotted in Fig. 10.51. Note that this plot has a minimum value of unity at $M_0 = 1$. Also note the jumps in value of A_{0i}/A_s corresponding to the transition between normal and oblique shocks at each ramp. (These also correspond to the jumps in total pressure shown in Fig. 10.36.)

The selected design point of an external compression inlet sets the value of A_s/A_1. Since $A_{0i} = A_1$ at the inlet design point, then $A_s/A_1 = 1/(A_{0i}/A_s)$ evaluated at the inlet's design point. For this example, let the inlet design point be $M_0 = 2$. Thus, $A_s/A_1 = 0.7681$ and the resulting values of A_{0i}/A_1 using Eq. (10.18a) are tabulated in Table 10.2.

Inlet size. Now that the mass flow ratio of the inlet has been determined, the inlet mass flow rate requirements must be established before it can be sized. Using these data, the maximum calculated value of the inlet size $(A_1/A_{0\,ref}^*)_{req}$

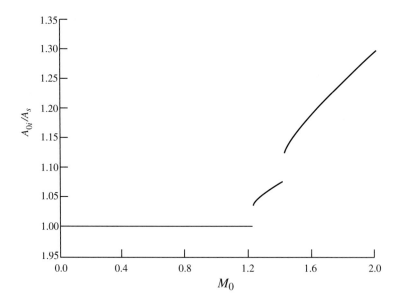

Fig. 10.51   Area ratio of Example 10.2 inlet (Fig. 10.35).

Table 10.2   Example 10.2 inlet performance

M_0	A_{0i}/A_1	M_0	A_{0i}/A_1
0.9	0.7749	1.5	0.8895
1.0	0.7681	1.6	0.9151
1.1	0.7885	1.7	0.9378
1.2	0.7688	1.8	0.9592
1.3	0.8125	1.9	0.9798
1.4	0.8267	2.0	1.0

from Eq. (10.20) sets the size of this fixed geometry inlet. Comparison of Figs. 10.50 and 10.51 indicates that the two most demanding operating points will most likely be at $M_0 = 1.23$ and $M_0 = 1.42$. Sizing calculations at these two Mach numbers are presented in Table 10.3. The flight condition at $M_0 = 1.42$ determines the inlet size as $A_1 = 1.425\, A^*_{0\,ref}$.

The resulting flow ratios of the sized inlet and its required performance are plotted for altitudes of between 36 and 60 kft in Fig. 10.52. This plot shows the difference in flow behavior of the inlet between actual and required flows. As the flight Mach number increases above 1.5, the inlet mass flow rate A_{0i}/A_1 increases while the required inlet mass flow rate $(A_{0i}/A_1)_{req}$ decreases. The difference between these mass flow rates is airflow that is either accepted by the inlet and then bypassed about the engine back to the atmosphere, or spilled about the inlet, or a combination of bypassed and spilled. At high Mach numbers, the large quantity of excess air for this example inlet will correspond to a high inlet installation loss. Nevertheless, over the required Mach range ($M_0 < 1.7$), the example inlet has good total pressure performance ($\eta_R > \eta_{R\,spec}$) and moderate excess air.

An inlet size based on the model variable geometry inlet of Chapter 6 would have an inlet capture area (A_1) of 1.24 $A^*_{0\,ref}$ (horizontal dashed line on Fig. 10.50) vs the capture area of 1.425 $A^*_{0\,ref}$ required for this example fixed geometry inlet. Also, the excess air for this example inlet is considerably larger than for the model inlet of Chapter 6. A better match of inlet and engine is needed, which requires a variable geometry inlet.

Variable geometry inlet.   The INLET program included with this textbook allows analysis of external compression inlets with variable ramps. The user can input the desired schedule into the program and the inlet's performance is calculated for that schedule.

As an example of a variable geometry inlet, consider our example double-ramp, external compression inlet of Fig 10.35 with ramp angles of 5 deg that becomes a

Table 10.3   Example 10.2 inlet sizing

M_0	$A_0/A^*_{0\,ref}$	$A_{0i\,req}/A^*_{0\,ref}$	A_{0i}/A_1	$A_{1\,req}/A^*_{0\,ref}$
1.23	1.0290	1.0854	0.7681	1.413
1.42	1.1004	1.1803	0.8283	1.425

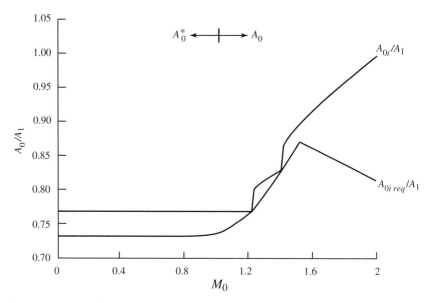

Fig. 10.52   Mass flow performance of sized Example 10.2 inlet at altitude and full throttle.

single ramp, external compression inlet with ramp angle of 5 deg for flight Mach numbers less than 1.42. This variable geometry inlet is shown in Fig. 10.53a. Since $A_1 = A_0$ at Mach 2 for the double-ramp inlet and A_1 is constant, basic geometry gives $A_{s'} = 1.131A_s$. If the inlet sizing flight condition is at a Mach number below 1.42, the variable ramp inlet will reduce the excess airflow about 13% for flight Mach numbers above 1.42. The actual and required inlet mass flow ratios for this example variable geometry inlet are plotted in Fig. 10.53b. Comparison of Fig. 10.53b with Fig. 10.52 shows that variable geometry has reduced the excess air that must be bypassed at high Mach numbers which will result in a corresponding reduction in installation losses.

10.2.3.10   *Inlet-airframe interference effects on inlet distortion.*   Both the location of the inlet and the aircraft attitude (angle of attack and angle of sideslip) influence the flow into the inlet and the resulting distortion of the flow to the compressor/fan. Figure 10.54 shows three typical inlet locations. The wing-shielded inlet and the fuselage-shielded inlet use the wing and fuselage, respectively, to help turn the air into the inlet at high angle of attack. The upwash flow around the fuselage increases the flow angularity for the side-mounted inlet. Both the fuselage- and wing-shielded inlets experience a significant reduction in angle of attack. However, the wing-shielded inlet can experience a higher angle of sideslip than the fuselage-shielded inlet.

The reader is directed to Chapter 13 of Ref. 1 for a thorough coverage of inlet-airframe interference at incidence. This reference also provides the reader with a good list of references on this topic.

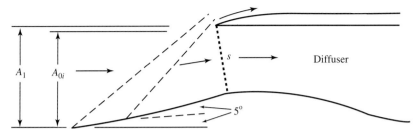

High Mach Operation, $M_0 > 1.42$

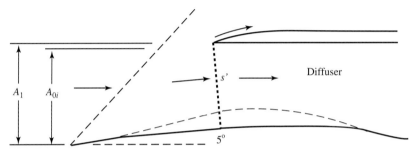

Low Mach Operation, $M_0 < 1.42$

Fig. 10.53a   Example 10.2 variable geometry inlet.

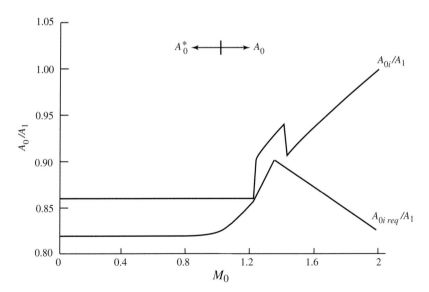

Fig. 10.53b   Mass flow performance of Example 10.2 variable geometry inlet at 40 kft and full throttle.

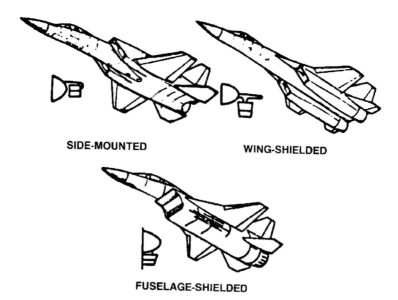

SIDE-MOUNTED   **WING-SHIELDED**

FUSELAGE-SHIELDED

Fig. 10.54   Three typical inlet locations.[10]

10.2.3.11 Subsonic diffuser. The subsonic diffuser portion of a subsonic or supersonic inlet must provide a smooth transition from the conditions at the inlet throat to those required at the face of the fan or compressor with minimal flow distortion and total pressure loss. In addition to a smooth variation in flow velocity, the diffuser may be required to transition from a rectangular cross-section to a circular one and/or to offset the flow when the inlet and engine are not aligned. The front and side views for a fighter aircraft diffuser are shown in Fig. 10.55. When this serpentine shape is combined with radar absorbing material (RAM), the inlet can effectively reduce the radar cross section of the aircraft (see Fig 10.18 in Sec. 10.2.3 and Ref. 12).

The most commonly used measure for the pressure recovery of a diffuser is the diffuser efficiency (η_D) which can be written as

$$\eta_D = \frac{h_{2s} - h_1}{h_2 - h_1} \tag{9.65}$$

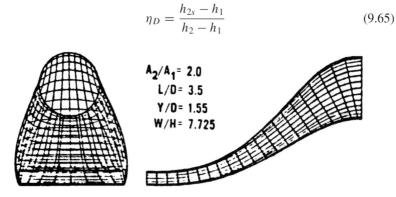

$A_2/A_1 = 2.0$
$L/D = 3.5$
$Y/D = 1.55$
$W/H = 7.725$

Fig. 10.55   Typical diffuser portion of supersonic inlet.[11]

where the subscript 1 denotes the entry of the diffuser and 2 denotes the exit. A typical range of values for η_D is 0.80–0.95 which corresponds to total pressure ratios (P_{te}/P_{ti}) of 0.92–0.98 for $M_i = 0.8$.

Although the flow through the diffuser is very complex with possible flow separation (see Fig. 9.21) in the regions of adverse pressure gradients, basic one-dimensional gas dynamic analysis will yield useful and meaningful results. When these results are incorporated with the diffuser efficiency, the overall performance of a diffuser design can be estimated.

10.2.3.12 Examples of existing inlet designs.

Two examples of supersonic inlet designs are shown in Figs. 10.56 and 10.57. Figure 10.56a shows the fixed, double-ramp (6 deg ramp followed by a 6.67 deg isentropic ramp[1]), external compression inlet with a throat slot bleed system developed for the J79 engine installation in the F-16 aircraft. The total pressure recovery of this inlet is shown in Fig. 10.56b.

The variable, triple-ramp, external compression inlet of the F-15 aircraft is shown in Fig. 10.57. This side view of the inlet shows the ramps as they would be positioned when operating at the supersonic design point (ramp angles of 7 deg, 8 deg, and 8 deg for the first, second, and third ramps, respectively). The first ramp angle is fixed and the second and third ramp angles are variable. The inlet capture area of this inlet is variable with movement of the first ramp/top of inlet assembly from −4 deg to +11 deg (this assembly is shown at 0 deg).

10.2.3.13 Flow separation from sharp lip inlets.

Airflow may separate from either the inside surface or outside surface of the sharp lip present on most supersonic inlets when operated at subsonic flight Mach numbers. Separation from the outside surface increases inlet drag and separation from the inside surface creates inlet flow distortion and reduces the total pressure recovery of the inlet (see Fig. 10.58), both of which reduce the installed engine performance. Auxiliary air inlets (also called blow-in doors) that reduce additive drag also reduce the flow separation from the inside surface of sharp lip inlets when operated at takeoff conditions.

10.3   Exhaust Nozzles

The purpose of the exhaust nozzle is to increase the velocity of the exhaust gas before discharge from the nozzle and to collect and straighten the gas flow. For large values of thrust, the kinetic energy of the exhaust gas must be high, which implies a high exhaust velocity. The pressure ratio across the nozzle controls the expansion process and the maximum uninstalled thrust for a given engine is obtained when the exit pressure (P_e) equals the ambient pressure (P_0).

The functions of the nozzle may be summarized by the following list:

1) Accelerate the flow to a high velocity with minimum total pressure loss.

2) Match exit and atmospheric pressure as closely as desired.

3) Permit afterburner operation without affecting main engine operation—requires variable throat area nozzle.

4) Allow for cooling of walls if necessary.

5) Mix core and bypass streams of turbofan if necessary.

6) Allow for thrust reversing if desired.

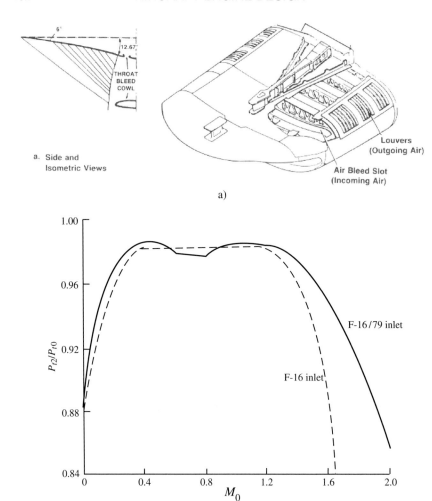

Fig. 10.56 F-16/J79 inlet.[13]

7) Suppress jet noise, radar reflection, and infrared radiation (IR) if desired.

8) Two-dimensional and axi-symmetric nozzles, thrust vector control if desired.

9) Do all of the above with minimal cost, weight, and boattail drag while meeting life and reliability goals.

The nozzle may be thought of as a device that converts enthalpy into kinetic energy with no moving parts. The perfect (no loss) nozzle would thus correspond to an isentropic (frictionless adiabatic) process. The nozzle adiabatic efficiency (η_n) is defined as

$$\eta_n = \frac{T_i - T_e}{T_i - T_{es}} = \frac{V_e^2 - V_i^2}{V_{es}^2 - V_i^2}$$

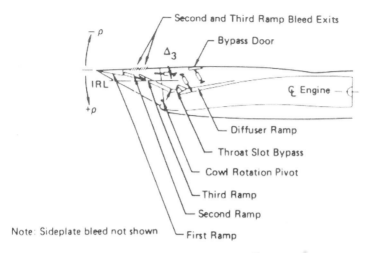

Fig. 10.57   F-15 inlet system.[14]

where the subscripts i, e, and es refer to the nozzle inlet, exit, and ideal exit conditions, respectively. For most cases, the inlet kinetic energy is small in comparison to the exit and can be neglected. Thus

$$\eta_n \cong \frac{T_{ti} - T_e}{T_{ti} - T_{es}} = \frac{1 - T_e/T_{ti}}{1 - T_{es}/T_{ti}} = \frac{V_e^2}{V_{es}^2} \qquad (10.22)$$

This expression can be recast in terms of a nozzle polytropic (e_n) efficiency by using $T_e/T_{ti} = (P_e/P_{ti})^{e_n(\gamma-1)/\gamma}$ and $T_{es}/T_{ti} = (P_e/P_{ti})^{(\gamma-1)/\gamma}$. Thus

$$e_n = \frac{\gamma}{\gamma - 1} \frac{\ln\left\{1 - \eta_n \left[1 - (P_e/P_{ti})^{(\gamma-1)/\gamma}\right]\right\}}{\ln(P_e/P_{ti})} \qquad (10.23)$$

The ratio of the actual exit velocity to the ideal exit velocity is the traditional nozzle

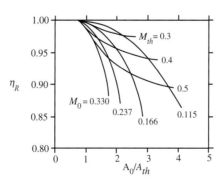

Fig. 10.58   Total pressure recovery characteristics of sharp lip axisymmetric pitot inlets.[1]

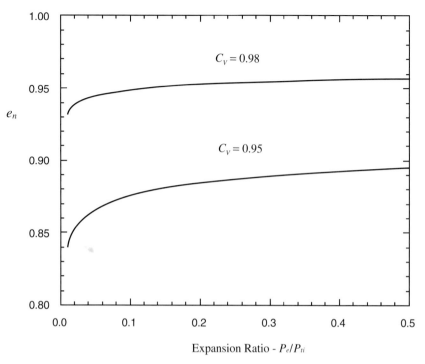

Fig. 10.59   Nozzle polytropic efficiency ($\gamma = 1.3$).

velocity coefficient (C_V) defined by

$$C_V \doteq \frac{V_e}{V_{es}} \tag{10.24}$$

From Eqs. (10.22) and (10.24), the nozzle adiabatic efficiency can be therefore approximated as

$$\eta_n \cong C_V^2 \tag{10.25}$$

Using Eqs. (10.23) and (10.25), the variation of nozzle polytropic efficiency versus nozzle expansion pressure ratio (P_e/P_{ti}) is given in Fig. 10.59. It is evident there that, for a given velocity coefficient (C_V), the equivalent nozzle polytropic efficiency is nearly constant with P_e/P_{ti}. Also, even for rather low values of C_V, the equivalent nozzle polytropic efficiency is equal to or greater than that of the turbine (see Table 4.4).

10.3.1   Nozzle Types

The two basic types of nozzles used in jet engines are the convergent and convergent-divergent (C-D) nozzle.

10.3.1.1   Convergent nozzle.
The convergent nozzle is a simple convergent duct as shown in Fig. 10.60. When the nozzle pressure ratio (P_{te}/P_0) is low

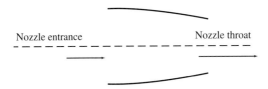

Fig. 10.60   Convergent exhaust nozzle.

(less than about 4), the convergent nozzle is used. The convergent nozzle has generally been used in engines for subsonic aircraft.

10.3.1.2   Convergent-divergent (C-D) nozzle.   The convergent-divergent nozzle is a convergent duct followed by a divergent duct as shown in Fig. 10.61. Where the cross-sectional area of the duct is at a minimum, the nozzle is said to have a throat. Most convergent-divergent nozzles used in aircraft are not simple ducts, but incorporate variable geometry and other aerodynamic features. The convergent-divergent nozzle is used if the nozzle pressure ratio is high (greater than about four). High-performance engines in supersonic aircraft generally have some form of a convergent-divergent nozzle. If the engine incorporates an afterburner, the nozzle throat is usually scheduled to leave the operating conditions of the engine upstream of the afterburner unchanged (in other words, the exit nozzle area is varied so that the engine doesn't know that the afterburner is operating). Also, the exit area must be varied to match the internal and external static pressures at exit for different flow conditions in order to produce the maximum available uninstalled thrust.

Earlier supersonic aircraft used ejector nozzles (Fig. 10.62) with their high performance turbojets. Use of the ejector nozzle permitted bypassing varying amounts of inlet air around the engine, providing engine cooling, good inlet recovery, and reduced boattail drag. Ejector nozzles can also receive air from outside the nacelle directly into the nozzle for better overall nozzle matching—these are called two-stage ejector nozzles. For the modern high-performance afterburning turbofan engines, simple convergent-divergent nozzles are used without secondary air as shown in Fig. 10.61 for the F100 engine.

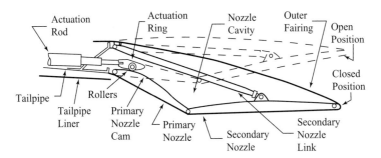

Fig. 10.61   Convergent-divergent (C-D) exhaust nozzle schematic.[15]

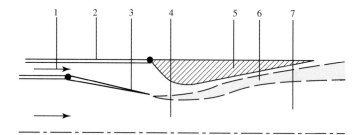

(*a*) Supersonic nozzle configuration with afterburning: (1) secondary flow; (2) outer case engine; (3) movable primary nozzle shown at maximum area; (4) primary flow, effective throat; (5) movable secondary nozzle shown at maximum exit area; (6) mixing layer between primary and secondary streams; and (7) supersonic primary flow

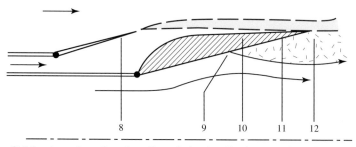

(*b*) Subsonic nozzle configuration with no afterburning: (8) primary nozzle at minimum area; (9) separation point of external flow; (10) secondary nozzle at minimum area; (11) sonic primary stream; and (12) region of separated flow in external flow

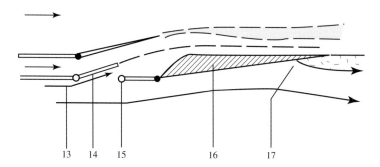

(*c*) Subsonic nozzle configuration, not afterburning, and blow-in door in use: (13) tertiary flow of ambient gas into nozzle; (14) blow-in door and inflow configuration; (15) reversible hinge/latch; (16) movable secondary nozzle; and (17) separation point of external flow.

Fig. 10.62   Ejector nozzle configuration.[15]

10.3.2 Nozzle Functions

One can also think of the exhaust nozzle as dividing the power available from the main burner exit gas between the requirements of the turbine and the jet power.[15] Thus, the nozzle serves as a back-pressure control for the engine and an acceleration device converting gas thermal energy into kinetic energy. A secondary function of the nozzle is providing required thrust reversing and/or thrust vectoring. The nozzle design can also reduce the infrared signature of the engine.

10.3.2.1 Engine back-pressure control.   The throat area of the nozzle is one of the main means available to control the thrust and fuel consumption characteristics of an existing engine. In preliminary engine cycle analysis, the selection of specific values for the engine design parameters and the design mass flow rate fixes the throat area of the nozzle. The off-design performance methods of Chapter 5 assume that the nozzle throat area and the other internal flow areas of the engine remain constant. This assumption of constant areas establishes the off-design operating characteristics of the engine and the resulting operating lines for each major component. It is important to realize, however, that changing the nozzle throat area from its original design value will change the engine design and the operating characteristics of the engine at both on- and off-design (see Appendix D). This is equivalent to displacing the operating line of the engine.

At times, it is necessary to change the off-design operation of an engine in only a few operating regions and variation of the throat area of the exhaust nozzle may provide the needed change. At reduced engine corrected mass flow rates (normally corresponding to reduced engine throttle settings), the operating line of a multistage compressor moves closer to the stall or surge line (see Fig. 10.63). Steady-state operation close to the stall or surge line is not desirable since transient operation may cause the compressor to stall or surge. The operating line can be moved away from the stall or surge line by increasing the exhaust nozzle throat area as shown in Fig. 10.61. This increase in nozzle throat area reduces the engine back-pressure and increases the corrected mass flow rate through the compressor.

Large changes in exhaust nozzle throat area are required for afterburning engines to compensate for the large changes in total temperature leaving the afterburner. The variable-area nozzle required for an afterburning engine can also be used for back-pressure control at its non-afterburning settings.

One advantage of the variable-area exhaust nozzle is that it improves the starting of the engine. Opening the nozzle throat area to its maximum value reduces the back-pressure on the turbine and increases its expansion ratio. Thus, the necessary turbine power for starting operation may be produced at a lower turbine inlet temperature. Also, since the back-pressure on the gas generator is reduced, the compressor may be started at a lower engine speed, which reduces the required size of the engine starter.

10.3.2.2 Exhaust nozzle area ratio.   Maximum uninstalled engine thrust is realized for ideal flow when the exhaust nozzle flow is expanded to ambient pressure $(P_e = P_0)$. When the nozzle pressure ratio is above choking, the supersonic expansion occurs between aft-facing surfaces. A small amount of underexpansion is less harmful to aircraft/engine performance than over-expansion.

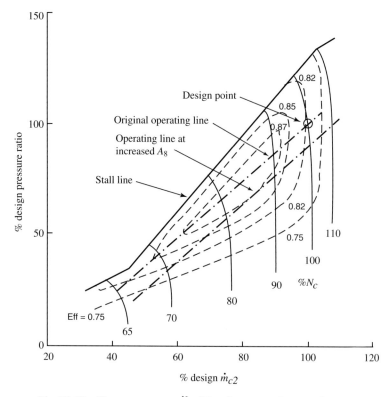

Fig. 10.63 Compressor map[16] with exhaust nozzle area change.

Over-expansion can produce regions of separated flow in the nozzle and on the aft end of the aircraft, reducing the aircraft performance.

The exhaust nozzle pressure ratio is a strong function of flight Mach number as is shown by Fig. 10.64. Whereas convergent nozzles are usually used on subsonic aircraft, convergent-divergent nozzles are usually used for supersonic aircraft. When afterburning engine operation is required, complex variable geometry nozzles must be used (see Fig. 10.65). Most of the nozzles shown in Fig. 10.64 are convergent-divergent nozzles with variable throat and exit areas. The throat area of the nozzle is controlled to satisfy engine back-pressure requirements and the exit area is scheduled with the throat area. The sophisticated nozzles of the F-15 and B-1 aircraft have two schedules, a low-speed mode and a high-speed mode.[15]

10.3.2.3 Thrust reversing and thrust vectoring.

The need for thrust reversing and thrust vectoring is normally determined by the required aircraft/engine system performance. Thrust reversers are used on commercial transports to supplement the brakes. In-flight thrust reversal has been shown to enhance combat effectiveness of fighter aircraft.[15] Thrust vectoring has been shown to enhance both takeoff and combat effectiveness of fighter aircraft.[15]

Two basic types of thrust reversers are used: the cascade-blocker type and the clam-shell type (Fig. 10.66). In the cascade-blocker type, the primary nozzle exit

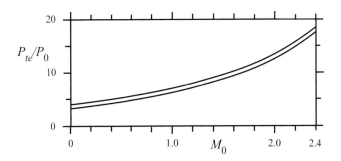

Fig. 10.64   Typical nozzle pressure ratios.

is blocked off and cascades are opened in the upstream portion of the nozzle duct to reverse the flow. In the clam-shell type, the exhaust jet is split and reversed by the clam shell. As shown in Fig. 10.67, the PW4000 high-bypass turbofan engine employs the cascade-blocker type in the bypass stream and no reverser in the core stream (some engines also employ reversers in the core stream). Since reversers usually provide a change in effective nozzle throat area during deployment or when deployed, most are designed such that it increases during the brief transitory period, thus lowering the operating line in order to prevent fan/compressor stalls.

Development of thrust vectoring nozzles for combat aircraft has increased in the last decade. Vectoring nozzles have been used on VTOL aircraft, such as the AV-8 Harrier, and are being used on new fighters to improve maneuvering and augment lift in combat. Thrust vectoring at augmented power settings has been developed for use in new fighters. However, cooling of the nozzle walls in contact

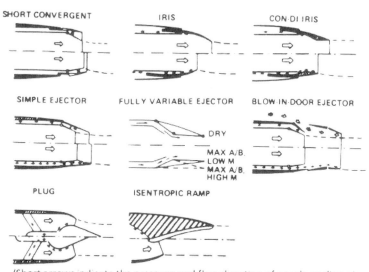

(Short arrows indicate the presence and flow direction of nozzle cooling air which is usually inlet bleed air, compressor bleed air, or fan discharge air)

Fig. 10.65   Typical nozzle concepts for afterburning engines.[15]

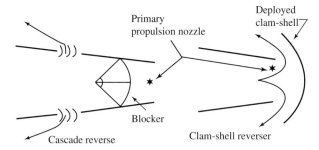

Fig. 10.66   Thrust reversers.[15]

with the hot turning or stagnating flows is very difficult and requires increased amounts of nozzle cooling airflow. Figure 10.68 shows the schematic of a two-dimensional convergent-divergent nozzle with thrust vectoring of ±15 deg and thrust reversing. The thrust vectoring is typical of the capabilities incorporated in the F-22 Raptor. The thrust vectoring nozzle of the Joint Strike Fighter (JSF) can turn the exhaust flow 90 deg for STOVL.

10.3.2.4   Infrared signature.   The rear of the engine is very hot and can produce a large infrared signature. Considerable effort is being used in modern military aircraft to reduce this signature. Most effective methods involve hiding

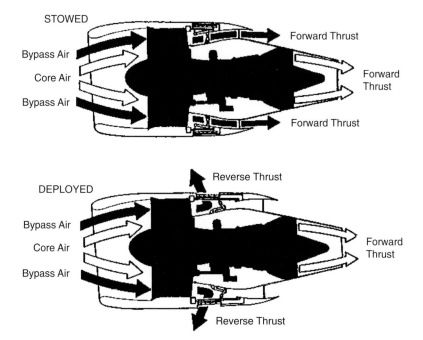

Fig. 10.67   PW4000 thrust reverser in stowed and deployed positions.

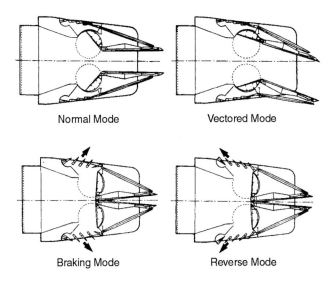

Normal Mode   **Vectored Mode**

Braking Mode   **Reverse Mode**

Fig. 10.68   Typical two-dimensional variable-area thrust vectoring nozzle with thrust reversing.[17]

the exit of the low-pressure turbine from direct view. Shown in Fig. 10.69 is the platypus exhaust duct used on the F-117A Nighthawk stealth fighter. This exhaust nozzle is canted up 10 degrees (Refs. 3 and 12) to prevent line-of-sight to the turbine face. For afterburning engines, the nozzle in concert with the devices (e.g., flameholders) downstream of the turbine can hide the turbine exit and thus reduce high temperature signatures. Generally speaking reduced performance is the cost of stealth.

10.3.3   Design Tools—Exhaust Nozzles

10.3.3.1   Total pressure loss.   The total pressure loss of an exhaust nozzle is primarily due to viscous effects. The fraction of total pressure loss can be expressed for one-dimensional flow in its differential form as

$$\frac{dP_t}{P_t} = -\frac{\gamma}{2}M^2 C_f \frac{P_w}{A}\,dx$$

where

$$C_f = \text{Friction coefficient}$$

and

$$P_w = \text{Wetted perimeter of the duct}$$

Comparison of the total pressure loss of a two-dimensional nozzle to that of an axisymmetric nozzle can be made using the above equation. Assuming the same axial distribution of Mach number, friction coefficient, and flow area, then the

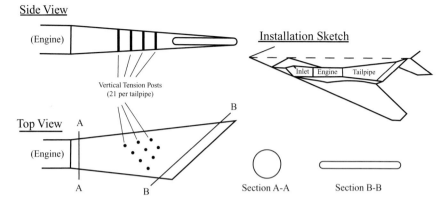

Fig. 10.69 Exhaust nozzle of F-117A [Originally published in *Have Blue and the F-117A: Evolution of the "Stealth Fighter,"* D. Aronstein and A. Piccirillo, AIAA, 1997 (Ref. 12). Copyright 1997 by AIAA. Reprinted with permission.]

total pressure loss is proportional to wetted perimeter (P_w), and the ratio of the total pressure loss of a rectangular cross-sectional nozzle to that of a circular can be written as

$$\frac{1 - (\pi_n)_{rectangular}}{1 - (\pi_n)_{circular}} = \frac{(\Delta P_t/P_t)_{rectangular}}{(\Delta P_t/P)_{circular}} = \frac{(P_w)_{rectangular}}{(P_w)_{circular}}$$

where the ratio of wetted perimeters can be expressed in terms of the aspect ratio ($AR = W/H$, where W is the duct width and H is the duct height) of a rectangular nozzle of the same flow area. The resulting relationship for total pressure loss comparing rectangular to circular cross-sectional nozzles is

$$\frac{1 - (\pi_n)_{rectangular}}{1 - (\pi_n)_{circular}} = \frac{(AR + 1)}{\sqrt{\pi AR}} \tag{10.26}$$

Thus, the total pressure loss of a rectangular nozzle with an aspect ratio of 2 will be 1.2 times that of a circular nozzle of the same area. Also, if $(\pi_n)_{circular} = 0.980$, then $(\pi_n)_{rectangular} = 0.976$.

10.3.3.2 Nozzle coefficients.
Nozzle performance is ordinarily evaluated by two dimensionless coefficients: the gross thrust coefficient and the discharge or flow coefficient. Figure 10.70 shows a convergent-divergent exhaust nozzle with the geometric parameters used in the definitions of nozzle coefficients to follow. Only total pressure losses downstream of station 8 are included in the gross thrust coefficient.

Gross thrust coefficient. The *gross thrust coefficient* (C_{fg}) is defined as the ratio of the actual gross thrust ($F_{g\,actual}$) to the ideal gross thrust ($F_{g\,ideal}$) or

$$C_{fg} \doteq F_{g\,actual}/F_{g\,ideal} \tag{10.27}$$

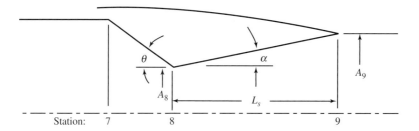

A_8 = Primary nozzle throat area
A_9 = Secondary nozzle exit area
α = Secondary nozzle half angle
θ = Primary nozzle half angle
L_s = Secondary nozzle length

Fig. 10.70 Nozzle geometric parameters.

Empirically derived coefficients are employed in Eq. (10.27) to account for the losses and directionality of the actual nozzle flow. Each engine organization uses somewhat different coefficients, but each of the following basic losses are accounted for:

1) Thrust loss due to the exhaust velocity vector angularity and/or dispersion;

2) Thrust loss due to reduction in velocity magnitude caused by friction in the boundary layers;

3) Thrust loss due to loss of mass flow between stations 7 and 9 from leakage through the nozzle walls;

4) Thrust loss due to flow non-uniformities.

Discharge or flow coefficient. The ratio of the actual mass flow ($\dot{m}_8$) to the ideal mass flow ($\dot{m}_{8i}$) is called the *discharge coefficient (C_D)*

$$C_D \doteq \dot{m}_8/\dot{m}_{8i}$$

This coefficient can be shown to be identically equal to the ratio of the effective one-dimensional flow area actually required to pass the total nozzle flow (A_{8e}) to the ideal nozzle throat area (A_8) of the engine cycle calculations as follows:

$$C_D = \frac{\dot{m}_8}{\dot{m}_{8i}} = \frac{\rho_8 V_8 A_8}{\rho_8 V_8 A_{8e}} = \frac{A_8}{A_{8e}} \tag{10.28}$$

The variation of the discharge coefficient with nozzle pressure ratio is shown in Fig. 10.71a for a conic convergent nozzle. When the nozzle is choked, the discharge coefficient reaches a maximum value ($C_{D\,max}$). The value of $C_{D\,max}$ is a function of the primary nozzle half-angle (θ) as shown in Fig. 10.71b. Figure 10.71c shows the variation in discharge coefficient for a convergent-divergent nozzle with nozzle pressure ratio. Note the change in behavior of C_D between that of the convergent-divergent (C-D) nozzle and that of the convergent nozzle as the nozzle pressure ratio drops below choking. This is due to the venturi behavior of the convergent-divergent nozzle.

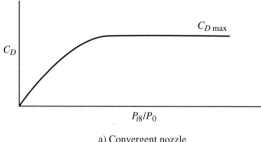

a) Convergent nozzle

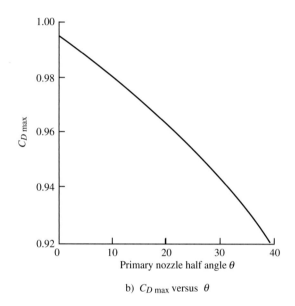

b) $C_{D\,max}$ versus θ

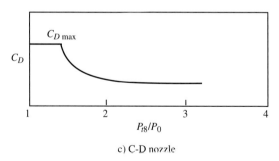

c) C-D nozzle

Fig. 10.71   Nozzle discharge coefficient:[15] a) convergent nozzle; b) convergent and C-D nozzle $C_{D\,max}$ vs θ; c) C-D nozzle.

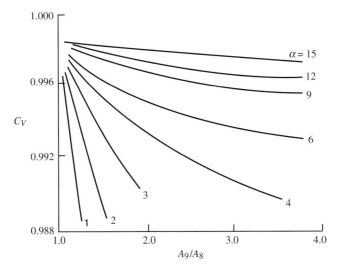

Fig. 10.72   C-D nozzle velocity coefficient.[15]

The discharge coefficient is used to size the nozzle throat area to pass the desired mass flow rate. For example, consider a nozzle with $\dot{m}_8 = 200$ lbm/s, $P_{t8} = 30$ psia, $T_{t8} = 2000°$R, $\gamma = 1.33$, and $\theta = 20$ deg. From Gas Tables, $MFP(@M_8 = 1) = 0.5224$ and thus $A_8 = 570.7$ in.[2] Figure 10.71b gives $C_{D\,max} \approx 0.96$ for $\theta = 20$ deg and thus the required throat area A_{8e} is 594.5 in.[2]

Velocity coefficient.   The *velocity coefficient* (C_V) is the ratio of the actual exit velocity (V_9) to the ideal exit velocity (V_{9i}) corresponding to $P_{t9} = P_{t8}$ or

$$C_V \doteq V_9/V_{9i} \tag{10.24}$$

represents the effect of frictional loss in the boundary layer of the nozzle and is a measure of the nozzle's efficiency [Eq. (10.25)]. It is mainly a function of the length of the nozzle, which depends on the nozzle area ratio (A_9/A_8) and the half-angle α as shown in Fig. 10.72.

Angularity coefficient.   The *angularity coefficient* (C_A) represents the axial fraction of the nozzle momentum and thus is proportional to the thrust loss due to the non-axial exit of the exhaust gas (see Fig. 10.73). For a differential element of flow, this coefficient is the cosine of the local exit flow angle (α_j). The local flow

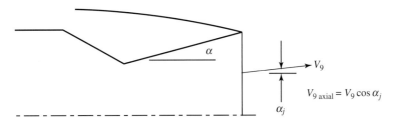

Fig. 10.73   Local angularity coefficient.[15]

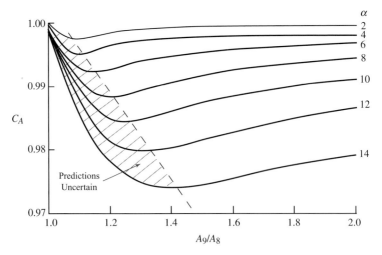

Fig. 10.74   C-D nozzle angularity coefficient.[15]

angle (α_j) varies from zero at the centerline to α at the outer wall and thus the nozzle angularity coefficient is the integral of α_j across the nozzle.

$$C_A \doteq \frac{1}{\dot{m}} \int \cos \alpha_j \, d\dot{m} \qquad (10.29)$$

Figure 10.74 presents the correlation of the angularity coefficient with the nozzle area ratio (A_9/A_8) and the half-angle, α. This figure is based on analytical evaluations of the inviscid flow field in convergent-divergent nozzles for a range of practical nozzle geometries.

One-dimensional flow.   Many of the nozzle flow coefficients simplify to algebraic expressions or become unity for the special case of one-dimensional adiabatic flow. This is a useful limit for understanding each coefficient and for preliminary analysis of nozzle performance using engine cycle analysis data.

For one-dimensional adiabatic flow, $C_A = 1$,

$$C_D = \frac{\dot{m}_8}{\dot{m}_{8i}} = \frac{A_8}{A_{8e}} = \frac{P_{t8}}{P_{t7}}$$

and the velocity coefficient (C_V) is given by

$$C_V \doteq V_9 / V_{9i} \qquad (10.24)$$

where V_9 is the exit velocity corresponding to T_{t8} and $A/A^*|_9 = (P_{t9}/P_{t8}) \times \{A_9/(C_D A_8)\}$ and V_{9i} is the ideal exit velocity corresponding to T_{t8} and $A/A^*|_{9i} = A_9/(C_D A_8)$. The discharge coefficient at station 9 has been taken to be one.

The uninstalled gross thrust for a one-dimensional flow is defined as

$$F_{g\,actual} = \dot{m}_8 V_9 / g_c + (P_9 - P_0)A_9 \qquad (10.30)$$

and the ideal gross thrust (corresponds to ($P_9 = P_0$) expressed as

$$F_{g\,ideal} = \dot{m}_{8i} V_s / g_c \qquad (10.31)$$

where V_s is the isentropic exit velocity based on P_{t8}/P_0 and T_{t8}. Please note that the uninstalled gross thrust differs from the uninstalled thrust of Eq. (4.1) only by the momentum of the incoming air, which is constant.

For one-dimensional flow of a calorically perfect gas, Eq. (10.30) can be written as

$$F_{g\,actual} = \frac{\dot{m}_8 V_9}{g_c} \left\{ 1 + \frac{\gamma - 1}{2\gamma} \frac{1 - P_0/P_9}{(P_{t9}/P_9)^{(\gamma-1)/\gamma} - 1} \right\} \qquad (10.32)$$

The uninstalled gross thrust coefficient for one-dimensional flow of a calorically perfect gas can be obtained by substituting Eqs. (10.31) and (10.32) into Eq. (10.27), giving

$$C_{fg} = C_D C_V \left\{ \frac{1 - \left(\frac{P_{9i}}{P_{t8}}\right)^{(\gamma-1)/\gamma}}{1 - \left(\frac{P_0}{P_{t8}}\right)^{(\gamma-1)/\gamma}} \right\}^{1/2} \left\{ 1 + \frac{\gamma - 1}{2\gamma} \frac{1 - P_0/P_9}{\left(\frac{P_{t9}}{P_9}\right)^{(\gamma-1)/\gamma} - 1} \right\} \qquad (10.33)$$

This equation reduces to $C_{fg} = C_D C_V$ for the case of ideal expansion ($P_9 = P_{9i} = P_0$). For isentropic flow, $P_9 = P_{9i}$, $P_{t9} = P_{t8}$, $C_V = 1$, and $C_D = 1$.

Equation (10.33) is plotted in Fig. 10.75 for isentropic flow vs the nozzle area ratio (A_9/A_8) for different nozzle pressure ratios (P_{t8}/P_0). Note that ideal expansion ($P_9 = P_0$) gives a gross thrust coefficient of unity and that both underexpansion ($P_9 > P_0$) and overexpansion ($P_9 < P_0$) reduce the gross thrust

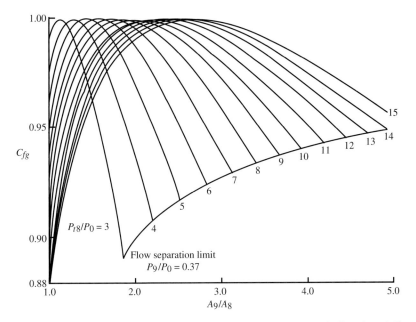

Fig. 10.75   Gross thrust coefficient for one-dimensional isentropic flow ($\gamma = 1.3$).

coefficient below unity. Both the uninstalled and installed thrust suffer as a result of non-ideal expansion.

The extent of overexpansion in nozzles is limited by flow separation resulting from the interaction of the nozzle boundary layer and the strong oblique shock waves at the exit of the nozzle. In extreme overexpansion, Summerfield et al.[18] noted that the oblique shock waves moved from the exit lip into the nozzle, the flow downstream of the shock waves was separated in the vicinity of the wall, and as a result the wall static pressure downstream of the shock waves was nearly equal to the ambient pressure (P_0). A simple estimate for the maximum allowable ratio of the pressure just preceding the shock waves (P_s) to the ambient pressure (P_0), suggested by Summerfield, is given by

$$P_s/P_0 \simeq 0.37 \qquad (10.34)$$

This flow separation limit can be included in the one-dimensional gross thrust coefficient of Eq. (10.33) for isentropic flow by considering the effective exit pressure ($P_9 = P_{9i}$) to be the pressure just preceding the shock wave (P_s). Equations (10.33) and (10.34) were used to obtain the flow separation limit shown on Fig. 10.75. The design area ratio (A_9/A_8) of convergent-divergent nozzles is selected such that the nozzle flow does not separate due to overexpansion for most throttle settings. This is because the increase in gross thrust coefficient associated with flow separation does not normally offset the accompanying increase in installation loss.

Nozzle pressure ratios are 3–5 in the subsonic cruise speed range of turbofan and turbojet engines. Typically, a subsonic engine uses a convergent exhaust nozzle. This is because, in the 3–5 nozzle pressure range, the convergent nozzle gross thrust (intercept of lines with vertical axis, $A_9/A_8 = 1$) is 1–3% below the peak gross thrust ($P_9 = P_0$) as shown in Fig. 10.75. Consequently, there may be insufficient gross thrust increase available in going to a convergent-divergent nozzle on a subsonic cruise turbofan or turbojet engine to pay for the added drag and weight of such a nozzle. In some applications, this loss in gross thrust coefficient of a convergent nozzle is too much and a C-D nozzle is used.

A band indicating the range of typical nozzle pressure ratios for turbojets is shown in Fig. 10.64 as a function of flight Mach number. The pressure ratio across the nozzle increases rapidly with supersonic flight Mach number. At a Mach number of 2, the pressure ratio is about 12. At this pressure ratio, the convergent nozzle gross thrust penalty is about 9% as shown in Fig. 10.76. This figure is a plot

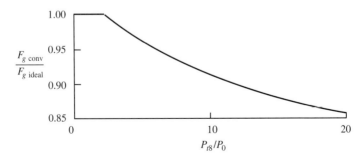

Fig. 10.76 Ratio of convergent nozzle gross thrust to ideal gross thrust vs pressure ratio ($\gamma = 1.3$).

of the ratio of the gross thrust in Fig. 10.75 of a convergent nozzle ($A_9/A_8 = 1$) to the peak thrust ($P_9 = P_0$) vs P_{t8}/P_0. Substitution of convergent-divergent nozzles for convergent nozzles provides large thrust gains for supersonic aircraft.

This method of calculating the performance of a one-dimensional nozzle, as demonstrated in the following example, is incorporated in the NOZZLE program provided with the AEDsys software package.

10.3.3.3 Example calculation based on one-dimensional flow.
Given:

$$\dot{m}_8 = 200 \text{ lbm/s} \quad P_{t8} = 30 \text{ psia} \quad T_{t8} = 2000°\text{R}$$

$$A_9/A_8 = 2.0 \quad \gamma = 1.33 \quad P_0 = 5 \text{ psia}$$

$$P_{t9}/P_{t8} = 0.98 \quad C_D = 0.98 \quad Rg_c = 1716 \text{ ft}^2/\text{s}^2\text{-}°\text{R}$$

Find the dimensions of an axisymmetric nozzle, C_{fg}, F_g, and C_V.
Solution:
From Gas Tables, $MFP(@ M_8 = 1) = 0.5224$, thus $A_8 = 570.7 \text{ in.}^2$
With $C_D = 0.98$, thus $A_{8e} = 582.3 \text{ in.}^2$ and $r_8 = 13.61 \text{ in.}$
Since $A_9/A_8 = 2.0$, then $A_9 = 1165 \text{ in.}^2$ and $r_9 = 19.25 \text{ in.}$

$$\left.\frac{A}{A^*}\right|_{9i} = \frac{A_9}{C_D A_8} = \frac{2.0}{0.98} = 2.041 \Rightarrow M_{9i} = 2.168 \quad \text{and} \quad \frac{P_{9i}}{P_{t9i}} = 0.0990$$

Thus, $P_{9i} = (0.0990)(30 \text{ psia}) = 2.970 \text{ psia}$,

$$V_{9i} = \sqrt{Rg_c T_{t8}} \sqrt{\frac{2\gamma}{\gamma - 1}\left\{1 - \left(\frac{P_{9i}}{P_{t9i}}\right)^{(\gamma-1)/\gamma}\right\}}$$

$$V_{9i} = \sqrt{(1716)(2000)}\sqrt{\frac{2(1.33)}{0.33}\left\{1 - (0.0990)^{0.33/1.33}\right\}} = 3475 \text{ ft/s}$$

$$\left.\frac{A}{A^*}\right|_{9i} = \frac{P_{t9}}{P_{t8}}\frac{A_9}{C_D A_8} = \frac{0.98 \times 2.0}{0.98} = 2.00 \Rightarrow M_9 = 2.146 \quad \text{and} \quad \frac{P_9}{P_{t9i}} = 0.1025$$

Thus $P_9 = (0.1025)(0.98)(30 \text{ psia}) = 3.014 \text{ psia}$,

$$V_{9i} = \sqrt{(1716)(2000)}\sqrt{\frac{2(1.33)}{0.33}\left\{1 - (0.1025)^{0.33/1.33}\right\}} = 3456 \text{ ft/s}$$

$$C_V = V_9/V_{9i} = 0.9945$$

$$C_{fg} = (0.98)(0.9945)\left\{\frac{1 - \left(\frac{2.97}{30}\right)^{0.33/1.33}}{1 - \left(\frac{5.0}{30}\right)^{0.33/1.33}}\right\}^{1/2}\left\{1 + \frac{0.33}{2.66}\frac{1 - 5.0/3.014}{\left(\frac{29.4}{3.014}\right)^{0.33/1.33} - 1}\right\}$$

$$C_{fg} = 0.9593$$

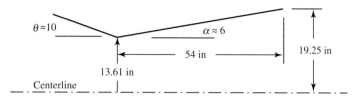

Fig. 10.77   Dimensions of example exhaust nozzle (one-dimensional calculation).

Figure 10.71b gives $\theta \approx 10$ deg for $C_D = 0.98$ and $A_9/A_8 = 2$. Likewise, Fig. 10.72 gives $\alpha \approx 6$ deg for $C_V = 0.9945$ and $A_9/A_8 = 2$. Thus $L_s \approx 54$ in. and the dimensions of the exhaust nozzle are shown in Fig. 10.77. The gross thrust can be calculated several ways: directly from Eq. (10.30)

$$F_g = \dot{m}_8 V_9/g_c + (P_9 - P_0)A_9$$

$$F_g = (200)(3456)/32.174 + (3.014 - 5.0)\,1165 = 19{,}170 \text{ lbf}$$

or from the ideal gross thrust and C_{fg} with

$$V_s = \sqrt{(1716)(2000)\,\frac{2(1.33)}{0.33}\left\{1 - \left(\frac{5}{30}\right)^{0.33/1.33}\right\}} = 3151 \text{ ft/s}$$

then

$$F_{gi} = \dot{m}_8 V_s/g_c = (200/0.98)(3151)/32.174 = 19{,}990 \text{ lbf}$$

$$F_g = C_{fg} F_{gi} = (0.9593)(19{,}990) = 19{,}170 \text{ lbf}$$

10.3.3.4   General thrust performance.   The gross *thrust coefficient* (C_{fg}) is a measure of the nozzle efficiency and accounts for nozzle losses due to friction, angularity, expansion, leakage and cooling air throttling. C_{fg} can be expressed in terms of the other nozzle coefficients as

$$C_{fg} = \frac{C_V C_A \dot{m}_7 V_{9i}/g_c + (P_{9i} - P_0)A_9}{\dot{m}_7 V_s/g_c} - \Delta C_{fg} \qquad (10.35)$$

where

C_V = Velocity coefficient, Eq. (10.24)
C_A = Angularity coefficient, Eq. (10.29)
$\dot{m}_7$ = Actual total mass flow rate supplied to the nozzle
V_{9i} = Ideal velocity at the nozzle exit based on A_9/A_8, C_D, and T_{t8}
P_{9i} = Ideal static pressure at the nozzle exit consistent with V_{9i}
A_9 = Nozzle physical exit area
V_s = Isentropic or fully expanded exit velocity based on P_{t8}/P_0 and T_{t8}
ΔC_{fg} = The sum of the loss in thrust coefficient due to leakage of gas from the nozzle and the loss due to changes in the cooling air flow

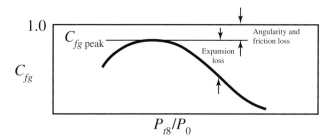

Fig. 10.78   Baseline gross thrust coefficient.

Basic aerodynamic analysis of nozzle efficiency includes the effects of thrust losses due to angularity and friction. The thrust losses due to over- or under-expansion are normally attributed to "off-design" operation. If losses due to leakage and cooling are neglected, then the other losses establish a base line gross thrust coefficient curve for a typical C-D nozzle as shown in Fig. 10.78. The one-dimensional analysis of the previous section did not include angularity losses, did include the expansion losses, and estimated frictional losses using π_d. The following analysis will include all three of the losses shown in Fig. 10.78.

From Eq. (10.35), the gross thrust coefficient of the base line nozzle (neglecting leakage and cooling) can be written as

$$C_{fg} = \frac{C_V C_A \dot{m}_7 V_{9i}/g_c + (P_{9i} - P_0)A_9}{\dot{m}_7 V_s/g_c} \tag{10.36}$$

At $C_{fg\,peak}$, $P_{9i} = P_0$ and $V_{9i} = V_s$. Therefore,

$$C_{fg} = C_V C_A \tag{10.37}$$

This method of calculating the performance of an axisymmetric two-dimensional nozzle, as demonstrated in the following example, is incorporated in the NOZZLE program provided with the AEDsys software package.

10.3.3.5   Example calculation—axisymmetric two-dimensional nozzle.
Given:

$$\dot{m}_8 = 200 \text{ lbm/s} \quad P_{t8} = 30 \text{ psia} \quad T_{t8} = 2000°\text{R}$$
$$A_9/A_8 = 2.0 \quad\quad \gamma = 1.33 \quad\quad P_0 = 5 \text{ psia}$$
$$\theta = 10 \deg \quad\quad\quad \alpha = 10 \deg \quad\quad R g_c = 1716 \text{ ft}^2/\text{s}^2\text{-°R}$$

Find the dimensions of an axisymmetric nozzle, C_{fg}, gross thrust, and approximate $\pi_n(P_{t9}/P_{t8})$.
Solution:

From Gas Tables, $MFP(@M_8 = 1) = 0.5224$, thus $A_8 = 570.7$ in.^{2}
From Fig. 10.71b, $C_D = 0.98$, thus $A_{8e} = 582.3$ in.^{2} and $r_8 = 13.61$ in.
Since $A_9/A_8 = 2.0$, then $A_9 = 1165$ in.^{2} and $r_9 = 19.25$ in.
With $r_8 = 13.61$ in., $r_9 = 19.25$ in., and $\alpha = 10$ deg, then $L_s = 32.0$ in.
The dimensions of the nozzle are shown in Fig. 10.79.

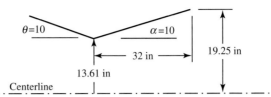

Fig. 10.79   Dimensions of example exhaust nozzle (axisymmetric two-dimensional calculation).

With $\alpha = 10$ deg and $A_9/A_8 = 2.0$, Fig. 10.72 gives $C_V = 0.9965$, Fig. 10.74 gives $C_A = 0.991$, and thus $C_{fg\ peak} = C_V C_A = 0.9875$.

$$\left.\frac{A}{A^*}\right|_{9i} = \frac{A_9}{C_D A_8} = \frac{2.0}{0.98} = 2.041 \Rightarrow M_{9i} = 2.168 \quad \text{and} \quad \frac{P_{9i}}{P_{t9i}} = 0.0990$$

Thus, $P_9 = (0.0990)(30\ \text{psia}) = 2.970\ \text{psia}$,

$$V_{9i} = \sqrt{Rg_c T_{t8}\,\frac{2\gamma}{\gamma-1}\left\{1 - \left(\frac{P_{9i}}{P_{t9i}}\right)^{(\gamma-1)/\gamma}\right\}}$$

$$V_{9i} = \sqrt{(1716)(2000)}\sqrt{\frac{2(1.33)}{0.33}\{1 - (0.0990)^{0.33/1.33}\}} = 3475\ \text{ft/s}$$

$$V_s = \sqrt{(1716)(2000)\,\frac{2(1.33)}{0.33}\left\{1 - \left(\frac{5}{30}\right)^{0.33/1.33}\right\}} = 3151$$

$$C_{fg} = \frac{C_{fg\ peak}\dot{m}_7 V_{9i}/g_c + (P_{9i} - P_0)A_9}{\dot{m}_7 V_s/g_c}$$

$$C_{fg} = \frac{(0.9875)(200)(3475)/32.174 + (2.970 - 5.0)1165}{(200)(3151)/32.174} = 0.9683$$

$$F_g = C_{fg\ peak}\dot{m}_7 V_{9i}/g_c + (P_{9i} - P_0)A_9$$

$$F_g = (0.9875)(200)(3475)/32.174 + (2.970 - 5.0)1165 = 18{,}966\ \text{lbf}$$

Since

$$C_V = \frac{V_9}{V_{9i}} = \sqrt{\frac{1 - (P_9/P_{t9})^{(\gamma-1)/\gamma}}{1 - (P_{9i}/P_{t8})^{(\gamma-1)/\gamma}}}$$

then

$$\frac{P_9}{P_{t9}} = \left\{1 - C_V^2\left[1 - \left(\frac{P_{9i}}{P_{t8}}\right)^{(\gamma-1)/\gamma}\right]\right\}^{\gamma/(\gamma-1)}$$

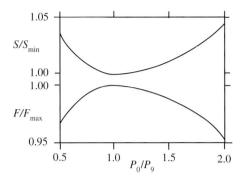

Fig. 10.80   Effect of P_0/P_9 on engine performance.

and

$$\frac{P_9}{P_{t9}} = \left\{1 - (0.9965)^2\left[1 - (0.0990)^{0.33/1.33}\right]\right\}^{1.33/0.33} = 0.1012$$

Thus, $M_9 = 2.154$, $A/A^*|_9 = 2.014$ and, finally, from one-dimensional flow,

$$\pi_n = \frac{P_{t9}}{P_{t8}} = C_D\frac{A/A^*|_9}{A_9/A_8} = (0.98)\frac{2.014}{2} = 0.9867$$

10.3.3.6 Off-design predicted performance.   The performance cycle equations developed in Chapter 5, listed in Appendix I, and implemented in AEDsys can be used to calculate the effects of non-perfect expansion at the nozzle exit. Figure 10.80 shows the effects of the pressure ratio P_0/P_9 on both uninstalled thrust and uninstalled thrust specific fuel consumption at a specific flight condition for a mixed-stream turbofan engine without afterburning. These plots show the trends that are typical for most turbojet and turbofan engines.

10.4   Example Engine Component Design: Inlet and Exhaust Nozzle

10.4.1   Inlet Design—AAF Engine

The requirements of the AAF inlet are specified in terms of required engine air mass flow rate by a plot of A_0 or A_0^* vs Mach number and altitude (see Fig. 7.E8) and in terms of total pressure recovery by military specification MIL-E-5008B [Eq. (4.12c)]. The type of inlet and its design are mainly determined by the type of aircraft, the required flight envelope, the range of angle of attack that the inlet will experience, and the maximum Mach number required. The AAF has a required maximum Mach number of 1.8 at 40 kft altitude. Since the lift coefficient increases 0.1 for each angle of attack, then the required 5g sustained turns at 0.9M/30 kft ($C_L = 0.7$ from Sec. 3.4.4) correspond to an angle of attack of about 7 deg and takeoff ($C_L = C_{L\,max}/k_{TO}^2 = 1.39$ from Sec. 3.4.4) will correspond to an angle of attack of about 12 deg. A two-dimensional external compression inlet is selected for this preliminary design of the AAF inlet because of its simplicity, ability to better match inlet airflow requirements of the AAF engine over the aircraft's mission, and ease of analysis.

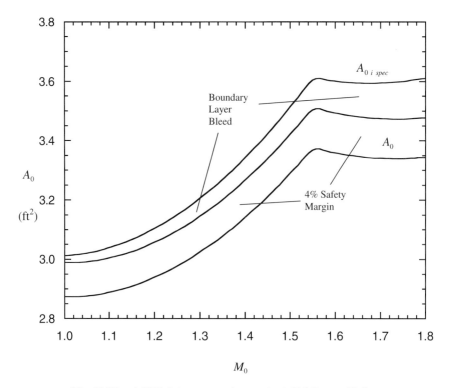

Fig. 10.E1   AAF inlet area requirements at 40 kft on cold day.

During preliminary engine sizing in Chapter 6, the sizing point for a fixed capture area, variable geometry inlet was selected to be 1.56M/40 kft on a cold day and resulted in a capture area (A_1) of 3.519 ft^2 (see Fig. 6.E3 in Sec. 6.4.5). Analysis and design of the AAF inlet is now performed at an altitude of 40 kft on a cold day over the range of Mach numbers of 1.0–1.8. The required engine flow area, required engine flow area plus 4% safety margin, and required inlet flow area are plotted in Fig. 10.E1 and tabulated in Table 10.E1 for the AAF. The required inlet flow area is composed of the required engine flow area, a 4% safety margin, and boundary layer bleed that varies linearly from 0% at 0.8M to 4% at 1.8M.

Figure 10.34 can be used to estimate the number of oblique shocks needed for an external compression inlet to meet the required total pressure recovery at the Mach 1.8 flight condition. Inspection of this figure shows that at least two oblique shocks plus a terminating normal shock are required for the AAF's external compression inlet. Equations (10.9) through (10.11) are the analytical tools needed to design 2-D external compression inlets and are imbedded in the INLET design program. They help us find the ramp angles of the external compression inlet that will meet or exceed the required total pressure recovery over the range of supersonic flight conditions (from MIL-E-5008B).

The AAF inlet needs to have excellent performance at supercruise to minimize fuel consumption and reasonable performance at Maximum Mach of 1.8. The

Table 10.E1   AAF inlet area requirements at 40 kft on cold day

	Inlet requirements based on engine performance cycle analysis calculations		Inlet area modified for safety margin and boundary layer bleed	
M_0	$\eta_{R\,spec}$	$A_{0\,spec}$, ft^2	$A_{0\,spec} + 4\%$, ft^2	$A_{0t\,spec}$, ft^2
1.0	1.0000	2.874	2.989	3.012
1.1	0.9966	2.889	3.005	3.039
1.2	0.9915	2.940	3.058	3.105
1.3	0.9852	3.025	3.146	3.207
1.4	0.9782	3.142	3.268	3.343
1.5	0.9706	3.290	3.422	3.514
1.52	0.9690	3.322	3.455	3.551
1.54	0.9674	3.357	3.491	3.591
1.56	0.9657	3.373	3.508	3.611
1.58	0.9641	3.365	3.500	3.605
1.6	0.9624	3.359	3.493	3.601
1.7	0.9537	3.341	3.475	3.595
1.8	0.9445	3.344	3.478	3.612

ramp angles of the AAF inlet will be designed for performance at supercruise and the inlet sized to meet the mass flow requirements over the range of flight Mach numbers. For a two-ramp external compression inlet, the inlet performance is presented in Fig. 10.E2 as total pressure recovery (η_R) contours from the INLET program for the supercruise Mach number of 1.5. This figure shows that the best total pressure recovery (η_R) of 0.9950 occurs at ramp angles 5.4° and 5.1° for the first and second ramps (θ_1, θ_2), respectively. Similarly ramp angles of 5° and 5° for θ_1 and θ_2 will give a total pressure recovery of 0.9947 and this combination is selected as for the AAF inlet at Mach 1.5. This provides more than the required total pressure recovery of 0.971 for this flight condition based on MIL-E-5008B.

Inlet design, like the design of other engine components, is iterative in nature. The INLET program helps this process enormously. Thus, the example design of the AAF inlet begins with the simplest inlet design (fixed inlet) and proceeds to more complex designs, if needed, until one is found that meets or exceeds the required performance.

10.4.1.1 *Inlet geometry and performance.*

Consider a fixed ramp, fixed area external compression inlet with ramp angles of 5° and 5° for the first and second ramps, respectively, as shown to scale in Fig. 10.E3. The location of the lower lip with respect to the intersection of the oblique shock wave is selected to be 1° further back than the angle of the first oblique shock. This location provides a small margin for subcritical operation of the inlet (normal shock moving forward from lip) without ingestion of the low total pressure layer that results when the normal shock intersects the second oblique shock.[19] The performance of the selected shock system was analyzed using the INLET program and the results are tabulated in Table 10.E2 under the heading of Selected Shock System. Since the required

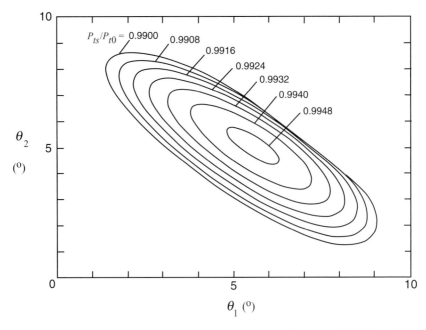

Fig. 10.E2   Total pressure recovery of a two-ramp external compression inlet at 1.5M.

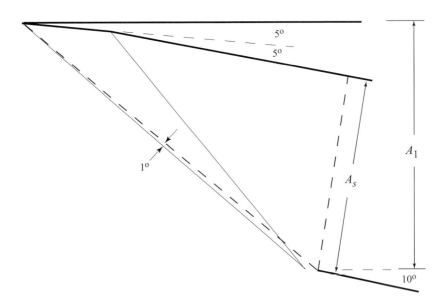

Fig. 10.E3   Two-ramp external compression inlet design.

Table 10.E2   Inlet design at 40 kft on cold day

	Selected shock system		Required			Selected		Resulting		
M_0	η_R	A_s/A_{0i}	A_0, ft^2	A_{0i}, ft^2	A_s, ft^2	A_1, ft^2	A_s, ft^2	A_{0i}, ft^2	$\dfrac{Fg_c}{\dot{m}_0 a_0}$	ϕ_{inlet}
1.0	1.0000	1.0000	2.874	3.012	3.012	4.000	3.203	3.203	3.500	0.0000
1.1	0.9989	0.9995	2.896	3.046	3.045	4.000	3.203	3.205	3.522	0.0025
1.2	0.9928	0.9990	2.944	3.109	3.106	4.000	3.203	3.206	3.542	0.0041
1.3	0.9972	0.9453	3.062	3.246	3.068	4.000	3.203	3.388	3.560	0.0073
1.4	0.9896	0.9290	3.179	3.382	3.142	4.000	3.203	3.447	3.576	0.0076
1.5	0.9947	0.8635	3.372	3.601	3.109	4.000	3.203	3.709	3.589	0.0112
1.52	0.9934	0.8582	3.406	3.640	3.124	4.000	3.203	3.732	3.590	0.0111
1.54	0.9916	0.8532	3.441	3.681	3.140	4.000	3.203	3.754	3.592	0.0109
1.56	0.9895	0.8484	3.456	3.700	3.139	4.000	3.203	3.775	3.588	0.0115
1.58	0.9871	0.8438	3.445	3.691	3.114	4.000	3.203	3.796	3.577	0.0132
1.6	0.9842	0.8394	3.435	3.683	3.091	4.000	3.203	3.816	3.565	0.0148
1.7	0.9654	0.8190	3.382	3.639	2.980	4.000	3.203	3.911	3.508	0.0247
1.8	0.9396	0.8007	3.327	3.593	2.877	4.000	3.203	4.000	3.453	0.0368

inlet areas of Table 10.E1 are based on the reference total pressure recovery of MIL-E-5008B, these are corrected for the inlet's shock system using Eq. (10.17). The required area A_s can then be calculated from the required A_{0i} and the A_0/A_s ratio of the inlet. The required inlet areas of Table 10.E2 show that the Mach 1.4 flight condition determines the size of the inlet with A_s selected to be 3.203 ft^2. Trigonometry gives the size of the inlet capture area (A_1) as 4.00 ft^2. The total pressure recovery and inlet flow area results are also presented in Figs. 10.E4 and 10.E5.

An analytical expression for estimating these inlet losses can be obtained by rewriting Eq. (6.8) in terms of the relevant flow areas for this inlet. Thus,

$$\phi_{inlet} = \frac{\left(\frac{A_{0i\,res}}{A_{0\,req}} - 1\right)\left\{M_0 - \left(\frac{2}{\gamma+1} + \frac{\gamma-1}{\gamma+1}M_0^2\right)^{1/2}\right\}}{Fg_c/(\dot{m}_0 a_0)} \qquad (10.E1)$$

The inlet's installation losses are listed in Table 10.E2 for cold day at 40 kft altitude. As an example of the inlet losses, ϕ_{inlet} at Mach 1.8 for inlet design ($A_{0i} = 4.000$ ft^2, $A_0 = 3.327$ ft^2, $Fg_c/\dot{m}_0 a_0 = 3.453$) using Eq. (10.E1) is 0.0368 vs 0.0420 estimated in Chapter 6. Their small values are encouraging in that this inlet design will meet the requirements, so an improved design will not be sought. If the installation losses were excessive, variable inlet geometry could be employed to reduce them.

10.4.1.2 Inlet diffuser duct.
The total pressure loss of the inlet due to friction was represented during engine cycle analysis by a value of 0.97 for $\pi_{d\,max}$. Assuming a total pressure loss of 0.5% for the boundary layer of the inlet up to its

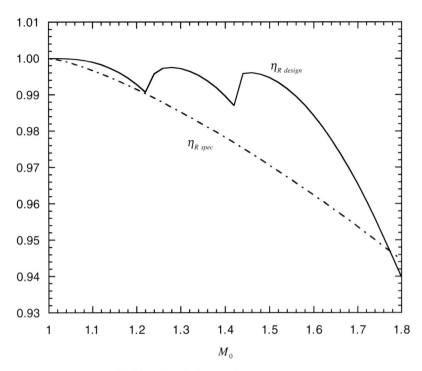

Fig. 10.E4   Inlet design total pressure recovery.

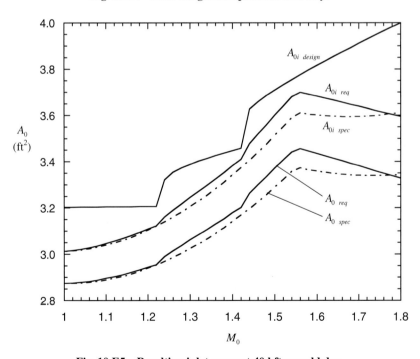

Fig. 10.E5   Resulting inlet areas at 40 kft on cold day.

throat, the total pressure loss remaining for the diffuser duct is 2.5% or $P_{te}/P_{ti} = 0.975$. Since the total pressure loss due to friction is proportional to the Mach number of the local flow, the maximum total pressure loss of the diffuser duct will occur at the maximum corrected mass flow rate (full throttle at 1.451M/36 kft on standard day) and the diffuser duct is designed at this condition.

At the design flight condition, the entrance area of the diffuser duct is 3.203 ft^2 and its exit area is 5.378 ft^2 (round duct of 15.7 in radius to match entrance of fan, see Sec. 8.3.1). The resulting area ratio AR is 1.679. For a corrected mass flow rate of 138.7 lbm/s at 1.451M/36 kft on cold day at station 0, the corrected mass flow at the entrance to the diffuser duct is

$$\dot{m}_{c\,diffuser\,entrance} = \frac{\dot{m}_{c0}}{\eta_R \times 0.995} = \frac{138.7}{0.956 \times 0.995} = 145.8 \text{ lbm/s}$$

where 0.956 is the AAF inlet total pressure recovery at 1.451M. The diffuser entrance Mach number (M_i) for $A_i = 3.203$ ft^2 is 0.713. For $P_{te}/P_{ti} = 0.975$, $M_i = 0.713$, $AR = 1.679$ and $\gamma = 1.4$, Eq. (9.67) gives the required diffuser effectiveness or efficiency (η_D) of 0.852. Figure 9.22 shows that this diffuser effectiveness can be obtained with a length-to-height ratio (L/H_i) of about 3.5. For a square inlet throat, the diffuser length will be about 6.26 ft.

The total pressure loss of the diffuser duct will be estimated at other engine operating conditions by assuming that the diffuser effectiveness (η_D) remains constant and the total pressure loss of the inlet before the throat remains constant at 0.5%. Thus for Combat Air Patrol (CAP) where $T_{req} = 1132$ lbf, $A_{0i}/A_0^* = 3.203/1.962 = 1.633$, and $M_{th} = 0.387$, the P_{te}/P_{ti} of the diffuser duct is given by

$$\frac{P_{te}}{P_{ti}} = 1 - \frac{\left(1 - \frac{1}{AR^2}\right)(1 - \eta_D)}{1 + \frac{2}{\gamma M_i^2}} \tag{9.67}$$

$$\frac{P_{te}}{P_{ti}} = 1 - \frac{\left(1 - \frac{1}{1.679^2}\right)(1 - 0.852)}{1 + \frac{2}{1.4 \times 0.387^2}} = 0.9909$$

Thus the total pressure ratio due to friction ($\pi_{d\,max}$) is 0.9859 (0.9909 $\times$ 0.995) versus the 0.97 value assumed in Chapter 6. Since the total pressure recovery of the inlet (η_R) is 1.0, then the total pressure ratio of the inlet (π_d) is 0.9859 resulting in lower fuel consumption for the Combat Air Patrol (CAP) leg.

10.4.1.3 Inlet size at zero flight speed.
The inlet size at zero flight speed is based on obtaining $\eta_R \geq 0.95$. First, the performance of the present AAF inlet design with $A_{th} = A_s = 3.203$ ft^2 is examined. From Chapter 6, the AAF engine at takeoff has $A_0^* = 2.842$ ft^2 for $\eta_R = 1.0$ and thus $A_{th}/A_0^* = 1.127$, which corresponds to $M_{th} = 0.660$. From Fig. 10.20 or Eq. (10.6), a sharp lip inlet ($A_{th}/A_b = \infty$) with $M_{th} = 0.66$ will have a total pressure recovery of 0.83. Thus, an auxiliary air inlet must be added to the AAF inlet design to reduce M_{th} and thus increase η_R.

Designing for $\eta_R = 0.95$, Eq. (10.6) gives $M_{th} = 0.285$. The required one-dimensional inlet throat area (A_{th}) is determined using

$$A_{th} = \frac{\dot{m}_c \sqrt{T_{std}}}{P_{std} MFP(M_{th})} \qquad (10.E2)$$

Thus

$$A_{th} = \frac{132.34\sqrt{518.7}}{2116 \times 0.2495} = 5.709 \text{ ft}^2$$

and an auxiliary air inlet whose throat area is 2.506 ft^2 (5.709 − 3.203) needs to be added to the AAF inlet design to meet the total pressure recovery goal of 0.95.

The AAF inlet with auxiliary air inlet door now has a total pressure recovery of 0.95 and ϕ_{inlet} of 0.0578 (assuming $A_1 = A_{th}$) as compared to the Chapter 6 values of $\eta_R = 1.0$ and $\phi_{inlet} = 0.0929$. The total pressure ratio of the diffuser duct with $AR \approx 1$ (5.378/5.709) is one. Thus, $\pi_{d\,max}$ is 0.995 and $\pi_d = (0.95)(0.995) = 0.9452$.

10.4.1.4 Inlet performance during takeoff.
Flow separation from the inside surface of the sharp lips of the inlet must be reduced during subsonic flight. An auxiliary air inlet was added to the AAF inlet to reduce the external flow separation at zero flight speed. This same auxiliary air inlet can be used to reduce flow separation at other subsonic flight conditions that have low total pressure recovery (η_R) with accompanying high inlet throat Mach number. The area ratio A_0/A_{th} can be used to identify those flight conditions at which lip flow separation may be a problem (see Fig. 10.58). Only Segments A, B, and C of Mission Phase 1-2 have A_0 larger than 4.0 ft^2 and Segments B and C have not yet been analyzed.

It is assumed that the auxiliary air inlet sized for zero flight speed is also used for Segments B and C, also giving them a total inlet throat area of 5.709 ft^2. Off-design engine cycle analyses give the required reference $A_{0\,spec}$ for Segments B and C of 16.55 ft^2 and 9.154 ft^2, respectively. The resulting A_0/A_{th}, M_{th}, and η_R (estimated from Fig. 10.58) are tabulated:

Segment	M_0	A_0/A_{th}	M_{th}	η_R
B	0.10	2.899	0.205	0.98
C	0.18	1.603	0.396	0.97

Based on a constant total pressure effectiveness (η_D) of the diffuser duct and Eq. (9.67), the inlet total pressure ratio (π_d) for Segments B and C are 0.97 and 0.98, respectively, as compared to the value of 0.97 used for both in the engine cycle analysis.

10.4.1.5 AAF inlet performance.
The performance of the AAF inlet design can now be calculated at all flight conditions and compared to the estimates

Table 10.E3 Inlet reference performance (Chapter 6)

Mission phases and segments		M_0/Alt, kft	T_{req}, lbf	$\dfrac{Fg_c}{\dot{m}_0 a_0}$	A_0^*, ft^2	$\dfrac{A_1}{A_0^*}$	ϕ_{inlet}	π_d[a]	$\dot{m}_{c0}$ lbm/s
1–2	A—Warm-up[b]	0.0/2	Mil	1.949	2.851	1.234	0.0558	0.970	142.3
1–2	B—Takeoff acceleration[b]	0.10/2	Max	2.980	2.842	1.238	0.0134	0.970	140.4
1–2	C—Takeoff rotation[b]	0.182/2	Max	2.906	2.822	1.247	0.0023	0.970	139.4
2–3	D—Horizontal acceleration[b]	0.441/2	Mil	1.559	2.691	1.308	0.0025	0.970	132.9
2–3	E—Climb/acceleration	0.875/16	Mil	1.610	2.879	1.222	0.0210	0.970	142.2
3–4	Subsonic cruise climb	0.900/42	1240	3.505	2.343	1.225	0.1032	0.970	115.5
5–6	Combat air patrol	0.700/30	1130	0.977	1.962	1.793	0.1239	0.970	96.92
6–7	F—Acceleration	1.090/30	Max	3.413	2.889	1.226	0.0048	0.957	141.8
6–7	G—Supersonic penetration	1.500/30	Max	1.503	2.882	1.436	0.0589	0.932	121.0
7–8	I—1.6M/5g turn	1.600/30	5370	2.326	2.930	1.502	0.0413	0.924	115.8
7–8	J—0.9M/5g turns	0.900/30	9210	3.202	2.878	1.223	0.0121	0.970	142.2
7–8	K—Acceleration	1.195/30	Max	3.429	2.940	1.232	0.0092	0.952	141.1
8–9	Escape dash	1.500/30	5320	1.497	2.872	1.441	0.0604	0.932	120.6
9–10	Zoom climb	1.326/39	Mil	1.692	3.053	1.242	0.0239	0.944	139.9
10–11	Subsonic cruise climb	0.900/48	929	3.509	2.330	1.226	0.1049	0.970	115.0
12–13	Loiter	0.397/10	844	4.995	1.428	2.464	0.0842	0.970	70.55
Maximum Mach number		1.80/40	9740	1.633	3.154	1.605	0.0445	0.907	108.3

[a] $\pi_{d\,max} = 0.97$. [b] $100°$F.

of Chapter 6 listed in Table 10.E3 where T is the installed thrust. The area listed under the A_0^* column for supersonic flight conditions are A_0. The inlet area (A_1) was 3.519 ft^2 and the auxiliary air inlet area (A_{1aux}) was also 3.519 ft^2. The value of A_0^* for the AAF inlet can be estimated by

$$A_0^* = A_{0spec}^* \times \eta_R / \eta_{R\,spec} \qquad (10.E3)$$

For supersonic operation of the inlet, the Mach number at the throat (entrance to the diffuser duct) is estimated by assuming constant corrected mass flow to the engine and is based on the throat area ($A_{th} = A_s$) having a value of 3.203 ft^2 for Mach numbers above 0.3 and a value of 5.709 ft^2 for Mach numbers below 0.3. The total pressure ratio of the diffuser duct is determined using Eq. (9.67) with $M_i = M_{th}$, $AR = 1.679$, and $\eta_D = 0.852$. The total pressure ratio of the inlet due to friction ($\pi_{d\,max}$) is estimated as 0.995 times the ratio across the diffuser duct. The net effect of the AAF inlet design on the installed thrust compared to the reference of Chapter 6 is estimated by the following relationship:

$$\frac{T}{T_{ref}} = \frac{F}{F_{ref}} \frac{(1 - \phi_{inlet} - \phi_{nozzle})}{(1 - \phi_{inlet} - \phi_{nozzle})_{ref}} \qquad (10.E4)$$

where

$$F / F_{ref} \approx \pi_d / \pi_{d\,spec}, \qquad \phi_{nozzle} = \phi_{nozzle\,ref}$$

and Eqs. (6.6), (10.E1), and (10.6) are used to find ϕ_{inlet}. The performance results for the AAF inlet design for the aircraft mission are given in Table 10.E4. Note that the resulting installed thrust (T) with the AAF inlet is greater than or nearly equal to the estimates of Chapter 6 (T_{ref}) for every mission phase. Most importantly, the AAF inlet has less installation drag on all the flight legs that consume the majority of the fuel except the Combat Air Patrol. Overall this inlet will give fuel saving for the mission due mainly to the reduced losses for the subsonic cruise, loiter, and supercruise flight conditions.

Figure 10.E6 shows the AAF inlet and diffuser duct design at two extreme flight conditions, takeoff and Mach 1.8 operation. Note the change in function of the top door from an auxiliary inlet at takeoff and low Mach number to a bypass exit for supersonic flight conditions.

10.4.2 Exhaust Nozzle Design—AAF Engine

The performance of the exhaust nozzle was modeled by one-dimensional adiabatic flow with constant total pressure ratio (π_n) for both the parametric and performance cycle analyses of the AAF engine. Also, the nozzle area ratio (A_9/A_8) and nozzle installation loss (ϕ_{nozzle}) at each flight condition were based on ideal expansion ($P_9/P_0 = 1$). The results of these preceding analyses are listed in Table 10.E5 for reference and serve as a starting point in the design of the AAF exhaust nozzle. The preliminary design of the AAF exhaust nozzle involves selection of the nozzle area schedule, design of the nozzle geometry, estimation of nozzle performance based on gross thrust coefficient, and determination of the installation losses.

10.4.2.1 Nozzle area schedule.
Providing the required throat area is a primary function of the nozzle control system. Working in conjunction with the afterburner fuel control, powered actuators are used to position the walls of the nozzle as shown in Fig. 10.61 to provide the desired nozzle throat area (A_8). The walls of the divergent section are mechanically linked to the remainder of the nozzle and thus the nozzle exit area (A_9) is determined by this linkage. The net effect of the actuator and linkage is an area ratio schedule for the exhaust nozzle like that shown in Fig. 10.E7. The nozzle design that follows assumes that the nozzle control system positions the nozzle throat at the required area (A_8). The schedule of nozzle area ratio (A_9/A_8) will be selected for the AAF.

The first task at hand is determining the desired nozzle schedule for the AAF engine. The logical starting point is to plot the required nozzle area ratio (A_9/A_8) versus throat area (A_8) from the data of Table 10.E5 to see if there are any general trends, as has been done in Fig. 10.E8. The mission flight legs that consume more than 400 lbf fuel are marked with a square and a triangle is used for those legs using less than 400 lbf fuel and these symbols are filled and unfilled for subsonic and supersonic flight conditions, respectively. Notice that this plot (Fig. 10.E8) for the AAF seems to be more of a random scattering of data points than a recognizable pattern—however supersonic flight conditions do generally require larger nozzle area ratios (A_9/A_8). A nozzle area ratio of about 1.28 is desired for subsonic cruise and a value of 1.96 is desired for supersonic cruise. For simplicity, a single value of the nozzle area ratio is first sought in the following section.

Table 10.E4 AAF design inlet performance

Mission phases and segments	η_R	A_0^*, ft²	A_1 or A_{0i}, ft²	$\dfrac{A}{A_0^*}$	ϕ_{inlet}	A_{th}, ft²	M_{th}	$\pi_{d\,max}$	$\dfrac{T}{T_{ref}}$
1–2 A—Warm-up[a]	0.95	2.708	5.709	1.949	0.0802	5.709	0.2885	0.9452	0.9492
1–2 B—Takeoff accel[a]	0.98	2.785	5.709	2.980	0.0209	5.709	0.2976	0.9751	0.9976
1–2 C—Takeoff rotation[a]	0.97	2.737	5.709	2.906	0.0067	5.709	0.2919	0.9652	0.9906
2–3 D—Horizontal accel[a]	1.0000	2.691	4.000	1.559	0.0000	3.203	0.5982	0.9749	1.0077
2–3 E—Climb/acceleration	1.0000	2.879	4.000	1.610	0.0519	3.203	0.6765	0.9707	0.9689
3–4 Subsonic cruise climb	1.0000	2.343	4.000	3.505	0.0610	3.203	0.4862	0.9807	1.0592
5–6 Combat air patrol	1.0000	1.962	4.000	0.977	0.1921	3.203	0.3874	0.9854	0.9368
6–7 F—Acceleration	0.9992	2.926	3.205	3.413	0.0021	3.203	0.9232	0.9572	1.0030
6–7 G—Supersonic penetration	0.9947	2.984	3.709	1.503	0.0648	3.203	0.8929	0.9544	1.0175
7–8 I—1.6M/5g turn	0.9842	3.027	3.816	2.326	0.0535	3.203	0.8136	0.9483	1.0132
7–8 J—0.9M/5g turns	1.0000	2.878	4.000	3.202	0.0288	3.203	0.676	0.9707	0.9838
7–8 K – Acceleration	0.9991	2.993	3.206	3.429	0.0033	3.203	0.8485	0.9608	1.0155
8–9 Escape dash	0.9947	2.973	3.709	1.497	0.0664	3.203	0.8929	0.9544	1.0174
9–10 Zoom climb	0.9959	3.124	3.426	1.692	0.0151	3.203	0.8656	0.9569	1.0228
10–11 Subsonic cruise climb	1.0000	2.330	4.000	3.509	0.0629	3.203	0.4826	0.9809	1.0593
12–13 Loiter	1.0000	1.428	4.000	4.995	0.0140	3.203	0.2694	0.9901	1.0989
Maximum mach number	0.9396	3.169	4.000	1.633	0.1008	3.203	0.7168	0.9101	0.9442

[a] 100°F.

Table 10.E5 Exhaust nozzle reference values

Mission phases and segments	M_0/Alt, kft	F_{req}, lbf	ϕ_{nozzle}	γ	A_8, ft^2	$\frac{P_{t9}}{P_0}$	A_9/A_8 $P_0/P_9 = 1$	$W_{F\,ref}$, lbf
1–2 A—Warm-up[a]	0.0/2	Mil	0.0	1.3362	1.576	2.993	1.140	214
1–2 B—Takeoff acceleration[a]	0.10/2	Max	0.0	1.3000	2.581	2.925	1.139	105
1–2 C—Takeoff rotation[a]	0.182/2	Max	0.0	1.3000	2.581	2.944	1.142	40
2–3 D—Horizontal acceleration[a]	0.441/2	Mil	0.0	1.3371	1.576	3.163	1.162	129
2–3 E—Climb/acceleration	0.875/23	Mil	0.0084	1.3361	1.576	5.010	1.425	428
3–4 Subsonic cruise climb	0.900/42	1403	0.0129	1.3405	1.576	3.996	1.279	524
5–6 Combat air patrol	0.700/30	1294	0.0001	1.3442	1.576	2.532	1.080	683
6–7 F—Acceleration	1.090/30	Max	0.0360	1.3000	2.688	6.235	1.627	391
6–7 G—Supersonic penetration	1.500/30	5730	0.0032	1.3383	1.576	9.052	1.961	1183
7–8 I—1.6M/5g turn	1.600/30	9612	0.0002	1.3000	2.054	9.772	2.077	470
7–8 J—0.9M/5g turns	0.900/30	7376	0.0042	1.3000	2.645	5.040	1.450	498
7–8 K—Acceleration	1.195/30	Max	0.0354	1.3000	2.640	7.079	1.747	346
8–9 Escape dash	1.500/30	5683	0.0033	1.3383	1.576	9.008	1.956	322
9–10 Zoom climb	1.326/39	Mil	0.0032	1.3361	1.576	8.377	1.925	44
10–11 Subsonic cruise climb	0.900/48	1054	0.0129	1.3409	1.576	3.989	1.278	491
12–13 Loiter	0.397/10	923	0.0001	1.3495	1.576	1.397	1.031	569
Total								6439
Maximum Mach number	1.80/40	Max	0.0006	1.3000	2.590	11.97	1.488[b]	—

[a]100°F. [b]From Table 6.E3, A_9 = 3.854.

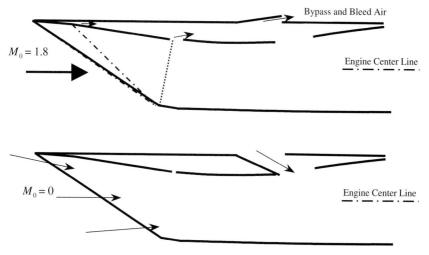

Fig. 10.E6   AAF inlet and diffuser duct design.

Single nozzle schedule.   A single nozzle schedule will give compromised performance resulting from the diverse requirements of the subsonic and supersonic cruise flight conditions. Nozzle area ratios from 1.3 to 1.7 are considered and input into the nozzle area schedule in the Mission window of the AEDsys program (does not include improved inlet estimates). Results of the mission calculations for A_9/A_8 of 1.4, 1.5, and 1.6 are listed in Table 10.E6 and plotted in Fig. 10.E9 for A_9/A_8 from 1.3 to 1.7. Note that the nozzle area ratio of about 1.5 gives the minimum overall mission fuel used that is 129 lbf greater that the reference values from Chapter 6 but 122 lbf less than the overall goal of 6690 lbf from Chapter 3.

Variable nozzle schedule.   Returning to the data of Table 10.E5, the first thing that can be noticed is that area ratios of 1.1–1.5 are desired at subsonic Mach numbers and area ratios of 1.9–2.0 are desired at supersonic Mach numbers. When

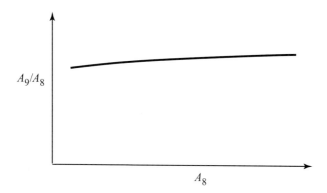

Fig. 10.E7   Example nozzle area schedule.

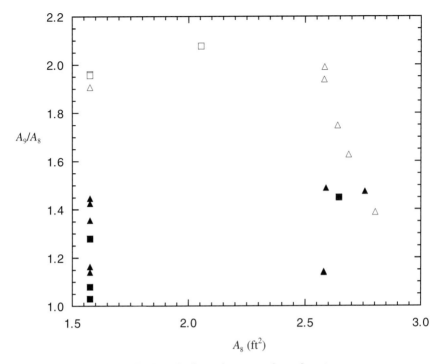

Fig. 10.E8 Required nozzle area ratio vs throat area.

Table 10.E6   AAF fuel burn for different exhaust nozzle area schedules

Mission phases and segments		M_0/Alt, kft	Mission fuel used—W_F, lbf			
			Ref	$A_9/A_8 = 1.4$	$A_9/A_8 = 1.5$	$A_9/A_8 = 1.6$
1–2	A—Warm-up[a]	0.0/2	214	214	214	214
1–2	B—Takeoff acceleration[a]	0.10/2	105	108	111	114
1–2	C—Takeoff rotation[a]	0.182/2	40	40	40	40
2–3	D—Horizontal acceleration[a]	0.441/2	129	132	134	138
2–3	E—Climb/acceleration	0.875/23	428	428	429	433
3–4	Subsonic cruise climb	0.900/42	524	526	530	534
5–6	Combat air patrol	0.700/30	683	719	738	759
6–7	F—Acceleration	1.090/30	391	398	394	393
6–7	G—Supersonic penetration	1.500/30	1183	1228	1211	1199
7–8	I—1.6M/5g turn	1.600/30	470	500	489	481
7–8	J—0.9M/5g turns	0.900/30	498	488	488	490
7–8	K—Acceleration	1.195/30	346	353	349	347
8–9	Escape dash	1.500/30	322	335	330	326
9–10	Zoom climb	1.326/39	44	46	45	45
10–11	Subsonic cruise climb	0.900/48	491	490	494	499
12–13	Loiter	0.397/10	569	566	566	565
Total		——	6439	6568	6561	6572

[a] $100°F$.

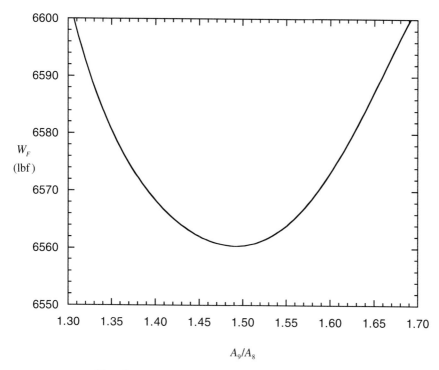

Fig. 10.E9   Mission fuel used vs nozzle area ratio.

the required nozzle area ratio (A_9/A_8) is plotted versus flight Mach number (M_0) for all mission legs, as was done in Fig. 10.E10, a definite pattern results. The variable nozzle area ratio shown by the solid line in Fig. 10.E10 is selected for the AAF and input into the nozzle area schedule in the Mission window of the AEDsys program (does not include improved inlet estimates). Results of the mission calculations for this variable nozzle area ratio are listed in Table 10.E7. Note that this nozzle area ratio schedule gives a mission fuel used that is only 25 lbf greater that the reference values from Chapter 6 and 226 lbf less than the overall goal of 6690 lbf from Chapter 3. Two nozzle actuators are required to obtain the schedule of Fig. 10.E10—one to set A_8 and the other to set A_9/A_8. The variable nozzle area schedule shown in Fig. 10.E10 is selected for the AAF.

10.4.2.2   AAF nozzle geometry.   The preliminary design of the exhaust nozzle geometry begins with selection of the maximum values for both the primary nozzle half-angle (θ) and the secondary nozzle half-angle (α) (see Figs. 10.71b, 10.72, and 10.74 in Sec. 10.3.3). The value of the primary nozzle half-angle directly affects the nozzle discharge coefficient (C_D) and thus the nozzle throat area (A_{8e}). An increase in θ reduces the length and weight of the primary nozzle, but may increase the overall weight of the nozzle due to the decrease in C_D that increases the secondary nozzle inlet and exit areas. The secondary nozzle

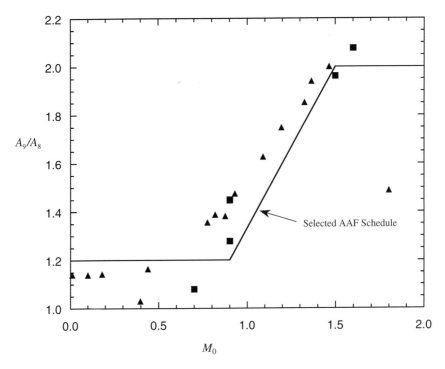

Fig. 10.E10   Required nozzle area ratio vs Mach number.

half-angle (α) affects both the velocity coefficient (C_V) and the angularity coefficient (C_A). For a fixed nozzle area ratio (A_9/A_8), an increase in α increases the velocity coefficient, decreases the angularity coefficient, decreases the nozzle length and weight, and changes the gross thrust coefficient. Hence, the selection of the nozzle half-angles (θ and α) is a complex design problem by itself when nozzle weight is included.

A maximum primary nozzle half-angle (θ) of 30 deg is selected, which corresponds to the nozzle throat at its military power setting. Likewise, a maximum secondary nozzle half-angle (α) of 12 deg is selected that corresponds to the 1.6M/5g turn with supersonic area ratio. The resulting nozzles at military and maximum power for area ratios of 1.2 and 2.0 are shown to scale in Fig. 10.E11 and Fig. 10.E12, respectively, using the NOZZLE program.

10.4.2.3   AAF nozzle performance.   The performance of the AAF exhaust nozzle of Figs. 10.E11 and 10.E12 is determined at each flight condition based on the general thrust performance method of Sec. 10.3.3, neglecting losses due to leakage and cooling ($\Delta C_{f_g} = 0$). Values for C_D, C_V, and C_A were obtained from Figs. 10.71b, 10.72, and 10.74, respectively. Equation (10.33) was used to calculate the gross thrust coefficient (C_{f_g}) where the gross thrust (F_g) is given by Eq. (10.27). The uninstalled thrust (F) was calculated by subtracting the

Table 10.E7   AAF fuel burn for variable exhaust nozzle area schedule

Mission phases and segments		M_0/Alt, kft	Mission fuel used— W_F, lbf		$\dfrac{A_9}{A_8}$	Power setting	F_{ref}, lbf
			Ref	Variable area ratio			
1–2	A—Warm-up[a]	0.0/2	214	214	1.200	Mil	8,846
1–2	B—Takeoff acceleration[a]	0.10/2	105	105	1.200	Max	13,563
1–2	C—Takeoff rotation[a]	0.182/2	40	40	1.200	Max	13,317
2–3	D—Horizontal acceleration[a]	0.441/2	129	129	1.200	Mil	7,493
2–3	E—Climb/acceleration	0.875/23	428	437	1.200	Mil	4,873
3–4	Subsonic cruise climb	0.900/42	524	522	1.200	$P_s = 0$	1,403
5–6	Combat air patrol	0.700/30	683	690	1.200	$P_s = 0$	1,294
6–7	F—Acceleration	1.090/30	391	393	1.453	Max	9,443
6–7	G—Supersonic penetration	1.500/30	1183	1183	2.000	$P_s = 0$	5,730
7–8	I—1.6M/5g turn	1.600/30	470	470	2.000	$P_s = 0$	9,612
7–8	J—0.9M/5g turns	0.900/30	498	509	1.200	$P_s = 0$	7,376
7–8	K—Acceleration	1.195/30	346	347	1.593	Max	10,596
8–9	Escape dash	1.500/30	322	322	2.000	$P_s = 0$	5,683
9–10	Zoom climb	1.326/39	44	45	1.769	Mil	3,948
10–11	Subsonic cruise climb	0.900/48	491	491	1.200	$P_s = 0$	1,054
12–13	Loiter	0.397/10	569	568	1.200	$P_s = 0$	923
Total		—	6439	6464	—	—	—
Maximum Mach number		1.80/40	—	—	2.000	Max	10,559

[a] 100°F.

momentum of the entering air $(\dot{m}_0 V_0/g_c)$ from F_g or

$$F = F_g - \dot{m}_0 V_0/g_c \qquad (10.E5)$$

The values used in calculating the nozzle performance and the results are presented in Table 10.E8. The ratio of the uninstalled thrust (F) based on this nozzle design to the uninstalled thrust from the performance analysis (F_{ref}) of Table 10.E7 is very close to unity for most flight conditions. Hence, the $\pi_n = 0.97$ and $P_0 = P_9$ used in the engine performance analysis predicts the performance of the AAF exhaust nozzle quite well over the flight conditions considered.

10.4.2.4 AAF nozzle installation losses.

The nozzle installation losses (ϕ_{nozzle}) of Chapter 6 were based on nozzle area ratios corresponding to ideal expansion ($P_9 = P_0$). Now that the geometry and nozzle area ratios of the AAF exhaust nozzle are known, a revised estimate of nozzle installation losses will be made based on the methods of Chapter 6 (see Sec. 6.2.3). The throat flow areas (A_8) listed in Table 10.E8 and the dimensions shown in Figs.10.E11 and 10.E12 are based on two-dimensional axisymmetric flow and result in nozzle areas that are 6.4% larger than the one-dimensional area calculated by the AEDsys cycle calculations. The minimum throat area was increased from its reference value by the reciprocal of the discharge coefficient ($1/C_D$) and the nozzle dimensions scaled accordingly. Based on the dimensions of Figs.10.E11 and 10.E12, the afterbody

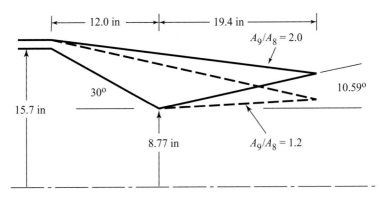

Fig. 10.E11   AAF exhaust nozzle—military power.

area (A_{10}) is estimated to be 6.30 ft^2 ($r_{10} = 17$ in.) and the afterbody length (L) is estimated to be 5 ft [two times the nozzle length of 31.4 in. (12.0 in. + 19.4 in.)]. These values are larger than the afterbody area of 5.153 ft^2 and afterbody length of 4.611 ft estimated in Chapter 6. The increase in afterbody area is mainly due to the 31.4 in inside diameter of the afterburner.

The AAF exhaust nozzle schedule was input into the Mission portion of the AEDsys program and the mission flown. The resulting installation losses for the AAF exhaust nozzle are listed in Table 10.E9. The ratios of installed thrust (T/T_{ref}) are also listed and are based on

$$\frac{T}{T_{ref}} \simeq \frac{F}{F_{ref}} \frac{(1 - \phi_{inlet} - \phi_{nozzle})}{(1 - \phi_{inlet} - \phi_{nozzle})_{ref}} \quad \text{where} \quad \phi_{inlet} = \phi_{inlet\ ref}$$

The results show that nozzle installation losses (ϕ_{nozzle}) do not appreciably change from the estimates of Chapter 6 (see Table 10.E9) except for the two acceleration flight conditions (segments 6–7 F and 7–8 K).

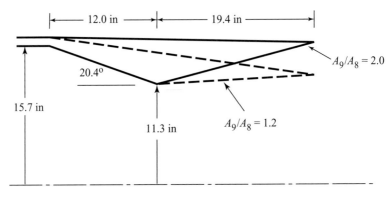

Fig. 10.E12   AAF exhaust nozzle—maximum power.

Table 10.E8 Exhaust nozzle performance

Mission phases and segments	A_{8ref}, ft²	θ	C_D	A_8, ft²	$\dfrac{A_9}{A_8}$	α	C_V	C_A	$\dot{m}_8$, lbm/s	P_{18}, psia	T_{18}, °R	F_g, lbf	$\dot{m}_0$, lbm/s	$\dot{m}_0 V_0/g$, lbf	F, lbf	F/F_{ref}
1–2 A—Warm-up[a]	1.576	30.00	0.939	1.679	1.200	2.467	0.9937	0.9980	127.10	42.17	1,553	8,875	126.04	45.4	8,829.6	0.99815
1–2 B—Takeoff acceleration[a]	2.581	20.54	0.956	2.698	1.200	3.127	0.9951	0.9973	132.24	41.20	3,600	14,048	126.40	456	13,592	1.00214
1–2 C—Takeoff rotation[a]	2.581	20.54	0.956	2.698	1.200	3.127	0.9951	0.9973	133.14	41.47	3,600	14,186	127.26	835	13,351	1.00255
2–3 D—Horizontal acceleration[a]	1.576	30.00	0.939	1.679	1.200	2.467	0.9937	0.9980	134.45	44.56	1,550	9,602	133.36	2,120	7,482	0.99853
2–3 E—Climb/acceleration	1.576	30.00	0.939	1.679	1.200	2.467	0.9937	0.9980	96.92	30.74	1,411	7,610	96.26	2,682	4,928	1.01129
3–4 Subsonic cruise climb	1.576	30.00	0.939	1.679	1.200	2.467	0.9937	0.9980	35.82	10.24	1,136	2,378	35.68	966	1,412	1.00641
5–6 Combat air patrol	1.576	30.00	0.939	1.679	1.200	2.467	0.9937	0.9980	43.13	11.49	983	2,206	43.05	932	1,274	0.98454
6–7 F—Acceleration	2.688	19.57	0.958	2.805	1.453	6.839	0.9956	0.9936	93.98	28.11	3,600	12,487	89.77	3,026	9,461	1.00191
6–7 G—Supersonic penetration	1.576	30.00	0.939	1.679	2.000	10.59	0.9971	0.9899	124.18	40.81	1,523	11,359	123.24	5,716	5,643	0.98482
7–8 I—1.6M/5g turn	2.054	25.43	0.947	2.168	2.000	12.00	0.9970	0.9869	136.64	44.05	2,442	16,187	133.61	6,610	9,577	0.99636
7–8 J—0.9M/5g turns	2.645	19.96	0.958	2.762	1.200	3.164	0.9951	0.9973	77.69	22.70	3,397	9,541	74.49	2,073	7,468	1.01247
7–8 K—Acceleration	2.640	20.01	0.957	2.757	1.593	8.628	0.9962	0.9914	104.79	31.92	3,600	14,276	100.12	3,700	10,576	0.99811
8–9 Escape dash	1.576	30.00	0.939	1.679	2.000	10.59	0.9971	0.9899	123.71	40.61	1,519	11,291	122.78	5,695	5,596	0.98469
9–10 Zoom climb	1.576	30.00	0.939	1.679	1.769	8.465	0.9958	0.9926	78.26	25.38	1,480	7,045	77.66	3,096	3,949	1.00025
10–11 Subsonic cruise climb	1.576	30.00	0.939	1.679	1.200	2.467	0.9937	0.9980	26.74	7.668	1,146	1,782	26.63	721	1,061	1.00664
12–13 Loiter	1.576	30.00	0.939	1.679	1.200	2.467	0.9937	0.9980	55.18	14.56	851	1,649	55.18	734	915	0.99133
Maximum Mach number	2.590	20.46	0.957	2.707	2.000	13.36	0.9963	0.9817	108.53	33.69	3,600	15,997	103.82	5,623	10,374	0.98248

[a]100°F.

Table 10.E9 Exhaust nozzle installation losses

Mission phases and segments	M_0/Alt, kft	$\dfrac{Fg_c}{\dot{m}_0 a_0}$	A_9, ft²	IMS[a]	C_D	A_0^*/A_0, ft²	ϕ_{nozzle}	T/T_{ref}
1–2 A—Warm-up[a]	0.0/2	1.946	1.888	0.2088	0.0002	2.851	0	0.9982
1–2 B—Takeoff acceleration[a]	0.10/2	2.976	3.086	0.0918	0.0001	2.842	0	1.0021
1–2 C—Takeoff rotation[a]	0.182/2	2.902	3.087	0.0918	0.0001	2.822	0	1.0026
2–3 D—Horizontal acceleration[a]	0.441/2	1.558	1.888	0.2088	0.0002	2.691	0	0.9985
2–3 E—Climb/acceleration[a]	0.875/23	1.590	1.888	0.2088	0.0002[c]	2.879	0.0104	1.0092
3–4 Subsonic cruise climb	0.900/42	1.609	1.888	0.2088	0.0002[c]	2.372	0.0157	1.0032
5–6 Combat air patrol	0.700/30	0.971	1.888	0.2088	0.0002	1.970	0.0002	0.9844
6–7 F—Acceleration	1.090/30	3.402	3.893	0.0466	0.1266[c]	2.889	0.0442	0.9933
6–7 G—Supersonic penetration	1.500/30	1.505	3.144	0.0879	0.0100	2.885	0.0055	0.9824
7–8 I—1.6M/5g turn	1.600/30	2.328	4.074	0.0390	0.0061	2.930	0.0016	0.9949
7–8 J—0.9M/5g turns	0.900/30	3.200	3.191	0.0847	0.0170[c]	2.878	0.0052	1.0114
7–8 K—Acceleration	1.195/30	3.422	4.192	0.0346	0.1160[c]	2.940	0.0434	0.9898
8–9 Escape dash	1.500/30	1.499	3.143	0.0879	0.0101	2.874	0.0055	0.9824
9–10 Zoom climb	1.326/39	1.690	2.778	0.1151	0.0156	3.053	0.0007	1.0028
10–11 Subsonic cruise climb	0.900/48	1.619	1.888	0.2088	0.0002[c]	2.335	0.0157	1.0034
12–13 Loiter	0.397/10	0.508	1.600	0.2512	0.0003	1.409	0.0003	0.9911
Maximum Mach number	1.80/40	1.642	3.343	0.0752	0.0116	3.154	0.0060	0.9769

[a]Based on $A_{10} = 6.30$ ft² and $L = 5.0$ ft.   [b]100°F.   [c]C_{DP}.

Table 10.E10 AAF installed performance

Mission phases and segments	M_0/Alt, kft	$(1 - \phi_i - \phi_n)_{ref}$	$1 - \phi_i - \phi_n$	$\pi_d/\pi_{d\,spec}$	F/F_{ref}	T/T_{ref}
1–2 A—Warm-up[a]	0.0/2	0.9444	0.9198	0.9354	0.9982	0.9093
1–2 B—Takeoff acceleration[a]	0.10/2	0.9866	0.9791	0.9954	1.0021	0.9900
1–2 C—Takeoff rotation[a]	0.182/2	0.9977	0.9933	0.9753	1.0000	0.9734
2–3 D—Horizontal acceleration[a]	0.441/2	0.9974	1.0000	1.0155	1.0000	1.0167
2–3 E—Climb/acceleration	0.875/23	0.9705	0.9377	1.0111	1.0113	0.9880
3–4 Subsonic cruise climb	0.900/42	0.8839	0.9233	1.0216	1.0064	1.0739
5–6 Combat air patrol	0.700/30	0.8761	0.8077	1.0265	0.9845	0.9317
6–7 F—Acceleration	1.090/30	0.9592	0.9537	0.9992	1.0019	0.9954
6–7 G—Supersonic penetration	1.500/30	0.9378	0.9297	1.0188	0.9848	0.9947
7–8 I—1.6M/5g turn	1.600/30	0.9584	0.9449	1.0102	0.9964	0.9923
7–8 J—0.9M/5g turns	0.900/30	0.9836	0.966	1.0111	1.0125	1.0054
7–8 K—Acceleration	1.195/30	0.9554	0.9533	1.0083	0.9981	1.0041
8–9 Escape dash	1.500/30	0.9362	0.9281	1.0188	1.0000	0.9945
9–10 Zoom climb	1.326/39	0.9729	0.9842	1.0094	1.0003	1.0214
10–11 Subsonic cruise climb	0.900/48	0.8823	0.9214	1.0218	1.0066	1.0741
12–13 Loiter	0.397/10	0.9156	0.9857	1.0314	0.9913	1.1007
Maximum Mach number	1.80/40	0.9549	0.8932	0.9431	0.9825	0.8667

[a] 100°F.

10.4.3 Closure

The present design configuration status is summarized by Figs. 10.E3, 10.E6, 10.E10, 10.E11, and 10.E12. Although this is a promising start because no real barriers to a successful design have been encountered, further iteration would focus on the following: 1) improvement of nozzle losses for Subsonic Cruise Climb legs; 2) improvement of inlet installation performance for Combat Air Patrol; and 3) impact of inlet and nozzle internal and external performance on the overall engine installed performance.

The combined influences of the inlet and nozzle designs on the installed thrust of the AAF with respect to the results of Chapter 6 (T/T_{ref}) are not apparent by viewing Tables 10.E4 and 10.E9. Since the AEDsys program does not currently include an improved inlet model, the overall performance of the AAF will be estimated using the data already gathered. The data now available in Tables 10.E3, 10.E4, 10.E5, 10.E8, and 10.E9 are used to estimate their combined influence on T/T_{ref} using

$$\frac{T}{T_{ref}} \simeq \frac{\pi_d}{\pi_{d\,spec}} \left. \frac{F}{F_{ref}} \right|_{nozzle} \frac{(1 - \phi_{inlet} - \phi_{nozzle})}{(1 - \phi_{inlet} - \phi_{nozzle})_{ref}}$$

where $F/F_{ref}|_{nozzle}$ is obtained from Table 10.E8. The results are presented in Table 10.E10. Note that the improvements in inlet performance more than compensate for the decrease in nozzle performance for the majority of mission phases and segments. The improved performance over the two Subsonic Cruise legs, Loiter leg, and other portions of the AAF mission will more than offset the lower installed thrust performance during the Combat Air Patrol and several other mission phase.

References

[1]Seddon, J., and Goldsmith, E. L., *Intake Aerodynamics*, 2nd ed., AIAA Education Series, AIAA, Reston, VA, 1999.

[2]Younghans, J., "Engine Inlet Systems and Integration with Airframe," *Lecture Notes for Aero Propulsion Short Course*, Univ. of Tennessee Space Inst., Tullahoma, TN, 1980.

[3]"Stealth Engine Advances Revealed in JSF Designs," *Aviation Week and Space Technology*, 19 March, 2001.

[4]Hawker Siddeley Aviation Ltd., *The Hawker Siddeley Harrier*, Bunhill Publications Ltd., London, 1970 (Reprint from *Aircraft Engineering*, Dec. 1969–Apr. 1970).

[5]Fabri, J. (ed), *Air Intake Problems in Supersonic Propulsion*, Pergamon, New York, 1958.

[6]Heiser, W., and Pratt, D., *Hypersonic Airbreathing Propulsion*, AIAA Education Series, AIAA, Reston, VA, 1994.

[7]Sedlock, D., and Bowers, D., *Inlet/Nozzle Airframe Integration*, Lecture Notes for Aircraft Design and Propulsion Design Courses, U.S. Air Force Academy, Colorado Springs, CO, 1984.

[8]Swan, W., "Performance Problems Related to Installation of Future Engines in Both Subsonic and Supersonic Transport Aircraft," March 1974.

[9]Oates, G. C., *Aerothermodynamics of Gas Turbine and Rocket Propulsion* (revised and enlarged), AIAA Education Series, AIAA, Reston, VA, 1988.

[10]Surber, L., "Trends in Airframe/Propulsion Integration," *Lecture Notes for Aircraft Design and Propulsion Design Courses*, U. S. Air Force Academy, Colorado Springs, CO, 1984.

[11]Kitchen, R., and Sedlock, D., "Subsonic Diffuser Development for Advanced Tactical Aircraft," AIAA Paper 83–168, 1983.

[12]Aronstein, D., and Piccirillo, A., *Have Blue and the F-117A: Evolution of the "Stealth Fighter,"* AIAA, Reston, VA, 1997.

[13]Hunter, L., and Cawthon, J., "Improved Supersonic Performance Design for the F-16 Inlet Modified for the J-79 Engine," AIAA Paper 84-1272, 1984.

[14]Stevens, C., Spong, E., and Oliphant, R., "Evaluation of a Statistical Method for Determining Peak Inlet Flow Distortion Using F-15 and F-18 Data," AIAA Paper 80-1109, 1980.

[15]Oates, G. C. (ed), *Aircraft Propulsion Systems Technology and Design*, AIAA Education Series, AIAA, Reston, VA, 1989.

[16]Oates, G. C. (ed), *Aerothermodynamics of Aircraft Engine Components*, AIAA Education Series, AIAA, Reston, VA, 1985.

[17]Stevens, H. L., "F-l5/Nonaxisymmetric Nozzle System Integration Study Support Program," NASA CR-135252, Feb. 1978.

[18]Summerfield, M., Foster, C. R., and Swan, W. C., "Flow Separation in Overexpanded Supersonic Exhaust Nozzles," *Jet Propulsion*, Vol. 24, Sept.–Oct. 1954, pp. 319–321.

[19]Tindell, R., "Inlet Drag and Stability Considerations for $M_0 = 2.00$ Design," AIAA Paper 80-1105, 1980.

Epilogue

The Air-to-Air Fighter (AAF) Engine design study has reached a successful conclusion. Satisfying solutions have been found to all of the important technical problems, and it is evident that the AAF systems requirements can be met. The competition may now proceed in earnest.

Further refinements and/or improvements, based on the quantitative results and physical insights gained during this first iteration, are certainly possible. The most likely candidates for further exploration have been noted along the way. We recommend, however, against doing this unless the system requirements change or superior analytical tools become available.

If no adequate AAF Engine design had been found, the next logical step would be to revise the engine cycle parameters and try again. It is even possible that no reasonable design point solution exists, in which case the aircraft parameters or even the mission requirements must be re-examined. Fortunately, that did not happen here, and we can happily close the book on the AAF Engine project.

We hope that you have found this journey as challenging, instructive, and rewarding as we have, and that you find the concepts, analyses, and software useful for their original purposes, and in ways that we have not envisioned.

Appendix A
Units and Conversion Factors

Table A.1   Basic definitions and constants

Constant	Definition
Time	1 h = 3600 s
Length	1 in. = 2.540 cm
	1 ft = 12 in.
	1 mile = 5280 ft
Mass	1 lbm = 0.45359 kg
	1 slug = 32.174 lbm
Force	1 lbf = 32.174 lbm-ft/s^2
	1 N = 1 kg-m/s^2
Energy	1 Btu = 778.16 ft-lbf
	1 J = 1 N-m
Power	1 hp = 550 ft-lbf/s
	1 W = 1 J/s
Pressure	1 atm = 14.696 lbf/in.^{2} = 2116.2 lbf/ft^2
	1 Pa = 1 N/m^2
Temperature	The Farenheit scale is $T(°F) = 1.8\ T(°C) + 32$
	where $T(°C)$ is the International Celsius scale.
	The Rankine scale is
	$\quad T(°R) = T(°F) + 459.69;$
	$\quad T(°R) = 1.8\ \{T(°C) + 273.16\};$
	$\quad T(°R) = 1.8\ T(K)$
	where $T(K)$ is the Kelvin scale.
Acceleration of standard gravity	$g_0 = 9.8067$ m/s^2 = 32.174 ft/s^2
Newton constant	$g_c = ma/F = 32.174$ lbm-ft/(lbf-s^2) for British Engineering
	$g_c = 1$ for SI

Table A.2   Scale factors

Number	Prefix	Symbol	Example
10^6	mega	M	megawatt (MW)
10^3	kilo	k	kilometer (km)
10^{-2}	centi	c	centimeter (cm)
10^{-3}	milli	m	milliwatt (mW)

Table A.3   Unit conversion factors

Quantity	British Engineering System unit	SI unit	Conversion factor (Multiply British Engineering system to get SI value)
Length	ft	m	0.3048
Mile	5280 ft	1.609 km	——
Nautical mile (NM)	6080 ft	1.853 km	——
Area	ft^2	m^2	0.09290
Mass	lbm	kg	0.4536
	slug	kg	14.59
Force	lbf	N	4.448
Pressure and	lbf/ft^2 (psf)	N/m^2 (Pa)	47.88
Stress	lbf/in.^{2} (psi)	kN/m^2 (kPa)	6.895
Density	lbm/ft^3	kg/m^3	16.02
Temperature difference	°R	K	1/1.8
Specific enthalpy and fuel heating value	Btu/lbm	kJ/kg	2.326
Specific heat (c_p, c_v)	Btu/(lbm-°R)	kJ/(kg-K)	4.187
Gas constant ($g_c R$)	ft^2/(s^2-°R)	m^2/(s^2-K)	0.1672
Rotational speed	rpm	rad/s	$2\pi/60 = 0.1047$
Specific thrust ($F/\dot{m}$)	lbf/(lbm/s)	N-s/kg = m/s	9.807
Thrust specific fuel consumption (S)	$\dfrac{\text{lbm fuel/h}}{\text{lbf thrust}} = \dfrac{\text{lbm}}{\text{lbf-h}}$	$\dfrac{\text{mg fuel/s}}{\text{N thrust}} = \dfrac{\text{mg}}{\text{N-s}}$	28.33
Power	hp	W	745.7
	Btu/hr	W	0.2931
Power specific fuel consumption (S_P)	$\dfrac{\text{lbm fuel/h}}{\text{hp}}$	$\dfrac{\text{mg/s}}{\text{W}} = \dfrac{\text{mg}}{\text{W-s}}$	0.1690

Appendix B
Altitude Tables

British Engineering (BE) units

h (kft)	δ (P/P_{std})	Standard day θ (T/T_{std})	Cold day θ (T/T_{std})	Hot day θ (T/T_{std})	Tropic day θ (T/T_{std})	h (kft)
0	1.0000	1.0000	0.7708	1.0849	1.0594	0
1	0.9644	0.9931	0.7972	1.0774	1.0520	1
2	0.9298	0.9863	0.8237	1.0700	1.0446	2
3	0.8963	0.9794	0.8501	1.0626	1.0372	3
4	0.8637	0.9725	0.8575	1.0552	1.0298	4
5	0.8321	0.9656	0.8575	1.0478	1.0224	5
6	0.8014	0.9588	0.8575	1.0404	1.0150	6
7	0.7717	0.9519	0.8575	1.0330	1.0076	7
8	0.7429	0.9450	0.8575	1.0256	1.0002	8
9	0.7149	0.9381	0.8575	1.0182	0.9928	9
10	0.6878	0.9313	0.8565	1.0108	0.9854	10
11	0.6616	0.9244	0.8502	1.0034	0.9780	11
12	0.6362	0.9175	0.8438	0.9960	0.9706	12
13	0.6115	0.9107	0.8375	0.9886	0.9632	13
14	0.5877	0.9038	0.8312	0.9812	0.9558	14
15	0.5646	0.8969	0.8248	0.9738	0.9484	15
16	0.5422	0.8901	0.8185	0.9664	0.9410	16
17	0.5206	0.8832	0.8121	0.9590	0.9336	17
18	0.4997	0.8763	0.8058	0.9516	0.9262	18
19	0.4795	0.8695	0.7994	0.9442	0.9188	19
20	0.4599	0.8626	0.7931	0.9368	0.9114	20
21	0.4410	0.8558	0.7867	0.9294	0.9040	21
22	0.4227	0.8489	0.7804	0.9220	0.8965	22
23	0.4051	0.8420	0.7740	0.9145	0.8891	23
24	0.3880	0.8352	0.7677	0.9071	0.8817	24
25	0.3716	0.8283	0.7613	0.8997	0.8743	25
26	0.3557	0.8215	0.7550	0.8923	0.8669	26
27	0.3404	0.8146	0.7486	0.8849	0.8595	27
28	0.3256	0.8077	0.7423	0.8775	0.8521	28
29	0.3113	0.8009	0.7360	0.8701	0.8447	29
30	0.2975	0.7940	0.7296	0.8627	0.8373	30
31	0.2843	0.7872	0.7233	0.8553	0.8299	31
32	0.2715	0.7803	0.7222	0.8479	0.8225	32

(continued)

British Engineering (BE) units (continued)

h (kft)	δ (P/P_{std})	Standard day θ (T/T_{std})	Cold day θ (T/T_{std})	Hot day θ (T/T_{std})	Tropic day θ (T/T_{std})	h (kft)
33	0.2592	0.7735	0.7222	0.8405	0.8151	33
34	0.2474	0.7666	0.7222	0.8331	0.8077	34
35	0.2360	0.7598	0.7222	0.8257	0.8003	35
36	0.2250	0.7529	0.7222	0.8183	0.7929	36
37	0.2145	0.7519	0.7222	0.8109	0.7855	37
38	0.2044	0.7519	0.7222	0.8035	0.7781	38
39	0.1949	0.7519	0.7222	0.7961	0.7707	39
40	0.1858	0.7519	0.7222	0.7939	0.7633	40
42	0.1688	0.7519	0.7222	0.7956	0.7485	42
44	0.1534	0.7519	0.7095	0.7973	0.7337	44
46	0.1394	0.7519	0.6907	0.7989	0.7188	46
48	0.1267	0.7519	0.6719	0.8006	0.7040	48
50	0.1151	0.7519	0.6532	0.8023	0.6892	50
52	0.1046	0.7519	0.6452	0.8040	0.6744	52
54	0.09507	0.7519	0.6452	0.8057	0.6768	54
56	0.08640	0.7519	0.6452	0.8074	0.6849	56
58	0.07852	0.7519	0.6452	0.8091	0.6929	58
60	0.07137	0.7519	0.6452	0.8108	0.7009	60
62	0.06486	0.7519	0.6514	0.8125	0.7090	62
64	0.05895	0.7519	0.6609	0.8142	0.7170	64
66	0.05358	0.7521	0.6704	0.8159	0.7251	66
68	0.04871	0.7542	0.6799	0.8166	0.7331	68
70	0.04429	0.7563	0.6894	0.8196	0.7396	70
72	0.04028	0.7584	0.6990	0.8226	0.7448	72
74	0.03665	0.7605	0.7075	0.8255	0.7501	74
76	0.03336	0.7626	0.7058	0.8285	0.7553	76
78	0.03036	0.7647	0.7042	0.8315	0.7606	78
80	0.02765	0.7668	0.7026	0.8344	0.7658	80
82	0.02518	0.7689	0.7009	0.8374	0.7711	82
84	0.02294	0.7710	0.6993	0.8403	0.7763	84
86	0.02091	0.7731	0.6976	0.8433	0.7816	86
88	0.01906	0.7752	0.6960	0.8463	0.7868	88
90	0.01738	0.7772	0.6944	0.8492	0.7921	90
92	0.01585	0.7793	0.6927	0.8522	0.7973	92
94	0.01446	0.7814	0.6911	0.8552	0.8026	94
96	0.01320	0.7835	0.6894	0.8581	0.8078	96
98	0.01204	0.7856	0.6878	0.8611	0.8130	98
100	0.01100	0.7877	0.6862	0.8640	0.8183	100

Density: $\rho = \rho_{std}\,\sigma = \rho_{std}\,(\delta/\theta)$. Speed of sound: $a = a_{std}\sqrt{\theta}$.
Reference values: $P_{std} = 2116.2\ \text{lbf/ft}^2$; $T_{std} = 518.69°\text{R}$; $\rho_{std} = 0.07647\ \text{lbm/ft}^3$; $a_{std} = 1116\ \text{ft/s}$.

System International (SI) units

h (km)	δ (P/P_{std})	Standard day θ (T/T_{std})	Cold day θ (T/T_{std})	Hot day θ (T/T_{std})	Tropic day θ (T/T_{std})	h (km)
0	1.0000	1.0000	0.7708	1.0849	1.0594	0
0.25	0.9707	0.9944	0.7925	1.0788	1.0534	0.25
0.50	0.9421	0.9887	0.8142	1.0727	1.0473	0.50
0.75	0.9142	0.9831	0.8358	1.0666	1.0412	0.75
1.00	0.8870	0.9774	0.8575	1.0606	1.0352	1.00
1.25	0.8604	0.9718	0.8575	1.0545	1.0291	1.25
1.50	0.8345	0.9662	0.8575	1.0484	1.0230	1.50
1.75	0.8093	0.9605	0.8575	1.0423	1.0169	1.75
2.00	0.7846	0.9549	0.8575	1.0363	1.0109	2.00
2.25	0.7606	0.9493	0.8575	1.0302	1.0048	2.25
2.50	0.7372	0.9436	0.8575	1.0241	0.9987	2.50
2.75	0.7143	0.9380	0.8575	1.0180	0.9926	2.75
3.00	0.6920	0.9324	0.8575	1.0120	0.9866	3.00
3.25	0.6703	0.9267	0.8523	1.0059	0.9805	3.25
3.50	0.6492	0.9211	0.8471	0.9998	0.9744	3.50
3.75	0.6286	0.9155	0.8419	0.9938	0.9683	3.75
4.00	0.6085	0.9098	0.8367	0.9877	0.9623	4.00
4.25	0.5890	0.9042	0.8315	0.9816	0.9562	4.25
4.50	0.5700	0.8986	0.8263	0.9755	0.9501	4.50
4.75	0.5514	0.8929	0.8211	0.9695	0.9441	4.75
5.00	0.5334	0.8873	0.8159	0.9634	0.9380	5.00
5.25	0.5159	0.8817	0.8107	0.9573	0.9319	5.25
5.50	0.4988	0.8760	0.8055	0.9512	0.9258	5.50
5.75	0.4822	0.8704	0.8003	0.9452	0.9198	5.75
6.00	0.4660	0.8648	0.7951	0.9391	0.9137	6.00
6.25	0.4503	0.8592	0.7899	0.9330	0.9076	6.25
6.50	0.4350	0.8535	0.7847	0.9269	0.9015	6.50
6.75	0.4201	0.8479	0.7795	0.9209	0.8955	6.75
7.00	0.4057	0.8423	0.7742	0.9148	0.8894	7.00
7.25	0.3916	0.8366	0.7690	0.9087	0.8833	7.25
7.50	0.3780	0.8310	0.7638	0.9027	0.8773	7.50
7.75	0.3647	0.8254	0.7586	0.8966	0.8712	7.75
8.00	0.3519	0.8198	0.7534	0.8905	0.8651	8.00
8.25	0.3393	0.8141	0.7482	0.8844	0.8590	8.25
8.50	0.3272	0.8085	0.7430	0.8784	0.8530	8.50
8.75	0.3154	0.8029	0.7378	0.8723	0.8469	8.75
9.00	0.3040	0.7973	0.7326	0.8662	0.8408	9.00
9.25	0.2929	0.7916	0.7274	0.8601	0.8347	9.25
9.50	0.2821	0.7860	0.7222	0.8541	0.8287	9.50
9.75	0.2717	0.7804	0.7222	0.8480	0.8226	9.75

(continued)

System International (SI) units (continued)

h (km)	δ (P/P_{std})	Standard day θ (T/T_{std})	Cold day θ (T/T_{std})	Hot day θ (T/T_{std})	Tropic day θ (T/T_{std})	h (km)
10.00	0.2615	0.7748	0.7222	0.8419	0.8165	10.00
10.25	0.2517	0.7692	0.7222	0.8358	0.8104	10.25
10.50	0.2422	0.7635	0.7222	0.8298	0.8044	10.50
10.75	0.2330	0.7579	0.7222	0.8237	0.7983	10.75
11.00	0.2240	0.7523	0.7222	0.8176	0.7922	11.00
11.25	0.2154	0.7519	0.7222	0.8116	0.7862	11.25
11.50	0.2071	0.7519	0.7222	0.8055	0.7801	11.50
11.75	0.1991	0.7519	0.7222	0.7994	0.7740	11.75
12.00	0.1915	0.7519	0.7222	0.7933	0.7679	12.00
12.25	0.1841	0.7519	0.7222	0.7940	0.7619	12.25
12.50	0.1770	0.7519	0.7222	0.7947	0.7558	12.50
12.75	0.1702	0.7519	0.7222	0.7954	0.7497	12.75
13.00	0.1636	0.7519	0.7222	0.7961	0.7436	13.00
13.25	0.1573	0.7519	0.7145	0.7968	0.7376	13.25
13.50	0.1513	0.7519	0.7068	0.7975	0.7315	13.50
13.75	0.1454	0.7519	0.6991	0.7982	0.7254	13.75
14.00	0.1399	0.7519	0.6914	0.7989	0.7193	14.00
14.25	0.1345	0.7519	0.6837	0.7996	0.7133	14.25
14.50	0.1293	0.7519	0.6760	0.8003	0.7072	14.50
14.75	0.1243	0.7519	0.6683	0.8010	0.7011	14.75
15.00	0.1195	0.7519	0.6606	0.8017	0.6951	15.00
15.25	0.1149	0.7519	0.6529	0.8024	0.6890	15.25
15.50	0.1105	0.7519	0.6452	0.8031	0.6829	15.50
15.75	0.1063	0.7519	0.6452	0.8037	0.6768	15.75
16.0	0.1022	0.7519	0.6452	0.8044	0.6708	16.0
16.5	0.09447	0.7519	0.6452	0.8058	0.6774	16.5
17.0	0.08734	0.7519	0.6452	0.8072	0.6839	17.0
17.5	0.08075	0.7519	0.6452	0.8086	0.6905	17.5
18.0	0.07466	0.7519	0.6452	0.8100	0.6971	18.0
18.5	0.06903	0.7519	0.6452	0.8114	0.7037	18.5
19.0	0.06383	0.7519	0.6531	0.8128	0.7103	19.0
19.5	0.05902	0.7519	0.6611	0.8142	0.7169	19.5
20.0	0.05457	0.7519	0.6691	0.8155	0.7235	20.0
20.5	0.05046	0.7534	0.6771	0.8169	0.7301	20.5
21.0	0.04667	0.7551	0.6851	0.8180	0.7367	21.0
21.5	0.04317	0.7568	0.6930	0.8204	0.7410	21.5
22.0	0.03995	0.7585	0.7010	0.8228	0.7453	22.0
23	0.03422	0.7620	0.7063	0.8277	0.7539	23

(continued)

System International (SI) units (continued)

h (km)	δ (P/P_{std})	Standard day θ (T/T_{std})	Cold day θ (T/T_{std})	Hot day θ (T/T_{std})	Tropic day θ (T/T_{std})	h (km)
24	0.02933	0.7654	0.7036	0.8326	0.7625	24
25	0.02516	0.7689	0.7009	0.8374	0.7711	25
26	0.02160	0.7723	0.6982	0.8423	0.7797	26
27	0.01855	0.7758	0.6955	0.8471	0.7883	27
28	0.01595	0.7792	0.6928	0.8520	0.7969	28
29	0.01372	0.7826	0.6901	0.8568	0.8056	29
30	0.01181	0.7861	0.6874	0.8617	0.8142	30

Density: $\rho = \rho_{std}$ $\sigma = \rho_{std}\,(\delta/\theta)$. Speed of sound: $a = a_{std}\sqrt{\theta}$.
Reference values: $P_{std} = 101{,}325$ N/m^2; $T_{std} = 288.15$ K; $\rho_{std} = 1.225$ kg/m^3; $a_{std} = 340.3$ m/s.

US Bureau of Standards, Standard Atmosphere 1976

A computer model (e.g., ATMOS program) of the standard day atmosphere can be written from the following material extracted from Ref. 4 of Chapter 1. All of the following is limited to geometric altitudes below 86 km—the original tables go higher, up to 1000 km. In addition, the correction for variation in mean molecular weight with altitude is very small below 86 km, so is neglected.

The geometric or actual altitude (h) is related to the geo-potential altitude (z), only used for internal calculations (a correction for variation of acceleration of gravity, used only for pressure and density calculations), by

$$z = r_0 h/(r_0 + h)$$

where $r_0 = 6{,}356.577$ km is the earth's radius.

The variation of temperature (T) with geo-potential altitude is represented by a continuous, piecewise linear relation,

$$T = T_i + L_i(z - z_i), \quad i = 0 \text{ through } 7,$$

with fit coefficients

i	z_i (km)	L_i (K/km)
0	0	−6.5
1	11	0.0
2	20	+1.0
3	32	+2.8
4	47	0.0
5	51	−2.8
6	71	−2.0
7	84.852	——

with $T_0 = 288.15$ K given, the corresponding values of temperature T_i can be readily generated from the given piecewise linear curve-fit. Note that z_7 corresponds exactly to $h = 86$ km.

The corresponding pressure (P), also a piecewise continuous function, is given by

$$P = P_i \left(\frac{T_i}{T}\right)^{\left(\frac{g_0 W_0}{R^* L_i}\right)}, \quad L_i \neq 0, \quad \text{or} \quad P = P_i \exp\left(\frac{-g_0 W_0 (z - z_i)}{R^* T_i}\right), \quad L_i = 0$$

where $g_0 = 9.80665$ m/s^2, $R^* = 8{,}314.32$ J/kmol-K, $W_0 = 28.9644$ kg/kmol, and the pressure calculations start from $P_0 = 101{,}325.0$ N/m^2.

The density (ρ) is given simply by the ideal gas law,

$$\rho = \frac{P W_0}{R^* T}$$

Cold, Hot, and Tropic Day Temperature Profiles

A computer model (e.g., ATMOS program) of the temperature profiles for Cold, Hot, and Tropic days can be written from the following material extracted from linear curve-fits of the data in Ref. 5 and 6 of Chapter 1. The following is limited to pressure altitudes below 30.5 km. The variation of temperature (T) with pressure altitude is represented by a continuous, piecewise linear relation,

$$T = T_i + L_i(h - h_i), \quad i = 0 \text{ through } 7,$$

with fit coefficients

| | Cold day | | Hot day | | Tropic day | |
i	h_i (km)	L_i (K/km)	h_i (km)	L_i (K/km)	h_i (km)	L_i (K/km)
0	0	+25	0	−7.0	0	−7.0
1	1	0	12	+0.8	16	+3.8
2	3	−6.0	20.5	+1.4	21	+2.48
3	9.5	0				
4	13	−8.88				
5	15.5	0				
6	18.5	+4.6				
7	22.5	−0.775				

With T_0 given below for the respective temperature profile, the corresponding values of temperature T_i can be readily generated from the given piecewise linear curve-fit.

Sea level base temperature

Day	Cold	Hot	Tropic
T_0 (K)	222.10	312.60	305.27

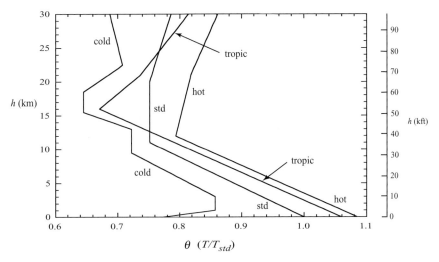

Fig. B.1   Four atmospheric temperature profiles vs pressure altitude (h).

The pressure at the pressure altitude comes directly from the standard atmosphere calculation for the geometric or actual altitude (h) equal to that pressure altitude. Figure B.1 shows the three non-standard day temperature profiles versus pressure altitude along with that of a standard day.

Appendix C
Gas Turbine Engine Data

Table C.1 Data for some military gas turbine engines

Model no.	Type	Max. thrust or power @ SLS	SFC[a] at max	Airflow, lbm/s	OPR[b] (stages)[c]	Maximum D, in.	Maximum L, in.	Maximum Weight, lbf	TTT[d], °F	Application
J57-P-23	TJ[e]	16,000 lbf	2.10	165	11.5 (16)	40	246	5,169	1,600	AB, F-102A, F-100D
J57-P-43WB	TJ	11,200 lbf	0.775	180	12 (16)	39	167.3	3,870	1,600	Water-injected, KC-135
J58-P[f]	TJ	32,500 lbf	—	450	6 (9)	—	—	—	—	AB, YF-12A, SR-71
J60-P-3	TJ	3,000 lbf	0.96	50	7 (9)	23.4	79.5	460	1,600	T-39A, C-140A
J69-T-25	TJ	1,025 lbf	1.14	20.5	3.9 (0.1)	22.3	43.3	364	1,525	T-37B
J75-P-17	TJ	24,500 lbf	2.15	252	12.0 (15)	43	237.6	5,875	1,610	AB, F-106A/B
J79-GE-17	TJ	17,820 lbf	1.965	170	13.5 (17)	39.1	208.7	3,855	1,210	AB, F-4E/G
J85-GE-5H	TJ	3,850 lbf	2.20	44	7 (8)	20.4	109.1	584	1,640	AB, T-38A/B
J85-GE-17	TJ	2,850 lbf	0.99	44	7 (8)	17.7	40.4	395	1,640	A-37B
J85-GE-21	TJ	5,000 lbf	2.13	51.9	8 (8)	20	116	667	1,790	AB, F-5E/F
PT6A-42	TP[g]	850 eshp	0.601	8.0	8 (3, 1)	19	67	391	—	C-12E
PT6A-45R	TP	1,197 eshp	0.553	8.6	8.7 (3, 1)	19	72	434	—	C-23A
T400-CP-400	TS[h]	1,800 shp	0.606	6.51	7 (3, 1)	43.5	66.3	716	1,920	Bell UH-1N
T406-AD-400	TS	6,150 shp	0.424	—	(14)	24.5	77.9	975	1,422	CV-22
T53-L-13	TS	1,400 shp	0.58	12.2	7 (5, 1)	23	47.6	549	1,720	Bell UH-1H, AH-1G
T55-L-11	TS	3,750 shp	0.52	—	8 (6, 1)	24.3	44	670	—	Boeing CH-47C
T56-A-7	TP	3,775 eshp	0.528	32.5	9.45 (14)	40.9	146	1,833	1,780	C-130B/E/F
T56-A-15	TP	4,591 eshp	0.54	32.5	9.55 (14)	44.6	146.3	1,848	1,970	C-130H/N/P
T58-GE-100	TS	1,500 shp	0.606	14	8.4 (10)	21.5	58.6	335	1,372	Sikorsky CH-3E, HH-3E, F
T64-GE-100	TS	4,330 shp	0.487	29.3	14 (14)	20.2	77.1	720	1,520	MH-53T
T700-GE-700	TS	1,622 shp	0.46	—	15 (5, 1)	25	47	423	1,563	UH-60A
T76-G-10	TS	715 shp	0.60	6.16	8.6 (2)	27.1	44.5	348	1,818	OV-IOA

[a]SFC = specific fuel consumption. [b]OPR = overall pressure ratio. [c](stages) = (axial, centrifugal) compressor stages.
[d]TIT = turbine inlet temperature. [e]TJ = turbojet. [f]J-58 Reference: Lockheed SR-71 by Jay Miller, Aerofax Minigraph 1, Aerofax, Inc., Arlington, TX, 1985.
[g]TP = turboprop. [h]TS = turboshaft.
(*Source:* Manufacturers' literature).

Table C.2 Data for some military turbofan engines

Model no.	Thrust, lbf	TSFC[a], (1/h)	Airflow, lbm/s	OPR[b]	Maximum		Weight (lbf)	TIT[c], °F	FPR[d]	BR[e]	Application
					D, in.	L, in.					
F100-PW-229	29,000 / 17,800	2.05 / 0.74	248	23.0	47	191	3,036	2,700	3.8	0.4	F-15, F16
F101-GE-102	30,780 / 17,390	2.460 / 0.562	356	26.8	55.2	180.7	4,448	2,550	2.31	1.91	B-1B
F103-GE-101	51,711	0.399	1,476	30.2	86.4	173	8,768	2,490	—	4.31	KC-10A
F107-WR-1C1	635	0.685	13.6	13.8	12	48.5	141	—	2.1	1.0	Air Launch Cruise Missile
F108-CF-100	21,634	0.363	785	23.7	72	115.4	4,610	2,228	1.5	6.0	KC-135R
F110-GE-100	28,620 / 18,330	2.08 / 1.47	254	30.4	46.5	182	3,895	—	2.98	0.80	F-16
F117-PW-100	41,700	0.33	—	31.8	84.5	146.8	7,100	—	—	5.8	(PW2040) C-17A
F118-GE-100	19,000	—	—	—	34.5	87	1,730	—	—	—	B-2
F404-GE-FID	10,000	—	—	25	35	159	—	—	—	0.34	F-117A
F404-GE-400	16,000	—	142	25	53	136.4	4,300	1,600	1.74	1.37	F-18, F-5G
JT3D-3B	18,000	0.535	458	13.6	45	123.7	3,252	1,076	—	1.03	(TF33-102) EC/RC-135
JT8D-7B	14,500	0.585	318	16.9	49	241.7	3,999	2,055	2.43	0.73	C-22, C-9, T-43A
TF30-P-111	25,100 / 14,560	2.450 / 0.686	260	21.8	53	136	3,900	1,600	1.7	1.55	F-111F
TF33-P-3	17,000	0.52	450	13.0	54	142	4,650	1,750	1.9	1.21	B-52H
TF33-P-7	21,000	0.56	498	16.0	50	100	1,421	2,234	1.5	6.42	C-141
TF34-GE-100	9,065	0.37	333	20.0	100	203	7,186	2,350	1.56	8.0	A-10
TF39-GE-1	40,805	0.315	1,549	26.0	40	114.5	3,511	2,165	2.45	0.76	C-5A
TF41-A-1B	14,500	0.647	260	20.0	40	50	625	—	1.54	2.67	A-7D, K
TFE731-2	3,500	0.504	113	17.7	50						C-21A

[a]TSFC = thrust specific fuel consumption. [b]OPR = overall pressure ratio. [c]TIT = turbine inlet temperature.
[d]FPR = fan pressure ratio. [e]BR = bypass ratio.
(*Sources*: Manufacturers' literature).

Table C.3   Data for some civil gas turbine engines

Model no.	Manufacturer	Takeoff				Cruise				Application
		Thrust, lbf	BR[a]	OPR[b]	Airflow, lbm/s	Alt, kft	Mach	Thrust, lbf	TSFC[c]	
CF6-50-C2	General Electric	52,500	4.31	30.4	1,476	35	0.80	11,555	0.630	DC10-10, A300B, 747-200
CF6-80-C2	General Electric	52,500	5.31	27.4	1,650	35	0.80	12,000	0.576	767-200, -300, -200ER
GE90-B4	General Electric	87,400	8.40	39.3	3,037	35	0.80	17,500	—	777
JT8D-15A	Pratt & Whitney	15,500	1.04	16.6	327	30	0.80	4,920	0.779	727, 737, DC9
JT9D-59A	Pratt & Whitney	53,000	4.90	24.5	1,639	35	0.85	11,950	0.646	DC1O-40, A300B, 747-200
PW2037	Pratt & Whitney	38,250	6.00	27.6	1,210	35	0.85	6,500	0.582	757-200
PW4052	Pratt & Whitney	52,000	5.00	27.5	1,700	—	—	—	—	767, A310-300
PW4084	Pratt & Whitney	87,900	6.41	34.4	2,550	35	0.83	—	—	777
CFM56-3	CFM International	23,500	5.00	22.6	655	35	0.85	4,890	0.667	737-300, -400, -500
CFM56-5C	CFM International	31,200	6.60	31.5	1,027	35	0.80	6,600	0.545	A340
RB211-524B	Rolls Royce	50,000	4.50	28.4	1,513	35	0.85	11,000	0.643	L1011-200, 747-200
RB211-535E	Rolls Royce	40,100	4.30	25.8	1,151	35	0.80	8,495	0.607	757-200
RB211-882	Rolls Royce	84,700	6.01	39.0	2,640	35	0.83	16,200	0.557	777
V2528-D5	International Aero Engines	28,000	4.70	30.5	825	35	0.80	5,773	0.574	MD-90
ALF5O2R-5	Textron Lycoming	6,970	5.70	12.2	—	25	0.70	2,250	0.720	BAe 146-200, -200
TFE731-5	Garrett	4,500	3.34	14.4	140	40	0.80	986	0.771	BAe 125-800
PW300	Pratt & Whitney Canada	4,750	4.50	23.0	180	40	0.80	1,113	0.675	BAe 1000
FJ44	Williams Rolls	1,900	3.28	12.8	63.3	30	0.70	600	0.750	
Olympus 593	Rolls Royce/SNECMA	38,000	0	11.3[d]	410	53	2.00	10,030	1.190	Concorde

[a]BR = bypass ratio.   [b]OPR = overall pressure ratio.   [d]At cruise.
[c]TSFC = thrust specific fuel consumption.
(*Sources:* Manufacturers' literature).

Table C.4   Temperature/pressure data for some engines

Temperature and pressure	Pegasus turbofan, separate exhaust	J57 turbojet w/AB exhaust	JT3D turbofan, separate exhaust	JT8D turbofan, mixed exhaust	JT9D turbofan, separate exhaust	F100-PW-100 turbofan, mixed w/AB exhaust
P_{t2}, psia	14.7	14.7	14.7	14.7	14.7	13.1
T_{t2}, °F	59	59	59	59	59	59
$P_{t2.5}$, psia	36.1	54	63	60	32.1	39.3
$T_{t2.5}$, °F	242	330	360	355	210	297
P_{t13}, psia	36.5	—	26	28	22.6	39.3
T_{t13}, °F	257	—	170	190	130	297
P_{t3}, psia	216.9	167	200	233	316	316
T_{t3}, °F	708	660	715	800	880	1,014
P_{t4}, psia	—	158	190	220	302	304
T_{t4}, °F	1,028	1,570	1,600	1,720	1,970	2,566
P_{t5} or P_{t6}, psia	29.3	36	—	2	20.9	38.0
T_{t5} or T_{t6}, °F	510	1,013	—	—	850	1,368
P_{t16}, psia	—	—	—	—	—	36.8
T_{t16}, °F	—	—	—	—	—	303
P_{t6A}, psia	—	—	—	29	—	37.5
T_{t6A}, °F	—	—	—	890	—	960
P_{t7}, psia	—	31.9	28	29	20.9	33.8
T_{t7}, °F	—	2,540	890	890	850	3,204
P_{t17}, psia	36.5	—	26	—	22.4	—
T_{t17}, °F	257	—	170	—	130	—
Bypass ratio α	1.4	0	1.36	1.1	5.0	0.69
Thrust, lbf	21,500	16,000	18,000	14,000	43,500	23,700
Airflow, lbm/s	444	167	460	315	1,495	224

Appendix D
Engine Performance:
Theta Break and Throttle Ratio

Aircraft engine designers have recently begun to capitalize on a fundamental cycle design choice most frequently referred to as either the theta break or throttle ratio in order to precisely tailor their machines for the expected range of flight conditions. In the development that follows, you will see that the theta break and throttle ratio are properties of the engine control system, so that this exploration takes us beyond the traditional boundaries of aerothermodynamics. This excursion has the added advantage of demonstrating how aircraft engines behave away from their reference or design conditions.

Although this development is based largely on a simplified model of the basic aircraft engine, namely, the single-shaft, uncooled turbojet, experience shows that the results apply equally well to all families of turbine engines. A special benefit of this development is the derivation of straightforward, transparent, algebraic equations that allow the basic workings of turbine engines to be understood and regulated. This presentation is based on material and nomenclature found in Chapters 4 and 5 of this textbook and draws heavily upon the foundational material found in Refs. 1 and 2.

Dimensionless Freestream Total Temperature

Because the freestream total temperature T_{t0} will be seen to exert a strong influence on the internal and overall behavior of the turbojet engine, it is useful to define a practical, dimensionless form. The dimensionless ratio of the freestream total temperature to the sea level static temperature of the standard atmosphere is called theta 0 and given the symbol θ_0. It is equal to the corrected freestream total temperature [cf. Eq. (5.22)] and is written as [cf. Eq. (1.1) or (4.5a-CPG)]

$$\theta_0 \doteq \frac{T_{t0}}{T_{std}} = \frac{T_0 \left(1 + \frac{\gamma_c - 1}{2} M_0^2\right)}{T_{std}} = \theta \tau_r \qquad (D.1)$$

Figure D.1 displays contours of constant θ_0 for the standard atmosphere of Ref. 3 and a wide range of flight conditions. The most important message of Fig. D.1 is that θ_0 can be used as a surrogate to condense various combinations of altitude and Mach number into a single parameter. That is, every point in the flight envelope possesses a specific value of θ_0, although the converse is not true. We will therefore refer hereinafter only to θ_0 rather than the associated flight conditions.

To increase your fluency with theta 0, it may be helpful to consider that for the standard atmosphere 1) $\theta_0 = 1$ at sea level static conditions; 2) θ_0 can be greater or less than 1; 3) θ_0 depends only on Mach number above 37 kft, the start of the

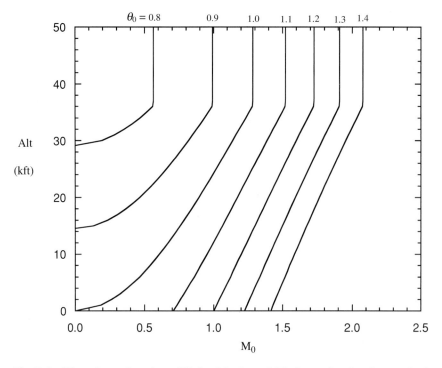

Fig. D.1   Theta 0 as a function of flight altitude and Mach number for the standard atmosphere of Ref. 3 with $\gamma = 1.4$.

constant static temperature tropopause; and 4) the entire range of θ_0 for modern aircraft operations is only about $0.8 < \theta_0 < 1.4$. Particular attention should be paid to the fact that the definition of theta 0 applies equally well to nonstandard atmospheres (e.g., Refs. 4 and 5), even though the standard atmosphere is generally found in textbooks because it is convenient, familiar, and relevant.

Single-Shaft Uncooled Turbojet Compressor Behavior

The behavior of a given single-shaft, uncooled turbojet compressor, sometimes referred to as its off-design behavior, can be evaluated as follows. To begin, Eq. (4.21a) for the power balance between the compressor and turbine is simplified and solved for the compressor total temperature ratio to yield

$$\tau_c - 1 = \eta_m(1 - \beta)(1 + f)(1 - \tau_t)\frac{1}{T_{std}}\frac{c_{pt}T_{t4}}{c_{pc}\theta_0} \tag{D.2}$$

Equation (D.2) reveals that compressor total temperature ratio depends only upon turbine total temperature ratio τ_t, throttle setting T_{t4}, and flight conditions θ_0. The other quantities in Eq. (D.2) are constant. The turbine total temperature ratio is now examined more closely.

Employing the logic and assumptions of Sec. 5.2.4, except that the choking downstream of the single shaft turbine occurs in the fixed area exhaust nozzle throat rather than the entry of the low-pressure turbine, the same two conclusions are reached, namely, the turbine total temperature ratio τ_t and turbine total pressure ratio π_t are constant. This result is valid for all important throttle settings, although it may fail when choking no longer occurs at very low throttle settings.

Consequently, Eq. (D.2) now reveals that τ_c varies only with the ratio of T_{t4} to θ_0. Moreover, the compressor total pressure ratio π_c, derived from the efficiency relationships of Eq. (4.9c-CPG), also varies only with the same ratio, to wit

$$\pi_c = [1 + \eta_c(\tau_c - 1)]^{\frac{\gamma_c}{\gamma_c - 1}} = \left(1 + C_1 \frac{T_{t4}}{\theta_0}\right)^{\frac{\gamma_c}{\gamma_c - 1}} \tag{D.3}$$

where

$$C_1 = \eta_c \eta_m (1 - \beta)(1 + f)(1 - \tau_t) \frac{1}{T_{std}} \frac{c_{pt}}{c_{pc}} \tag{D.4}$$

It is imperative that the reader pauses to absorb the significance of these results. First, the compressor responds primarily to the throttle setting and the flight condition. The causal chain of events is evidently remarkably short. Second, τ_c and π_c increase as the ratio T_{t4}/θ_0 increases. For example, π_c will increase when flight Mach number and T_{t4} are fixed and the aircraft climbs to higher altitudes, and decrease when flight altitude and T_{t4} are fixed and the aircraft is accelerated to higher Mach numbers.

Turbomachinery Limits: The Role of the Control System

Control systems must be designed to prevent aircraft engines from destroying themselves (see Appendix O). Two of the most stringent turbomachinery limitations are the maximum allowable values of π_c and T_{t4}. The control system situation can be easily grasped with the aid of Fig. D.2, which graphically depicts Eq. (D.3) for a typical, example compressor.

Figure D.2 makes several things clear. First, if θ_0 is decreased from a large initial value while T_{t4} is fixed at $T_{t4\,max}$, then $\pi_{c\,max}$ is reached when $\theta_0 = 1.1$. As θ_0 is further decreased, T_{t4} must then be reduced in order to protect the compressor from stalling. In fact, according to Eq. (D.3), the ratio of T_{t4}/θ_0 must remain constant at $3300/1.1 = 3000$ in order to maintain π_c constant at $\pi_{c\,max}$. Second, if θ_0 is increased from a small initial value while holding T_{t4}/θ_0 constant at 3000, then π_c will remain fixed at $\pi_{c\,max}$ as T_{t4} increases until, of course, $T_{t4\,max}$ is reached at $\theta_0 = 1.1$. As θ_0 further increases, $\pi_{c\,max}$ cannot any longer be maintained, and π_c gradually decreases. Third, and of *paramount* importance, is the fact that π_c and T_{t4} simultaneously reach their upper limits *only* at $\theta_0 = 1.1$. Finally, Fig. D.2 shows how θ_0 and T_{t4} may be chosen to reach lower values of π_c.

The Theta Break

The unique point, so visually striking in Fig. D.2, at which the control logic must switch from limiting π_c to limiting T_{t4}, is known as the theta break, or $\theta_{0\,break}$. Returning briefly to Fig. D.1, you will find it very convenient to visualize that at any

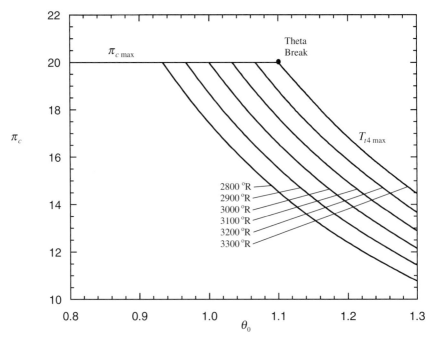

Fig. D.2 Compressor pressure ratio as a function θ_0 of and T_{t4} for a compressor with a reference point of $\pi_c = \pi_{c\,max} = 20$, $T_{t4} = T_{t4\,max} = 3300\,°R$ (1833 K), and $\theta_0 = 1.1$ [i.e., $C_1 = 0.0004512\ 1/°R$ (0.0008122 1/K) in Eq. (D.3)].

point in the flight envelope to the left of the theta break $\pi_c = \pi_{c\,max}$ and $T_{t4} < T_{t4\,max}$, while at any point to the right of the theta break $\pi_c < \pi_{c\,max}$ and $T_{t4} = T_{t4\,max}$. The relationship of the instantaneous value of θ_0 to $\theta_{0\,break}$ has important consequences to engine cycle performance. On the one hand, when $\theta_0 < \theta_{0\,break}$ and $T_{t4} < T_{t4\,max}$, the specific thrust of the engine is less than its inherent material capabilities would make possible. On the other hand, when $\theta_0 > \theta_{0\,break}$ and $\pi_c < \pi_{c\,max}$, the specific fuel consumption is more than its inherent thermal efficiency would make possible.

The designer would therefore strongly prefer to have the engine always operate at or very near $\theta_0 = \theta_{0\,break}$, but this is impossible because every aircraft has a flight envelope with a range of θ_0 (see Fig. D.1). The best available compromise is to chose a $\theta_{0\,break}$ that provides the best balance of engine performance over the expected range of flight conditions.

It is interesting to note that because early commercial and military aircraft primarily flew at or near $\theta_0 = 1$ they were successfully designed with $\theta_{0\,break} = 1$. Consequently, several generations of propulsion engineers took it for granted that aircraft engines always operated at $\pi_{c\,max}$ and $T_{t4\,max}$ under standard sea level static conditions. However, the special requirements of more recent aircraft such as the AAF of this textbook ($\theta_0 = 1.151$ at supercruise) have forced designers to select theta breaks different from one. These engines may operate either at $\pi_{c\,max}$ or $T_{t4\,max}$ at standard sea level static conditions, but never both.

The Throttle Ratio

We now determine how the designer can set the theta break for the engine. Assuming for the moment that $\theta_{0\,break} > 1$, which is the usual case, and returning to our earlier conclusion regarding the constancy of the ratio T_{t4}/θ_0, it follows immediately that, for the standard atmosphere

$$\frac{T_{t4\,max}}{\theta_{0\,break}} = \frac{T_{t4}}{\theta_0} = T_{t4\,SLS} \qquad (D.5)$$

because $\theta_{0SLS} = 1$, and that the throttle ratio, or TR, is therefore given by

$$TR \doteq \frac{T_{t4\,max}}{T_{t4\,SLS}} = \theta_{0\,break} \qquad (D.6)$$

The result is surprisingly simple. The engine must merely be designed to have the $T_{t4\,SLS}$ given by Eq. (D.5) at standard sea level static conditions and must have a control system that limits π_c to $\pi_{c\,max}$ and T_{t4} to $T_{t4\,max}$. Everything else follows directly. The terms throttle ratio and theta break are used interchangeably in the propulsion industry. This should present no problems because, as Eq. (D.6) shows, they are identical.

It is interesting and useful to determine the sea level flight Mach number at which the theta break is reached. Returning to Eq. (D.1) and recognizing that $\theta = 1$ at standard sea level conditions, it follows immediately that

$$M_{0\,break} = \sqrt{\frac{2}{\gamma_c - 1}(\theta_{0\,break} - 1)} \qquad (D.7)$$

Equation (D.7) offers the option of selecting a design or reference point at $M_{0\,break}$ and standard sea level static conditions with $\pi_c = \pi_{c\,max}$ and $T_{t4} = T_{t4\,max}$. For example, if it is desired to have $\theta_{0\,break} = 1.1$, then Eq. (D.7) shows that $M_{0\,break} = 0.707$.

It is satisfying to find that the results of AEDsys performance calculations always precisely and simultaneously obey both Eqs. (D.6) and (D.7).

In the rare case that $\theta_0 < 1$, a different concept is needed because $T_{t4\,SLS} = T_{t4\,max}$ and $\pi_c < \pi_{c\,max}$. One approach would be to use Eq. (D.3) to determine the value of π_c that exists at standard sea level static conditions. Figure D.1 shows that there is no relevant $M_{0\,break}$ for this case. Another approach would be to specify the standard day altitude (h) for $M_0 = 0$, as obtained from Eq. (D.1), as the altitude at which

$$\theta = \theta_{0\,break} \qquad (D.8)$$

We could, of course, refer to this as the h_{break}.

The Compressor or Engine Operating Line

Another pleasant discovery is that it is now possible to define and construct the required compressor or engine operating line with little further ado (cf. Secs. 5.3.2 and 7.4.3). It is often surprising, but nevertheless true, that this critical component characteristic can be determined from first principles. Applying conservation of mass to the compressor and turbine, and using the mass flow parameter of Sec. 1.9.3 and the corrected flow quantity definitions of Sec. 5.3.1, we find that

$$\dot{m}_{c2} = \frac{\pi_c \, \pi_b \, P_{std} A_4 MFP(M_4)}{(1 - \beta)(1 + f)} \sqrt{\frac{\theta_0}{T_{t4}}} = C_2 \pi_c \sqrt{\frac{\theta_0}{T_{t4}}} \tag{D.9}$$

where M_4 and $MFP(M_4)$ are constant because the turbine entry is presumed to be choked, and

$$C_2 = \frac{\pi_b \, P_{std} A_4 MFP(M_4)}{(1 - \beta)(1 + f)} \tag{D.10}$$

Figure D.3 corresponds to the example compressor of Fig. D.2 with a corrected mass flow rate of 100 lbm/s at the theta break. The straight lines portray Eq. (D.9) for several constant values of the ratio T_{t4}/θ_0. It should be noted that, because π_c cannot be less than one (and M_4 drops as the turbine entry unchokes at very low power), the straight lines do not continue to the origin.

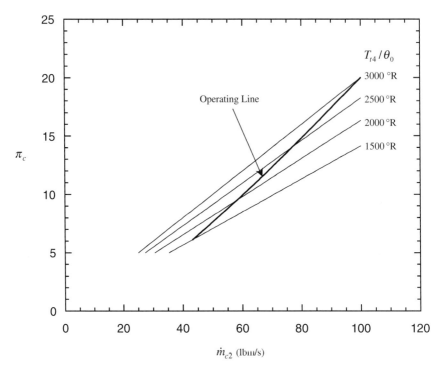

Fig. D.3 **The required operating line for a compressor with a reference point of** $\pi_c = \pi_{c\,max} = 20$, $T_{t4} = T_{t4\,max} = 3300\,°R$ (1833 K), $\theta_{0\,break} = 1.1$, **and** $\dot{m}_{c2} = 100$ **lbm/s** (45.36 kg/s) [i.e., $C_1 = 0.0004512\ 1/°R$ (0.0008122 1/K) **and** $C_2 = 273.9$ **lbm** $\sqrt{°R}/s$ (92.60 kg $\sqrt{K}/s$) **in Eq. (D.11)].**

Equation (D.9) may now be combined with Eq. (D.3) to yield the required compressor operating line, which also appears on Fig. D.3:

$$\dot{m}_{c2} = C_2 \pi_c \sqrt{\frac{C_1}{\pi_c^{(\gamma_c-1)/\gamma_c} - 1}} \qquad (D.11)$$

Because the operating line connects the dots on a series of rays radiating from the origin, it always has the characteristic shape found in Fig. D.3, which is quite similar to that of Figs. 5.5 and 7.E11.

The nature of the predicted and observed compressor operating line is obviously dictated by the choking of the fixed A_4 turbine inlet guide vane. We are therefore frequently asked at this point whether superior turbine engines could be designed if the choking assumption were revised. Indeed, a great deal of attention (Refs. 1 and 6) has been given to experimental turbines having a variable A_4 for cycle purposes. This work is stimulating and worth investigating. However, because the vast preponderance of aircraft engines are deliberately designed to operate with choked, fixed A_4 turbine guide vanes, it is the appropriate model for this textbook.

Uncooled Nonafterburning Single-Shaft Turbojet Performance: $\theta_0 < \theta_{0\,break}$

This line of attack is now carried to a higher level, namely, the evaluation of the overall performance of the entire engine. You will see that this has many benefits, including added insight into the behavior of engines and strong analytical support for the performance correlations of Secs. 2.3.2 and 3.3.2. The inspiration for this work is Sec. 7.3 of Ref. 1, and several intermediate steps are given next to guide the reader. Once again, even though the analysis strictly pertains only to a narrow class of engines, experience shows that it is broadly applicable. To the best of our knowledge, this is the first time that the complete algebraic analysis of overall engine performance *with control limits imposed* has been presented.

In this first case, the engine is operating at maximum thrust with $\theta_0 < \theta_{0\,break}$, so that T_{t4}/θ_0, τ_c, π_c, τ_t, and π_t are constant. Six quite reasonable assumptions are made that retain the underlying physics and provide adequate accuracy while greatly simplifying the analysis. They are that f and β are negligible compared with one, that π_d is constant, that $\eta_m = 1$, that the engine is always perfectly expanded (i.e., $P_9 = P_0$), and that in Eq. (4.18) $c_{pt}T_{t4}$ is negligible compared with h_{PR} (i.e., the energy density of the fuel greatly exceeds that of the combustion gases).

Following Ref. 1 closely, the uninstalled specific thrust of the engine is given by the expression

$$\frac{F}{\dot{m}_0} = \frac{a_0}{g_c}\left(M_0\frac{V_9}{V_0} - M_0\right) \qquad (D.12)$$

where

$$M_0\frac{V_9}{V_0} = \sqrt{\frac{2\tau_\lambda \tau_t}{\gamma_c - 1}\left[1 - \left(\frac{1}{\pi_r\,\pi_d\,\pi_c\,\pi_b\,\pi_t\,\pi_n}\right)^{\frac{\gamma_t-1}{\gamma_t}}\right]} \qquad (D.13)$$

so that

$$\frac{F}{\dot{m}_0 \sqrt{\theta}} = \frac{a_{std}}{g_c} f_1\{M_0\}$$　(D.14)

where

$$f_1\{M_0\} = \left\{ \sqrt{C_3 \tau_r \left[1 - \left(\frac{1}{\pi_d \, \pi_c \, \pi_b \, \pi_t \, \pi_n \, \pi_r} \right)^{\frac{\gamma_t - 1}{\gamma_t}} \right]} - M_0 \right\}$$　(D.15)

and

$$C_3 = \frac{2\tau_t}{\gamma_c - 1} \frac{1}{T_{std}} \frac{c_{pt}}{c_{pc}} \frac{T_{t4}}{\theta_0}$$　(D.16)

where it is important to note that, for the case at hand, f_1 is a function only of the instantaneous flight Mach number M_0 through M_0, π_r, and τ_r.

The amazing result of Eqs. (D.14–D.16) is that the uninstalled specific thrust behavior of this engine collapses into a single line, as shown in Fig. D.4 for the typical reference point turbojet engine that will be used as the example for the remainder of this exposition. Example turbojet engine reference point data are as follows: $T_{t4}/\theta_0 = 3000$; $\theta_{0\,break} = 1.1$; $h_{PR} = 18,000$ Btu/lbm; $\pi_c = 20$; $\tau_c = 2.592$; $\eta_c = 0.85$; $\tau_t = 0.7626$; $\pi_t = 0.2957$; $\eta_t = 0.91$; $\pi_d = 0.98$; $\gamma_c = 1.40$; $c_{pc} = 0.238$

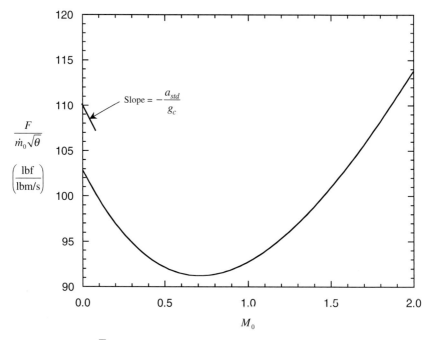

Fig. D.4　$F/(\dot{m}_0 \sqrt{\theta})$ vs M_0 according to Eqs. (D.14–D.16) for the example reference point uncooled, single-shaft turbojet engine ($C_3 = 25.57$, $\pi_d \pi_c \pi_b \pi_t \pi_n = 5.451$, and $\gamma_t = 1.33$).

Btu/lbm-°R; $\pi_b = 0.95$; $\gamma_t = 1.33$; $c_{pt} = 0.276$ Btu/lbm-°R; $\pi_n = 0.99$; $\eta_b = 0.95$; $\eta_m = 1$; $\beta = 0$; $1 + f \approx 1$. Figure D.4 clearly displays the thrust minimum or "bucket" normally experienced by turbojet engines as they accelerate but not usually captured by simple models. At first, $F/(\dot{m}_0\sqrt{\theta})$ decreases, reflecting the penalty of the captured freestream momentum, but it then increases as π_r, T_{t4}, and cycle thermal efficiency increase. At very small Mach numbers, where π_r and τ_r are essentially constant, Eq. (D.14) can be differentiated to reveal that the slope is $-a_{std}/g_c[34.7 \text{ lbf}/(\text{lmb/s})]$, as noted in Fig. D.4.

It should also be noted for later use that, using the definition of corrected compressor mass flow $\dot{m}_{c2}$ [cf. Eq. (5.23)], Eq. (D.14) becomes

$$F = \frac{a_{std}\delta_2\dot{m}_{c2}}{g_c}f_1\{M_0\} \tag{D.17}$$

Continuing to follow Ref. 1, the uninstalled specific fuel consumption of the engine is given by the expression

$$S = \frac{\dot{m}_f}{F} = \frac{f}{F/\dot{m}_0} = \frac{g_c}{a_{std}}\frac{c_{pc}T_0}{\eta_b h_{PR}}\frac{\tau_\lambda - \tau_r\tau_c}{\sqrt{\theta}f_1\{M_0\}} \tag{D.18}$$

which reduces to

$$\frac{S}{\sqrt{\theta}} = C_4\frac{\tau_r}{f_1\{M_0\}} \tag{D.19}$$

where

$$C_4 = \frac{g_c a_{std}}{\eta_b h_{PR}(\gamma_c - 1)}\left(\frac{c_{pt}}{c_{pc}}\frac{1}{T_{std}}\frac{T_{t4}}{\theta_0} - \tau_c\right) \tag{D.20}$$

The right-hand side of Eq. (D.19) is again independent of theta and collapses the uninstalled specific fuel consumption behavior of this engine into a single, almost straight line, as shown for the example reference point engine in Fig. D.5. The approximate linear curve fit shown in Fig. D.5 for the results given by Eq. (D.19) is

$$\frac{S}{\sqrt{\theta}} = 1.08 + 0.26M_0 \tag{D.21}$$

which compares very favorably with the installed specific fuel consumption correlation for the entire class of turbojet engines presented in Sec. 3.3.2.

Hot Day Flat Rating

An important footnote to these proceedings is to clarify a term often found in the propulsion literature, namely "hot day flat rating." It is imperative that commercial and military aircraft engines retain their standard day static thrust on "hot days," which generally means up to temperatures in the range of 90–110 °F (32–43 °C), as dictated by the specific application. Otherwise, some undesirable compromise to aircraft performance is required, such as leaving payload, fuel, and/or passengers behind. This is clearly a case of a nonstandard atmosphere.

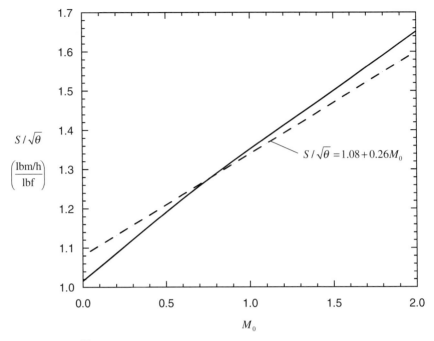

Fig. D.5 $S/\sqrt{\theta}$ vs M_0 according to Eqs. (D.19) and (D.21) for the example reference point uncooled, single-shaft turbojet engine [$C_4 = 3.012$ lbm/lbf-h (85.31 mg/N-s)].

Since Eq. (D.11) shows that the corrected mass flow is constant when θ_0 is less than or equal to $\theta_{0\,break}$, then Eq. (D.17) reveals that the static thrust is also constant there. Consequently, setting $\theta_{0\,break}$ [cf. Eq. (D.6)] at or above the ratio of the absolute hot day flat rating temperature to T_{std} guarantees that the constant static thrust requirement will be met. This is in every way equivalent to picking a theta break or throttle ratio for the engine that is greater than one, and leads to the conclusion that T_{t4} is actually somewhat less than $T_{t\,max}$ for most engines at standard sea level static conditions. For example, if $T_{t4\,max}$ first occurs at $1.1\,T_{std} = 1.1(518.7)\,°R = 570.6\,°R\ (111.9\,°F = 299.2\,K = 44.4\,°C)$, then the $\theta_{0\,break} = 1.1$ at $M_0 = 0$.

Uncooled Nonafterburning Single-Shaft Turbojet Performance: $\theta_0 > \theta_{0\,break}$

An entirely analogous and parallel development, with equally appealing results, is now carried out for the second case of maximum thrust with $\theta_0 > \theta_{0\,break}$. The corresponding situation is that $T_{t4} = T_{t4\,max}$, τ_t, and π_t are fixed and the same six assumptions are made.

Equations (D.12) and (D.13) become

$$\frac{F}{\dot{m}_0\sqrt{\theta}} = \frac{a_{std}}{g_c} f_2\{M_0, \theta\} \tag{D.22}$$

where

$$f_2\{M_0, \theta\} = \left\{ \sqrt{\frac{C_5}{\theta}\left[1 - \left(\frac{1}{\pi_d \pi_b \pi_t \pi_n}\right)^{\frac{\gamma_t - 1}{\gamma_t}}\left(\frac{1}{\tau_r + C_6/\theta}\right)^{\frac{\gamma_c}{\gamma_t}\frac{\gamma_t - 1}{\gamma_c - 1}}\right]} - M_0 \right\}$$

(D.23)

and

$$\tau_\lambda^* = \frac{c_{pt} T_{t4\,max}}{c_{pc} T_{std}}$$

(D.24)

and

$$C_5 = \frac{2\tau_t \tau_\lambda^*}{\gamma_c - 1}$$

(D.25)

and

$$C_6 = \eta_c(1 - \tau_t)\tau_\lambda^*$$

(D.26)

The results of Eqs. (D.22–D.26) are shown in Fig. D.6 for the example reference point engine. $F/(\dot{m}_0\sqrt{\theta})$ decreases continuously with increasing M_0 because π_c is decreasing while $T_{t4} = T_{t4\,max}$ remains constant. When M_0 is small, the slope is $-a_{std}/g_c$, for the same reason as in the preceding case, as noted in Fig. D.6.

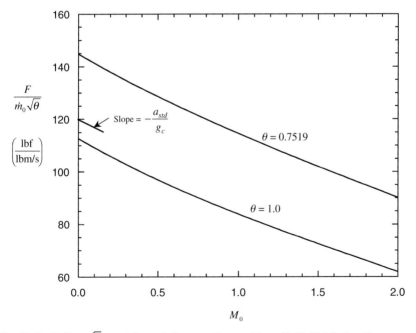

Fig. D.6 $F/(\dot{m}_0\sqrt{\theta})$ vs M_0 and θ according to Eqs. (D.22–D.26) for the example reference point uncooled, single-shaft turbojet engine ($C_5 = 28.15$, $C_6 = 1.489$, $\pi_d \pi_b \pi_t \pi_n = 0.2725$, and $\gamma_t = 1.33$).

Continuing, the uninstalled specific fuel consumption of the engine is given by the expression

$$S = \frac{\dot{m}_f}{F} = \frac{f}{F/\dot{m}_0} = \frac{c_{pc}T_0}{\eta_b\, h_{PR}} \frac{(\tau_\lambda - \tau_t\, \tau_c)}{F/\dot{m}_0} \tag{D.27}$$

which reduces to

$$\frac{S}{\sqrt{\theta}} = \frac{C_7 \left\{ \dfrac{\tau_t\, \tau_\lambda^*}{\theta} - \tau_r \right\}}{F/(\dot{m}_0\sqrt{\theta})} \tag{D.28}$$

where

$$C_7 = \frac{c_{pc}T_{std}}{\eta_b\, h_{PR}} \tag{D.29}$$

The results of Eqs. (D.28) and (D.29) are shown in Fig. D.7 for the example reference point engine. Because of compensating changes in the numerator and denominator, the right-hand side of Eq. (D.28) is weakly dependent on θ for the entire range of standard day values of θ. The linear curve fit of Eq. (D.21) again shows excellent agreement with the simple model, further supporting the turbojet correlation of Sec. 3.3.2.

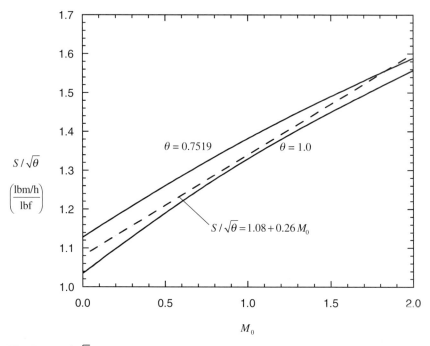

Fig. D.7 $S/\sqrt{\theta}$ vs M_0 and θ according to Eqs. (D.28), (D.29), and (D.21) for the example reference point uncooled, single-shaft turbojet engine ($C_7 = 0.006998$ and $\tau_\lambda^* = 7.378$).

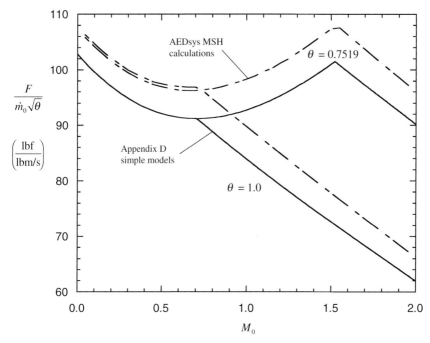

Fig. D.8   Comparison of $F/(\dot{m}_0\sqrt{\theta})$ vs M_0 and θ for the simple models versus AEDSys MSH performance computations for the example reference point turbojet engine with $\theta_{0\,break} = 1.1$.

Figure D.8 compares the results of the simple model calculations of $F/(\dot{m}_0\sqrt{\theta})$ with those of the AEDsys modified specific heat (MSH) performance model computations for the same example reference point turbojet engine. They are very similar because the two methods solve essentially the same equations. The majority of the approximately 5% difference is due to the fact that AEDsys accounts for the added mass flow of fuel that is neglected by the simple models. Similar agreement is obtained for the quantity $S/\sqrt{\theta}$. Based on these results, one may comfortably conclude that the simple models provide a reasonable representation of reality.

Above and Beyond

It should be obvious that the groundwork just developed can be extended to investigate a wide variety of variations on the turbojet theme. On the one hand, more complex cycles, including bypass or afterburning, can be analyzed using this approach. We encourage you to explore them on your own. You will find these journeys stimulating and rewarding.

On the other hand, important questions about individual component operation can be answered as they arise. For example, the definitions of cycle parameters and Eq. (D.2) can be used to reveal the behavior of the compressor discharge total temperature T_{t3} as a function of flight condition for the turbojet cycle of this appendix. This quantity is extremely important from the design standpoint because it controls the cycle thermal efficiency (see Appendix E) and is limited by available material capabilities (see Sec. 8.2.3). After some exhilarating algebraic manipulations, it can be shown that

$$T_{t3}/T_{std} = \theta_3 = \theta_0 \tau_{c\,max} \qquad \text{for } \theta_0 \leq \theta_{0\,break} \quad \text{(D.30)}$$

and

$$T_{t3}/T_{std} = \theta_3 = \theta_0 + \theta_{0\,break}(\tau_{c\,max} - 1) \qquad \text{for } \theta_0 > \theta_{0\,break} \quad \text{(D.31)}$$

These remarkably simple expressions reveal that T_{t3} is always directly proportional to θ_0, although the slope is less after the theta break than before. The consequences of this situation are swift and clear. For fighter aircraft that have a large flight envelope and spend a small fraction of their flight time at their maximum θ_0, the compressor discharge temperature is usually less than the maximum allowable value. For supersonic transport aircraft that cruise at their maximum θ_0, the compressor discharge temperature is usually at the maximum allowable value. Thus, the T_{t3} material selection problem can be much more difficult for the transport aircraft than for the fighter aircraft.

But the fun is not over yet. Equations (D.30) and (D.31) allow the possibility that $T_{t3\,max}$ will be reached before the design $\theta_{0\,break}$, and the throttle will have to be retarded. For a typical value of $T_{t3\,max}/T_{std}$ of 3.5 and the $\tau_{c\,max} = 2.592$ and $\theta_{0\,break} = 1.1$ of the example turbojet, Eq. (D.31) shows that θ_0 must exceed 1.75 (i.e., $M_0 > 1.94$ at $\theta = 1$) before the compressor discharge materials limitation is reached. Although there is no conflict for this example case, we have discovered another boundary that could be placed on Fig. D.1 that must be examined for every new engine. And once this boundary is reached, another break in all of the performance parameters will occur. Can you use Eq. (D.31) to determine the general behavior of τ_c and T_{t4} once $T_{t3\,max}$ is reached?

You will find it worthwhile to repeat this investigation for the compressor discharge pressure, which is also limited by available materials.

And so it goes. We hope that these and the other examples found in this textbook encourage you to use this framework as the *first* resort when trying to understand the fundamentals of jet engine operation.

References

[1] Oates, G. C., *The Aerothermodynamics of Gas Turbine and Rocket Propulsion*, 3rd ed., AIAA Education Series, AIAA, Reston, VA, 1997.

[2] Mattingly, J. D., *Elements of Gas Turbine Propulsion*, McGraw–Hill, New York, 1996.

[3] *U. S. Standard Atmosphere, 1976*, U.S. Government Printing Office, Washington, DC, Oct. 1976.

[4] "Climatic Information to Determine Design and Test Requirements for Military Equipment," U.S. Dept. of Defense, *MIL-STD-210C*, Rev. C, Jan. 1997.

[5] "Climatic Information to Determine Design and Test Requirements for Military Equipment," U.S. Dept. of Defense, *MIL-STD-210A*, Nov. 1958.

[6] Oates, G. C. (ed.), *Aerothermodynamics of Aircraft Engine Components*, AIAA Education Series, AIAA, Reston, VA, 1985, p. 263.

Appendix E
Aircraft Engine Efficiency and Thrust Measures

The goal of this appendix is to provide a deeper appreciation and understanding of the efficiency and thrust measures that you will encounter in this textbook and in practice. The title immediately reveals that there is no single, universal measure of engine efficiency or thrust that serves all purposes. Engineers and designers have found it necessary instead to define and use many different efficiency and thrust measures. Three efficiency measures and four of the most frequently cited thrust measures will be developed here in detail. All flows are assumed to be steady in the cyclic time average, propulsion sense.

Please note that the definition of each is plain and unambiguous and that, although this material is based on a single exhaust flow engine configuration, it can easily be extended to multiple exhaust flow situations. The material that follows has benefited greatly from Refs. 1 and 2 and repeatedly employs the impulse function as described in Sec. 1.9.5.

Overall Efficiency

The function of the airbreathing engine, viewed as a thermodynamic cycle, is to convert the chemical energy stored in the fuel into mechanical energy for the aerospace system. This leads to a performance measure called overall efficiency that, although always introduced but seldom intensely pursued in the literature, is particularly revealing and is presented in all AEDsys engine computations (see Secs. 4.2.7 and 4.2.8). The rate at which the engine makes mechanical energy available to the aerospace system is known as the thrust power and is given by the expression

$$\text{Thrust power} = F V_0 \tag{E.1}$$

where it has been assumed that the thrust is parallel to the direction of flight.

Placing an unambiguous value on the rate at which the chemical reactions make energy available to the engine cycle requires some thought. The standard practice in the propulsion and power industry is to represent the actual combustion process by a fictitious one in which the pressure is constant and there are no heat or work interactions, namely the heat of reaction or heating value of the fuel h_{PR}, as defined in Chapter 9. The rate at which the chemical reactions make energy available to the engine cycle for the overall fuel flow rate of $\dot{m}_{f_o}$ is therefore

$$\text{Chemical energy rate} = \dot{m}_{f_o} h_{PR} \tag{E.2}$$

An alternative approach would be to add the kinetic energy of the fuel being consumed (i.e., $V_0^2/2$) to the heat of reaction in order to account for the energy required to make the fuel available to the engine. We have not used this method for several reasons. First, on philosophical grounds, one has no choice but to carry the fuel aloft, and the thermodynamic cycle has no way to capitalize on this kinetic energy because it vanishes in the aircraft/engine frame of reference. Second, because the kinetic energy is less than about 1% of the heat of reaction over the normal operating envelope of turbine engines, it would have a negligible effect on the numerical results.

Based on the foregoing, the overall efficiency η_O of the airbreathing engine cycle is defined as

$$\text{Overall Efficiency} = \eta_O = \frac{\text{Thrust power}}{\text{Chemical energy rate}} = \frac{F V_0}{\dot{m}_{f_o} h_{PR}} \qquad \text{(E.3)}$$

It should be emphasized that the overall efficiency is a direct indicator of how well the engine uses the energy originally deposited in the fuel tanks or, conversely, how much fuel must be put onboard in order to provide the propulsive energy needed for a given mission. Moreover, common-sense application of the second law of thermodynamics leads to the conclusion that overall efficiency cannot exceed 1; otherwise the chemical energy of the fuel could be restored and the surplus of mechanical energy used to create perpetual motion.

Thermal Efficiency and Propulsive Efficiency

It can be very enlightening to further break down the airbreathing engine overall efficiency into its "grass roots" constituents as follows:

$$\eta_O = \underbrace{\frac{\text{Engine mechanical power}}{\text{Chemical energy rate}}}_{\text{Thermal efficiency } \eta_{TH}} \underbrace{\frac{\text{Thrust power}}{\text{Engine mechanical power}}}_{\text{Propulsive efficiency } \eta_P}$$

This word equation reveals that our purpose is to follow the energy along its "food chain" from chemical (in the fuel tank) to mechanical (generated by the engine) to the aerospace system (thrust power). Provided that the exhaust flow is perfectly expanded to atmospheric pressure and no bleed air or shaft takeoff power, the mechanical power generated by the engine manifests itself only as a change in kinetic energy of the flow, so that

$$\text{Engine mechanical power} = \frac{1}{g_c}\left\{(\dot{m}_0 + \dot{m}_{f_o})\frac{V_9^2}{2} - \dot{m}_0\frac{V_0^2}{2}\right\}$$

$$= \frac{\dot{m}_0}{g_c}\left\{(1+f_o)\frac{V_9^2}{2} - \frac{V_0^2}{2}\right\}$$

and, therefore, that

$$\eta_O = \eta_{TH}\eta_P = \frac{\dfrac{1}{g_c}\left\{(1+f_o)\dfrac{V_9^2}{2} - \dfrac{V_0^2}{2}\right\}}{f_o h_{PR}} \quad \frac{F V_0}{\dfrac{\dot{m}_0}{g_c}\left\{(1+f_o)\dfrac{V_9^2}{2} - \dfrac{V_0^2}{2}\right\}} \qquad \text{(E.4)}$$

where $f_o = \dot{m}_{f_o}/\dot{m}_0$ was incorporated.

Thermodynamic analysis of engine cycles teaches us that thermal efficiency primarily increases with $T_{t3}/T_0 = \tau_r \tau_c$, and therefore with π_c, although η_{TH} cannot exceed 1 (Ref. 1). This is the driving force behind high-pressure ratio aircraft engine cycles. Furthermore, because the uninstalled thrust when the exhaust flow is perfectly matched to atmospheric pressure is merely the change in momentum flux from entry to exhaust, then

$$F = \frac{1}{g_c}\{(\dot{m}_0 + \dot{m}_{f_o})V_9 - \dot{m}_0 V_0\} = \frac{\dot{m}_0}{g_c}\{(1 + f_o)V_9 - V_0\} \qquad \text{(E.5)}$$

so that the propulsive efficiency portion of Eq. (E.4) becomes

$$\eta_P = 2\left\{(1 + f_o)\frac{V_9}{V_0} - 1\right\} \Big/ \left\{(1 + f_o)\left(\frac{V_9}{V_0}\right)^2 - 1\right\} \qquad \text{(E.6)}$$

which shows that propulsive efficiency primarily increases as the ratio of the exhaust velocity to the freestream velocity decreases. This is the driving force behind high bypass ratio aircraft engine cycles, which spread the available engine mechanical power across more air in order to reduce this velocity ratio. By noting that the fuel/air ratio is small compared 1 even for stoichiometric combustion (see Sec. 9.1.2), a reasonable approximation and the most revealing formula for propulsive efficiency is obtained by using this fact to reduce Eq. (E.6) to

$$\eta_P \simeq \frac{2}{V_9/V_0 + 1} \qquad \text{(E.7)}$$

This is the most transparent and frequently encountered form and, because exhaust velocity must exceed inlet velocity in order to obtain positive thrust, this approximation for propulsive efficiency never exceeds 1.

The exact value of propulsive efficiency given by Eq. (E.6) is always slightly larger than the approximate value given by Eq. (E.7) as a result of the presence of the very small additional fuel mass over which the energy is spread. Close examination of Eq. (E.6) will reveal, for example, that the exact propulsive efficiency will always be less than 1 even for arbitrarily large fuel air ratios provided that V_9/V_0 is greater than 2. You are encouraged to calculate both versions of propulsive efficiency and draw your own conclusions.

Performance Measure Interrelationships

The conventional definitions may be arranged to yield a complete set of exact interrelationships between the airbreathing engine performance measures. The results of these manipulations are presented in Table E.1.

One important and immediate conclusion that can be drawn from these interrelationships is that, for a fixed value of η_O, S is directly proportional to V_0 while $F/\dot{m}_0$ is inversely proportional to V_0. Knowledge of these trends is often a shortcut to useful conclusions.

Airbreathing Engine Performance Measure Example

It is generally true that specifying the flight speed, the fuel heating value, and any two performance measures allows all of the others to be calculated. The example that follows will demonstrate a typical case of this assertion, as well as

Table E.1   Interrelationships between the three primary airbreathing engine performance measures. (For example, in order to express the specific thrust $F/\dot{m}_0$ in terms of the specific fuel consumption S and the overall fuel/air ratio f_o, read across the $F/\dot{m}_0$ row to the S column to find that $F/\dot{m}_0 = f_o/S$.)

Measure	$F/\dot{m}_0$	S	η_O
$\dfrac{F}{\dot{m}_0} =$	$\dfrac{F}{\dot{m}_0}$	$\dfrac{f_o}{S}$	$\dfrac{f_o h_{PR}}{V_0}\eta_O$
$S =$	$\dfrac{f_o}{F/\dot{m}_0}$	S	$\dfrac{V_0}{h_{PR}\eta_O}$
$\eta_O =$	$\dfrac{V_0}{f_o h_{PR}}\dfrac{F}{\dot{m}_0}$	$\dfrac{V_0}{h_{PR}S}$	η_O

providing a method for estimating the levels and trends of typical turbojet engine performance.

A turbojet is being flown at a velocity of 1000 ft/s and is burning a hydrocarbon fuel with a heating value of 19,000 Btu/lbm. The uninstalled specific thrust $F/\dot{m}_0$ is 75 lbf-s/lbm and the specific fuel consumption S is 1.0 lbm/(lbf-h). We wish to determine the remaining engine performance measures.

$$f_o = \frac{F}{\dot{m}_0} \cdot S = \frac{75 \times 1.0}{3600} = 0.0208 \text{ lbm fuel/lbm air} \qquad \text{from Table E.1}$$

$$\eta_O = \frac{V_0}{h_{PR}S} = \frac{1000 \times 3600}{19{,}000 \times 778.2 \times 1.0} = 0.243 \qquad \text{from Table E.1}$$

$$\frac{V_9}{V_0} = \left(\frac{1}{1+f_o}\right)\left(\frac{F g_c}{\dot{m}_0 V_0} + 1\right)$$

$$= \frac{1}{1.0208}\left(\frac{75 \times 32.174}{1000} + 1\right) = 3.34 \qquad \text{from Eq. (E.5)}$$

$$\eta_P = 2\left\{(1+f_o)\frac{V_9}{V_0} - 1\right\} \Big/ \left\{(1+f_o)\left(\frac{V_9}{V_0}\right)^2 - 1\right\} = 0.464 \quad \text{from Eq. (E.6)}$$

$$\eta_P \simeq \frac{2}{\dfrac{V_9}{V_0}+1} = 0.461 \quad [0.65\% \text{ lower than Eq. (E.6)}] \qquad \text{from Eq. (E.7)}$$

$$\eta_{TH} = \frac{\eta_O}{\eta_P} = 0.524 \qquad \text{from Eq. (E.4)}$$

Internal Thrust

The internal thrust F_i of an engine is defined as the net axial force exerted on all of the wetted surfaces inside the engine by the fluid within the engine flowpath control volume. It is the equal and opposite reaction force to the force exerted on that fluid. The sign convention is that F_i is positive when it acts in the direction of flight (i.e., opposite to the direction of the freestream flow). Because the fuel and bleed airflows may be assumed to have negligible axial momentum when they cross their respective control volume boundaries, they contribute nothing to the internal thrust. The impulse function of Sec. 1.9.5 may therefore be applied directly to show that the internal thrust is given by the simple expression

$$F_i = I_9 - I_1 \tag{E.8}$$

The internal engine thrust F_i may be easily evaluated from quantities provided by ONX or AEDsys by means of Eq. (E.8).

Uninstalled Thrust

The uninstalled thrust F of an engine is an extremely useful engineering idealization that allows all parties concerned to communicate about this important property with clarity and precision. It is also the primary thrust measure used in this textbook. The uninstalled thrust F is defined as the net axial force that would be produced by an engine immersed in a perfect or inviscid external flow. It is equal and opposite to the force exerted on all of the fluid influenced by the engine and is positive when it acts in the direction of flight. The derivation of the relationships governing uninstalled thrust is greatly simplified by the careful selection of appropriate control volumes.

The control volume for the external airflow is shown in Fig. E.1. Please note that 1) the flow is treated as axisymmetric only in order to minimize the algebraic complexity and increase the transparency of the results; 2) the inner boundary of the control volume is the streamtube that divides external flow from internal engine flow (i.e., it consists of the streamtubes approaching and leaving the engine plus the outer surface of the engine); 3) the axial extent of the control volume is sufficiently large compared with the engine that the static pressure equals atmospheric pressure and the streamlines are parallel to the centerline over the entire upstream and downstream boundaries; 4) the upstream frontal area A_{CV} of the control volume is sufficiently large compared with the engine that the static pressure equals atmospheric pressure over the entire outer boundary, and the outer boundary is a streamtube; 5) the A and dA of the inner boundary are measured perpendicular to the centerline (consistent with throughflow area terminology) and dA is taken as positive when the throughflow area of the internal boundary increases in the axial direction (see detailed sketch); and 6) the supporting pylon that holds the engine in place and transmits the uninstalled thrust F via stresses exacted on the control volume boundary to the vehicle exerts no axial force on the external flow.

Because the external flow is inviscid or isentropic, traditional streamline arguments lead to the conclusion that the freestream velocity and density are constant along the upstream and downstream boundaries. Consequently, the external flow experiences no change of axial momentum and the net axial force exerted over the control volume boundary must be zero. Further, mass conservation leads to the conclusion that the upstream and downstream frontal areas are equal. Finally, because the inviscid external flow generates no frictional boundary forces, the

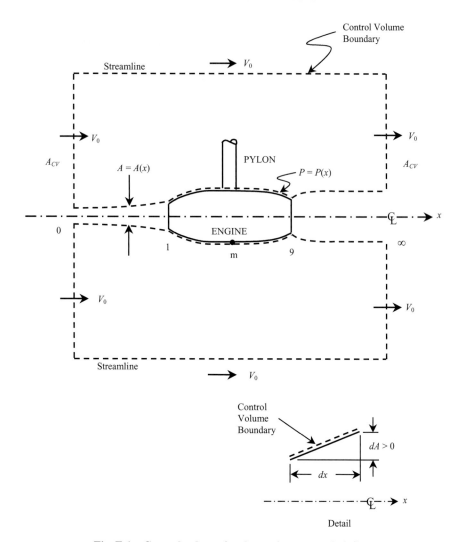

Fig. E.1   Control volume for the engine external airflow.

condition of perfect external flow requires that the axial pressure integral over the control volume boundary of Fig. E.1 be zero, or

$$P_0 A_{CV} + P_0(A_\infty - A_0) - P_0 A_{CV} - \int_0^\infty P\, dA = 0 \qquad (E.9)$$

or, since $\int_0^\infty dA = A_\infty - A_0$, then

$$\int_0^\infty (P - P_0)\, dA = 0 \qquad (E.10)$$

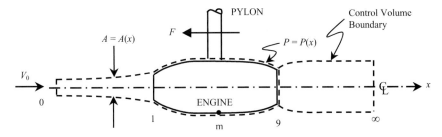

Fig. E.2   Control volume for evaluating uninstalled engine thrust.

This interesting and universal result reveals that the axial area average of the pressure P over the internal boundary must be equal to P_0 for perfect external flows.

The control volume for evaluating the uninstalled thrust is shown in Fig. E.2. The same rules as those of Fig. E.1 and Sec. 1.9.5 apply, except that the dividing streamtube is the outer boundary for this case. Assuming that the fuel and bleed airflows contribute no axial momentum, the axial direction control volume momentum analysis yields

$$F + \int_0^\infty P \, dA = I_\infty - I_0 \tag{E.11}$$

The nature of the free exhaust jet is such that the ambient static pressure is impressed essentially over its entire external surface. Thus, applying control volume analysis separately to the exhaust stream downstream of the exit plane, we find that

$$I_\infty = I_9 + P_0(A_\infty - A_9) \tag{E.12}$$

Finally, Eqs. (E.10–E.12) and $\int_0^\infty dA = A_\infty - A_0$ are combined to yield the desired expression for the uninstalled thrust:

$$F = I_9 - I_0 - P_0(A_9 - A_0) = \frac{1}{g_c}(\dot{m}_9 V_9 - \dot{m}_0 V_0) + A_9(P_9 - P_0) \tag{E.13}$$

Equation (E.13), which is identical to Eq. (4.1), allows the uninstalled thrust F to be easily evaluated from quantities provided by ONX or AEDsys. Because the uninstalled thrust depends only upon flow quantities governed by cycle parameters, it is an inherent property of the engine cycle, is independent of installation effects, and is used as the standard of engine performance.

Installed Thrust

Because the external flow is actually viscous and imperfect, there is a downstream axial drag on the engine control volume equal and opposite to the upstream axial drag on the external flow control volume (see Figs. E.1 and E.2). Thus, the installed thrust T must be equal to the uninstalled thrust F minus this drag. The drag is due both to frictional stresses acting along the dividing streamtube (primarily the boundary layer on the outer surface of the engine) and to pressure or form drag resulting from boundary layer separation (caused either by adverse pressure gradients or by shock-boundary layer interactions). Because the frictional drag is included in the vehicle account, engine designers are responsible only for the pressure drag.

The pressure drag is variously referred to as the installation or integration "drag," "penalty," or "effect" in the literature. Because the pressure drag obviously depends on the entire shape of the dividing streamtube, it also depends on the flight conditions and the engine throttle setting (e.g., A_0 and A_9) and is therefore deservedly referred to also as the "throttle-dependent drag." Several specific examples of installation drag are provided in Sec. 6.2. The following material provides a general introduction to the analysis of installation drag as well as the background necessary for the design work of this textbook.

The conventional approach to accounting for the installation penalties is to separate the drags associated with the forward and rearward portions of the engine, commonly referred to as the inlet and nozzle drags, as in Secs. 6.1 and 6.2. Referring to Fig. E.1 and choosing an arbitrary but convenient midpoint m at which the external flow is reasonably parallel to the freestream flow and the static pressure most nearly equals P_0, control volume analysis of the external flow shows that the momentum loss or drag is equal to the axial pressure integral over the control volume boundary, or

$$D = \int_0^\infty (P - P_0)\, dA = \int_0^9 (P - P_0)\, dA = \int_0^m (P - P_0)\, dA + \int_m^9 (P - P_0)\, dA$$

$$= D_{inlet} + D_{nozzle} \geq 0 \qquad (E.14)$$

where the forward or inlet drag is defined as

$$D_{inlet} \doteq \int_0^m (P - P_0)\, dA \geq 0 \qquad (E.15)$$

and the rearward or nozzle drag is defined as

$$D_{nozzle} \doteq \int_m^9 (P - P_0)\, dA \geq 0 \qquad (E.16)$$

The drag on the forward portion (where dA is positive) arises because boundary layer separation causes the average value of P to exceed P_0, while drag on the rearward portion (where dA is negative) arises because boundary layer separation causes the average value of P to be less than P_0.

Referring to Fig. E.2, the axial direction control volume analysis for the real flow [identical to the derivation of Eq. (E.11) for perfect flow] combined with Eqs. (E.12–E.14) and $\int_0^\infty dA = A_\infty - A_0$ yields the desired expression for the installed thrust, namely,

$$T = I_9 - I_0 - P_0(A_9 - A_0) - \int_0^9 (P - P_0)\, dA$$

$$= F - (D_{inlet} + D_{nozzle}) \leq F \qquad (E.17)$$

Equation (E.17) is not only a very practical result, but it is also rich with meaning. Two of the most important messages are that designers require the means to evaluate D_{inlet} and D_{nozzle} in order to derive T from F, and that T is directly dependent upon installation effects and therefore should not be used as a standard of engine performance.

Ground Test Determination of Uninstalled Thrust

One practical difficulty with the uninstalled thrust is that there is no way to measure this idealized quantity directly in a ground test facility. In particular, F is not equal to the force exerted on the test facility thrust stand, usually referred to as the scale force F_s. Because the correct determination of the uninstalled thrust is of paramount importance to aircraft and engine designers and their customers, the process of deriving F from F_s is described next. It is important to note that because the real engine inlet and exhaust flows are nonuniform, integral methods must be used in place of the one-dimensional approach. Nevertheless, the integral impulse function retains its original significance, namely, that the net axial force exerted on the fluid flowing through a control volume is the difference between the exit and inlet impulse functions (see Sec. 1.9.5).

Figure E.3 shows the control volume for an engine mounted in a direct-connect ground test facility, the most common and best characterized type of altitude testing (Ref. 2). Please note that the engine is isolated from any axial forces exerted by the test facility bellmouth by means of a labyrinth air seal. First, the measured airflow conditions at engine station 2 are used to evaluate the integral I_2 and then used in concert with an accurate model of the inlet compression (or acceleration) process to either correspond to predetermined freestream conditions or to determine the corresponding freestream conditions. This allows the upstream impulse function I_0

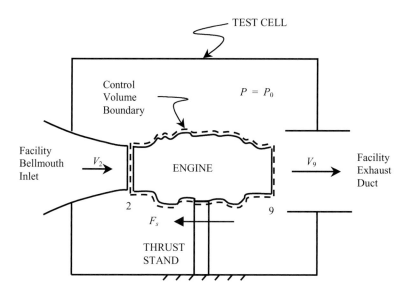

Fig. E.3 Control volume for evaluating engine uninstalled thrust.

to be evaluated. Next, the facility exhaust system is used to set the static pressure surrounding the engine and nozzle exit station 9 equal to the freestream static pressure P_0. Finally, the axial direction control volume analysis is used to show that

$$I_9 = I_2 + F_s + P_0(A_9 - A_2) \tag{E.18}$$

where I_2 and I_9 are integrated impulse functions, F_s is the scale force measured by the thrust stand, and I_2 is obtained from station 2 measurements as just described.

Two types of corrections are required before Eq. (E.18) can provide a sufficiently accurate value for I_9 at a specific test condition. First, test cell calibrations must be used to reduce or eliminate such deterministic errors in F_s as test stand and load cell ambient pressure and temperature effects, aerodynamic and mechanical tares, test cell static pressure distribution forces (buoyancy), and the consequences of leakage flows. Second, empirical relationships in the form of influence coefficients must be applied to adjust I_9 for differences between the desired and actual test cell conditions and engine control settings. An interesting observation is that, because the state of the flow at station 2 can be quite far from freestream conditions, F_s can be zero or less.

The expression for the uninstalled thrust is obtained by combining Eqs. (E.13) and (E.18) in order to yield the desired relationship

$$F = F_s + (I_2 - I_0) - P_0(A_2 - A_0) \tag{E.19}$$

Modern, highly developed, direct-connect ground test facilities use this process to provide uninstalled thrust measurements with an uncertainty in the range of $+/-$ 0.5 to 1.0%, depending on the engine configuration and flight conditions. You may well imagine how much more difficult the determination of F must be in flight testing. The close control over simulated flight conditions, large amounts and variety of data, excellent accuracy of results, and reduced risk to personnel make ground testing the approach overwhelmingly employed for engine development.

References

[1]Oates, G. C., *The Aerothermodynamics of Gas Turbine and Rocket Propulsion*, 3rd ed., AIAA Education Series, AIAA, Reston, VA, 1997.

[2]Smith, R. E., Jr., and Wehofer, S., "Measurement of Engine Thrust in Altitude Ground Test Facilities," AIAA Paper 82-0572, 1982.

Appendix F
Compressible Flow Functions for Gas
with Variable Specific Heats

Consider a perfect gas with variable specific heats in thermodynamic equilibrium. The gas properties are based on the NASA Glenn thermochemical data and the Gordon–McBride equilibrium algorithm (see Chapter 9). Given the total temperature (T_t), fuel/air ratio (f), and one of the following four input properties, the Mach number (M), the isentropic temperature ratio (T_t/T), isentropic pressure ratio (P_t/P), and mass flow parameter (MFP), the subroutine RGCOMPR determines the other three using the subroutines FAIR and MASSFP. In addition, the high- and low-turbines have an iterative system of equations (Sec. 5.2.4) that determine their off-design performance with variable gas properties. Outlines of the subroutines TURBC and TURB are given here for the high-pressure cooled turbine and the low-pressure turbine, respectively.

Subroutine RGCOMPR (Item, T_t, f, M, T_t/T, P_t/P, MFP)
    Inputs: Item, T_t, f, and one of the following: M, T_t/T, P_t/P, and MFP
    Outputs: M, T_t/T, P_t/P, and MFP
    Select Case Item
        Case 1—Mach known
            MASSFP $(T_t$, f, M, T_t/T, P_t/P, $MFP)$
        Cases 2 and 3—T_t/T or P_t/P known
            FAIR $(1$, f, T_t, h_t, P_{rt}, ϕ_t, c_{pt}, R_t, γ_t, $a_t)$
            If Item $= 2$ then
$$T = \frac{T_t}{T_t/T}$$
                FAIR $(2$, f, T, h, P_r, ϕ, c_p, R, γ, $a)$
            Else
$$P_r = \frac{P_{rt}}{P_t/P}$$
                FAIR $(3$, f, T, h, P_r, ϕ, c_p, R, γ, $a)$
            End if
            $V^2 = 2(h_t - h)g_c$
            If $V^2 < 0$ then
                $M = 0$
                $T = T_t$
            Else
$$M = \frac{\sqrt{V^2}}{a}$$
            End If

$\quad$ MASSFP $(T_t, f, M, T_t/T, P_t/P, MFP)$
$\quad$ Cases 4 and 5—MFP known
$\quad\quad$ If Item $= 4$ then $M = 2$ else $M = 0.5$
$\quad\quad$ $\Delta M = 0.1$
$\quad\quad$ MASSFP $(T_t, f, M, T_t/T, P_t/P, MFP_0)$
$\quad$ 4 $\quad M = M + \Delta M$
$\quad\quad$ MASSFP $(T_t, f, M, T_t/T, P_t/P, MFP_n)$
$\quad\quad$ $MFP_{error} = |MFP_n - MFP_0|$
$\quad\quad$ If $MFP_{error} > 0.00001$ then

$$\Delta M = \frac{MFP - MFP_n}{MFP_n - MFP_0} \Delta M$$

$\quad\quad\quad$ $MFP_0 = MFP_n$
$\quad\quad\quad$ GOTO 4
$\quad\quad$ End If
$\quad$ End Select
$\quad$ Return

Subroutine MASSFP $(T_t, f, M, T_t/T, P_t/P, MFP)$
$\quad$ Inputs: Case, T_t, f, and M
$\quad$ Outputs: T_t/T, P_t/P, and MFP
$\quad$ FAIR $(1, f, T_t, h_t, P_{rt}, \phi_t, c_{pt}, R_t, \gamma_t, a_t)$

$$V = \frac{Ma_t}{1 + \{(\gamma_t - 1)/2\}M^2}$$

A $\quad h = h_t - \dfrac{V^2}{2g_c}$

$\quad$ FAIR $(2, f, T, h, P_r, \phi, c_p, R, \gamma, a)$
$\quad$ $V_n = Ma$
$\quad$ If $V \neq 0$ then $V_{error} = \dfrac{V - V_n}{V}$ else $V_{error} = V - V_n$
$\quad$ If $|V_{error}| > 0.00001$ then $V = V_n$; Go to A
$\quad$ $T_t/T = \dfrac{T_t}{T}$

$\quad$ $P_t/P = \dfrac{P_{rt}}{P_r}$

$\quad$ $MFP = \dfrac{M}{P_t/P} \sqrt{\dfrac{\gamma g_c}{R} \dfrac{T_t}{T}}$

$\quad$ Return

Subroutine TURBC $\quad \{T_{t4}, f, (A_4/A_{4.5}), M_4, M_{4.5}, \eta_{tH}, T_{t4.5R}, T_{t3}, \beta, \varepsilon_1, \varepsilon_2; \pi_{tH},$
$\quad\quad\quad\quad\quad\quad\quad\quad\quad\quad\quad\quad \tau_{tH}, T_{t4.5}\}$
$\quad$ Inputs: $\quad\quad\quad\quad T_{t4}, f, (A_4/A_{4.5}), M_4, M_{4.5}, \eta_{tH}, T_{t4.5R}, T_{t3}, \beta, \varepsilon_1, \varepsilon_2$
$\quad$ Outputs: $\quad\quad\quad \pi_{tH}, \tau_{tH}, T_{t4.5}$
$\quad$ FAIR $(1, f, T_{t4}, h_{t4}, P_{rt4}, \phi_{t4}, c_{pt4}, R_{t4}, \gamma_{t4}, a_{t4})$
$\quad$ MASSFP $(T_{t4}, f, M_4, T_4, MFP_4)$
$\quad$ FAIR $(1, 0, T_{t3}, h_{t3}, P_{rt3}, \phi_{t3}, c_{pt3}, R_{t3}, \gamma_{t3}, a_{t3})$

$\dot{m}_f = f(1 - \beta - \varepsilon_1 - \varepsilon_2)$

$\dot{m}_4 = (1 + f)(1 - \beta - \varepsilon_1 - \varepsilon_2)$

$\dot{m}_{4.1} = (1 + f)(1 - \beta - \varepsilon_1 - \varepsilon_2) + \varepsilon_1$

$\dot{m}_{4.5} = (1 + f)(1 - \beta - \varepsilon_1 - \varepsilon_2) + \varepsilon_1 + \varepsilon_2$

$f_{4.1} = \dot{m}_f / (\dot{m}_{4.1} - \dot{m}_f)$

$f_{4.5} = \dot{m}_f / (\dot{m}_{4.5} - \dot{m}_f)$

$$h_{t4.1} = \frac{\dot{m}_4 h_{ti} + \varepsilon_1 h_{t3}}{\dot{m}_4 + \varepsilon_1}$$

FAIR $(2, f_{4.1}, T_{t4.1}, h_{t4.1}, P_{rt4.1}, \phi_{t4.1}, c_{pt4.1}, R_{t4.1}, \gamma_{t4.1}, a_{t4.1})$

$T_{t4.5} = T_{t4.5R}$

1　MASSFP $(T_{t4.5}, f_{4.5}, M_{4.5}, T_{4.5}, MFP_{4.5})$

$$\pi_{tH} = \frac{\dot{m}_{4.5}}{\dot{m}_4} \frac{MFP_4}{MFP_{4.5}} \frac{A_4}{A_{4.5}} \sqrt{\frac{T_{t4.5}}{T_{t4}}}$$

FAIR $(1, f_{4.5}, T_{t4.5}, h_{t4.5}, P_{rt4.5}, \phi_{t4.5}, c_{pt4.5}, R_{t4.5}, \gamma_{t4.5}, a_{t4.5})$

$P_{rt4.4i} = \pi_{tH} P_{rt4.1}$

FAIR $(3, f_{4.1}, T_{t4.4i}, h_{t4.4i}, P_{rt4.4i}, \phi_{t4.4i}, c_{pt4.4i}, R_{t4.4i}, \gamma_{t4.4i}, a_{t4.4i})$

$h_{t4.4} = h_{t4.1} - \eta_t(h_{t4.1} - h_{t4.4i})$

$\tau_{tH} = h_{t4.4} / h_{t4.1}$

$$h_{t4.5} = \frac{\dot{m}_{4.1} h_{t4.4} + \varepsilon_2 h_{t3}}{\dot{m}_{4.1} + \varepsilon_2}$$

FAIR $(2, f_{4.5}, T_{t4.5n}, h_{t4.5}, P_{rt4.5}, \phi_{t4.5}, c_{pt4.5}, R_{t4.5}, \gamma_{t4.5}, a_{t4.5})$

if $|T_{t4.5} - T_{t4.5n}| > 0.01$ then

　　$T_{t4.5} = T_{t4.5n}$

　　goto 1

End if

Return

Subroutine TURB $\{T_{ti}, f, (A_i/A_e), M_i, M_e, \eta_t, T_{teR}; \pi_t, \tau_t, T_{te}\}$

　　Inputs:　$T_{ti}, f, (A_i/A_e), M_i, M_e, \eta_t, T_{teR}$

　　Outputs: π_t, τ_t, T_{te}

　　FAIR $(1, f, T_{ti}, h_{ti}, P_{rti}, \phi_{ti}, c_{pti}, R_{ti}, \gamma_{ti}, a_{ti})$

　　MASSFP $(T_{ti}, f, M_i, T_i, MFP_i)$

　　$T_{te} = T_{teR}$

1　MASSFP $(T_{te}, f, M_e, T_e, MFP_e)$

　　FAIR $(1, f, T_{te}, h_{te}, P_{rte}, \phi_{te}, c_{pte}, R_{te}, \gamma_{te}, a_{te})$

$$\pi_t = \frac{MFP_i}{MFP_e} \frac{A_i}{A_e} \sqrt{\frac{T_{te}}{T_{ti}}}$$

$P_{rtei} = \pi_t P_{rti}$

FAIR $(3, f, T_{tei}, h_{tei}, P_{rtei}, \phi_{tei}, c_{ptei}, R_{tei}, \gamma_{tei}, a_{tei})$

$$h_{te} = h_{ti} - \eta_t(h_{ti} - h_{tei})$$

$$\tau_t = \frac{h_{te}}{h_{ti}}$$

FAIR $(2, f, T_{ten}, h_{te}, P_{rte}, \phi_{te}, c_{pte}, R_{te}, \gamma_{te}, a_{te})$

$[T_{te}]_{error} = |T_{te} - T_{ten}|$

if $[T_{te}]_{error} > 0.01$ then

   $T_{te} = T_{ten}$

   GOTO 1

end if

Return

Appendix G
Constant-Area Mixer Analysis

Consider an ideal (no wall friction) subsonic constant-area mixer (Fig. G.1) with perfect gases having variable specific heats entering at stations 6 and 16. From either the parametric or performance cycle analysis up to the mixer, all gas properties at stations 6 and 16 are known as well as the following ratios at the mixer inlet stations:

$$\alpha' \doteq \frac{\dot{m}_6}{\dot{m}_{16}} = \frac{\alpha}{(1 - \beta - \varepsilon_1 - \varepsilon_2)(1 + f) + \varepsilon_1 + \varepsilon_2} \tag{G.1}$$

$$\frac{P_{t16}}{P_{t6}} = \frac{\pi_f}{\pi_{cL}\pi_{cH}\pi_b\pi_{tH}\pi_{tL}} \tag{G.2}$$

$$\frac{h_{t16}}{h_{t6}} = \frac{\tau_r\tau_f}{\tau_\lambda\tau_{m1}\tau_{tH}\tau_{m2}\tau_{tL}} \tag{G.3}$$

The mixer total pressure ratio, P_{t6A}/P_{t6}, is required for performance calculations. Toward this end, the energy balance on the mixer gives

$$\dot{m}_6 h_{t6} + \dot{m}_{16} h_{t16} = \dot{m}_{6A} h_{t6A}$$

from which the total enthalpy ratio becomes

$$\tau_M \doteq \frac{h_{t6A}}{h_{t6}} = \frac{1 + \alpha' h_{t16}/h_{t6}}{1 + \alpha'} \tag{G.4}$$

An expression for the mixer total pressure ratio in terms of τ_M and the other properties at stations 6, 16, and 6A is obtained directly from the mass flow parameter

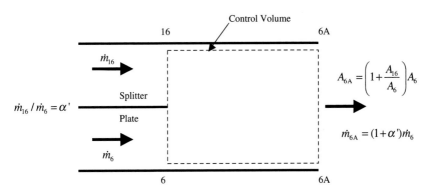

Fig. G.1   Constant-area mixer.

(MFP) defined in Eq. (4.24) as

$$MFP \doteq \frac{\dot{m}\sqrt{T_t}}{P_t A} = M\sqrt{\frac{\gamma g_c}{R}}\sqrt{\frac{T_t/T}{P_t/P}} = MFP(M, T_t, f) \qquad (G.5)$$

Solving Eq. (G.5) for P_t and forming the ratio P_{t6A}/P_{t6} yields

$$\pi_M = \frac{P_{t6A}}{P_{t6}} = (1 + \alpha')\sqrt{\tau_M}\frac{A_6}{A_{6A}}\frac{MFP(M_6, T_{t6}, f_6)}{MFP(M_{6A}, T_{t6A}, f_{6A})} \qquad (G.6)$$

where $\dot{m}_{6A}/\dot{m}_6 = 1 + \alpha'$ and $h_{t6A}/h_{t6} = \tau_M$ were used and where

$$\frac{A_6}{A_{6A}} = \frac{1}{1 + A_{16}/A_6} \qquad (G.7)$$

$$f_{6A} = \frac{f_6}{1 + \alpha'} \qquad (G.8)$$

If M_6 in Eq. (G.6) is specified, then M_{6A} need only be determined to find π_M because M_6 fixes M_{16} and, hence, A_{16}/A_6 and A_6/A_{6A} as shown by the following.

Using the Kutta condition at the splitter plate end, $P_6 = P_{16}$, and total to static pressure ratio (P_t/P), gives

$$\left(\frac{P_t}{P}\right)_{16} = \left(\frac{P_t}{P}\right)_6 \frac{P_{t16}}{P_{t6}} \qquad (G.9)$$

and using the compressible flow functions yields the Mach number at station 16. From the mass flow parameter, we can write

$$\frac{A_{16}}{A_6} = \alpha'\sqrt{\frac{T_{t16}}{T_{t6}}}\frac{P_{t6}}{P_{t16}}\frac{MFP(M_6, T_{t6}, f_6)}{MFP(M_{16}, T_{t16}, f_{16})} \qquad (G.10)$$

Any one of the three variables M_6, M_{16}, or A_{16}/A_6 in Eqs. (G.9) and (G.10) may be specified and the remaining two determined. Because, generally, the desirable Mach number range for M_6 and M_{16} is known, a Mach number is specified instead of A_{16}/A_6 in the analysis.

For the ideal constant-area mixer, application of the momentum equation provides a solution for M_{6A} and, hence, for $\pi_{M\,ideal}$. The momentum equation in terms of the impulse function (I) is, for the constant-area mixer,

$$I_6 + I_{16} = I_{6A} \qquad (G.11)$$

where

$$I = PA(1 + \gamma M^2) \qquad (G.12)$$

Thus

$$P_{6A}A_{6A}(1 + \gamma_{6A}M_{6A}^2) = P_6 A_6(1 + \gamma_6 M_6^2) + P_{16}A_{16}(1 + \gamma_{16}M_{16}^2)$$

Using the Kutta condition at the splitter plate end, $P_6 = P_{16}$, gives

$$P_{6A}A_{6A}(1 + \gamma_{6A}M_{6A}^2) = P_6 A_6\left\{(1 + \gamma_6 M_6^2) + \frac{A_{16}}{A_6}(1 + \gamma_{16}M_{16}^2)\right\} \qquad (G.13)$$

Since

$$PA = P\frac{\dot{m}}{\rho V} = \dot{m}\frac{RT}{V} = \dot{m}\frac{RT}{M\sqrt{\gamma R g_c T}} = \frac{\dot{m}}{M}\sqrt{\frac{RT}{\gamma g_c}}$$

then the (PA) terms in Eq. (G.13) can be replaced to yield

$$\frac{\dot{m}_{6A}}{M_{6A}}\sqrt{\frac{R_{6A}T_{6A}}{\gamma_{6A}g_c}}\left(1 + \gamma_{6A}M_{6A}^2\right) = \frac{\dot{m}_6}{M_6}\sqrt{\frac{R_6 T_6}{\gamma_6 g_c}}\left\{\left(1 + \gamma_6 M_6^2\right) + \frac{A_{16}}{A_6}\left(1 + \gamma_{16}M_{16}^2\right)\right\}$$

and solving for M_{6A} yields

$$\sqrt{\frac{R_{6A}T_{6A}}{\gamma_{6A}}}\frac{1 + \gamma_{6A}M_{6A}^2}{M_{6A}} = \sqrt{\frac{R_6 T_6}{\gamma_6}}\frac{\left(1 + \gamma_6 M_6^2\right) + A_{16}/A_6\left(1 + \gamma_{16}M_{16}^2\right)}{M_6(1 + \alpha')} \quad \text{(G.14)}$$

where the right-hand side is a known constant. This is a nonlinear equation for M_{6A} that can be solved by functional iteration in combination with the compressible flow functions. The resulting value of M_{6A} is placed in Eq. (G.6) to give $\pi_{M\,ideal}$ and, finally,

$$\pi_M = \pi_{M\,max}\pi_{M\,ideal} \quad \text{(G.15)}$$

where $\pi_{M\,max}$ is the mixer total pressure ratio caused by wall friction only (no mixing losses).

Gross Thrust

It is interesting to compare the gross thrust capabilities of mixed and unmixed streams for the case of correctly expanded ideal exhaust nozzles. The gross thrusts are, using subscript e for the exhaust nozzle exit stations,

$$F_{G_{UM}} = \dot{m}_6 V_{e6} + \dot{m}_{16}V_{e16} \quad \text{for unmixed streams} \quad \text{(G.16)}$$

$$F_{G_{MX}} = (\dot{m}_6 + \dot{m}_{16})V_{e6A} \quad \text{for mixed streams} \quad \text{(G.17)}$$

where

$$V_e^2 = 2g_c h_t\left(1 - \frac{h_e}{h_t}\right)$$

It follows immediately that

$$\frac{F_{G_{MX}}}{F_{G_{UM}}} = \frac{(1 + \alpha')\sqrt{h_{t6A}(1 - h_{6Ae}/h_{t6A})}}{\sqrt{h_{t6}(1 - h_{6e}/h_{t6})} + \alpha'\sqrt{h_{t16}(1 - h_{16e}/h_{t16})}} \quad \text{(G.18)}$$

Example Results

Contours for parametric values of $F_{G_{MX}}/F_{G_{UM}}$ are plotted in Fig. G.2 for the following input data to the system of equations listed below:

$$\alpha' = 2, \quad M_6 = 0.5, \quad P_e/P_{t6} = 0.3, \quad T_{t6} = 1600\ R, \quad f_6 = 0.03,$$

$$f_{16} = 0, \quad \pi_{M\,max} = 0.97$$

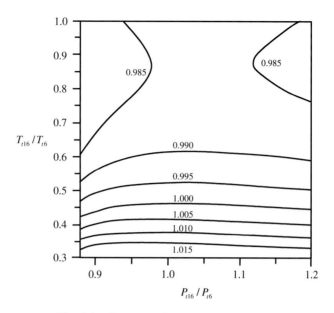

Fig. G.2   Contours of constant $F_{G_{MX}}/F_{G_{UM}}$.

Although the mixer can actually augment (or increase) the ideal thrust under some conditions, it is most sensitive to T_{t16}/T_{t6} and ordinarily results in a reduction. For typical values of turbofan cycles $T_{t16}/T_{t6} \approx 0.7$ and $P_{t16}/P_{t6} \approx 1.0$, the loss is negligible with $\pi_{M\,max} = 0.97$ (see Fig. G.2); however it is about 2% with $\pi_{M\,max} = 0.92$.

Summary of Equations—Constant-Area Mixer

Inputs

$$\alpha',\, T_{t6},\, M_6,\, \frac{P_e}{P_{t6}},\, \frac{T_{t16}}{T_{t6}},\, \frac{P_{t16}}{P_{t6}},\, f_6,\, f_{16},\, \pi_{M\,max}$$

Outputs

$$\frac{A_{16}}{A_6},\, \pi_M,\, \tau_M,\, M_{16},\, M_{6A},\, \frac{F_{G_{MX}}}{F_{G_{UM}}}$$

Equations

FAIR $(1,\, f_6,\, T_{t6},\, h_{t6},\, P_{rt6},\, \phi_{t6},\, c_{pt6},\, R_{t6},\, \gamma_{t6},\, a_{t6})$

$$T_{t16} = T_{t6}\frac{T_{t16}}{T_{t6}}$$

FAIR $(1,\, f_{16},\, T_{t16},\, h_{t16},\, P_{rt16},\, \phi_{t16},\, c_{pt16},\, R_{t16},\, \gamma_{t16},\, a_{t16})$

$$h_{t6A} = \frac{h_{t6} + \alpha' h_{t16}}{1 + \alpha'}$$

$$\tau_M = h_{t6A}/h_{t6}$$

RGCOMPR $(T_{t6}, M_6, f_6, (T_t/T)_6, (P_t/P)_6, MFP_6)$

$$T_6 = T_{t6}/(T_t/T)_6$$

$$(P_t/P)_{16} = (P_t/P)_6 \frac{P_{t16}}{P_{t6}}$$

$$P_{r16} = \frac{P_{rt16}}{(P_t/P)_{16}}$$

FAIR $(3, 0, T_{16}, h_{16}, P_{r16}, \phi_{16}, c_{p16}, R_{16}, \gamma_{16}, a_{16})$

$$V_{16} = \sqrt{2g_c(h_{t16} - h_{16})}$$

$$M_{16} = V_{16}/a_{16}$$

RGCOMPR $(T_{t16}, M_{16}, f_{16}, (T_t/T)_{16}, (P_t/P)_{16}, MFP_{16})$

$$\frac{A_{16}}{A_6} = \alpha' \sqrt{\frac{T_{t16}}{T_{t6}}} \frac{P_{t6}}{P_{t16}} \frac{MFP_6}{MFP_{16}}$$

$$\frac{A_6}{A_{6A}} = \frac{1}{1 + A_{16}/A_6}$$

$$\text{Constant} = \sqrt{\frac{R_6 T_6}{\gamma_6}} \frac{(1 + \gamma_6 M_6^2) + \dfrac{A_{16}}{A_6}(1 + \gamma_{16} M_{16}^2)}{M_6(1 + \alpha')}$$

Set initial value of Mach number at station $6A = M_{6Ai}$

B RGCOMPR $(T_{t6A}, M_{6A}, f_{6A}, (T_t/T)_{6A}, (P_t/P)_{6A}, MFP_{6A})$

$$T_{6A} = T_{t6A}(T_t/T)_{6A}$$

FAIR $(1, f_{6A}, T_{6A}, h_{6A}, P_{r6A}, \phi_{6A}, c_{p6A}, R_{6A}, \gamma_{6A}, a_{6A})$

$$M_{6A} = \sqrt{\frac{R_{6A} T_{6A}}{\gamma_{6A}}} \frac{1 + \gamma_{6A} M_{6Ai}^2}{\text{Constant}}$$

If $| M_{6A} - M_{6Ai} | > 0.0001$, then $M_{6Ai} = M_{6A}$ and go to B; else continue

$$\pi_{M\,ideal} = (1 + \alpha')\sqrt{\tau_M} \frac{A_6}{A_{6A}} \frac{MFP_6}{MFP_{6A}}$$

$$\pi_M = \pi_{M\,max}\,\pi_{M\,ideal}$$

$$P_{r6e} = P_{rt6}(P_e/P_{t6})$$

FAIR $(3, f_6, T_{6e}, h_{6e}, P_{r6e}, \phi_{6e}, c_{p6e}, R_{6e}, \gamma_{6e}, a_{6e})$

$$P_{r16e} = P_{rt16}(P_e/P_{t6})/(P_{t16}/P_{t6})$$

FAIR $(3, f_{16}, T_{16e}, h_{16e}, P_{r16e}, \phi_{16e}, c_{p16e}, R_{16e}, \gamma_{16e}, a_{16e})$

$$P_{r6Ae} = P_{rt6}(P_e/P_{t6})\pi_M$$

FAIR $(3, f_{6A}, T_{6Ae}, h_{6Ae}, P_{r6Ae}, \phi_{6Ae}, c_{p6Ae}, R_{6Ae}, \gamma_{6Ae}, a_{6Ae})$

$$\frac{F_{G_{MX}}}{F_{G_{UM}}} = \frac{(1 + \alpha')\sqrt{h_{t6A}(1 - h_{6Ae}/h_{t6A})}}{\sqrt{h_{t6}(1 - h_{6e}/h_{t6})} + \alpha'\sqrt{h_{t16}(1 - h_{16e}/h_{t16})}}$$

Appendix H
Mixed Flow Turbofan Engine Parametric Cycle Analysis Equations

Appendix H summarizes the complete parametric or design point cycle analysis equations for the mixed flow, afterburning, two-spool turbofan engine with bleed, turbine cooling, and power extraction. For convenience in computer programming, the required computer inputs and principal computer outputs are given. These are followed by the cycle equations in their order of solution. Eqs. (H.1–16) in the listing represents the 16 independent equations in terms of the 16 dependent component performance variables in the order τ_f, τ_{cL}, τ_{cH}, f, τ_{m1}, τ_{tH}, π_{tH}, τ_{m2}, τ_{tL}, π_{tL}, a', τ_M, M_{16}, M_{6A}, π_M, and f_{AB}. Note this solution procedure requires no iteration.

Inputs

Flight parameters:	M_0, T_0, P_0
Aircraft system parameters:	β, C_{TOL}, C_{TOH}
Design limitations:	
Fuel heating value:	h_{PR}
Component figures	ε_1, ε_2
of merit:	π_b, $\pi_{d\,max}$, $\pi_{M\,max}$, π_{AB}, π_n
	e_f, e_{cL}, e_{cH}, e_{tH}, e_{tL}
	η_b, η_{AB}, η_{mL}, η_{mH}, η_{mPL}, η_{mPH}
Design choices:	π_f, π_{cL}, π_{cH}, α, T_{t4}, T_{t7}, M_6, P_0/P_9

Outputs

Overall performance:	$F/\dot{m}_0$, S, f_o, η_P, η_{TH}, V_9/a_0, P_{t9}/P_9
Component behavior:	π_{tH}, π_{tL}, π_M
	τ_f, τ_{cL}, τ_{cH}, τ_{tH}, τ_{tL}, τ_λ, $\tau_{\lambda AB}$
	f, f_{AB}
	η_f, η_{cL}, η_{cH}, η_{tH}, η_{tL}
	M_{16}, M_{6A}, M_9

Equations

FAIR $(1, 0, T_0, h_0, P_{r0}, \phi_0, C_{p0}, R_0, \gamma_0, a_0)$

$V_0 = M_0 a_0$

$$h_{t0} = h_0 + \frac{V_0^2}{2g_c}$$

$\text{FAIR}\,(2, 0, T_{t0}, h_{t0}, P_{rt0}, \phi_{t0}, c_{pt0}, R_{t0}, \gamma_{t0}, a_{t0})$

$\tau_r = h_{t0}/h_0$

$\pi_r = P_{rt0}/P_{r0}$

$\eta_{R\;spec} = 1$ for $M_0 \le 1$

$\eta_{R\;spec} = 1 - 0.075(M_0 - 1)^{1.35}$ for $1 < M_0 < 5$

$\eta_{R\;spec} = \dfrac{800}{M_0^4 + 935}$ for $1 < M_0 < 5$

$\pi_d = \pi_{d\,\max}\,\eta_{R\;spec}$

$h_{t2} = h_{t0}$

$P_{rt2} = P_{rt0}$

$P_{rt13} = P_{rt2}\pi_f^{1/e_f}$

$\text{FAIR}\,(3, 0, T_{t13}, h_{t13}, P_{rt13}, \phi_{t13}, c_{pt13}, R_{t13}, \gamma_{t13}, a_{t13})$

$\tau_f = h_{t13}/h_{t2}$ (H.1)

$P_{rt13i} = P_{rt2}\pi_f$

$\text{FAIR}\,(3, 0, T_{t13i}, h_{t13i}, P_{rt13i}, \phi_{t13i}, c_{pt13i}, R_{t13i}, \gamma_{t13i}, a_{t13i})$

$\eta_f = \dfrac{h_{t13i} - h_{t2}}{h_{t13} - h_{t2}}$

$P_{rt2.5} = P_{rt2}\pi_{cL}^{1/e_{cL}}$

$\text{FAIR}\,(3, 0, T_{t2.5}, h_{t2.5}, P_{rt2.5}, \phi_{t2.5}, c_{pt2.5}, R_{t2.5}, \gamma_{t2.5}, a_{t2.5})$

$\tau_{cL} = h_{t2.5}/h_{t2}$ (H.2)

$P_{rt2.5i} = P_{rt2}\pi_{cL}$

$\text{FAIR}\,(3, 0, T_{t2.5i}, h_{t2.5i}, P_{rt2.5i}, \phi_{t2.5i}, c_{pt2.5i}, R_{t2.5i}, \gamma_{t2.5i}, a_{t2.5i})$

$\eta_{cL} = \dfrac{h_{t2.5i} - h_{t2}}{h_{t2.5} - h_{t2}}$

$P_{rt3} = P_{rt2.5}\pi_{cH}^{1/e_{cH}}$

$\text{FAIR}\,(3, 0, T_{t3}, h_{t3}, P_{rt3}, \phi_{t3}, c_{pt3}, R_{t3}, \gamma_{t3}, a_{t3})$

$\tau_{cH} = h_{t3}/h_{t2.5}$ (H.3)

$P_{rt3} = P_{rt2.5}\pi_{cH}$

$\text{FAIR}\,(3, 0, T_{t3i}, h_{t3i}, P_{rt3i}, \phi_{t3i}, c_{pt3i}, R_{t3i}, \gamma_{t3i}, a_{t3i})$

$\eta_{cH} = \dfrac{h_{t3i} - h_{t2.5}}{h_{t3} - h_{t2.5}}$

Set initial value of fuel/air ratio at station 4 $= f_{4i}$

A $\text{FAIR}\,(1, f_{4i}, T_{t4}, h_{t4}, P_{rt4}, \phi_{t4}, c_{pt4}, R_{t4}, \gamma_{t4}, a_{t4})$

$f = \dfrac{h_{t4} - h_{t3}}{\eta_b h_{PR} - h_{t4}}$ (H.4)

If $|f - f_{4i}| > 0.0001$, then $f_{4i} = f$ and go to A; else continue.

$\tau_\lambda = h_{t4}/h_0$

$$\tau_{m1} = \frac{(1 - \beta - \varepsilon_1 - \varepsilon_2)(1 + f) + \varepsilon_1 \tau_r \tau_{cL} \tau_{cH}/\tau_\lambda}{(1 - \beta - \varepsilon_1 - \varepsilon_2)(1 + f) + \varepsilon_1} \tag{H.5}$$

$$\tau_{tH} = 1 - \frac{\tau_r \tau_{cL}(\tau_{cH} - 1) + (1 + \alpha)C_{TOH}/\eta_{mPH}}{\eta_{mH}\tau_\lambda\{(1 - \beta - \varepsilon_1 - \varepsilon_2)(1 + f) + \varepsilon_1 \tau_r \tau_{cL} \tau_{cH}/\tau_\lambda\}} \tag{H.6}$$

$$h_{t4.1} = h_{t4}\tau_{m1}$$

$$f_{4.1} = \frac{f}{1 + f + \varepsilon_1/(1 - \beta - \varepsilon_1 - \varepsilon_2)}$$

FAIR $(2, f_{4.1}, T_{t4.1}, h_{t4.1}, P_{rt4.1}, \phi_{t4.1}, c_{pt4.1}, R_{t4.1}, \gamma_{t4.1}, a_{t4.1})$

$$h_{t4.4} = h_{t4.1}\tau_{tH}$$

FAIR $(2, f_{4.1}, T_{t4.4}, h_{t4.4}, P_{rt4.4}, \phi_{t4.4}, c_{pt4.4}, R_{t4.4}, \gamma_{t4.4}, a_{t4.4})$

$$\pi_{tH} = \left(\frac{P_{rt4.4}}{P_{rt4.1}}\right)^{1/e_{tH}} \tag{H.7}$$

$$P_{rt4.4i} = \pi_{tH}P_{rt4.1}$$

FAIR $(3, f_{4.1}, T_{t4.4i}, h_{t4.4i}, P_{rt4.4i}, \phi_{t4.4i}, c_{pt4.4i}, R_{t4.4i}, \gamma_{t4.4i}, a_{t4.4i})$

$$\eta_{tH} = \frac{h_{t4.1} - h_{t4.4}}{h_{t4.1} - h_{t4.4i}}$$

$$\tau_{m2} = \frac{(1 - \beta - \varepsilon_1 - \varepsilon_2)(1 + f) + \varepsilon_1 + \varepsilon_2\{\tau_r \tau_{cL} \tau_{cH}/(\tau_\lambda \tau_{m1} \tau_{tH})\}}{(1 - \beta - \varepsilon_1 - \varepsilon_2)(1 + f) + \varepsilon_1 + \varepsilon_2} \tag{H.8}$$

$$h_{t4.5} = h_{t4.4}\tau_{m2}$$

$$f_{4.5} = \frac{f}{1 + f + (\varepsilon_1 + \varepsilon_2)/(1 - \beta - \varepsilon_1 - \varepsilon_2)}$$

FAIR $(2, f_{4.5}, T_{t4.5}, h_{t4.5}, P_{rt4.5}, \phi_{t4.5}, c_{pt4.5}, R_{t4.5}, \gamma_{t4.5}, a_{t4.5})$

$$\tau_{tL} = 1 - \frac{\tau_r\{(\tau_{cL} - 1) + \alpha(\tau_f - 1)\} + (1 + \alpha)C_{TOL}/\eta_{mPL}}{\eta_{mL}\tau_\lambda \tau_{tH}\left\{(1 - \beta - \varepsilon_1 - \varepsilon_2)(1 + f) + \left(\varepsilon_1 + \dfrac{\varepsilon_2}{\tau_{tH}}\right)\dfrac{\tau_r \tau_{cL} \tau_{cH}}{\tau_\lambda}\right\}} \tag{H.9}$$

$$h_{t5} = h_{t4.5}\tau_{tL}$$

FAIR $(2, f_{4.5}, T_{t5}, h_{t5}, P_{rt5}, \phi_{t5}, c_{pt5}, R_{t5}, \gamma_{t5}, a_{t5})$

$$\pi_{tL} = \left(\frac{P_{rt5}}{P_{rt4.5}}\right)^{1/e_{tL}} \tag{H.10}$$

$$P_{rt5i} = \pi_{tH}P_{rt4.5}$$

FAIR $(3, f_{4.5}, T_{t5i}, h_{t5i}, P_{rt5i}, \phi_{t5i}, c_{pt5i}, R_{t5i}, \gamma_{t5i}, a_{t5i})$

$$\eta_{tL} = \frac{h_{t4.5} - h_{t5}}{h_{t4.5} - h_{t5i}}$$

$$h_{t6} = h_{t5}; \quad T_{t6} = T_{t5}; \quad f_6 = f_{4.5}$$

$$h_{t16} = h_{t13}; \quad T_{t16} = T_{t13}; \quad P_{rt16} = P_{rt13}; \quad f_{16} = 0$$

$$\alpha' = \frac{\alpha}{(1 - \beta - \varepsilon_1 - \varepsilon_2)(1 + f) + \varepsilon_1 + \varepsilon_2} \tag{H.11}$$

$$f_{6A} = f_6/(1 + \alpha')$$

$$h_{t6A} = \frac{h_{t6} + \alpha'h_{t16}}{1 + \alpha'}$$

$$\tau_M = h_{t6A}/h_{t6} \tag{H.12}$$

$$\frac{P_{t16}}{P_{t6}} = \frac{\pi_f}{\pi_{cL}\,\pi_{cH}\,\pi_b\,\pi_{tH}\,\pi_{tL}}$$

RGCOMPR $(1, T_{t6}, M_6, f_{4.5}, (T_t/T)_6, (P_t/P)_6, MFP_6)$

$$T_6 = T_{t6}/(T_t/T)_6$$

$$(P_t/P)_{16} = (P_t/P)_6 \frac{P_{t16}}{P_{t6}}$$

$$P_{r16} = \frac{P_{rt16}}{(P_t/P)_{16}}$$

FAIR $(3, 0, T_{16}, h_{16}, P_{r16}, \phi_{16}, c_{p16}, R_{16}, \gamma_{16}, a_{16})$

$$V_{16} = \sqrt{2g_c(h_{t16} - h_{16})}$$

$$M_{16} = V_{16}/a_{16} \tag{H.13}$$

RGCOMPR $(1, T_{t16}, M_{16}, f_{16}, (T_t/T)_{16}, (P_t/P)_{16}, MFP_{16})$

$$\frac{A_{16}}{A_6} = \alpha'\sqrt{\frac{T_{t16}}{T_{t6}}\,\frac{P_{t6}}{P_{t16}}\,\frac{MFP_6}{MFP_{16}}}$$

$$\frac{A_6}{A_{6A}} = \frac{1}{1 + A_{16}/A_6}$$

$$\text{Constant} = \sqrt{\frac{R_6 T_6}{\gamma_6}}\left\{(1 + \gamma_6 M_6^2) + \frac{A_{16}}{A_6}\left(1 + \gamma_{16}M_{16}^2\right)\right\}\bigg/\{M_6(1 + \alpha')\}$$

Set initial value of Mach number at station $6A = M_{6Ai}$

B   RGCOMPR $(T_{t6A}, M_{6A}, f_{6A}, (T_t/T)_{6A}, (P_t/P)_{6A}, MFP_{6A})$

$$T_{6A} = T_{t6A}(T_t/T)_{6A}$$

FAIR $(1, f_{6A}, T_{6A}, h_{6A}, P_{r6A}, \phi_{6A}, c_{p6A}, R_{6A}, \gamma_{6A}, a_{6A})$

$$M_{6A} = \sqrt{\frac{R_{6A}T_{6A}}{\gamma_{6A}}\,\frac{1 + \gamma_{6A}M_{6Ai}^2}{\text{Constant}}} \tag{H.14}$$

If $|M_{6A} - M_{6Ai}| > 0.0001$, then $M_{6Ai} = M_{6A}$ and go to B; else continue

$$\pi_{M\,ideal} = (1 + \alpha')\sqrt{\tau_M}\,\frac{A_6}{A_{6A}}\,\frac{MFP_6}{MFP_{6A}}$$

$$\pi_M = \pi_{M\,max}\,\pi_{M\,ideal} \tag{H.15}$$

Set initial value of fuel/air ratio at station $7 = f_{7i}$

C   FAIR $(1, f_{7i}, T_{t7}, h_{t7}, P_{rt7}, \phi_{t7}, c_{pt7}, R_{t7}, \gamma_{t7}, a_{t7})$

$$\tau_{\lambda AB} = \frac{h_{t7}}{h_0}$$

$$f_{AB} = \left(1 + f\frac{1 - \beta - \varepsilon_1 - \varepsilon_2}{1 + \alpha - \beta}\right)\frac{\tau_{\lambda AB} - \tau_\lambda \tau_{m1}\tau_{tH}\tau_{m2}\tau_{tL}\tau_M}{h_{PR}\eta_{AB}/h_0 - \tau_{\lambda AB}} \tag{H.16}$$

$$f_7 = f_{6A} + f_{AB}$$

If $|f_7 - f_{7i}| > 0.0001$, then $f_{7i} = f_7$ and go to C; else continue.

$$f_o = f_7$$

$$T_{t9} = T_{t7};\quad h_{t9} = h_{t7};\quad P_{rt9} = P_{r7t}$$

$$\frac{P_{t9}}{P_9} = \left(\frac{P_0}{P_9}\right)\pi_r\,\pi_d\,\pi_{cL}\,\pi_{cH}\,\pi_b\,\pi_{tH}\,\pi_{tL}\,\pi_M\,\pi_{AB}\,\pi_n$$

$$P_{r9} = P_{rt9}\left(\frac{P_{t9}}{P_9}\right)$$

FAIR $(3,\,f_o,\,T_9,\,h_9,\,P_{r9},\,\phi_9,\,c_{p9},\,R_9,\,\gamma_9,\,a_9)$

$$V_9 = \sqrt{2g_c(h_{t9} - h_9)}$$

$$M_9 = V_9/a_9$$

$$\frac{F}{\dot{m}_0} = \frac{a_0}{g_c}\left\{\left(1 + f_o - \frac{\beta}{1+\alpha}\right)\frac{V_9}{a_0} - M_0\right.$$
$$\left. + \left(1 + f_o - \frac{\beta}{1+\alpha}\right)\frac{R_9}{R_0}\frac{T_9/T_0}{V_9/a_0}\frac{(1 - P_0/P_9)}{\gamma_0}\right\}$$

$$S = \frac{f_o}{F/\dot{m}_0}$$

$$\eta_P = \frac{\dfrac{2g_c M_0}{a_0}\dfrac{F}{\dot{m}_0}}{\left\{1 + f_o - \dfrac{\beta}{1+\alpha}\right\}\left(\dfrac{V_9}{a_0}\right)^2 - M_0^2}$$

$$\eta_{TH} = \frac{\dfrac{1}{2g_c}\left\{\left[1 + f_o - \left(\dfrac{\beta}{1+\alpha}\right)\right]V_9^2 - V_0^2\right\} + (C_{TOL} + C_{TOH})h_o}{f_o h_{PR}}$$

$$\eta_O = \eta_{TH}\eta_P$$

Appendix I
Mixed Flow Turbofan Engine Performance Cycle Analysis Equations

Appendix I summarizes the complete performance or off-design cycle analysis equations for mixed flow, afterburning, two-spool turbofan engine with bleed, turbine cooling, and power extraction. For convenience in computer programming, the required computer inputs and principal computer outputs are given. These are followed by the cycle equations in their order of solution. Note that the iterative solution procedure for M_6, α', and $\dot{m}_0$ follows that described in Sec. 5.2.6 and depicted in Figs. 5.3a and 5.3b.

Inputs

Performance choices:

Flight parameters:	M_0, T_0, P_0
Throttle setting:	T_{t4}, T_{t7}
Exhaust nozzle setting:	P_0/P_9

Design constants:

π:	$\pi_{d\,max}, \pi_b, \pi_{M\,max}, \pi_{ABR}, \pi_n$
η:	$\eta_f, \eta_{cL}, \eta_{cH}, \eta_{tH}, \eta_{tL}, \eta_b, \eta_{mL}, \eta_{mH}, \eta_{mPL}, \eta_{mPH}$
A:	$A_4, A_{4.5}, A_6, A_{16}, A_{6A}, A_{8wo/AB}$
Others:	$\beta, \varepsilon_1, \varepsilon_2, h_{PR}, P_{TOL}, P_{TOH}$

Reference condition:

Flight parameters:	M_{0R}, T_{0R}, P_{0R}
Component behavior:	$\pi_{fR}, \pi_{cLR}, \pi_{cHR}, \pi_{tHR}, \pi_{tLR}$
	$\tau_{fR}, \tau_{cLR}, \tau_{cHR}, \tau_{tHR}, \tau_{tLR}$
	$M_{6R}, M_{16R}, M_{6AR}, M_{8R}$
Others:	$\tau_{m1R}, \tau_{m2R}, f_R, f_{ABR}, M_{9R}, M_{19R}, \alpha_R, \alpha'_R$
	$F_R, \dot{m}_{0R}, S_R$
Engine control limits:	$\pi_{c\,max}, T_{t3\,max}, P_{t3\,max}, \%N_L, \%N_H$

Outputs

Overall performance:	$F, \dot{m}_0, S, f_o, \eta_P, \eta_{TH}, V_9/a_0, \alpha$
	$P_{t9}/P_9, P_9/P_0, T_9/T_0$
Component behavior:	$\pi_f, \pi_{cL}, \pi_{cH}, \pi_{tH}, \pi_{tL}$
	$\tau_f, \tau_{cL}, \tau_{cH}, \tau_{tH}, \tau_{tL}, \tau_\lambda$
	$\tau_{m1}, \tau_{m2}, f, f_{AB}$
	$M_6, M_{16}, M_{6A}, M_8, M_9$

Equations

Preliminary computations:

$\text{FAIR}\,(1, 0, T_0, h_0, P_{r0}, \phi_0, c_{p0}, R_0, \gamma_0, a_0)$

$V_0 = M_0 a_0$

$h_{t0} = h_0 + \dfrac{V_0^2}{2g_c}$

$\text{FAIR}\,(2, 0, T_{t0}, h_{t0}, P_{rt0}, \phi_{t0}, c_{pt0}, R_{t0}, \gamma_{t0}, a_{t0})$

$\tau_r = h_{t0}/h_0$

$\pi_r = P_{rt0}/P_{r0}$

$\eta_{R\,spec} = 1 \qquad\qquad\qquad\qquad \text{for } M_0 \le 1$

$\eta_{R\,spec} = 1 - 0.075(M_0 - 1)^{1.35} \text{ for } 1 < M_0 < 5$

$\eta_{R\,spec} = \dfrac{800}{M_0^4 + 935} \qquad\qquad \text{for } 1 < M_0 < 5$

$\pi_d = \pi_{d\,max}\eta_{R\,spec}$

$h_{t2} = h_{t0}$

$P_{rt2} = P_{rt0}$

$\pi_{ABdry} = 1 - (1 - \pi_{ABR})/2$

Set initial values:

$\pi_{tH} = \pi_{tHR}, \quad \pi_{tL} = \pi_{tLR}, \quad \tau_{tH} = \tau_{tHR}, \quad \tau_{tL} = \tau_{tLR}$

$\pi_f = \pi_{fR}, \quad \pi_{cL} = \pi_{cLR}, \quad \pi_{cH} = \pi_{cHR}$

$\tau_f = \tau_{fR}, \quad \tau_{cL} = \tau_{cLR}, \quad \tau_{cH} = \tau_{cHR}$

$\tau_{m1} = \tau_{m1R}, \quad \tau_{m2} = \tau_{m2R}, \quad f = f_R$

$M_4 = 1, \quad M_{4.5} = 1, \quad M_{6A} = M_{6AR}, \quad M_8 = M_{8R}$

$\text{FAIR}\,(1, f, T_{t4}, h_{t4}, P_{rt4}, \phi_{t4}, c_{pt4}, R_{t4}, \gamma_{t4}, a_{t4})$

$h_{t4.5} = h_{t4}\tau_{m1}\tau_{tH}\tau_{m2}$

$f_{4.5} = f(1 - \beta - \varepsilon_1 - \varepsilon_2)/(1 - \beta)$

$\text{FAIR}\,(2, f_{4.5}, T_{t4.5i}, h_{t4.5}, P_{rt4.5}, \phi_{t4.5}, c_{pt4.5}, R_{t4.5}, \gamma_{t4.5}, a_{t4.5})$

$h_{t5} = h_{t4.5}\tau_{tL}$

$\text{FAIR}\,(2, f_{4.5}, T_{t5i}, h_{t5}, P_{rt5}, \phi_{t5}, c_{pt5}, R_{t5}, \gamma_{t5}, a_{t5})$

$h_{t6A} = h_{t5}\tau_{mR}$

$f_{6A} = f_{4.5}(1 - \beta)/(1 + \alpha - \beta)$

$\text{FAIR}\,(2, f_{6A}, T_{t6A}, h_{t6A}, P_{rt6A}, \phi_{t6A}, c_{pt6A}, R_{t6A}, \gamma_{t6A}, a_{t6A})$

1 $\quad h_{t3} = h_{t0}\tau_{cL}\tau_{cH}$

$\text{FAIR}\,(2, 0, T_{t3}, h_{t3}, P_{rt3}, \phi_{t3}, c_{pt3}, R_{t3}, \gamma_{t3}, a_{t3})$

$\alpha' = \alpha/\{(1 + f)(1 - \beta - \varepsilon_1 - \varepsilon_2) + \varepsilon_1 + \varepsilon_2\}$

$\text{FAIR}\,(1, f, T_{t4}, h_{t4}, P_{rt4}, \phi_{t4}, c_{pt4}, R_{t4}, \gamma_{t4}, a_{t4})$

$f_{4.5} = f(1 - \beta - \varepsilon_1 - \varepsilon_2)/(1 - \beta)$

$\text{TURBC}\,(T_{t4}, f, A_4/A_{4.5}, M_4, M_{4.5}, \eta_{tH}, T_{t4.5i}, T_{t3}, \beta, \varepsilon_1, \varepsilon_2, \pi_{tH}, \tau_{tH}, T_{t4.5})$

$\text{TURB}\,(T_{t4.5}, f_{4.5}, A_{4.5}/A_6, M_{4.5}, M_6, \eta_{tL}, T_{t5i}, \pi_{tL}, \tau_{tL}, T_{t5})$

$\tau_\lambda = h_{t4}/h_0$

$$\tau_f = 1 + \left[(1 - \tau_{tL})\eta_{mL}\left\{\begin{array}{l}(1 - \beta - \varepsilon_1 - \varepsilon_2)(1+f)\dfrac{\tau_\lambda \tau_{tH}}{\tau_r} \\ + (\varepsilon_1 \tau_{tH} + \varepsilon_2)\tau_{cL}\tau_{cH}\end{array}\right\} - \dfrac{(1+\alpha)}{\tau_r \eta_{mPL}}\dfrac{P_{TOL}}{\dot{m}_0 h_0}\right] \Big/$$

$$\times \{(\tau_{cL} - 1)_R/(\tau_f - 1)_R + \alpha\}$$

$$\tau_{cL} = 1 + (\tau_f - 1)\frac{(\tau_{cL} - 1)_R}{(\tau_f - 1)_R}$$

$$\tau_{cH} = 1 + (1 - \tau_{tH})\eta_{mH}\left\{(1 - \beta - \varepsilon_1 - \varepsilon_2)(1+f)\frac{\tau_\lambda}{\tau_r \tau_{cL}} + \varepsilon_1 \tau_{cH}\right\}$$

$$- \frac{(1+\alpha)}{\tau_r \tau_{cL}\eta_{mPH}}\frac{P_{TOH}}{\dot{m}_0 h_0}$$

$h_{t2} = h_{t0}$

$P_{rt2} = P_{rt0}$

$h_{t13} = h_{t2}\tau_f$

$h_{t2.5} = h_{t2}\tau_{cL}$

$h_{t3} = h_{t2.5}\tau_{cH}$

$h_{t13i} = h_{t2}\{1 + \eta_f(\tau_f - 1)\}$

$h_{t2.5i} = h_{t2}\{1 + \eta_{cL}(\tau_{cL} - 1)\}$

$h_{t3i} = h_{t2.5}\{1 + \eta_{cH}(\tau_{cH} - 1)\}$

FAIR $(2, 0, T_{t13}, h_{t13}, P_{rt13}, \phi_{t13}, c_{pt13}, R_{t13}, \gamma_{t13}, a_{t13})$

FAIR $(2, 0, T_{t13i}, h_{t13i}, P_{rt13i}, \phi_{t13i}, c_{pt13i}, R_{t13i}, \gamma_{t13i}, a_{t13i})$

FAIR $(2, 0, T_{t2.5}, h_{t2.5}, P_{rt2.5}, \phi_{t2.5}, c_{pt2.5}, R_{t2.5}, \gamma_{t2.5}, a_{t2.5})$

FAIR $(2, 0, T_{t2.5i}, h_{t2.5i}, P_{rt2.5i}, \phi_{t2.5i}, c_{pt2.5i}, R_{t2.5i}, \gamma_{t2.5i}, a_{t2.5i})$

FAIR $(2, 0, T_{t3}, h_{t3}, P_{rt3}, \phi_{t3}, c_{pt3}, R_{t3}, \gamma_{t3}, a_{t3})$

FAIR $(2, 0, T_{t3i}, h_{t3i}, P_{rt3i}, \phi_{t3i}, c_{pt3i}, R_{t3i}, \gamma_{t3i}, a_{t3i})$

$\pi_f = P_{rt13i}/P_{rt2}$

$\pi_{cL} = P_{rt2.5i}/P_{rt2}$

$\pi_{cH} = P_{rt3i}/P_{rt2.5}$

$\pi_c = \pi_{cL}\pi_{cH}$

$\tau_c = \tau_{cL}\tau_{cH}$

2    $f_{temp} = f$

FAIR $(1, f, T_{t4}, h_{t4}, P_{rt4}, \phi_{t4}, c_{pt4}, R_{t4}, \gamma_{t4}, a_{t4})$

$$f = \frac{h_{t4} - h_{t3}}{h_{PR}\eta_b - h_{t4}}$$

if $|f - f_{temp}| > 0.0001$ goto 2

$h_{t6} = h_{t5}$

$T_{t6} = T_{t5}$

$h_{t16} = h_{t13}$

$T_{t16} = T_{t13}$

$P_{t6} = P_0 \pi_r \pi_d \pi_{cL} \pi_{cH} \pi_b \pi_{tH} \pi_{tL}$

$f_{4.5} = f(1 - \beta - \varepsilon_1 - \varepsilon_2)/(1 - \beta)$

RGCOMPR $(1, T_{t6}, M_6, f_{4.5}, TtT, PtP, MFP_6)$

$P_6 = P_{t6}/PtP$

$T_6 = T_{t6}/TtT$

$P_{t16} = P_0 \pi_r \pi_d \pi_f$

$$\left(\frac{P_t}{P}\right)_{16} = P_{t16}/P_6$$

RGCOMPR $(1, T_{t16}, 1, 0, TtT, PtP, MFP_{16})$

if $(P_t/P)_{16} > PtP$ then $M_6 = M_6 - 0.01$ goto 1

if $(P_t/P)_{16} < 1$ then $M_6 = M_6 - 0.01$ goto 1

RGCOMPR $(3, T_{t16}, M_{16}, 0, TtT, (P_t/P)_{16}, MFP_{16})$

$T_{16} = T_{t16}/TtT$

$$\alpha'_{new} = \frac{P_{t16} A_{16} MFP_{16}}{P_{t6} A_6 MFP_6} \sqrt{\frac{T_{t6}}{T_{t16}}}$$

$$\alpha'_{error} = \left|\frac{\alpha'_{new} - \alpha'}{\alpha'}\right|$$

$\alpha = \alpha'_{new}\{(1 + f)(1 - \beta - \varepsilon_1 - \varepsilon_2) + \varepsilon_1 + \varepsilon_2\}$

if $\alpha'_{error} > 0.001$ then

    calculate a new α' using Newtonian iteration

    goto 1

end if

FAIR $(1, f_{4.5}, T_6, h_6, P_{r6}, \phi_6, c_{p6}, R_6, \gamma_6, a_6)$

FAIR $(1, 0, T_{16}, h_{16}, P_{r16}, \phi_{16}, c_{p16}, R_{16}, \gamma_{16}, a_{16})$

$$h_{t6A} = \frac{h_{t6} + \alpha' h_{t16}}{1 + \alpha'}$$

$$\tau_M = \frac{h_{t6A}}{h_{t6}}$$

$f_{6A} = f_{4.5}(1 - \beta)/(1 + \alpha - \beta)$

FAIR $(2, f_{6A}, T_{t6A}, h_{t6A}, P_{rt6A}, \phi_{t6A}, c_{pt6A}, R_{t6A}, \gamma_{t6A}, a_{t6A})$

$$\text{Constant} = \frac{1}{1 + \alpha'}\left\{\sqrt{\frac{R_6 T_6}{\gamma_6}}\frac{1 + \gamma_6 M_6^2}{M_6} + \alpha'\sqrt{\frac{R_{16} T_{16}}{\gamma_{16}}}\frac{1 + \gamma_{16} M_{16}^2}{M_{16}}\right\}$$

3   RGCOMPR $(1, T_{t6A}, M_{6A}, f_{6A}, TtT_{6A}, PtP_{6A}, MFP_{6A})$

$$T_{6A} = \frac{T_{t6A}}{TtT_{6A}}$$

   FAIR $(1, f_{6A}, T_{6A}, h_{6A}, P_{r6A}, \phi_{6A}, c_{p6A}, R_{6A}, \gamma_{6A}, a_{6A})$

$$M_{6Anew} = \sqrt{\frac{R_{6A} T_{6A}}{\gamma_{6A}}\frac{1 + \gamma_{6A} M_{6A}^2}{\text{Constant}}}$$

   $M_{6Aerror} = |M_{6Anew} - M_{6A}|$

   if $M_{6Aerror} > 0.001$ then $M_{6A} = M_{6Anew}$ goto 3

$$\pi_{M\,ideal} = \sqrt{\frac{T_{t6A}}{T_{t6}}} \frac{MFP_6}{MFP_{6A}} \frac{1+\alpha'}{1+A_{16}/A_6}$$

$$\pi_M = \pi_{M\,max}\, \pi_{M\,ideal}$$

$$\frac{P_{t9}}{P_0} = \pi_r\, \pi_d\, \pi_{cL}\, \pi_{cH}\, \pi_b\, \pi_{tH}\, \pi_{tL}\, \pi_M\, \pi_{AB\,dry}\, \pi_n$$

RGCOMPR $(3, T_{t6A}, M_9, f_{6A}, TtT_9, P_{t9}/P_0, MFP_9)$

if $M_9 > 1$ then $M_8 = 1$ else $M_8 = M_9$

RGCOMPR $(1, T_{t6A}, M_8, f_{6A}, TtT_8, PtP_8, MFP_8)$

$$MFP_6 = MFP_8 \frac{\pi_M\, \pi_{AB\,dry}}{1+\alpha'} \frac{A_8}{A_6} \sqrt{\frac{T_{t6}}{T_{t6A}}}$$

RGCOMPR $(4, T_{t6}, M_{6\,new}, f_{4.5}, TtT_6, PtP_6, MFP_6)$

$M_{6\,error} = |M_6 - M_{6\,new}|$

if $M_{6\,error} > 0.0005$ then

    if $M_6 > M_{6\,new}$ then $M_6 = M_6 - 0.0001$ else $M_6 = M_6 + 0.002$

    goto 1

end if

RGCOMPR $(1, T_{t4}, M_4, f, TtT, PtP, MFP_4)$

$$\dot{m}_{0\,new} = \dot{m}_{0R} \frac{1+f_R}{1+f} \frac{P_0(1+\alpha)\pi_r\, \pi_d\, \pi_{cL}\, \pi_{cH}}{\{P_0(1+\alpha)\,\pi_r\, \pi_d\, \pi_{cL}\, \pi_{cH}\}_R} \frac{MFP_4}{MFP_{4R}} \sqrt{\frac{T_{t4R}}{T_{t4}}}$$

$$\dot{m}_{0\,error} = \left| \frac{\dot{m}_{0\,new} - \dot{m}_0}{\dot{m}_{0R}} \right|$$

if $\dot{m}_{0\,error} > 0.001$ then $\dot{m}_0 = \dot{m}_{0\,new}$ goto 1

$f_7 = f_{6A}$

4   FAIR $(1, f_7, T_{t7}, h_{t7}, P_{rt7}, \phi_{t7}, c_{pt7}, R_{t7}, \gamma_{t7}, a_{t7})$

$$f_{AB} = \frac{h_{t7} - h_{t6A}}{\eta_{AB}h_{PR} - h_{t6A}}$$

$f_{7\,new} = f_{6A} + f_{AB}$

$f_{7\,error} = |f_{7\,new} - f_7|$

if $\dot{m}_{7\,error} > 0.00001$ then $f_7 = f_{7\,new}$ goto 4

$$\%AB = 100\frac{T_{t7} - T_{t6A}}{T_{t7R} - T_{t6A}}$$

$$\pi_{AB} = \pi_{AB\,dry} + 0.01 \times \%AB(\pi_{ABR} - \pi_{AB\,dry})$$

$$\frac{P_{t9}}{P_0} = \pi_r\, \pi_d\, \pi_{cL}\, \pi_{cH}\, \pi_b\, \pi_{tH}\, \pi_{tL}\, \pi_M\, \pi_{AB}\, \pi_n$$

$$\frac{P_{t9}}{P_9} = \frac{P_{t9}}{P_0} \frac{P_9}{P_0}$$

$$T_{t9} = T_{t7}$$

RGCOMPR $(3, T_{t9}, M_9, f_7, TtT, P_{t9}/P_9, MFP_9)$

$$\dot{m}_9 = \dot{m}_0 (1 + f_7) \left(1 - \frac{\beta}{1 + \alpha} \right)$$

$$P_{t9} = P_0 \, \pi_r \, \pi_d \, \pi_{cL} \, \pi_{cH} \, \pi_b \, \pi_{tH} \, \pi_{tL} \, \pi_M \, \pi_{AB} \, \pi_n$$

$$A_9 = \frac{\dot{m}_9 \sqrt{T_{t9}}}{P_{t9} MFP_9}$$

$$T_9 = T_{t9}/TtT$$

FAIR $(1, \, f_7, \, T_9, \, h_9, \, P_{r9}, \, \phi_9, \, c_{p9}, \, R_9, \, \gamma_9, \, a_9)$

$$V_9 = M_9 a_9$$

$$f_o = \frac{f(1 - \beta - \varepsilon_1 - \varepsilon_2) + f_{AB}(1 + \alpha - \beta)}{1 + \alpha}$$

$$\frac{F}{\dot{m}_0} = \frac{a_0}{g_c} \left\{ \left(1 + f_o - \frac{\beta}{1 + \alpha} \right) \frac{V_9}{a_0} - M_0 \right.$$
$$\left. + \left(1 + f_o - \frac{\beta}{1 + \alpha} \right) \frac{R_9}{R_0} \frac{T_9/T_0}{V_9/a_0} \frac{(1 - P_0/P_9)}{\gamma_0} \right\}$$

$$S = \frac{f_o}{F/\dot{m}_0}$$

$$F = \dot{m}_0 \left(\frac{F}{\dot{m}_0} \right)$$

RGCOMPR $(1, \, T_{t0}, \, M_0, \, 0, \, TtT, \, PtP, \, MFP_0)$

$$A_0 = \frac{\dot{m}_0 \sqrt{T_{t0}}}{P_{t0} MFP_0}$$

$$\%RPM_{LP \; Spool} = 100 \sqrt{\frac{h_0 \tau_r (\tau_f - 1)}{[h_0 \tau_r (\tau_f - 1)]_R}}$$

$$\%RPM_{HP \; Spool} = 100 \sqrt{\frac{h_0 \tau_r \tau_{cL} (\tau_{cH} - 1)}{[h_0 \tau_r \tau_{cL} (\tau_{cH} - 1)]_R}}$$

$$\eta_P = \frac{2 g_c M_0}{a_0} \frac{F}{\dot{m}_0} \left/ \left\{ \left(1 + f_o - \frac{\beta}{1 + \alpha} \right) \left(\frac{V_9}{a_0} \right)^2 - M_0^2 \right\} \right.$$

$$\eta_{TH} = \frac{1}{2 g_c} \left\{ \left[\left(1 + f_o - \frac{\beta}{1 + \alpha} \right) V_9^2 - V_0^2 \right] + (C_{TOL} + C_{TOH}) h_0 \right\} \left/ f_o h_{PR} \right.$$

$$\eta_O = \eta_{TH} \eta_P$$

If any of the control limits (π_c, T_{t3}, P_{t3}, etc.) are exceeded, then reduce T_{t4} and go to 1. A Newtonian iteration scheme is used to rapidly converge on the value of T_{t4} that meets the most constraining control limit.

Appendix J
High Bypass Ratio Turbofan Engine Cycle Analysis

This material is included in case nonafterburning, separate exhaust flow, high bypass ratio turbofan engine cycles are under consideration. They are strong candidates for any application where high thrust and low fuel consumption are required and the flight Mach number never exceeds approximately 0.9. Consider the high bypass ratio turbofan engine shown in Figs. J.1a and J.1b. The station numbers of locations indicated there will be used throughout this appendix and include the following:

Station	Location
0	Far upstream or freestream
1	Inlet or diffuser entry
2	Inlet or diffuser exit, fan entry
13	Fan exit
2.5	Low-pressure compressor exit
	High-pressure compressor entry
3	High-pressure compressor exit
3.1	Burner entry
4	Burner exit
	Nozzle vanes entry
	Modeled coolant mixer 1 entry
	High-pressure turbine entry
	for π_{tH} definition
4.1	Nozzle vanes exit
	Coolant mixer 1 exit
	High-pressure turbine entry
	for τ_{tH} definition
4.4	High-pressure turbine exit
	Modeled coolant mixer 2 entry
4.5	Coolant mixer 2 exit
	Low-pressure turbine entry
5	Low-pressure turbine exit
7	Core exhaust nozzle entry
9	Core exhaust nozzle exit
17	Bypass exhaust nozzle entry
19	Bypass exhaust nozzle exit

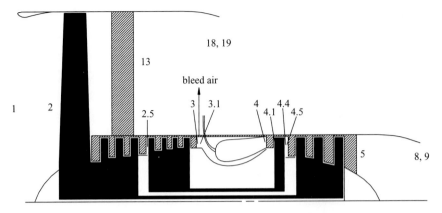

Fig. J.1a   Reference stations—high bypass ratio turbofan engine.

The component τ, π, efficiencies, and assumptions of Chapter 4 apply to this engine with the exception of those referring to the mixer and afterburner. Unlike the engine of Chapters 4 and 5, this turbofan does not have afterburning, and both the core ($\dot{m}_C$) and bypass ($\dot{m}_F$) airflows pass through separate nozzles. The total pressure ratio of the bypass air stream's nozzle is defined as

$$\pi_{nf} = P_{t19}/P_{t17}$$

The mass flow ratios of Eqs. (4.4a), (4.4b), (4.4c), (4.4d), (4.4e), (4.4h), (4.8i), and (4.8j) apply as does the turbine cooling model of Chapter 4 shown in Fig. 4.2.

This turbofan engine is modeled as having fixed convergent nozzles for both the core and bypass air streams. Thus, the exit pressure is equal to the ambient pressure for unchoked nozzle operation and the exit pressure is greater than the ambient pressure when the nozzle flow is choked.

The following sections outline development of both parametric and performance cycle analysis equations for this turbofan engine.

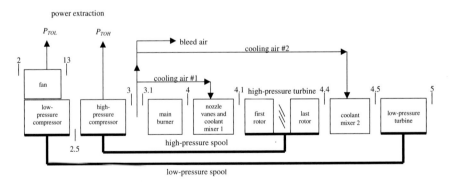

Fig. J.1b   Reference stations—bleed and turbine cooling airflows.

Parametric Analysis

The uninstalled thrust for a turbofan engine with separate exhausts streams is given by

$$F = \frac{1}{g_c}(\dot{m}_9 V_9 + \dot{m}_{19} V_{19} - \dot{m}_0 V_0) + A_9(P_9 - P_0) + A_{19}(P_{19} - P_0)$$

which can be rearranged into its nondimensional form as

$$\frac{F g_c}{\dot{m}_0 a_0} = \frac{1}{1+\alpha} \left\{ \begin{array}{l} (1 + f_o(1+\alpha) - \beta)\dfrac{V_9}{a_0} + \alpha \dfrac{V_{19}}{a_0} - (1+\alpha)M_0 \\[2ex] + (1 + f_o(1+\alpha) - \beta)\dfrac{R_9}{R_0}\dfrac{T_9/T_0}{V_9/a_0}\dfrac{(1 - P_0/P_9)}{\gamma_0} \\[2ex] + \alpha \dfrac{R_{19}}{R_0}\dfrac{T_{19}/T_0}{V_{19}/a_0}\dfrac{(1 - P_0/P_{19})}{\gamma_0} \end{array} \right\} \quad (J.1)$$

The velocity and temperature ratios required in Eq. (J.1) are obtained using the methods of Chapter 4. For the core airstream, they are

$$\left(\frac{V_9}{a_0}\right)^2 = \frac{M_0^2 \tau_\lambda \tau_{m1} \tau_{tH} \tau_{m2} \tau_{tL}}{\tau_r - 1}\left\{ 1 - \frac{h_9}{h_{t9}} \right\}$$

where h_9 is determined from h_{t9} and the pressure ratio

$$\frac{P_{t9}}{P_9} = \left(\frac{P_0}{P_9}\right) \pi_r \pi_d \pi_{cL} \pi_{cH} \pi_b \pi_{tH} \pi_{tL} \pi_n$$

For the bypass airstream, they are

$$\left(\frac{V_{19}}{a_0}\right)^2 = \frac{M_0^2 \tau_r \tau_f}{\tau_r - 1}\left\{ 1 - \frac{h_{19}}{h_{t19}} \right\}$$

where h_{19} is determined from h_{t19} and the pressure ratio

$$\frac{P_{t19}}{P_{19}} = \left(\frac{P_0}{P_{19}}\right) \pi_r \pi_d \pi_f \pi_{nf}$$

The independent design variables for this engine are the fan pressure ratio (π_f), the overall cycle pressure ratio (π_c), and the bypass ratio (α). The pressure ratio across the high-pressure compressor is obtained from

$$\pi_{cH} = \pi_c / \pi_{cL}$$

The temperature ratios across the fan (τ_f), the low-pressure compressor (τ_{cL}), and the high-pressure compressor (τ_{cH}) are related to their pressure ratios by Eqs. (4.7b), (4.7c), and (4.7d), respectively. The temperature ratios across the high-pressure turbine (τ_{tH}) and low-pressure turbine (τ_{tL}) are obtained from power balances of the high- and low-pressure spools resulting in Eqs. (4.21a) and (4.22a). The temperature ratios across the two cooling air mixing processes (τ_{m1} and τ_{m2}) are given by Eqs. (4.20a) and (4.20b). The pressure ratios across the high-pressure turbine (π_{tH}) and low-pressure turbine (π_{tL}) are related to their respective temperature ratio and polytropic efficiency by Eqs. (4.9d) and (4.9e). The fuel-air ratio (f) is given by Eq. (4.18). Thus, the only unknowns for solution of Eq. (J.1) are the static pressure ratios, P_0/P_9 and P_0/P_{19}.

Two flow regimes exist for flow through a convergent nozzle, unchoked and choked. For unchoked flow, the exit static pressure (P_e) is equal to the ambient pressure (P_0), and the exit Mach number is less than or equal to one. Unchoked flow will exist when

$$\frac{P_{te}}{P_0} < \left(\frac{P_t}{P}\right)_{M=1}$$

Then $P_e = P_0$ and the exit Mach number (M_e) is determined using the compressible flow functions. On the other hand, choked flow will exist when

$$\frac{P_{te}}{P_0} \geq \left(\frac{P_t}{P}\right)_{M=1}$$

and then $M_e = 1$, $P_{te}/P_e = (P_t/P)_{M=1}$, and

$$P_0/P_e = \frac{P_{te}/P_e}{P_{te}/P_0}$$

where P_{te}/P_0 is obtained by the product of the ram and component π for the respective airstream.

The thrust specific fuel consumption is given by Eq. (4.31), which can be expressed as

$$S = \frac{f_o}{F/\dot{m}_0} = \frac{f(1 - \beta - \varepsilon_1 - \varepsilon_2)}{(1 + \alpha)F/\dot{m}_0}$$

All of the equations needed for on-design cycle analysis of this turbofan engine have now been identified. The following section presents these equations in the order of solution.

Summary of High Bypass Ratio Turbofan Engine Parametric Cycle Analysis Equations

This section presents the complete parametric cycle analysis equations for non-afterburning, separate exhaust flow, two-spool turbofan engine with bleed, turbine cooling, power extraction, and convergent nozzles. For convenience in computer programming, the required computer inputs and principal computer outputs are given. These are followed by the cycle equations in their order of solution.

Inputs

Flight parameters: $\quad\quad\quad\quad$ M_0, T_0, P_0

Aircraft system parameters: $\quad$ β, C_{TOL}, C_{TOH}

Design limitations:

$\quad$ Fuel heating value: $\quad\quad$ h_{PR}

$\quad$ Component figures $\quad\quad$ $\varepsilon_1, \varepsilon_2$

$\quad\quad$ of merit: $\quad\quad\quad\quad$ $\pi_b, \pi_{d\,max}, \pi_n, \pi_{nf}$

$\quad\quad\quad\quad\quad\quad\quad\quad$ $e_f, e_{cL}, e_{cH}, e_{tH}, e_{tL}$

$\quad\quad\quad\quad\quad\quad\quad\quad$ $\eta_b, \eta_{mL}, \eta_{mH}, \eta_{mPL}, \eta_{mPH}$

Design choices: $\quad\quad\quad\quad$ $\pi_f, \pi_{cL}, \pi_{cH}, \alpha, T_{t4}$

Outputs

Overall performance: $\quad$ $F/\dot{m}_0, S, f_o, \eta_P, \eta_{TH}, V_9/a_0, V_{19}/a_0$

Component behavior: $\quad$ π_{tH}, π_{tL}

$\quad\quad\quad\quad\quad\quad\quad\quad$ $\tau_f, \tau_{cL}, \tau_{cH}, \tau_{tH}, \tau_{tL}, \tau_\lambda$

$\quad\quad\quad\quad\quad\quad\quad\quad$ f

$\quad\quad\quad\quad\quad\quad\quad\quad$ $\eta_f, \eta_{cL}, \eta_{cH}, \eta_{tH}, \eta_{tL}$

$\quad\quad\quad\quad\quad\quad\quad\quad$ $M_9, P_{t9}/P_9, P_9/P_0, T_9/T_0$

$\quad\quad\quad\quad\quad\quad\quad\quad$ $M_{19}, P_{t19}/P_{19}, P_{19}/P_0, T_{19}/T_0$

Equations

FAIR $(1, 0, T_0, h_0, P_{r0}, \phi_0, c_{p0}, R_0, \gamma_0, a_0)$

$V_0 = M_0 a_0$

$$h_{t0} = h_0 + \frac{V_0^2}{2g_c}$$

FAIR $(2, 0, T_{t0}, h_{t0}, P_{rt0}, \phi_{t0}, c_{pt0}, R_{t0}, \gamma_{t0}, a_{t0})$

$\tau_r = h_{t0}/h_0$

$\pi_r = P_{rt0}/P_{r0}$

$\eta_r = 1 \quad\quad\quad\quad\quad\quad\quad\quad$ for $M_0 \le 1$

$\eta_r = 1 - 0.075(M_0 - 1)^{1.35} \quad$ for $M_0 > 1$

$\pi_d = \pi_{d\,max}\eta_r$

$h_{t2} = h_{t0}$

$P_{rt2} = P_{rt0}$

$P_{rt13} = P_{rt2}\pi_f^{1/e_f}$

FAIR $(3, 0, T_{t13}, h_{t13}, P_{rt13}, \phi_{t13}, c_{pt13}, R_{t13}, \gamma_{t13}, a_{t13})$

$\tau_f = h_{t13}/h_{t2}$

$P_{rt13i} = P_{rt2}\pi_f$

FAIR $(3, 0, T_{t13i}, h_{t13i}, P_{rt13i}, \phi_{t13i}, c_{pt13i}, R_{t13i}, \gamma_{t13i}, a_{t13i})$

$$\eta_f = \frac{h_{t13i} - h_{t2}}{h_{t13} - h_{t2}}$$

$$P_{rt2.5} = P_{rt2}\pi_{cL}^{1/e_{cL}}$$

FAIR $(3, 0, T_{t2.5}, h_{t2.5}, P_{rt2.5}, \phi_{t2.5}, c_{pt2.5}, R_{t2.5}, \gamma_{t2.5}, a_{t2.5})$

$$\tau_{cL} = h_{t2.5}/h_{t2}$$

$$P_{rt2.5i} = P_{rt2}\,\pi_{cL}$$

FAIR $(3, 0, T_{t2.5i}, h_{t2.5i}, P_{rt2.5i}, \phi_{t2.5i}, c_{pt2.5i}, R_{t2.5i}, \gamma_{t2.5i}, a_{t2.5i})$

$$\eta_{cL} = \frac{h_{t2.5i} - h_{t2}}{h_{t2.5} - h_{t2}}$$

$$P_{rt3} = P_{rt2.5}\,\pi_{cH}^{1/e_{cH}}$$

FAIR $(3, 0, T_{t3}, h_{t3}, P_{rt3}, \phi_{t3}, c_{pt3}, R_{t3}, \gamma_{t3}, a_{t3})$

$$\tau_{cH} = h_{t3}/h_{t2.5}$$

$$P_{rt3i} = P_{rt2.5}\,\pi_{cH}$$

FAIR $(3, 0, T_{t3i}, h_{t3i}, P_{rt3i}, \phi_{t3i}, c_{pt3i}, R_{t3i}, \gamma_{t3i}, a_{t3i})$

$$\eta_{cH} = \frac{h_{t3i} - h_{t2.5}}{h_{t3} - h_{t2.5}}$$

Set initial value of fuel/air ratio at station $4 = f_{4i}$

A   FAIR $(1, f_{4i}, T_{t4}, h_{t4}, P_{rt4}, \phi_{t4}, c_{pt4}, R_{t4}, \gamma_{t4}, a_{t4})$

$$f = \frac{h_{t4} - h_{t3}}{\eta_b h_{PR} - h_{t4}}$$

If $|f - f_{4i}| > 0.0001$, then $f_{4i} = f$ and go to A, else continue.

$$\tau_\lambda = h_{t4}/h_0$$

$$\tau_{m1} = \frac{(1 - \beta - \varepsilon_1 - \varepsilon_2)(1 + f) + \varepsilon_1 \tau_r \tau_{cL} \tau_{cH}/\tau_\lambda}{(1 - \beta - \varepsilon_1 - \varepsilon_2)(1 + f) + \varepsilon_1}$$

$$\tau_{tH} = 1 - \frac{\tau_r \tau_{cL}(\tau_{cH} - 1) + (1 + \alpha)C_{TOH}/\eta_{mPH}}{\eta_{mH}\tau_\lambda\{(1 - \beta - \varepsilon_1 - \varepsilon_2)(1 + f) + \varepsilon_1 \tau_r \tau_{cL} \tau_{cH}/\tau_\lambda\}}$$

$$h_{t4.1} = h_{t4}\tau_{m1}$$

$$f_{4.1} = \frac{f}{1 + f + \varepsilon_1/(1 - \beta - \varepsilon_1 - \varepsilon_2)}$$

FAIR $(2, f_{4.1}, T_{t4.1}, h_{t4.1}, P_{rt4.1}, \phi_{t4.1}, c_{pt4.1}, R_{t4.1}, \gamma_{t4.1}, a_{t4.1})$

$$h_{t4.4} = h_{t4.1}\tau_{tH}$$

FAIR $(2, f_{4.1}, T_{t4.4}, h_{t4.4}, P_{rt4.4}, \phi_{t4.4}, c_{pt4.4}, R_{t4.4}, \gamma_{t4.4}, a_{t4.4})$

$$\pi_{tH} = \left(\frac{P_{rt4.4}}{P_{rt4.1}}\right)^{1/e_{tH}}$$

$$P_{rt4.4i} = \pi_{tH}P_{rt4.1}$$

FAIR $(3, f_{4.1}, T_{t4.4i}, h_{t4.4i}, P_{rt4.4i}, \phi_{t4.4i}, c_{pt4.4i}, R_{t4.4i}, \gamma_{t4.4i}, a_{t4.4i})$

$$\eta_{tH} = \frac{h_{t4.1} - h_{t4.4}}{h_{t4.1} - h_{t4.4i}}$$

$$\tau_{m2} = \frac{(1 - \beta - \varepsilon_1 - \varepsilon_2)(1 + f) + \varepsilon_1 + \varepsilon_2\{\tau_r \tau_{cL} \tau_{cH}/(\tau_\lambda \tau_{m1} \tau_{tH})\}}{(1 - \beta - \varepsilon_1 - \varepsilon_2)(1 + f) + \varepsilon_1 + \varepsilon_2}$$

$$h_{t4.5} = h_{t4.4}\tau_{m2}$$

$$f_{4.5} = \frac{f}{1 + f + (\varepsilon_1 + \varepsilon_2)/(1 - \beta - \varepsilon_1 - \varepsilon_2)}$$

FAIR $(2, f_{4.5}, T_{t4.5}, h_{t4.5}, P_{rt4.5}, \phi_{t4.5}, c_{pt4.5}, R_{t4.5}, \gamma_{t4.5}, a_{t4.5})$

$$\tau_{tL} = 1 - \frac{\tau_r\{(\tau_{cL} - 1) + \alpha(\tau_f - 1)\} + (1 + \alpha)C_{TOL}/\eta_{mPL}}{\eta_{mH}\tau_\lambda\tau_{tH}\{(1 - \beta - \varepsilon_1 - \varepsilon_2)(1 + f) + (\varepsilon_1 + \varepsilon_2/\tau_{tH})\tau_r\tau_{cL}\tau_{cH}/\tau_\lambda\}}$$

$$h_{t5} = h_{t4.5}\tau_{tL}$$

FAIR $(2, f_{4.5}, T_{t4.5}, h_{t4.5}, P_{rt4.5}, \phi_{t4.5}, c_{pt4.5}, R_{t4.5}, \gamma_{t4.5}, a_{t4.5})$

$$\pi_{tL} = \left(\frac{P_{rt5}}{P_{rt4.5}}\right)^{1/e_{tL}}$$

$$P_{rt5i} = \pi_{tL}P_{rt4.5}$$

FAIR $(3, f_{4.5}, T_{t5i}, h_{t5i}, P_{rt5i}, \phi_{t5i}, c_{pt5i}, R_{t5i}, \gamma_{t5i}, a_{t5i})$

$$\eta_{tL} = \frac{h_{t4.5} - h_{t5}}{h_{t4.5} - h_{t5i}}$$

$$h_{t9} = h_{t5}; \quad T_{t9} = T_{t5}; \quad P_{rt9} = P_{rt5}; \quad f_9 = f_{4.5}$$

$$M_9 = 1$$

RGCOMPR $(1, T_{t9}, f_9, M_9, (T_t/T)_9, (P_t/P)_9, MFP_9)$

$$\frac{P_{t9}}{P_0} = \pi_r \pi_d \pi_{cL} \pi_{cH} \pi_b \pi_{tH} \pi_{tL} \pi_n$$

If $\dfrac{P_{t9}}{P_0} \geq \left(\dfrac{P_t}{P}\right)_9$ then

$$T_9 = \frac{T_{t9}}{(T_t/T)_9}$$

FAIR $(1, f_9, T_9, h_9, P_{r9}, \phi_9, c_{p9}, R_9, \gamma_9, a_9)$

$$\frac{P_0}{P_9} = \frac{(P_t/P)_9}{P_{t9}/P_0}$$

Else

$$P_{r9} = \frac{P_{rt9}}{P_{t9}/P_0}$$

FAIR $(3, f_9, T_9, h_9, P_{r9}, \phi_9, c_{p9}, R_9, \gamma_9, a_9)$

$$\frac{P_0}{P_9} = 1$$

End if

$$V_9 = \sqrt{2g_c(h_{t9} - h_9)}$$

$$M_9 = V_9/a_9$$

$$h_{t19} = h_{t13}; \quad T_{t19} = T_{t13}; \quad P_{rt19} = P_{rt13}; \quad f_{19} = 0$$

$$M_{19} = 1$$

RGCOMPR $(1, T_{t19}, f_{19}, M_{19}, (T_t/T)_{19}, (P_t/P)_{19}, MFP_{19})$

$$\frac{P_{t19}}{P_0} = \pi_r \pi_d \pi_f \pi_{nf}$$

If $\dfrac{P_{t19}}{P_0} \geq \left(\dfrac{P_t}{P}\right)_{19}$ then

$$T_{19} = \frac{T_{t19}}{(T_t/T)_{19}}$$

FAIR $(1, f_{19}, T_{19}, h_{19}, P_{r19}, \phi_{19}, c_{p19}, R_{19}, \gamma_{19}, a_{19})$

$$\frac{P_0}{P_{19}} = \frac{(P_t/P)_{19}}{P_{t19}/P_0}$$

Else

$$P_{r19} = \frac{P_{rt19}}{P_{t19}/P_0}$$

FAIR $(3, f_{19}, T_{19}, h_{19}, P_{r19}, \phi_{19}, c_{p19}, R_{19}, \gamma_{19}, a_{19})$

$$\frac{P_0}{P_{19}} = 1$$

End if

$$V_{19} = \sqrt{2g_c(h_{t19} - h_{19})}$$
$$M_{19} = V_{19}/a_{19}$$
$$f_o = f(1 - \beta - \varepsilon_1 - \varepsilon_2)/(1 + \alpha)$$

$$\frac{F}{\dot{m}_0} = \frac{a_0}{g_c(1+\alpha)} \left\{ \begin{array}{l} [1 + f_o(1+\alpha) - \beta]\dfrac{V_9}{a_0} + \alpha\dfrac{V_{19}}{a_0} - (1+\alpha)M_0 \\[2mm] + [1 + f_o(1+\alpha) - \beta]\dfrac{R_9}{R_0}\dfrac{T_9/T_0}{V_9/a_0}\dfrac{(1 - P_0/P_9)}{\gamma_0} \\[2mm] + \alpha\dfrac{R_{19}}{R_0}\dfrac{T_{19}/T_0}{V_{19}/a_0}\dfrac{(1 - P_0/P_{19})}{\gamma_0} \end{array} \right\}$$

$$S = \frac{f_o}{F/\dot{m}_0}$$

$$\eta_P = \frac{2g_c M_0(1+\alpha)F/(\dot{m}_0 a_0)}{\{1 + f_o(1+\alpha) - \beta\}\left(\dfrac{V_9}{a_0}\right)^2 + \alpha\left(\dfrac{V_{19}}{a_0}\right)^2 - (1+\alpha)M_0^2}$$

$$\eta_{TH} = \frac{1}{2g_c}\left\{\left[\frac{[1 + f_o(1+\alpha) - \beta]V_9^2 + \alpha V_{19}^2}{1 + \alpha} - V_0^2\right] + (C_{TOL} + C_{TOH})h_0\right\}\Bigg/ f_o h_{PR}$$

Example Parametric Analysis Results

Consider a turbofan engine with a fan pressure ratio (π_f) of 1.4 to be designed for a flight Mach number of 0.8 at standard altitude of 40 kft using the variable specific

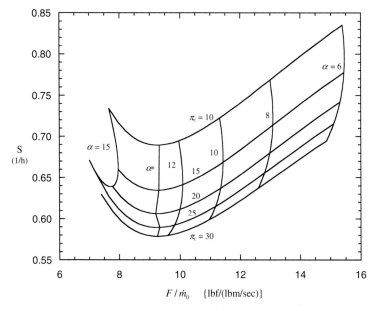

Fig. J.2   Specific performance of high bypass turbofan engines.

heat (VSH) gas model with the inputs listed here: $e_f = 0.89$; $\pi_{d\,max} = 0.99$; $\eta_b = 0.995$; $T_{t4} = 2600°R$; $e_{cL} = 0.90$; $\pi_b = 0.96$; $\eta_{mL} = 0.995$; $h_{PR} = 18{,}400$ Btu/lbm; $e_{cH} = 0.90$; $\pi_n = 0.99$; $\eta_{mH} = 0.995$; $\varepsilon_1 = 0.04$, $\varepsilon_2 = 0.03$; $e_{tH} = 0.89$; $\pi_{nf} = 0.99$; $\eta_{mPL} = 1.00$; $\eta_{mPH} = 0.99$; $e_{tL} = 0.91$; $\beta = 0.03$; $C_{TOL} = 0.00$; and $C_{TOH} = 0.01$.

Figure J.2 presents the parametric results for variation in the remaining two design variables, π_c and α. These results were obtained using the equations just listed for $\pi_{cL} = 4$ and values $10 < \pi_c < 30$ and $6 < \alpha < 15$. As can be seen in this figure, increasing either the bypass ratio or the compressor pressure ratio generally reduces the specific fuel consumption (see Appendix E), while increasing the bypass ratio naturally reduces the specific thrust. Also, for the bypass ratio range $12 < \alpha < 14$, increasing the bypass ratio no longer reduces the specific fuel consumption because the bypass and core velocities are so disparate. Consequently, for each compressor pressure ratio, there is a bypass ratio that gives the minimum thrust specific fuel consumption. This is commonly referred to as the optimum bypass ratio (α^*). A performance curve for this optimum bypass ratio is also plotted in Fig. J.2. The value of the optimum bypass ratio for this engine is plotted vs the compressor pressure ratio in Fig. J.3.

Performance Analysis

The performance of a selected design point high bypass turbofan engine of the type shown in Figs. J.1a and J.1b is desired at off-design flight conditions and throttle settings. In this off-design problem, there are 19 dependent and 4 independent variables as shown in Table J.1.

The assumptions of Sec. 5.2.2 apply, except those referring to the exhaust mixer and afterburner, and the exit nozzles have fixed areas. As a result of these

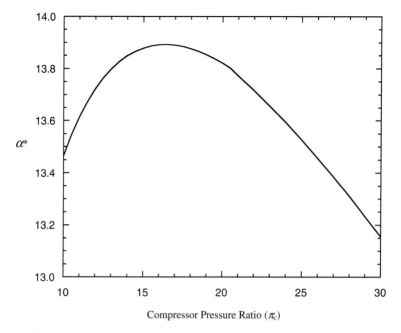

Fig. J.3   Optimum bypass ratio of the high bypass turbofan engines.

Table J.1   Engine performance variables

Component	Variable		
	Independent	Constant or known	Dependent
Engine	M_0, T_0, P_0	β	$\dot{m}_0, \alpha$
Diffuser	——	$\pi_d = f(M_0)$	——
Fan	——	η_f	π_f, τ_f
Low-pressure compressor	——	η_{cL}	π_{cL}, τ_{cL}
High-pressure compressor	——	η_{cH}	π_{cH}, τ_{cH}
Burner	T_{t4}	π_b	f
Coolant mixer 1	——	ε_1	τ_{m1}
High-pressure turbine	——	η_{tH}	π_{tH}, τ_{tH}
Coolant mixer 2	——	ε_2, π_{m2}	τ_{m2}
Low-pressure turbine	——	η_{tL}	π_{tL}, τ_{tL}
Core nozzle	——	π_n	$M_9, P_9/P_0$
Fan nozzle	——	π_{nf}	$M_{19}, P_{19}/P_0$
Total number	4	——	19

assumptions, Eqs. (5.1) and (5.2) apply to the high-pressure turbine. Since the flow is adiabatic between stations 5 and 9, then $A_6 MFP_6 = \pi_n A_9 MFP_9$, and Eq. (5.3) can be rewritten as

$$\frac{\pi_{tL}}{\sqrt{T_{t5}/T_{t4.5}}} = \frac{A_{4.5}}{\pi_n A_9} \frac{MFP(M_{4.5}, T_{t4.5}, f_{4.5})}{MFP(M_9, T_{t5}, f_{4.5})} \tag{J.2}$$

In addition, Eqs. (5.4–5.8), and (5.17) also apply to this engine. These equations allow solution for 14 of the dependent variables, and new relationships are required for the bypass ratio (α) and the four exhaust nozzle dependent variables (M_9, M_{19}, P_9/P_0, and P_{19}/P_0). An expression for the engine bypass ratio (α) follows directly from its definition written in terms of properties at stations 4 and 19. We write

$$\alpha = \frac{\dot{m}_F}{\dot{m}_C}$$

where

$$\dot{m}_F = \frac{P_{t19} A_{19}}{\sqrt{T_{t19}}} MFP_{19} = \frac{P_0 \, \pi_r \, \pi_d \, \pi_f \, \pi_{nf} \, A_{19}}{\sqrt{T_{t13}}} MFP_{19}$$

and

$$\dot{m}_4 = \dot{m}_C (1 - \beta - \varepsilon_1 - \varepsilon_2)(1 + f) = \frac{P_{t4} A_4}{\sqrt{T_{t4}}} MFP_4 = \frac{P_0 \, \pi_r \, \pi_d \, \pi_{cL} \, \pi_{cH} \, \pi_b \, A_4}{\sqrt{T_{t4}}} MFP_4$$

Thus the engine bypass ratio can be written as

$$\alpha = \frac{(1 - \beta - \varepsilon_1 - \varepsilon_2)(1 + f)}{\pi_{cL} \, \pi_{cH} \, \pi_b / (\pi_f \, \pi_{nf})} \sqrt{\frac{T_{t4}}{T_{t13}} \frac{MFP_{19}}{MFP_4} \frac{A_{19}}{A_4}} \tag{J.3}$$

The pressure ratio P_0/P_e depends on whether or not a convergent nozzle is choked. This is the same criterion that applied to the parametric cycle analysis of this engine. Two flow regimes exist for flow through a convergent nozzle, unchoked and choked. For unchoked flow, the exit static pressure (P_e) is equal to the ambient pressure (P_0), and the exit Mach number is less than or equal to one. Unchoked flow will exist when

$$\frac{P_{te}}{P_0} < \left(\frac{P_t}{P}\right)_{M=1}$$

Then $P_0 = P_e$ and the exit Mach number (M_e) is determined using the compressible flow functions. On the other hand, choked flow will exist when

$$\frac{P_{te}}{P_0} \geq \left(\frac{P_t}{P}\right)_{M=1}$$

and then $M_e = 1$, $P_{te}/P_e = (P_t/P)_{M=1}$, and

$$P_0/P_e = \frac{P_{te}/P_e}{P_{te}/P_0}$$

where P_{te}/P_0 is obtained by the product of the ram and component π for the respective airstream.

Summary of High Bypass Ratio Turbofan Engine Performance Cycle Analysis Equations

This section presents the complete performance cycle analysis equations for nonafterburning, separate exhaust flow, two-spool turbofan engine with bleed, turbine cooling, and power extraction. For convenience in computer programming, the required computer inputs and principal computer outputs are given. These are followed by the cycle equations in their order of solution.

Inputs

Performance choices:

Flight parameters:	M_0, T_0, P_0
Throttle setting:	T_{t4}

Design constants:

π:	$\pi_{d\,max}, \pi_b, \pi_n, \pi_{nf}$
η:	$\eta_f, \eta_{cL}, \eta_{cH}, \eta_{tH}, \eta_{tL}, \eta_b, \eta_{mL}, \eta_{mH}, \eta_{mPL}, \eta_{mPH}$
A:	$A_4, A_{4.5}, A_8, A_{18},$
Others:	$\beta, \varepsilon_1, \varepsilon_2, h_{PR}, P_{TOL}, P_{TOH}$

Reference condition:

Flight parameters:	M_{0R}, T_{0R}, P_{0R}
Component behavior:	$\pi_{fR}, \pi_{cLR}, \pi_{cHR}, \pi_{tHR}, \pi_{tLR}$
	$\tau_{fR}, \tau_{cLR}, \tau_{cHR}, \tau_{tHR}, \tau_{tLR}$
Others:	$\tau_{m1R}, \tau_{m2R}, f_R, M_{9R}, M_{19R}, \alpha_R$
	$F_R, \dot{m}_{0R}, S_R$
Engine control limits:	$\pi_{c\,max}, T_{t3\,max}, P_{t3\,max}, \%N_L, \%N_H$

Outputs

Overall performance:	$F, \dot{m}_0, S, f_o, \eta_P, \eta_{TH}, V_9/a_0, V_{19}/a_0, \alpha$
	$P_{t9}/P_9, P_9/P_0, T_9/T_0, P_{t19}/P_{19}, P_{19}/P_0, T_{19}/T_0$
Component behavior:	$\pi_f, \pi_{cL}, \pi_{cH}, \pi_{tH}, \pi_{tL}$
	$\tau_f, \tau_{cL}, \tau_{cH}, \tau_{tH}, \tau_{tL}, \tau_\lambda$
	$\tau_{m1}, \tau_{m2}, f, M_9, M_{19}$

Equations

Preliminary computations:

FAIR $(1, 0, T_0, h_0, P_{r0}, \phi_0\, c_{p0}, R_0, \gamma_0, a_0)$

$V_0 = M_0\, a_0$

$$h_{t0} = h_0 + \frac{V_0^2}{2g_c}$$

FAIR $(2, 0, T_{t0}, h_{t0}, P_{rt0}, \phi_{t0}, c_{pt0}, R_{t0}, \gamma_{t0}, a_{t0})$

$\tau_r = h_{t0}/h_0$

$$\pi_r = P_{rt0}/P_{r0}$$

$$\eta_{R\ spec} = 1 \qquad\qquad\qquad \text{for } M_0 \le 1$$

$$\eta_{R\ spec} = 1 - 0.075(M_0 - 1)^{1.35} \quad \text{for } 1 < M_0 < 5$$

$$\pi_d = \pi_{d\max}\eta_{R\ spec}$$

$$h_{t2} = h_{t0}$$

$$P_{rt2} = P_{rt0}$$

Set initial values:

$$\pi_{tH} = \pi_{tHR}, \quad \pi_{tL} = \pi_{tLR}, \quad \tau_{tH} = \tau_{tHR}, \quad \tau_{tL} = \tau_{tLR}$$

$$\pi_f = \pi_{fR}, \quad \pi_{cL} = \pi_{cLR}, \quad \pi_{cH} = \pi_{cHR}$$

$$\tau_f = \tau_{fR}, \quad \tau_{cL} = \tau_{cLR}, \quad \tau_{cH} = \tau_{cHR}$$

$$\tau_{m1} = \tau_{m1R}, \quad \tau_{m2} = \tau_{m2R}, \quad f = f_R$$

$$M_4 = 1, \quad M_{4.5} = 1, \quad M_9 = M_{9R}, \quad M_{19} = M_{19R}$$

FAIR $(1, f, T_{t4}, h_{t4}, P_{rt4}, \phi_{t4}, c_{pt4}, R_{t4}, \gamma_{t4}, a_{t4})$

$$h_{t4.5} = h_{t4}\tau_{m1}\tau_{tH}\tau_{m2}$$

$$f_{4.5} = f(1 - \beta - \varepsilon_1 - \varepsilon_2)/(1 - \beta)$$

FAIR $(2, f_{4.5}, T_{t4.5i}, h_{t4.5}, P_{rt4.5}\ \phi_{t4.5}, c_{pt4.5}, R_{t4.5}\ \gamma_{t4.5}, a_{t4.5})$

$$h_{t5} = h_{t4.5}\tau_{tL}$$

FAIR $(2, f_{4.5}, T_{t5i}, h_{t5}, P_{rt5}, \phi_{t5}, c_{pt5}, R_{t5}, \gamma_{t5}, a_{t5})$

1 $h_{t3} = h_{t0}\tau_{cL}\tau_{cH}$

FAIR $(2, 0, T_{t3}, h_{t3}, P_{rt3}, \phi_{t3}, c_{pt3}, R_{t3}, \gamma_{t3}, a_{t3})$

FAIR $(1, f, T_{t4}, h_{t4}, P_{rt4}, \phi_{t4}, c_{pt4}, R_{t4}, \gamma_{t4}, a_{t4})$

$$f_{4.5} = f(1 - \beta - \varepsilon_1 - \varepsilon_2)/(1 - \beta)$$

$TURBC$ $(T_{t4}, f, A_4/A_{4.5}, M_4, M_{4.5}, \eta_{tH}, T_{t4.5i}, T_{t3}, \beta, \varepsilon_1, \varepsilon_2, \pi_{tH}, \tau_{tH}, T_{t4.5})$

$TURB$ $(T_{t4.5}, f_{4.5}, A_{4.5}/(A_9\pi_n), M_{4.5}, M_9, \eta_{tL}, T_{t5i}, \pi_{tL}, \tau_{tL}\ T_{t5})$

$$\tau_\lambda = h_{t4}/h_0$$

$$\tau_f = 1 + \left\{(1 - \tau_{tL})\eta_{mL}\left[\begin{array}{c}(1 - \beta - \varepsilon_1 - \varepsilon_2)(1 + f)\dfrac{\tau_\lambda\tau_{tH}}{\tau_r} \\[4pt] + (\varepsilon_1\tau_{tH} + \varepsilon_2)\tau_{cL}\tau_{cH}\end{array}\right]\right.$$

$$\left. - \frac{(1 + \alpha)}{\tau_r\eta_{mPL}}\frac{P_{TOL}}{\dot{m}_0 h_0}\right\} \bigg/ \{(\tau_{cL} - 1)_R/(\tau_f - 1)_R + \alpha\}$$

$$\tau_{cL} = 1 + (\tau_f - 1)\frac{(\tau_{cL} - 1)_R}{(\tau_f - 1)_R}$$

$$\tau_{cH} = 1 + (1 - \tau_{tH})\eta_{mH}\left\{(1 - \beta - \varepsilon_1 - \varepsilon_2)(1 + f)\frac{\tau_\lambda}{\tau_r\tau_{cL}} + \varepsilon_1\tau_{cH}\right\}$$

$$- \frac{(1 + \alpha)}{\tau_r\tau_{cL}\eta_{mPH}}\frac{P_{TOH}}{\dot{m}_0 h_0}$$

$$h_{t2} = h_{t0}$$

$$P_{rt2} = P_{rt0}$$

$$h_{t13} = h_{t2}\tau_f$$

$$h_{t2.5} = h_{t2}\tau_{cL}$$

$$h_{t3} = h_{t2.5}\tau_{cH}$$

$$h_{t13i} = h_{t2}\{1 + \eta_f(\tau_f - 1)\}$$
$$h_{t2.5i} = h_{t2}\{1 + \eta_{cL}(\tau_{cL} - 1)\}$$
$$h_{t3i} = h_{t2.5}\{1 + \eta_{cH}(\tau_{cH} - 1)\}$$

FAIR $(2, 0, T_{t13}, h_{t13}, P_{rt13}, \phi_{t13}, c_{pt13}, R_{t13}, \gamma_{t13}, a_{t13})$

FAIR $(2, 0, T_{t13i}, h_{t13i}, P_{rt13i}, \phi_{t13i}, c_{pt13i}, R_{t13i}, \gamma_{t13i}, a_{t13i})$

FAIR $(2, 0, T_{t2.5}, h_{t2.5}, P_{rt2.5}, \phi_{t2.5}, c_{pt2.5}, R_{t2.5}, \gamma_{t2.5}, a_{t2.5})$

FAIR $(2, 0, T_{t2.5i}, h_{t2.5i}, P_{rt2.5i}, \phi_{t2.5i}, c_{pt2.5i}, R_{t2.5i}, \gamma_{t2.5i}, a_{t2.5i})$

FAIR $(2, 0, T_{t3}, h_{t3}, P_{rt3}, \phi_{t3}, c_{pt3}, R_{t3}, \gamma_{t3}, a_{t3})$

FAIR $(2, 0, T_{t3i}, h_{t3i}, P_{rt3i}, \phi_{t3i}, c_{pt3i}, R_{t3i}, \gamma_{t3i}, a_{t3i})$

$$\pi_f = P_{rt13i}/P_{rt2}$$
$$\pi_{cL} = P_{rt2.5i}/P_{rt2}$$
$$\pi_{cH} = P_{rt3i}/P_{rt2.5}$$
$$\pi_c = \pi_{cL}\pi_{cH}$$
$$\tau_c = \tau_{cL}\tau_{cH}$$

2   $f_{temp} = f$

FAIR $(1, f, T_{t4}, h_{t4}, P_{rt4}, \phi_{t4}, c_{pt4}, R_{t4}, \gamma_{t4}, a_{t4})$

$$f = \frac{h_{t4} - h_{t3}}{h_{PR}\eta_b - h_{t4}}$$

if $|f - f_{temp}| > 0.0001$ goto 2

$$\frac{P_{t19}}{P_0} = \pi_r \, \pi_d \, \pi_f \, \pi_{nf}$$

RGCOMP $(3, T_{t13}, 0, M_{19}, T_{t19}/T_0, P_{t19}/P_0, MFP_{19})$

if $M_{19} > 1$ then

    $M_{19} = 1$

    RGCOMP $(1, T_{t13}, 0, M_{19}, T_{t19}/T_{19}, P_{t19}/P_{19}, MFP_{19})$

$$P_0/P_{19} = \frac{P_{t19}/P_{19}}{P_{t19}/P_0}$$

$$T_{19} = \frac{T_{t13}}{T_{t19}/T_{19}}$$

else

    $P_0/P_{19} = 1$

    $P_{t19}/P_{19} = P_{t19}/P_0$

$$T_{19} = \frac{T_{t13}}{T_{t19}/T_0}$$

endif

FAIR $(1, 0, T_{19}, h_{19}, P_{r19}, \phi_{19}, c_{p19}, R_{19}, \gamma_{19}, a_{19})$

$$\alpha_{new} = \frac{(1 - \beta - \varepsilon_1 - \varepsilon_2)(1 + f)}{\pi_{cL}\pi_{cH}\pi_b/(\pi_f \pi_{nf})}\sqrt{\frac{T_{t4}}{T_{t13}}}\frac{MFP_{19}}{MFP_4}\frac{A_{19}}{A_4}$$

if $\left|\dfrac{\alpha - \alpha_{new}}{\alpha_R}\right| > 0.001$ then

$\alpha = \alpha_{new}$

goto 1

endif

$$\frac{P_{t9}}{P_0} = \pi_r\,\pi_d\,\pi_{cL}\,\pi_{cH}\,\pi_b\,\pi_{tH}\,\pi_{tL}\,\pi_n$$

RGCOMP $(3, T_{t5}, f_{4.5}, M_9, T_{t9}/T_0, P_{t9}/P_0, MFP_9)$

if $M_9 > 1$ then

$\quad M_9 = 1$

$\quad$ RGCOMP $(1, T_{t5}, f_{4.5}, M_9, T_{t9}/T_9, P_{t9}/P_9, MFP_9)$

$$P_0/P_9 = \frac{P_{t9}/P_9}{P_{t9}/P_0}$$

$$T_9 = \frac{T_{t5}}{T_{t9}/T_9}$$

else

$\quad P_0/P_9 = 1$

$\quad P_{t9}/P_9 = P_{t9}/P_0$

$$T_9 = \frac{T_{t5}}{T_{t9}/T_0}$$

endif

FAIR $(1, f_{4.5}, T_9, h_9, P_{r9}, \phi_9, c_{p9}, R_9, \gamma_9, a_9)$

RGCOMPR $(1, T_{t4}, f, M_4, TtT, PtP, MFP_4)$

$$\dot{m}_{0\,new} = \dot{m}_{0R}\,\frac{1+f_R}{1+f}\,\frac{P_0(1+\alpha)\pi_r\,\pi_d\,\pi_{cL}\,\pi_{cH}}{\{P_0(1+\alpha)\pi_r\,\pi_d\,\pi_{cL}\,\pi_{cH}\}_R}\,\frac{MFP_4}{MFP_{4R}}\sqrt{\frac{T_{t4R}}{T_{t4}}}$$

$$\dot{m}_{0\,error} = \left|\frac{\dot{m}_{0\,new} - \dot{m}_0}{\dot{m}_{0R}}\right|$$

if $\dot{m}_{0\,error} > 0.001$ then

$\quad \dot{m}_0 = \dot{m}_{0\,new}$

$\quad$ goto 1

endif

$V_9 = M_9 a_9$

$V_{19} = M_{19} a_{19}$

$f_o = f(1 - \beta - \varepsilon_1 - \varepsilon_2)/(1+\alpha)$

$$\frac{F}{\dot{m}_0} = \frac{a_0}{g_c(1+\alpha)}\left\{\begin{array}{l}[1 + f_o(1+\alpha) - \beta]\dfrac{V_9}{a_0} + \alpha\dfrac{V_{19}}{a_0} - (1+\alpha)M_0\\[2mm] + [1 + f_o(1+\alpha) - \beta]\dfrac{R_9}{R_0}\dfrac{T_9/T_0}{V_9/a_0}\dfrac{(1 - P_0/P_9)}{\gamma_0}\\[2mm] + \alpha\dfrac{R_{19}}{R_0}\dfrac{T_{19}/T_0}{V_{19}/a_0}\dfrac{(1 - P_0/P_{19})}{\gamma_0}\end{array}\right\}$$

$$F = \dot{m}_0 \left(\frac{F}{\dot{m}_0} \right)$$

$$S = \frac{f_o}{F/\dot{m}_0}$$

$$\eta_P = \frac{2g_c M_0 (1+\alpha) F/(\dot{m}_0 a_0)}{\{1 + f_o(1+\alpha) - \beta\}(V_9/a_0)^2 + \alpha (V_{19}/a_0)^2 - (1+\alpha)M_0^2}$$

$$\eta_{TH} = \frac{1}{2g_c} \left\{ \left[\frac{[1 + f_o(1+\alpha) - \beta]V_9^2 + \alpha V_{19}^2}{1+\alpha} - V_0^2 \right] + (C_{TOL} + C_{TOH})h_0 \right\} \bigg/ f_o h_{PR}$$

$$\eta_O = \eta_{tH}\eta_P$$

RGCOMPR $(1, T_{t0}, 0, M_0, T_tT, P_tP, MFP_0)$

$$A_0 = \frac{\dot{m}_0 \sqrt{T}_{t0}}{P_{t0}MFP_0}$$

$$\%N_L = 100 \sqrt{\frac{h_0 \tau_r (\tau_f - 1)}{[h_0 \tau_r (\tau_f - 1)]_R}}$$

$$\%N_H = 100 \sqrt{\frac{h_0 \tau_r \tau_{cL}(\tau_{cH} - 1)}{[h_0 \tau_r \tau_{cL}(\tau_{cH} - 1)]_R}}$$

If any of the control limits (π_c, T_{t3}, P_{t3}, etc.) are exceeded, then reduce T_{t4} and go to 1. A Newtonian iteration scheme is used to rapidly converge on the value of T_{t4} that meets the most constraining control limit.

Example Performance Results

Consider a turbofan engine designed for a Mach number of 0.8 at a standard day altitude of 30 kft using the variable specific heat (VSH) gas model with a compressor pressure ratio of 30 ($\pi_{cL} = 4$, $\pi_{cH} = 7.5$), a fan pressure ratio of 1.5, a bypass ratio of 8, and the other inputs given here: $e_f = 0.89$; $\pi_{d\,max} = 0.99$; $\eta_b = 0.995$; $T_{t4} = 2860°R$; $e_{cL} = 0.90$; $\pi_b = 0.96$; $\eta_{mL} = 0.995$; $h_{PR} = 18{,}400$ Btu/lbm; $e_{cH} = 0.90$; $\pi_n = 0.99$; $\eta_{mH} = 0.995$; $\beta = 0.03$; $e_{tH} = 0.89$; $\pi_{nf} = 0.99$; $C_{TOL} = 0.00$; $\eta_{mPL} = 1.0$; $e_{tL} = 0.91$; ε_1, $\varepsilon_2 = 0.05$; $C_{TOH} = 0.005$; and $\eta_{mPH} = 0.99$. The performance variation of the fan pressure ratio, the compressor pressure ratio, and the bypass ratio with changes in flight Mach number and altitude are presented in Figs. J.4–J.6, respectively, for full throttle operation with maximum compressor pressure ratio of 30 and maximum T_{t4} of 3200°R. These are the same trends observed in Figs. 4.9, 4.10, and 4.11. Because the component performance curves of Figs. J.4–J.6 break at about a Mach number of 0.45 at sea level on a standard day, this engine has a theta break (App. D) and throttle ratio (TR) of about 1.04.

Figure J.7 shows the variation in full throttle uninstalled thrust with changes in Mach number and altitude for an engine sized for a static sea level thrust of 50,000 lbf. The variation of the uninstalled thrust specific fuel consumption at full throttle is shown in Fig. J.8. The partial throttle performance at an altitude of 30 kft is presented in Fig. J.9 for selected flight Mach numbers.

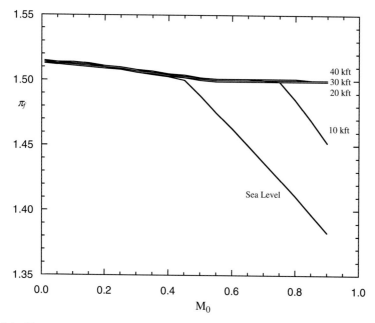

Fig. J.4   Fan pressure ratio of example turbofan engine at full throttle (standard day).

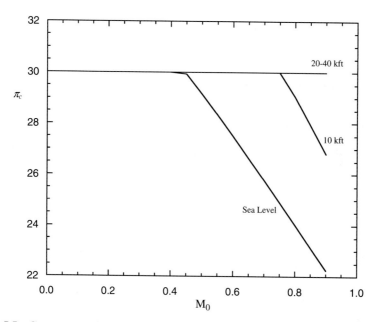

Fig. J.5   Compressor pressure ratio of example turbofan engine at full throttle (standard day).

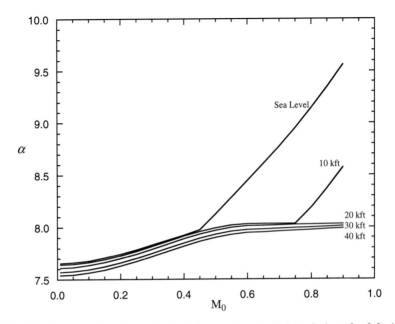

Fig. J.6   Bypass ratio of example turbofan engine at full throttle (standard day).

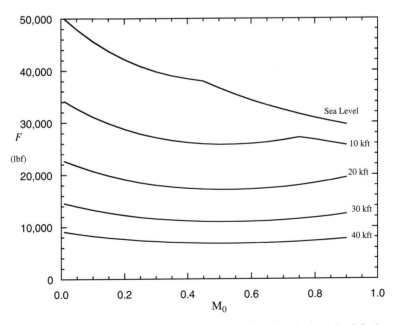

Fig. J.7   Thrust of example turbofan engine at full throttle (standard day).

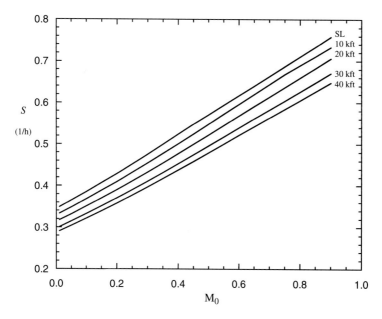

Fig. J.8   Thrust specific fuel consumption of example turbofan engine at full throttle (standard day).

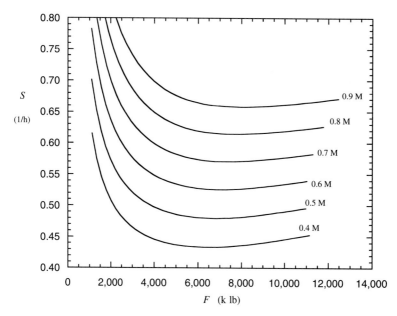

Fig. J.9   Partial throttle performance of example turbofan engine at 30 kft (standard day).

Appendix K
Turboprop Engine Cycle Analysis

This material is included in case turboprop engine cycles are under consideration. They are strong candidates for any application where high thrust and low fuel consumption are required and the flight Mach number never exceeds about 0.8. Consider the turboprop engine shown in Figs. K.1a and K.1b. The station numbers of locations indicated there will be used throughout this appendix and include the following:

Station	Location
0	Far upstream or freestream
1	Inlet or diffuser entry
2	Inlet or diffuser exit
	Compressor entry
3	Compressor exit
3.1	Burner entry
4	Burner exit
	Nozzle vanes entry
	Modeled coolant mixer 1 entry
	High-pressure turbine entry for π_{tH} definition
4.1	Nozzle vanes exit
	Coolant mixer 1 exit
	High-pressure turbine entry for τ_{tH} definition
4.4	High-pressure turbine exit
	Modeled coolant mixer 2 entry
4.5	Coolant mixer 2 exit
	Low-pressure turbine entry
5	Low-pressure turbine exit
7	Core exhaust nozzle entry
9	Core exhaust nozzle exit

The component τ, π, efficiencies, and assumptions of Chapter 4 apply to this engine with the exception of those referring to the exhaust mixer and afterburner. Unlike the engine of Chapters 4 and 5, this engine has neither a fan nor a bypass airflow. The mass flow ratios of Eqs. (4.8a–4.8e) and (4.8i) apply as does the turbine cooling model of Chapter 4 shown in Fig. 4.2.

The compressor of this turboprop engine and high-pressure spool power takeoff are powered by the high-pressure turbine, while the low-pressure turbine provides

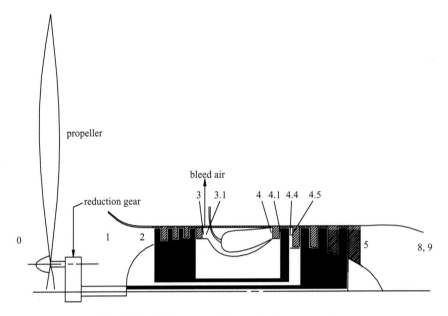

Fig. K.1a   Reference stations—turboprop engine.

mechanical power to both the propeller and the low-pressure spool power takeoff. The engine's nozzle is modeled as a fixed convergent nozzle.

The following sections outline development of both parametric and performance cycle analysis equations for this turbofan engine.

Parametric Analysis

The "work interaction coefficient" (C) is introduced for use in analysis of the work interaction of this engine with the vehicle rather than the thrust. The dimensionless coefficient is defined by

$$C \doteq \frac{\text{Total power interaction with vehicle}}{\text{Mass flow of air through core engine}} \Big/ h_0 \qquad \text{(K.1)}$$

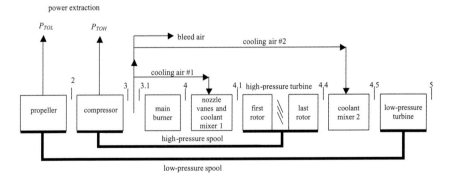

Fig. K.1b   Reference stations—bleed and turbine cooling airflows.

The use of such coefficients is commonplace in the turboprop industry because turboprop designers see themselves as converting engine power into flight power.

Please note that the bypass ratio (α) does not appear in this development because the propeller is treated as a power exchange device. For the propeller, the total work interaction with the vehicle is given by $\eta_{prop} P_{prop}/\dot{m}_0$ where η_{prop} is the efficiency of the power transfer from the propeller to the air and P_{prop} is the power transferred to the propeller. The total power interaction of the propeller is also equal to the effective thrust of the propeller (F_{prop}) times the velocity of the vehicle (V_0) or

$$\text{Total work interaction of the propeller} = \eta_{prop} P_{prop} = F_{prop} V_0$$

Thus from Eq. (K.1)

$$C_{prop} \doteq \frac{\eta_{prop} P_{prop}}{\dot{m}_0 h_0} = \frac{F_{prop} V_0}{\dot{m}_0 h_0} \tag{K.2}$$

Similarly, the work interaction coefficient for the core engine is defined with respect to the power transferred to the vehicle (thrust $\times$ velocity) or

$$C_C \doteq \frac{F_C V_0}{\dot{m}_0 h_0} \tag{K.3}$$

The total work interaction coefficient of the turboprop engine is the sum of C_{prop} and C_C, or

$$C_{TOTAL} = C_{prop} + C_C \tag{K.4}$$

Thus, C_{TOTAL} is related to the total power transferred to the vehicle. The effective uninstalled thrust (F) of the engine can be found from Eqs. (K.1) and (K.4) to be

$$F \doteq F_{prop} + F_C = \frac{C_{TOTAL} \dot{m}_0 h_0}{V_0} \tag{K.5}$$

The uninstalled specific thrust ($F_C/\dot{m}_0$) of the core is given by

$$\frac{F_C}{\dot{m}_0} = \frac{a_0}{g_c}\left\{(1 + f_o - \beta)\frac{V_9}{a_0} - M_0 + (1 + f_o - \beta)\frac{R_9\,T_9/T_0}{R_0\,V_9/a_0}\frac{(1 - P_0/P_9)}{\gamma_0}\right\}$$

where $f_o = f\,(1 - \beta - \varepsilon_1 - \varepsilon_2)$. Thus, the work interaction coefficient of the core can be written as

$$C_C = (\gamma_0 - 1)M_0\left\{(1 + f_o - \beta)\frac{V_9}{a_0} - M_0 + (1 + f_o - \beta)\frac{R_9\,T_9/T_0}{R_0\,V_9/a_0}\frac{(1 - P_0/P_9)}{\gamma_0}\right\} \tag{K.6}$$

The velocity and temperature ratios required in Eq. (K.6) are obtained using the methods of Chapter 4. We have

$$\left(\frac{V_9}{a_0}\right)^2 = \frac{M_0^2\,\tau_\lambda\,\tau_{m1}\,\tau_{tH}\,\tau_{m2}\,\tau_{tL}}{\tau_r - 1}\left\{1 - \frac{h_9}{h_{t9}}\right\}$$

where h_9 is determined from h_{t9} and the pressure ratio

$$\frac{P_{t9}}{P_9} = \left(\frac{P_0}{P_9}\right) \pi_r \, \pi_d \, \pi_c \, \pi_b \, \pi_{tH} \, \pi_{tL} \, \pi_n$$

The independent design variables for this engine are the compressor pressure ratio (π_c) and the turbine total enthalpy ratio (τ_t). The enthalpy ratio across the low-pressure turbine is obtained from

$$\tau_{tL} = \tau_t / (\tau_{m1} \tau_{tH} \tau_{m2})$$

The enthalpy ratio across the compressor (τ_c) is related to its pressure ratio by Eq. (4.9c). The enthalpy ratio across the high-pressure turbine (τ_{tH}) is obtained from the power balance of the high-pressure spool, which gives

$$\dot{m}_{4.1}(h_{t4.1} - h_{t4.4})\eta_{mH} = \dot{m}_C(h_{t3} - h_{t2}) + \frac{P_{TOH}}{\eta_{mPH}}$$

and rearrangement allows the calculation of the high-pressure turbine total enthalpy ratio

$$\tau_{tH} = 1 - \frac{\tau_r(\tau_c - 1) + C_{TOH}/\eta_{mPH}}{\eta_{mH}\tau_\lambda\{(1 - \beta - \varepsilon_1 - \varepsilon_2)(1 + f) + \varepsilon_1 \tau_r \tau_c / \tau_\lambda\}} \qquad \text{(K.7)}$$

The enthalpy ratios across the two cooling air mixing processes $(\tau_{m1}$ and $\tau_{m2})$ are given by Eqs. (4.20a) and (4.20b). The pressure ratios across the high-pressure turbine (π_{tH}) and low-pressure turbine (π_{tL}) are related to their respective enthalpy ratios and polytropic efficiencies by Eqs. (4.9d) and (4.9e). The fuel-air ratio (f) is given by Eq. (4.18). Thus, the only unknown for solution of Eq. (K.6) is the static pressure ratio, P_0/P_9.

Two flow regimes exist for flow through a convergent nozzle, unchoked flow and choked. For unchoked flow, the exit static pressure (P_9) is equal to the ambient pressure (P_0) and the exit Mach number is less than or equal to one. Unchoked flow will exist when

$$\frac{P_{t9}}{P_0} \leq \left(\frac{P_t}{P}\right)_{M=1}$$

then $P_9 = P_0$, and the exit Mach number (M_9) is determined using the compressible flow functions. On the other hand, choked flow will exist when

$$\frac{P_{t9}}{P_0} > \left(\frac{P_t}{P}\right)_{M=1}$$

thus

$$M_9 = 1, \quad \frac{P_{t9}}{P_9} = \left(\frac{P_t}{P}\right)_{M=1}, \quad \text{and} \quad P_0/P_9 = \frac{P_{t9}/P_9}{P_{t9}/P_0}$$

where P_{t9}/P_0 is obtained by the product of the ram and component π for the core airstream.

Development of an expression for the propeller work interaction coefficient (C_{prop}) starts with a power balance on the low-pressure spool, which gives

$$\dot{m}_{4.5}(h_{t4.5} - h_{t5})\eta_{mL} = \frac{P_{prop}}{\eta_g} + \frac{P_{TOL}}{\eta_{mPL}}$$

Solution for the power of the propeller (P_{prop}) in terms of enthalpy and mass flow ratios and using Eq. (K.2) yields

$$C_{prop} = \eta_{prop}\eta_g \left\{ \eta_{mL}(1 + f_o - \beta)\,\tau_\lambda \tau_{m1} \tau_{tH} \tau_{m2}(1 - \tau_{tL}) - \frac{C_{TOL}}{\eta_{mPL}} \right\} \quad \text{(K.8)}$$

The uninstalled specific power of the engine ($P/\dot{m}_0$) is given by

$$\frac{P}{\dot{m}_0} = C_{TOTAL}h_0 \quad\quad \text{(K.9)}$$

and the uninstalled power specific fuel consumption (S_P) is given by

$$S_P = \frac{\dot{m}_f}{P} = \frac{f_o}{C_{TOTAL}h_0} \quad\quad \text{(K.10)}$$

The uninstalled equivalent specific thrust of the turboprop engine ($F/\dot{m}_0$) is given by

$$\frac{F}{\dot{m}_0} = \frac{C_{TOTAL}h_0}{V_0} \quad\quad \text{(K.11)}$$

and the uninstalled thrust specific fuel consumption (S) is given by

$$S = \frac{\dot{m}_f}{F} = \frac{f_o V_0}{C_{TOTAL}h_0} \quad\quad \text{(K.12)}$$

The propulsive efficiency (η_P) of the turboprop engine is defined as the ratio of the total power interaction with the vehicle producing propulsive power to the total energy available for producing propulsive power. Thus,

$$\eta_P = \frac{\dot{m}_0 h_0 C_{TOTAL}}{P_{prop} + \left(\dot{m}_9 V_9^2 - \dot{m}_0 V_0^2\right)/2g_c}$$

or

$$\eta_P = C_{TOTAL} \left/ \left\{ \frac{C_{prop}}{\eta_{prop}} + \frac{\gamma_0 - 1}{2}\left[(1 + f_o - \beta)\left(\frac{V_9}{a_0}\right)^2 - M_0^2\right] \right\} \right. \quad \text{(K.13)}$$

The thermal efficiency (η_{TH}) of the turboprop engine is defined as the ratio of the total power produced by the engine to the energy made available by the fuel. Thus,

$$\eta_{TH} = \frac{\dot{m}_0 h_0 (C_{TOTAL} + C_{TOL} + C_{TOH})}{\dot{m}_f h_{PR}}$$

or

$$\eta_{TH} = \frac{C_{TOTAL} + C_{TOL} + C_{TOH}}{f_o h_{PR}/h_0} \quad\quad \text{(K.14)}$$

All of the equations needed for parametric cycle analysis of this turboprop engine have now been identified. The following section presents these equations in the order of solution.

Summary of Turboprop Engine Parametric Cycle Analysis Equations

This section presents the complete parametric cycle analysis equations for the turboprop engine with bleed, turbine cooling, and power extraction. For convenience in computer programming, the required computer inputs and principal computer outputs are given. These are followed by the cycle equations in their order of solution. Please note that iteration is required to calculate f.

Inputs

Flight parameters:	M_0, T_0, P_0
Aircraft system parameters:	β, C_{TOL}, C_{TOH}
Design limitations:	
Fuel heating value:	h_{PR}
Component figures	$\varepsilon_1, \varepsilon_2$
of merit:	$\pi_b, \pi_{d\max}, \pi_n$
	e_c, e_{tH}, e_{tL}
	$\eta_b, \eta_{mL}, \eta_{mH}, \eta_{mPL}, \eta_{mPH}, \eta_{prop}$
Design choices:	π_c, τ_t, T_{t4}

Outputs

Overall performance:	$F/\dot{m}_0, S, P/\dot{m}_0, S_P, f_o, C_C, C_{prop}, \eta_P, \eta_{TH}, V_9/a_0$
Component behavior:	π_{tH}, π_{tL}
	$\tau_c, \tau_{tH}, \tau_{tL}, \tau_\lambda$
	f
	$\eta_c, \eta_{tH}, \eta_{tL}$
	$M_9, P_{t9}/P_9, P_9/P_0, T_9/T_0$

Equations

$\text{FAIR}\,(1, 0, T_0, h_0, P_{r0}, \phi_0, c_{p0}, R_0, \gamma_0, a_0)$

$V_0 = M_0 a_0$

$$h_{t0} = h_0 + \frac{V_0^2}{2g_c}$$

$\text{FAIR}\,(2, 0, T_{t0}, h_{t0}, P_{rt0}, \phi_{t0}, c_{pt0}, R_{t0}, \gamma_{t0}, a_{t0})$

$\tau_r = h_{t0}/h_0$

$\pi_r = P_{rt0}/P_{r0}$

$\pi_d = \pi_{d\max} \quad \text{for } M_0 \leq 1$

$h_{t2} = h_{t0}$

$P_{rt2} = P_{rt0}$

$P_{rt3} = P_{rt2}\pi_c^{1/e_c}$

FAIR $(3, 0, T_{t3}, h_{t3}, P_{rt3}, \phi_{t3}, c_{pt3}, R_{t3}, \gamma_{t3}, a_{t3})$

$$\tau_{cL} = h_{t3}/h_{t2}$$

$$P_{rt3i} = P_{rt2}\pi_c$$

FAIR $(3, 0, T_{t3i}, h_{t3i}, P_{rt3i}, \phi_{t3i}, c_{pt3i}, R_{t3i}, \gamma_{t3i}, a_{t3i})$

$$\eta_c = \frac{h_{t3i} - h_{t2}}{h_{t3} - h_{t2}}$$

Set initial value of fuel/air ratio at station $4 = f_{4i}$

A   FAIR $(1, f_{4i}, T_{t4}, h_{t4}, P_{rt4}, \phi_{t4}, c_{pt4}, R_{t4}, \gamma_{t4}, a_{t4})$

$$f = \frac{h_{t4} - h_{t3}}{\eta_b h_{PR} - h_{t4}}$$

If $|f - f_{4i}| > 0.0001$, then $f_{4i} = f$ and go to A; else continue.

$$\tau_\lambda = h_{t4}/h_0$$

$$\tau_{m1} = \frac{(1 - \beta - \varepsilon_1 - \varepsilon_2)(1 + f) + \varepsilon_1 \tau_r \tau_c/\tau_\lambda}{(1 - \beta - \varepsilon_1 - \varepsilon_2)(1 + f) + \varepsilon_1}$$

$$\tau_{tH} = 1 - \frac{\tau_r(\tau_c - 1) + C_{TOH}/\eta_{mPH}}{\eta_{mH}\tau_\lambda\{(1 - \beta - \varepsilon_1 - \varepsilon_2)(1 + f) + \varepsilon_1 \tau_r \tau_c/\tau_\lambda\}}$$

$$h_{t4.1} = h_{t4}\tau_{m1}$$

$$f_{4.1} = \frac{f}{1 + f + \varepsilon_1/(1 - \beta - \varepsilon_1 - \varepsilon_2)}$$

FAIR $(2, f_{4.1}, T_{t4.1}, h_{t4.1}, P_{rt4.1}, \phi_{t4.1}, c_{pt4.1}, R_{t4.1}, \gamma_{t4.1}, a_{t4.1})$

$$h_{t4.4} = h_{t4.1}\tau_{tH}$$

FAIR $(2, f_{4.1}, T_{t4.4}, h_{t4.4}, P_{rt4.4}, \phi_{t4.4}, c_{pt4.4}, R_{t4.4}, \gamma_{t4.4}, a_{t4.4})$

$$\pi_{tH} = \left(\frac{P_{rt4.4}}{P_{rt4.1}}\right)^{1/e_{tH}}$$

$$P_{rt4.4i} = \pi_{tH} P_{rt4.1}$$

FAIR $(3, f_{4.1}, T_{t4.4i}, h_{t4.4i}, P_{rt4.4i}, \phi_{t4.4i}, c_{pt4.4i}, R_{t4.4i}, \gamma_{t4.4i}, a_{t4.4i})$

$$\eta_{tH} = \frac{h_{t4.1} - h_{t4.4}}{h_{t4.1} - h_{t4.4i}}$$

$$\tau_{m2} = \frac{(1 - \beta - \varepsilon_1 - \varepsilon_2)(1 + f) + \varepsilon_1 + \varepsilon_2\{\tau_r \tau_c/(\tau_\lambda \tau_{m1} \tau_{tH})\}}{(1 - \beta - \varepsilon_1 - \varepsilon_2)(1 + f) + \varepsilon_1 + \varepsilon_2}$$

$$h_{t4.5} = h_{t4.4}\tau_{m2}$$

$$f_{4.5} = \frac{f}{1 + f + (\varepsilon_1 + \varepsilon_2)/(1 - \beta - \varepsilon_1 - \varepsilon_2)}$$

FAIR $(2, f_{4.5}, T_{t4.5}, h_{t4.5}, P_{rt4.5}, \phi_{t4.5}, c_{pt4.5}, R_{t4.5}, \gamma_{t4.5}, a_{t4.5})$

$$\tau_{tL} = \frac{\tau_t}{\tau_{m1} \tau_{tH} \tau_{m2}}$$

$$h_{t5} = h_{t4.5}\tau_{tL}$$

FAIR $(2, f_{4.5}, T_{t4.5}, h_{t4.5}, P_{rt4.5}, \phi_{t4.5}, c_{pt4.5}, R_{t4.5}, \gamma_{t4.5}, a_{t4.5})$

$$\pi_{tL} = \left(\frac{P_{rt5}}{P_{rt4.5}}\right)^{1/e_{tL}}$$

$$P_{rt5i} = \pi_{tL} P_{rt4.5}$$

FAIR $(3, f_{4.5}, T_{t5i}, h_{t5i}, P_{rt5i}, \phi_{t5i}, c_{pt5i}, R_{t5i}, \gamma_{t5i}, a_{t5i})$

$$\eta_{tL} = \frac{h_{t4.5} - h_{t5}}{h_{t4.5} - h_{t5i}}$$

$$h_{t9} = h_{t5}; \quad T_{t9} = T_{t5}; \quad P_{rt9} = P_{rt5}; \quad f_9 = f_{4.5}$$

$$M_9 = 1$$

RGCOMPR $(T_{t9}, M_9, f_9, (T_t/T)_9, (P_t/P)_9, MFP_9)$

$$\frac{P_{t9}}{P_0} = \pi_r \, \pi_d \, \pi_c \, \pi_b \, \pi_{tH} \, \pi_{tL} \, \pi_n$$

If $\dfrac{P_{t9}}{P_0} \geq \left(\dfrac{P_t}{P}\right)_9$ then

$$T_9 = \frac{T_{t9}}{(T_t/T)_9}$$

FAIR $(1, f_9, T_9, h_9, P_{r9}, \phi_9, c_{p9}, R_9, \gamma_9, a_9)$

$$\frac{P_0}{P_9} = \frac{(P_t/P)_9}{P_{t9}/P_0}$$

Else

$$P_{r9} = \frac{P_{rt9}}{P_{t9}/P_0}$$

FAIR $(3, f_9, T_9, h_9, P_{r9}, \phi_9, c_{p9}, R_9, \gamma_9, a_9)$

$$\frac{P_0}{P_9} = 1$$

End if

$$V_9 = \sqrt{2g_c(h_{t9} - h_9)}$$

$$M_9 = V_9/a_9$$

$$f_o = f(1 - \beta - \varepsilon_1 - \varepsilon_2)$$

$$C_C = (\gamma_0 - 1)M_0 \left\{ (1 + f_o - \beta)\frac{V_9}{a_0} - M_0 + (1 + f_o - \beta)\frac{R_9}{R_0}\frac{T_9/T_0}{V_9/a_0}\frac{(1 - P_0/P_9)}{\gamma_0} \right\}$$

$$C_{prop} = \eta_{prop}\eta_g \left\{ \eta_{mL}(1 + f_o - \beta)\tau_\lambda \tau_{m1} \tau_{tH} \tau_{m2}(1 - \tau_{tL}) - \frac{C_{TOL}}{\eta_{mPL}} \right\}$$

$$C_{TOTAL} = C_{prop} + C_C$$

$$\frac{P}{\dot{m}_0} = C_{TOTAL}h_0$$

$$S_P = \frac{f_o}{C_{TOTAL}h_0}$$

$$\frac{F}{\dot{m}_0} = \frac{C_{TOTAL}h_0}{V_0}$$

$$S = \frac{f_o V_0}{C_{TOTAL}h_0}$$

$$S = \frac{f_o}{F/\dot{m}_0}$$

$$\eta_P = C_{TOTAL} \Bigg/ \left\{ \frac{C_{prop}}{\eta_{prop}} + \frac{\gamma_0 - 1}{2} \left[(1 + f_o - \beta) \left(\frac{V_9}{a_0} \right)^2 - M_0^2 \right] \right\}$$

$$\eta_{TH} = \frac{C_{TOTAL} + C_{TOL} + C_{TOH}}{f_o h_{PR}/h_0}$$

Example Design Point Results

Consider a turboprop engine to be designed for a Mach of 0.8 at a standard day altitude of 25 kft with the inputs listed here: $e_c = 0.90$; $\pi_d = 0.97$; $\eta_b = 0.995$; $T_{t4} = 3200°R$; $e_{tH} = 0.89$; $\pi_b = 0.96$; $\eta_{mL} = 0.99$; $h_{PR} = 18{,}400$ Btu/lbm; $e_{tL} = 0.91$; $\pi_n = 0.99$; $\eta_{mH} = 0.98$; $\eta_{prop} = 0.82$; $\eta_g = 0.99$; $\varepsilon_1 = \varepsilon_2 = 0.05$; $\gamma_c = 1.4$; $c_{pc} = 0.240$ Btu/lbm-°R; $\beta = 0$; $C_{TOH} = C_{TOL} = 0$; $\gamma_t = 1.4$; and $c_{pt} = 0.295$ Btu/lbm-°R. Figures K.2 and K.3 present the parametric performance results for variation in the two design variables, π_c and τ_t. These results were obtained using the methods of the preceding sections for values of $5 \leq \pi_c \leq 35$ and $0.45 \leq \tau_t \leq 0.75$. Of the three thermodynamic models available with the ONX program, we have chosen to use for this exercise the modified specific heat model MSH.

Figures K.2 and K.3 reveal that for any π_c there is a turbine enthalpy ratio (τ_t^*) for which $F/\dot{m}_0$ is maximized and S is minimized. This is referred to as the optimum turbine enthalpy ratio.

Example Design Point Results—Optimum τ_t

The design point performance of a family of optimum turboprop engines was calculated for values of $5 \leq \pi_c \leq 35$ using the inputs from the preceding section. The performance results are plotted as a dashed line in Figs. K.2 and K.3 vs the compressor pressure ratio. The optimum turbine enthalpy ratio (τ_t^*) for each compressor pressure ratio is plotted in Fig. K.4.

Performance Analysis

The performance of a selected design point turboprop engine of the type shown in Figs. K.1a and K.1b is desired at off-design flight conditions and throttle settings. In this off-design problem, there are 10 dependent and four independent variables as shown in Table K.1.

The assumptions of Sec. 5.2.2 apply, except those referring to the exhaust mixer and afterburner, and the exit nozzle has a fixed area. As a result of these assumptions, Eqs. (5.1) and (5.2) apply to this engine. Because the high-pressure turbine drives the compressor, the power balance of the high-pressure spool yields the expression for calculating the total temperature ratio of the compressor (τ_c) at off-design conditions. The power balance of the high-pressure spool gives

$$\dot{m}_{4.1}(h_{t4.1} - h_{t4.4})\eta_{mH} = \dot{m}_C(h_{t3} - h_{t2}) + \frac{P_{TOH}}{\eta_{mPH}}$$

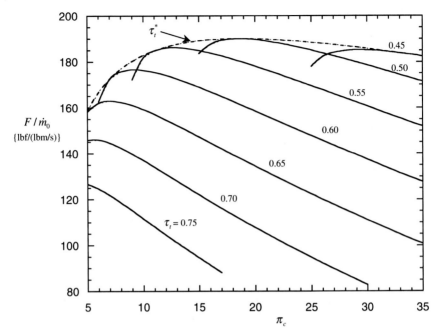

Fig. K.2   Design point specific thrust of turboprop engines.

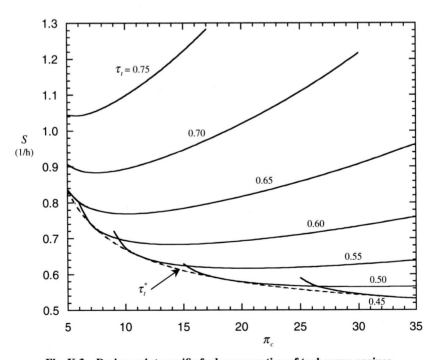

Fig. K.3   Design point specific fuel consumption of turboprop engines.

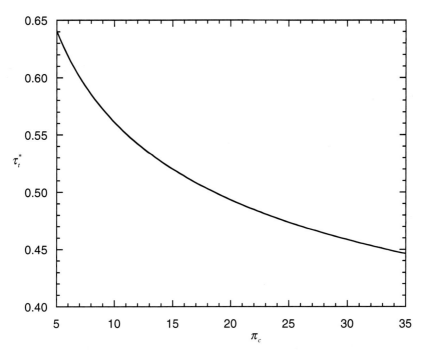

Fig. K.4   Optimum turbine enthalpy ratio.

Table K.1   Performance variables

Component	Independent	Constant or known	Dependent
Engine	M_0, T_0, P_0	β	$\dot{m}_0$
Diffuser	——	$\pi_d = f(M_0)$	——
Compressor	——	η_c	π_c, τ_c
Burner	T_{t4}	π_b	——
Coolant mixer 1	——	ε_1	τ_{m1}
High-pressure turbine	——	η_{tH}	π_{tH}, τ_{tH}
Coolant mixer 2	——	ε_2, π_{m2}	τ_{m2}
Low-pressure turbine	——	η_{tL}	π_{tL}, τ_{tL}
Nozzle	——	π_n	M_9
Propeller	——	$\eta_{prop} = f(M_0)$	——
Total number	4	——	10

which can be written as

$$\tau_c = 1 + \eta_{mH}\{(1 - \beta - \varepsilon_1 - \varepsilon_2)(1 + f) + \varepsilon_1\}\frac{\tau_\lambda \tau_{m1}(1 - \tau_{tH})}{\tau_r} - \frac{C_{TOH}}{\eta_{mPH}} \quad \text{(K.15)}$$

The total pressure ratio of the compressor (π_c) is determined from Eq. (4.9c) and the ideal exit state $t3i$, or

$$h_{t3i} = h_{t2}\{1 + \eta_c(\tau_c - 1)\} \quad \text{and} \quad \pi_c = P_{rt3i}/P_{rt2} \quad \text{(K.16)}$$

An expression for the mass flow rate of air through the turboprop engine ($\dot{m}_0$) at any conditions can be obtained by using Eq. (5.17) for the case when $\alpha = 0$ and $\pi_c = \pi_{cL}\pi_{cH}$, yielding

$$\dot{m}_0 = (1 - \beta - \varepsilon_1 - \varepsilon_2)(1 + f)P_0 \pi_r \pi_d \pi_c \pi_b A_4 MFP_4/\sqrt{T_{t4}} \quad \text{(K.17)}$$

The power produced by the low-pressure turbine at off-design is determined by its total pressure ratio (π_{tL}). The total enthalpy ratio of the low-pressure turbine (τ_{tL}) is related to its dependent variables by the uncooled turbine subroutine (TURB) of Chapter 5 and Appendix F written as

$$TURB\,[(T_{t4.5}, f_{4.5}, A_{4.5}/(A_9\pi_n), M_{4.5}, M_8, \eta_{tL}, T_{t5i}, \pi_{tL}, \tau_{tL}, T_{t5})] \quad \text{(K.18)}$$

This subroutine includes the conservation of mass between stations 4.5 and 9, constant turbine efficiency, and the variation of gas properties with temperature and fuel-to-air ratio. For a calorically perfect gas, this relationship becomes

$$\tau_{tL} = 1 - \eta_{tL}\left\{1 - (\pi_{tL})^{(\gamma_t - 1/\gamma_t)}\right\} \quad \text{(K.18-CPG)}$$

The work interaction coefficient for the propeller (C_{prop}) is obtained by a power balance of the low-pressure spool. For a constant value of P_{TOL}, C_{prop} is given by

$$C_{prop} = \eta_{prop}\eta_g\{\eta_{mL}(1 + f_o - \beta)\tau_\lambda \tau_{m1} \tau_{tH}\tau_{m2}(1 - \tau_{tL})\} - \frac{(C_{TOL})_R}{\eta_{mPL}}\frac{\dot{m}_{0R}}{\dot{m}_0}\frac{h_{0R}}{h_0} \quad \text{(K.19)}$$

Determination of the value of C_{prop} thus depends mainly on $T_{t4}(\tau_\lambda)$ and τ_{tL} because η_{prop}, η_g, and η_{mL}, τ_{m1}, τ_{tH}, and τ_{m2} are constant or essentially constant in Eq. (K.19). Equation (K.18-CPG) shows the direct dependence of τ_{tL} on π_{tL} for a constant η_{tL}. The off-design π_{tL} depends on the total pressure ratio imposed across the low-pressure turbine. Note that the flow is choked at the entrance to the low-pressure turbine (station 4.5) and is normally unchoked at the engine exit (station 9).

The total pressure at station 4.5 is related to the flight condition and throttle setting by

$$P_{t4.5} = P_0 \pi_r \pi_d \pi_c \pi_b \pi_{tH}$$

The total pressure at station 5 is related to the nozzle operation by

$$P_{t5} = \frac{P_0}{\pi_n}\left(\frac{P_{t9}}{P_0}\right)$$

and thus

$$\pi_{tL} = \frac{P_{t9}/P_0}{\pi_r \, \pi_d \, \pi_c \, \pi_b \, \pi_{tH} \, \pi_n} \tag{K.20}$$

The pressure ratio P_0/P_9 is determined by the nozzle operation with

$$\frac{P_{t9}}{P_9} = \left(\frac{P_t}{P}\right)_{M=1} \quad \text{and} \quad \frac{P_0}{P_9} = \frac{P_{t9}/P_9}{P_{t9}/P_0} \qquad \text{for choked flow}$$

and

$$\frac{P_0}{P_9} = 1 \quad \text{and} \quad \frac{P_{t9}}{P_9} = \left(\frac{P_t}{P}\right)_{M=1} \qquad \text{for unchoked flow}$$

Equating the mass flow rate of air at stations 4.5 and 9 yields the following equation for the total pressure ratio of the low-pressure turbine in terms of the exit Mach number and the total temperature ratio of the low-pressure turbine:

$$\frac{\pi_{tL}}{\sqrt{T_{t5}/T_{t4.5}}} = \frac{A_{4.5}}{\pi_n \, A_9} \frac{MFP(M_{4.5}, T_{t4.5}, f_{4.5})}{MFP(M_9, T_{t5}, f_{4.5})} \tag{K.21}$$

where M_9 is determined by the conditions at the exit. Thus, $M_9 = 1$ for choked flow, and M_9 is given by the compressible flow function RGCOMP for P_t/P, T_t, and f at station 9.

Determination of the conditions downstream of station 4.5 requires an iterative solution of Eqs. (K.18), (K.20), and (K.21). The method used is as follows:

1) Initially assume $= \pi_{tL} = \pi_{tLR}$.
2) Calculate τ_{tL} using Eq. (K.18).
3) Calculate P_{t9}/P_0 and conditions at exit including M_9.
4) Calculate new π_{tL} using Eq. (K.21).
5) Compare new π_{tL} with earlier value. If the difference is greater than 0.0001, then go to step 2 using the new π_{tL}.

The performance of the propeller can be simply modeled as a function of the flight Mach number (see Appendix L); one such model, which is used in the AEDsys computer program of this textbook, is shown in Fig. K.5 and expressed algebraically as

$$\eta_{prop} = 10 M_0 \eta_{prop \, max} \qquad\qquad M_0 \leq 0.1$$

$$\eta_{prop} = \eta_{prop \, max} \qquad\qquad 0.1 < M_0 \leq 0.7$$

$$\eta_{prop} = \left(1 - \frac{M_0 - 0.7}{3}\right) \eta_{prop \, max} \qquad 0.7 < M_0 \leq 0.85$$

The equation for the Mach range of 0.7–0.85, just given, models the drop in η_{prop} experienced in this flight regime as a result of transonic flow losses in the tip region of the propeller.

The following section summarizes the performance equations in the order of calculation.

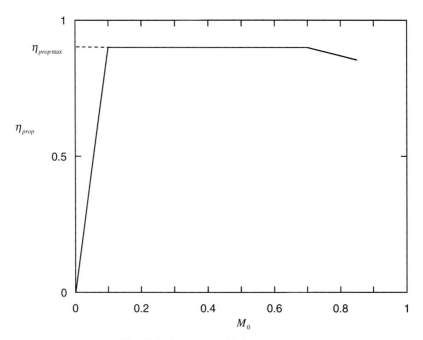

Fig. K.5   Propeller efficiency vs M_0.

Summary of Turboprop Engine Performance Cycle Analysis Equations

This section presents the complete performance cycle analysis equations for the turboprop engine with bleed, turbine cooling, and power extraction. For convenience in computer programming, the required computer inputs and principal computer outputs are given. These are followed by the cycle equations in their order of solution. Note that iteration is required for solution.

Inputs

Performance choices:
  Flight parameters: $\quad\quad M_0, T_0, P_0$
  Throttle setting: $\quad\quad\quad T_{t4}$
Design constants:
  π: $\quad\quad\quad\quad\quad\quad\quad \pi_{d\,max}, \pi_b, \pi_n$
  η: $\quad\quad\quad\quad\quad\quad\quad \eta_c, \eta_{tH}, \eta_{tL}, \eta_b, \eta_{mL}, \eta_{mH}, \eta_{mPL}, \eta_{mPH}, \eta_{prop\,max}$
  A: $\quad\quad\quad\quad\quad\quad\quad A_4, A_{4.5}, A_8$
  Others: $\quad\quad\quad\quad\quad\quad \beta, \varepsilon_1, \varepsilon_2, h_{PR}, P_{TOL}, P_{TOH}$
Reference condition:
  Flight parameters: $\quad\quad M_{0R}, T_{0R}, P_{0R}$
  Component behavior: $\quad \pi_{cR}, \pi_{tHR}, \pi_{tLR}$
  $\quad\quad\quad\quad\quad\quad\quad\quad\quad \tau_{cR}, \tau_{tHR}, \tau_{tLR}$
  Others: $\quad\quad\quad\quad\quad\quad T_{t4R}, \tau_{m1R}, \tau_{m2R}, f_R, M_{0R}, M_{8R}, C_{TOL\,R}, C_{TOH\,R}$
  $\quad\quad\quad\quad\quad\quad\quad\quad\quad F_R, \dot{m}_{0R}, S_R$
Engine control limits: $\quad \pi_{c\,max}, T_{t3\,max}, P_{t3\,max}, \%N_L, \%N_H$

Outputs

Overall performance: F, P, $\dot{m}_0$, S, S_P, f_o, η_P, η_{TH}, η_0, C_c, C_{prop}
V_9/a_0, P_{t9}/P_9, P_9/P_0, T_9/T_0

Component behavior: π_c, π_{tH}, π_{tL}, τ_c, τ_{tH}, τ_{tL}, τ_λ
τ_{m1}, τ_{m2}, f, M_8, M_9

Equations

Preliminary computations:

FAIR $(1, 0, T_0, h_0, P_{r0}, \phi_0, c_{p0}, R_0, \gamma_0, a_0)$

$V_0 = M_0 a_0$

$$h_{t0} = h_0 + \frac{V_0^2}{2g_c}$$

FAIR $(2, 0, T_{t0}, h_{t0}, P_{rt0}, \phi_{t0}, c_{pt0}, R_{t0}, \gamma_{t0}, a_{t0})$

$\tau_r = h_{t0}/h_0$

$\pi_r = P_{rt0}/P_{r0}$

$\pi_d = \pi_{d\,max}$ $\hspace{6cm}$ $M_0 \le 1$

$\eta_{prop} = 10 M_0 \eta_{prop\,max}$ $\hspace{4cm}$ $M_0 \le 0.1$

$\eta_{prop} = \eta_{prop\,max}$ $\hspace{4.5cm}$ $0.1 < M_0 \le 0.7$

$\eta_{prop} = \left(1 - \dfrac{M_0 - 0.7}{3}\right) \eta_{prop\,max}$ $\hspace{2cm}$ $0.7 < M_0 \le 0.85$

$h_{t2} = h_{t0}$

$P_{rt2} = P_{rt0}$

Set initial values:

$\pi_{tH} = \pi_{tHR}, \quad \pi_{tL} = \pi_{tLR}, \quad \tau_{tH} = \tau_{tHR}, \quad\quad \tau_{tL} = \tau_{tLR}$

$\pi_c = \pi_{cR}, \quad\quad \tau_c = \tau_{cR}, \quad\quad \dot{m}_0 = \dot{m}_{0R}$

$\tau_{m1} = \tau_{m1R}, \quad \tau_{m2} = \tau_{m2R}, \quad f = f_R$

$M_4 = 1, \quad\quad\quad M_{4.5} = 1, \quad\quad M_9 = M_8 = M_{8R}$

High-pressure and low-pressure turbines:

FAIR $(1, f, T_{t4}, h_{t4}, P_{rt4}, \phi_{t4}, c_{pt4}, R_{t4}, \gamma_{t4}, a_{t4})$

$h_{t4.5} = h_{t4} \tau_{m1} \tau_{tH} \tau_{m2}$

$f_{4.5} = f(1 - \beta - \varepsilon_1 - \varepsilon_2)/(1 - \beta)$

FAIR $(2, f_{4.5}, T_{t4.5i}, h_{t4.5}, P_{rt4.5}, \phi_{t4.5}, c_{pt4.5}, R_{t4.5}, \gamma_{t4.5}, a_{t4.5})$

$h_{t5} = h_{t4.5} \tau_{tL}$

FAIR $(2, f_{4.5}, T_{t5i}, h_{t5}, P_{rt5}, \phi_{t5}, c_{pt5}, R_{t5}, \gamma_{t5}, a_{t5})$

1   $h_{t3} = h_{t2} \tau_c$

FAIR $(2, 0, T_{t3}, h_{t3}, P_{rt3}, \phi_{t3}, c_{pt3}, R_{t3}, \gamma_{t3}, a_{t3})$

FAIR $(1, f, T_{t4}, h_{t4}, P_{rt4}, \phi_{t4}, c_{pt4}, R_{t4}, \gamma_{t4}, a_{t4})$

$f_{4.5} = f(1 - \beta - \varepsilon_1 - \varepsilon_2)/(1 - \beta)$

TURBC $(T_{t4}, f, A_4/A_{4.5}, M_4, M_{4.5}, \eta_{tH}, T_{t4.5i}, T_{t3}, \beta, \varepsilon_1, \varepsilon_2, \pi_{tH}, \tau_{tH}, T_{t4.5})$

$TURB\,(T_{t4.5},\, f_{4.5},\, A_{4.5}/A_8,\, M_{4.5},\, M_8,\, \eta_{tL},\, T_{t5i},\, \pi_{tL},\, \pi_n,\, \tau_{tL},\, T_{t5})$

$\tau_\lambda = h_{t4}/h_0$

Compressor and engine mass flow:

$$\tau_c = 1 + \eta_{mH}\{(1 - \beta - \varepsilon_1 - \varepsilon_2)(1 + f) + \varepsilon_1\}\frac{\tau_\lambda \tau_{m1}(1 - \tau_{tH})}{\tau_r} - \frac{C_{TOH}}{\eta_{mPH}}$$

$h_{t3} = h_{t2}\tau_c$

$h_{t3i} = h_{t2}\{1 + \eta_{cH}(\tau_{cH} - 1)\}$

$FAIR\,(2,\, 0,\, T_{t3},\, h_{t3},\, P_{rt3},\, \phi_{t3},\, c_{pt3},\, R_{t3},\, \gamma_{t3},\, a_{t3})$

$FAIR\,(2,\, 0,\, T_{t3i},\, h_{t3i},\, P_{rt3i},\, \phi_{t3i},\, c_{pt3i},\, R_{t3i},\, \gamma_{t3i},\, a_{t3i})$

$\pi_c = P_{rt3i}/P_{rt2}$

2 $f_{temp} = f$

$FAIR\,(1,\, f,\, T_{t4},\, h_{t4},\, P_{rt4},\, \phi_{t4},\, c_{pt4},\, R_{t4},\, \gamma_{t4},\, a_{t4})$

$$f = \frac{h_{t4} - h_{t3}}{h_{PR}\eta_b - h_{t4}}$$

if $|f - f_{temp}| > 0.0001$ goto 2

$$\frac{P_{t9}}{P_0} = \pi_r\,\pi_d\,\pi_c\,\pi_b\,\pi_{tH}\,\pi_{tL}\,\pi_n$$

$RGCOMPR\,(3,\, T_{t5},\, M_{9new},\, f_{4.5},\, TtT9,\, P_{t9}/P_0,\, MFP9)$

$M_{9\,error} = |M_9 - M_{9new}|$

if $M_{9\,error} > 0.01$ then

  $M_9 = M_{9new}$

   goto 1

end if

if $M_9 > 1$ then $M_8 = 1$ else $M_8 = M_9$

$RGCOMPR\,(1,\, T_{t4},\, M_4,\, f,\, TtT,\, PtP,\, MFP_4)$

$$\dot{m}_{0\,new} = \dot{m}_{0R}\frac{1 + f_R}{1 + f}\frac{P_0\pi_r\pi_d\pi_c}{\{P_0\pi_r\pi_d\pi_c\}_R}\frac{MFP_4}{MFP_{4R}}\sqrt{\frac{T_{t4R}}{T_{t4}}}$$

$$\dot{m}_{0\,error} = \left|\frac{\dot{m}_{0new} - \dot{m}_0}{\dot{m}_{0R}}\right|$$

if $\dot{m}_{0\,error} > 0.001$ then $\dot{m}_0 = \dot{m}_{0\,new}$ goto 1

$T_{t9} = T_{t5}$

$RGCOMPR\,(1,\, T_{t9},\, M_9,\, f_{4.5},\, TtT,\, P_{t9}/P_9,\, MFP9)$

$$P_0/P_9 = \frac{P_{t9}/P_9}{P_{t9}/P_0}$$

$T_9 = T_{t9}/TtT9$

   $FAIR\,(1,\, f_{4.5},\, T_9,\, h_9,\, P_{r9},\, \phi_9,\, c_{p9},\, R_9,\, \gamma_9,\, a_9)$

$V_9 = M_9 a_9$

$f_o = f(1 - \beta - \varepsilon_1 - \varepsilon_2)$

$$C_{TOL} = (C_{TOH})_R \frac{\dot{m}_{0R}}{\dot{m}_0} \frac{h_{0R}}{h_0}$$

$$C_{TOH} = (C_{TOH})_R \frac{\dot{m}_{0R}}{\dot{m}_0} \frac{h_{0R}}{h_0}$$

$$C_c = (\gamma_0 - 1)M_0 \left\{ (1 + f_o - \beta)\frac{V_9}{a_0} - M_0 + (1 + f_o - \beta) \right.$$
$$\left. \times \frac{R_9}{R_0} \frac{T_9/T_0}{V_9/a_0} \frac{(1 - P_0/P_9)}{\gamma_0} \right\}$$

$$C_{prop} = \eta_{prop}\eta_g \left\{ \eta_{mL}(1 + f_o - \beta)\tau_\lambda \tau_{m1} \tau_{tH} \tau_{m2}(1 - \tau_{tL}) - \frac{C_{TOL}}{\eta_{mPL}} \right\}$$

$$C_{TOTAL} = C_{prop} + C_C$$

$$\frac{P}{\dot{m}_0} = C_{TOTAL}h_0$$

$$P = \dot{m}_0 C_{TOTAL}h_0$$

$$S_P = \frac{f_o}{C_{TOTAL}h_0}$$

$$\frac{F}{\dot{m}_0} = \frac{C_{TOTAL}h_0}{V_0}$$

$$F = \dot{m}_0 C_{TOTAL}h_0 V_0$$

$$S = \frac{f_o}{F/\dot{m}_0}$$

$$\eta_P = C_{TOTAL} \left/ \left\{ \frac{C_{prop}}{\eta_{prop}} + \frac{\gamma_0 - 1}{2}\left[(1 + f_o - \beta)\left(\frac{V_9}{a_0}\right)^2 - M_0^2 \right] \right\} \right.$$

$$\eta_{TH} = \frac{C_{TOTAL} + C_{TOL} + C_{TOH}}{f_o h_{PR}/h_0}$$

$$\eta_O = \eta_{TH}\eta_P$$

RGCOMPR $(1, T_{t0}, 0, M_0, TtT, PtP, MFP_0)$

$$A_0 = \frac{\dot{m}_0 \sqrt{T}_{t0}}{P_{t0}MFP_0}$$

FAIR $(1, f_{4.5}, T_{t4.5}, h_{t4.5}, P_{rt4.5}, \phi_{t4.5}, c_{pt4.5}, R_{t4.5}, \gamma_{t4.5}, a_{t4.5})$

$$f_{4.5R} = f_R(1 - \beta - \varepsilon_1 - \varepsilon_2)/(1 - \beta)$$

FAIR $(1, f_R, T_{t4R}, h_{t4R}, P_{rt4R}, \phi_{t4R}, c_{pt4R}, R_{t4R}, \gamma_{t4R}, a_{t4R})$

$$h_{t4.5R} = h_{t4R}\tau_{m1R}\tau_{tHR}\tau_{m2R}$$

$$\%N_L = 100\sqrt{\frac{h_{t4.5}(1 - \tau_{tL})}{[h_{t4.5}(1 - \tau_{tL})]_R}}$$

$$\%N_H = 100\sqrt{\frac{h_0\tau_r(\tau_c - 1)}{[h_0\tau_r(\tau_c - 1)]_R}}$$

If any of the control limits (π_c, T_{t3}, P_{t3}, etc.) are exceeded, then reduce T_{t4} and go to 1. A Newtonian iteration scheme is used to rapidly converge on the value of T_{t4} that meets the most constraining limit.

Example Performance Results

Consider a turboprop engine designed for a Mach number of 0.8 at a standard day altitude of 25 kft with a compressor pressure ratio of 30, a turbine enthalpy ratio of 0.6, and the other information given in the Example Design Point Results Section. Engine controls limit the compressor pressure ratio to 30, the combustor exit temperature (T_{t4}) to 3200°R, and the compressor exit temperature (T_{t3}) to 1600°R. The performance of the engine is desired at other altitudes, Mach numbers, and partial throttle. The variation of the compressor pressure ratio (π_c) with changes in flight Mach number and altitude is presented in Fig. K.6 for full throttle operation. This is the same trend as observed before and corresponds to a θ_0 break of 0.933.

Figure K.7 shows the variation in full throttle uninstalled thrust with changes in flight Mach number and altitude for an engine sized for a static sea level thrust of 14,000 lbf. The variation of uninstalled thrust specific fuel consumption at full throttle is shown in Fig. K.8. The sharp break at $M_0 = 0.1$ in Figs. K.7 and K.8 is due to the assumed η_{prop} of Fig. K.5. The partial throttle performance at an altitude of 15 kft is presented in Fig. K.9 for selected flight Mach numbers. Note that S is very low compared with other turbine engine cycles.

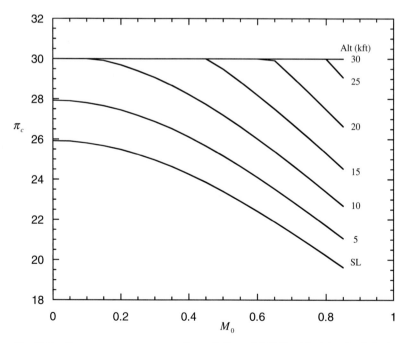

Fig. K.6   Compressor pressure ratio variation at full throttle (standard day).

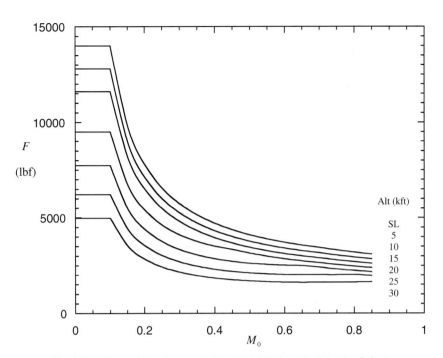

Fig. K.7 **Example turboprop's thrust at full throttle (standard day).**

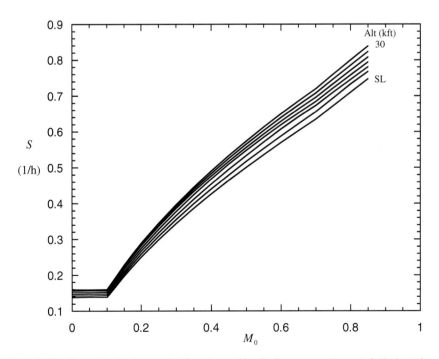

Fig. K.8 **Example turboprop's thrust specific fuel consumption at full throttle (standard day).**

607

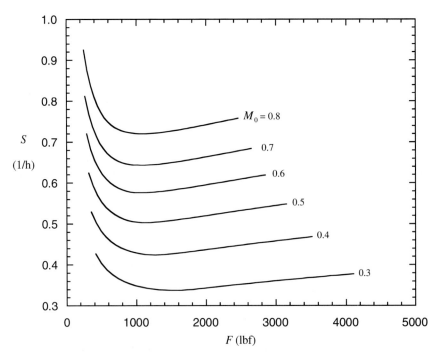

Fig. K.9   Partial throttle performance of example turboprop at 15 kft (standard day).

Appendix L
Propeller Design Tools

When turboprop cycles are being studied, it is important to have realistic design tools for the propeller because most of the thrust is provided by the propeller and because the behavior of propellers is far from simple. The emphasis here is on the efficiency of conversion of mechanical or shaft power to thrust power because that is the main function of the propeller.

The propeller accomplishes its purpose by spreading the mechanical energy that would otherwise reside in the core jet exhaust flow over a much greater flow of the oncoming air (Fig. L.1). This greatly increases the propulsive efficiency of the turboprop cycle and gives it the characteristics of a very high bypass ratio turbofan engine. However, the absence of a diffuser to reduce the Mach number of the approaching flow leads to supersonic relative speeds at the propeller blade tips while the flight speed is still subsonic. This, in turn, leads to unacceptably high propeller drag losses as the speed of sound is neared.

Propeller technology has been pursued by outstanding aerodynamicists for more than a century, including W. J. M. Rankine, R. E. Froude, S. Drzewiecki, L. Prandtl, A. Betz, H. Glauert,[1] S. Goldstein, and T. Theodorsen.[2,3] One of their legacies to us is a number of extremely clever analyses with fascinating results. It is worthwhile understanding what they have accomplished, whether or not you care about propellers.

Propeller Momentum or Actuator Disk Theory

This analysis is remarkable for the wealth of information brought forth by the simple, but insightful, model shown in Fig. L.2.

The assumptions are as follows:

1) The flow is everywhere inviscid; in particular, the slipstream allows a discontinuity between the freestream velocity and the velocity of the air that has passed through the propeller disk.

2) The entire effect of the propeller is a uniform increase in the static pressure across the "actuator disk" (which represents the smeared-out influence of the propeller) of magnitude ΔP_p.

3) Because the propeller spreads the available mechanical power over a relatively large quantity of air, the density of the air may be taken as constant at ρ_0.

4) Because the streamlines are parallel at sections far upstream and far downstream, the static pressure there equals P_0. This is not true near the propeller disk where there is considerable streamline curvature.

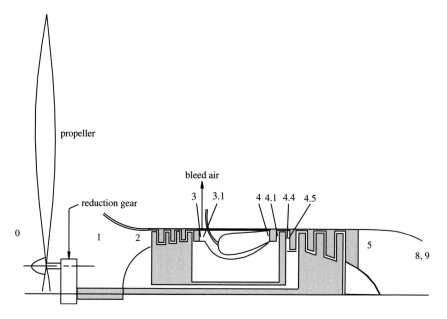

Fig. L.1   Turboprop engine.

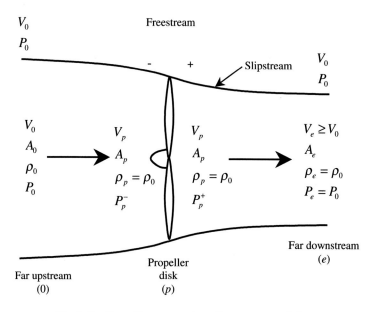

Fig. L.2   Propeller momentum theory nomenclature.

Conservation of Mass

Since

$$\rho_0 V_0 A_0 = \rho_0 V_p A_p$$

then

$$A_p = \frac{V_0 A_0}{V_p} \tag{L.1}$$

Incompressible Bernoulli Equation

Since

$$P_p^- = P_0 + \frac{\rho_0 V_0^2}{2} - \frac{\rho_0 V_p^2}{2}$$

and

$$P_p^+ = P_0 + \frac{\rho_0 V_e^2}{2} - \frac{\rho_0 V_p^2}{2}$$

then their difference is

$$P_p^+ - P_p^- \doteq \Delta P_p = \frac{\rho_0}{2}\left(V_e^2 - V_0^2\right) \tag{L.2}$$

Propeller Thrust

The thrust of the propeller can be obtained either from using Eq. (L.2)

$$F = A_p \Delta P_p = \frac{\rho_0 A_p}{2}\left(V_e^2 - V_0^2\right)$$

or from

$$F = \dot{m}_p(V_e - V_0) = \rho_0 V_0 A_0(V_e - V_0) \tag{L.3}$$

Setting these equal yields

$$A_p = \left(\frac{2}{1 + V_e/V_0}\right) A_0 \le A_0 \tag{L.4}$$

which may be combined with Eq. (L.1) to produce the very useful result:

$$V_p = (V_e + V_0)/2 \tag{L.5}$$

In words, the flow velocity at the propeller actuator disk is the exact average of the far upstream and far downstream values.

Ideal Propulsive Efficiency (η_P^*)

Using the definition

$$\eta_P^* = \frac{\text{Propulsive power}}{\text{Rate of kinetic energy input}}$$

$$\eta_P^* = \frac{F V_0}{\rho_0 V_0 A_0 \left(V_e^2 - V_0^2 \right)/2} \tag{L.6}$$

and Eq. (L.3) gives

$$\eta_P^* = \frac{2}{1 + V_e/V_0} = \frac{A_p}{A_0} \le 1 \tag{L.7}$$

This is a familiar result that confirms the earlier assertion that the more air the propeller power is distributed amongst, the more thrust power is generated.

Ideal Thrust Coefficient (C_T^*)

This quantity is a measure of the thrust per unit actuator disk area (or thrust loading). As it grows larger, the required propeller diameter for a given thrust grows smaller, in accordance with the definition

$$C_T^* = \frac{F}{\rho_0 V_0^2 A_p/2}$$

This may be combined with Eqs. (L.3) and (L.4) to yield

$$C_T^* = \left(\frac{V_e}{V_0} \right)^2 - 1 = \frac{4(1 - \eta_P^*)}{(\eta_P^*)^2} \tag{L.8}$$

Ideal Power Coefficient (C_P^*)

This quantity is a measure of the ability of the propeller to transfer power to the airstream and is defined as

$$C_P^* = \frac{\text{Rate of kinetic energy input}}{\rho_0 V_0^3 A_p/2}$$

$$C_P^* = \frac{\rho_0 V_0 A_0 \left(V_e^2 - V_0^2 \right)/2}{\rho_0 V_0^3 A_p/2}$$

which becomes, using Eq. (L.4),

$$C_P^* = \frac{1}{2} \left(1 + \frac{V_e}{V_0} \right) \left\{ \left(\frac{V_e}{V_0} \right)^2 - 1 \right\}$$

$$C_P^* = \frac{C_T^*}{\eta_P^*} = \frac{4(1 - \eta_P^*)}{(\eta_P^*)^3} \tag{L.9}$$

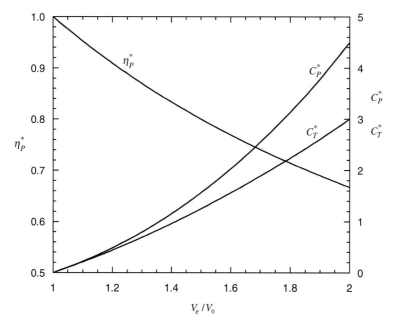

Fig. L.3   Ideal propeller performance indicators.

The three ideal propeller performance parameters are displayed together in Fig. L.3. Comparison reveals that high η_P^* can be obtained only at the cost of large size of A_p. Putting this in more precise, quantitative terms, in order for η_P^* to be at least 0.80, then V_e/V_0 must be less than 1.5, C_T^* must be less than 1.25, C_P^* must be less than 1.56, and A_p/A_0 must be greater than 0.8.

These expressions represent the ideal performance—something that can never be fully achieved in practice. The underlying assumption is that the propeller generates only the kinetic energy of axial velocity. In reality, several sources of energy loss occur, including frictional drag on the propeller blades, kinetic energy of rotation of the wake, and nonuniform axial velocities in the wake. Actual efficiencies are about 85% of the ideal value, with the most important loss mechanism being frictional drag. The next section will shed more light on this subject.

Propeller Blade Element or Strip Theory

This amounts to the equivalent of two-dimensional or infinite aspect ratio theory for propeller blades and is closely related to wing airfoil theory. It deals with the local conversion of mechanical power into thrust power of the propeller exhaust jet. To determine the behavior of the entire propeller, it is necessary to integrate from hub to tip across all blade elements and then to make corrections for end effects. The purposes of this section are completely served, however, by considering only one infinitesimal radial increment or blade element.

An important feature of this analysis is that the moving propeller blades do not "see" the undisturbed, freestream velocity V_0. Equation (1.5) has already shown

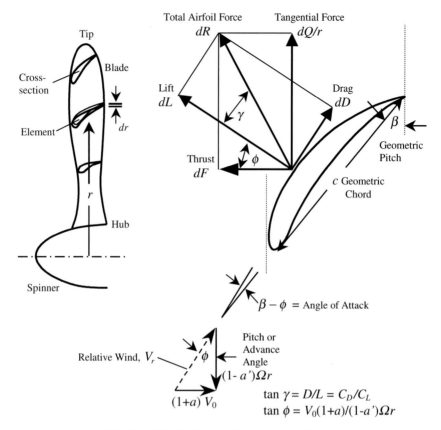

Fig. L.4   Blade element theory nomenclature.

that the axial component of velocity is larger than V_0 and is, in the general case, represented by $(1 + a)V_0$, where a is known as the "axial interference factor." Similarly, it has been found that the trailing vortex system reduces the relative tangential velocity to $(1 - a')r\Omega$, where a' is known as the "rotational interference factor." Whereas a depends primarily upon V_e/V_0 and can have a wide range of values (it can even be negative when the thrust is reversed), a' is merely of the order of 1%.

The thrust on the blade element (Fig. L.4) follows directly from

$$dF = dL\frac{\cos(\phi + \gamma)}{\cos \gamma} = \frac{\rho_0 \{(1 + a)V_0\}^2}{2 \sin^2\phi}\frac{\cos(\phi + \gamma)}{\cos \gamma}C_L c\, dr \qquad (L.10)$$

so that the total thrust is

$$F = \int_{r_{hub}}^{r_{tip}} dF \qquad (L.11)$$

The tangential torque on the blade element follows directly from

$$dQ = rdL\frac{\sin(\phi + \gamma)}{\cos \gamma} = \frac{\rho_0\{(1+a)V_0\}^2}{2\sin^2 \phi}\frac{\sin(\phi + \gamma)}{\cos \gamma}C_L c\, rdr \qquad (L.12)$$

so that the total torque is

$$Q = \int_{r_{hub}}^{r_{tip}} dQ \qquad (L.13)$$

The most interesting relationship, which allows the evaluation of the local or blade element efficiency of conversion of mechanical power into thrust power, comes from the definition of the blade element efficiency η_e.

$$\eta_e \doteq \frac{V_0\, dF}{\Omega\, dQ} = \left(\frac{V_0}{\Omega r}\right)\left(\frac{dF}{dQ/r}\right)$$

which, from the relative wind velocity and total airfoil force triangles of Fig. L.4, becomes

$$\eta_e = \frac{1 - a'}{1 + a}\frac{\tan \phi}{\tan(\phi + \gamma)} \qquad (L.14)$$

The local conversion efficiency therefore depends primarily upon a, γ, and ϕ. If a and ϕ are held constant, η_e must decrease as γ increases, which certainly makes sense because that decreases dF while increasing dQ/r. The behavior of Eq. (L.14) with constant a and γ and changing ϕ is more complex, as indicated in Fig. L.5. It can be shown, for example, that there is a maximum at $\phi = 45° - \gamma/2$, at which point

$$\eta_{e\,max} = \frac{1 - a'}{1 + a}\frac{\tan(45 - \gamma/2)}{\tan(45 + \gamma/2)} \qquad (L.15)$$

The curve also passes through zero at $\phi = 0$ and $90° - \gamma$, which correspond to no thrust power ($V_0 = 0$) and the total force being in the tangential direction, respectively. Finally, it should be noted that, as the propeller aerodynamics approach the ideal situation where a' and γ are zero and a is $(V_e - V_0)/2V_0$, then η_e approaches the η_P^* of Eq. (L.7), an outcome having great intuitive appeal.

Real propeller blade elements do not, of course, have constant γ because ϕ at a given radius varies as a result of flight and propeller speed changes, but have their lowest γ and best performance in the vicinity of $\phi = \beta$ (design angle of attack). One way to improve the range of operation near minimum γ, at the cost of mechanical complexity, has been to provide "variable pitch" in order to match β to ϕ as flight and propeller speeds change. If sufficient turning is provided, this also makes "reverse thrust" possible.

It should also be noted that the naturally occurring values of ϕ are in the range of 10–15 deg, which has prompted the use of geared propellers in order to reduce Ω and therefore increase both ϕ and η_e.

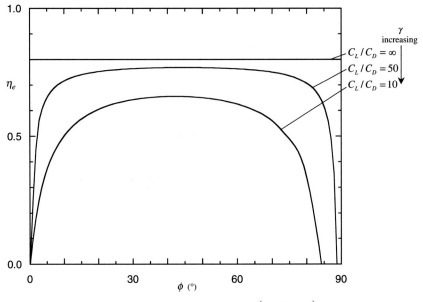

Fig. L.5 η_e **as a function of** $\phi\left(\frac{1-a'}{1+a} = 0.8\right)$**.**

Radial Variations

Because the propeller moves in solid body rotation, ϕ must decrease, and V_r must increase with radius. The first result of this fact is that β is designed to decrease with radius in order to maintain the design angle of attack near zero. This gives the propeller its twisted appearance and makes it impossible to maintain zero angle of attack at all radii at off-design conditions.

More importantly, the relative Mach number M_r given by

$$M_r = (1 + a)M_0/\sin \phi \qquad (L.16)$$

increases with freestream Mach number M_0 and radius and always exceeds M_0. When M_r approaches unity, blade element shock wave and boundary layer separation drag cause γ to rapidly increase and η_e to decrease below any reasonable value. Turboprop operation must therefore be restricted to subsonic forward speeds. This condition is also relieved somewhat by gearing down Ω and thereby increasing ϕ.

Real Propeller Behavior

Two questions that often arise while designing propellers cannot be answered using these fundamental methods, namely, the size and off-design performance.

Sizing is usually done on the basis of static thrust and often uses experimental or empirical information. Thanks to the brilliant work of Theodorsen[2] on the vortex theory of propellers, it is possible to understand and compute the observed behavior of the "standard" correlation parameters for thrust

$$C_T \doteq \frac{F}{660\sigma(N/1000)^2(D/10)^4} \tag{L.17}$$

and horsepower

$$C_P \doteq \frac{HP}{2000\sigma(N/1000)^3(D/10)^5} \tag{L.18}$$

where F, N, D, and HP are in units of lbf, rpm, ft, and hp, respectively. Note that these have little to do with C_T^* and C_P^* defined earlier, but are used by engineers to correlate real propeller behavior.

The complete calculations of Theodorsen, done by Amatt et al.,[4] show that the quantity

$$\frac{C_T^{3/2}}{C_P} = \frac{2000\,F^{3/2}}{(6605)^{3/2}\sigma^{1/2}(D/10)HP}$$

is not only independent of N, but is nearly constant over the usual range of operating parameters. As a result, it is possible to solve the preceding equation for D and use the resulting approximate correlation

$$D = \left\{ \frac{F^3}{589\sigma HP^2(blades)^{1/3}} \right\}^{1/2} \tag{L.19}$$

as a starting point. This clearly shows that the same thrust can be obtained from less HP by increasing the airflow, i.e., D!

Example

Suppose a four-bladed propeller is to be designed to produce 15,000 lbf of thrust from 4000 hp at standard sea level static conditions. Then Eq. (L.19) shows that

$$D = \left\{ \frac{(15,000)^3}{589(1)(4000)^2(4)^{1/3}} \right\}^{1/2} = 15.0\,\text{ft}$$

If the same job were to be done with two rows of propellers, each producing half the thrust and using half the power, whether on the same or separate engines, then

$$D = \left\{ \frac{(15,000/2)^3}{589(1)(4000/2)^2(4)^{1/3}} \right\}^{1/2} = 10.6\,\text{ft}$$

Propeller Map

The most accurate method for computing off-design propeller behavior, which also requires the most initial data, is the "propeller map" containing contours of constant η_{prop}, an obvious relative of the well-known compressor map. A typical propeller map is shown in Fig. L.6.

The type of propeller map to be used in any situation depends on which input parameters are known. In the typical propulsion case of selecting propellers for

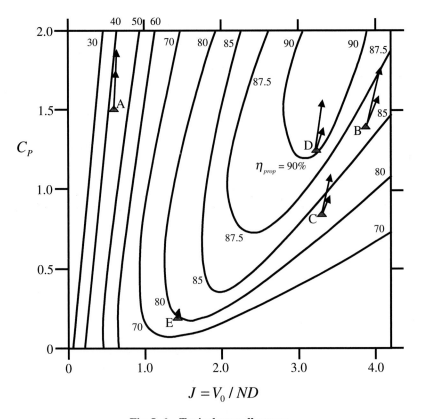

Fig. L.6   Typical propeller map.

turboprop cycles, it is most advantageous to employ C_P [Eq. (L.18)] and the "advance ratio" or "slip function"

$$J \doteq \frac{V_0}{ND} \qquad (L.20)$$

as the independent variables. The reason for the choice of C_P and J is simply that HP and V_0 are usually known and the propeller design goal is to determine values for D and N (which are often fixed for mechanical and control reasons) that result in acceptable values of the propeller efficiency η_{prop} over the entire mission. Each set of C_P and J uniquely determines D and N.

An example of this method can be found in Fig. L.6, which is data representative of a counterrotating, tandem (or dual) propeller operating below the critical relative Mach number. The benefits of variable pitch have been included by presenting the highest attainable value of η_{prop} at each point and the effects of gearing appear directly in both C_P and J. Such data can and should be obtained from the propeller manufacturer.

The general features of this map can be understood in terms of propeller blade element theory. The highest efficiencies occur in the vicinity of $J = \pi$, which

Table L.1 **Example turboprop design**

Label	Flight condition	M_0/Alt, kft	Power (avail)	Thrust (required)	η_{prop}, %	Thrust (actual)	J/C_P
A	Takeoff	0.088/0	2387 hp	6660 lbf	43.0	6660 lbf	0.60/1.50
B	Sea level dash	0.529/0	2259	3452	85.0	3576.1	3.88/1.38
C	Low cruise	0.454/0	1411	2540	83.7	2570.3	3.30/0.85
D	High cruise	0.5/35	619	1152	90.0	4067.8	3.20/1.24
E	Loiter	0.2/10	218	916	81.9	1229.3	1.45/0.18

$D = 14$ ft and $N = 663.4$ rpm.

corresponds to $\phi = 45$ deg. Beyond this, the efficiency "islands" are the result of angle of attack effects on the propeller blades. In the regions where η_{prop} falls off rapidly, it is clear that stall is occurring because the relative angle of attack is too positive or too negative.

Five points labeled A through E have been spotted on Fig. L.6 and portray the "best" solution for the multipurpose transport aircraft of Table L.1 with many conflicting requirements, including short takeoff, high-speed sea level dash, and great range. Also shown in Fig. L.6 are the locations to which each of these five points would move if D were reduced 5% (longer lines) and if N were reduced 5% (shorter lines). Although η_{prop} could be slightly increased at the four flight conditions (B through E), particularly by reducing the diameter D, sufficient thrust for takeoff would no longer be available at condition A. Reversing this reasoning quickly leads to the conclusion that providing excessive takeoff thrust will unnecessarily penalize η_{prop} at the four flight conditions. Other propellers, with different performance maps, should also be explored for any such application.

Structural Design

The method of designing propeller blades for a specified service life follows the lines already described for compressor rotor airfoils with one overwhelming change: Because propeller blades have the protential for so much destruction, they cannot be allowed to separate. In the jargon of the trade, they must be "prime reliable." This only increases the need for good analytical tools, exhaustive and realistic testing, and high-quality manufacturing.

Beyond this, there are significant differences because bending and twisting moments can be more important than centrifugal forces and because composite materials with nonisentropic properties (such as wood) are frequently employed.

The net result is that propeller structural design,[4] like many other things, is a field that requires its own special expertise. Nevertheless, there are certain structural aspects that warrant some discussion here.

In reviewing the typical turbofan or turbojet engine, a number of components and design features are readily apparent that optimize inflow angle and flow velocity. Such is the case with inlet ducts, inlet guide vanes, and variable compressor stator vanes. As a result of these design features, the engine is nearly impervious to aircraft altitude changes. The propeller, however, always operates in the freestream and aircraft pitch, yaw, and roll motions constantly change the inflow angle into the blades. More often than not, the inflow angle is such that the velocity vector is not normal to the propeller blade plane of rotation. This condition results in cyclic aerodynamic loads that peak one time per (1XP) revolution. This cyclic loading is known as the "1XP" moment and is directly proportional to the product of inflow angle and dynamic pressure. In aft-mounted (pusher) propeller, the wing and nacelle flowfield interactions result in other moments, referred to as "2XP," etc., that must be considered. These cyclic loads are of paramount importance to the structural integrity of propellers, especially in view of their "prime reliable" requirements.

It was just mentioned that the twisting and bending moments on propeller blades are more significant than those on axial compressor blades. A typical compressor rotor has upward of 100 blades, giving high solidity (which means greater ability to absorb power), with a low aspect ratio on the blades (of the order of 1 to 2). In contrast, a typical propeller has four blades of high aspect ratio (greater than six). This means that fewer blades must absorb all the power, which translates into very high loading. This has an impact on the severity of bending moments, which grow rapidly with radius and are greatest at the root. The high loading also affects the twisting moments because the pressure distribution on the highly twisted blades is asymmetric.

These differences between compressor blades and propeller blades highlight the complexity of structural considerations in propellers. These problems are made more acute by the need to install anti-ice or de-ice devices on the leading edge of propeller blades. In compressors this is done by injecting hot air bleed from the compressor into the inlet, but this is not easily accomplished with a propeller blade rotating in the freestream. Although there are various methods, such as circulation of hot oil along the leading edge, the most common is the resistive heater, in which an electrical heating element is installed along the leading edge of the blade.

Variable Speed vs Constant Speed

One of the advantages of turboprop and turboshaft engines lies in the fact that their purpose allows for operation at constant speeds. By simply changing the blade pitch, and hence the load, a pilot can control thrust. Throttle movements will increase or decrease fuel flow to the engine, with a consequent tendency to increase or decrease rpm. The propeller governor will sense the change and adjust propeller pitch, thereby adjusting the load corresponding to engine power output and hence maintaining constant rpm. Such a mode of operation allows for rugged, simple engines, constructed with a single compressor tied to the turbine by just one shaft, which also drives the propeller reduction gearbox. On the other hand, constant speed does not allow for most efficient propeller operation at all aircraft airspeeds. Under constant N conditions, given that the diameter is constant, the advance ratio will vary only with flight airspeed. At the same time, power setting will change the value of the power coefficient. The end result is that, at low flight speeds and power settings, the propeller is not operating at optimum efficiency for the flight condition. To remedy this problem, given a set at low airspeed, the rotational speed must be decreased in order to increase the value of the advance ratio. At greater values of J, the operating point on the propeller map moves to the right and up on efficiency. This can have a significant impact on fuel consumption and aircraft loiter time. The drawback of the variable speed propeller is that the engine must now operate in a more conventional way, that is through an extended range of rotational speeds. This will increase the complexity of controls, structures, and manufacture, and ultimately cost. It is thus extremely important to take into consideration the intended duty cycle or mission profile in order to make the most advantageous choice—constant speed or variable speed.

Turboprop Cycle Performance Characteristics

A novel feature of turboprop engines is the simplicity with which their general behavior can be understood. Returning to the initial view of the propeller as a device for converting engine-generated mechanical power into thrust power and ignoring the usually negligible amount of thrust generated by the core flow, then from the definition of η_{prop}

$$\eta_{prop} \doteq \frac{\text{Thrust power}}{\text{Propeller shaft power}} = \frac{F V_0}{P_{prop}} \tag{L.21}$$

there follows

$$F = \frac{\eta_{prop} P_{prop}}{V_0} = \frac{\eta_{prop} P_{prop}}{a_0 M_0} \tag{L.22}$$

Recognizing that P_{prop} is only slightly affected by M_0, but does decrease faster than a_0 with altitude, it is possible to conclude immediately that F decreases with altitude and varies almost inversely with M_0 at constant altitude (see Fig. K.7). The latter has tremendous implications for high-speed turboprop flight. Because aircraft drag increases in proportion to M_0^2 and η_{prop} diminishes with M_0, the P_{prop} required to fly faster at fixed altitude varies at least as M_0^3. Small wonder that the record speed for a turboprop-powered aircraft, which was set in 1960 by the Soviet TU-114, is a Mach number of only about 0.77.

Something about static thrust can be learned by differentiating Eq. (L.22) using L'Hospital's rule, whence

$$F|_{M_0=0} = \frac{P_{prop}}{a_0} \left(\frac{d\eta_{prop}}{dM_0} \right)_{M_0=0} \tag{L.23}$$

Even though this thrust is often too great for some other part of the propulsion system, such as the gears or shafts, it allows the maximum thrust capability of the engine to be calculated only from the slope of propeller efficiency at $M_0 = 0$. An important conclusion about turboprop thrust behavior, as noted at the outset, is that it provides high thrust at low speed.

The other important performance parameter is specific fuel consumption, which, using the definition of overall efficiency ($\eta_{prop} \times \eta_{TH}$), is given by

$$S = \frac{\dot{m}_f}{F} = \frac{a_0 M_0}{\eta_{prop} \eta_{TH} h_{PR}} \tag{L.24}$$

where $\eta_{TH} = P_{prop}/(\dot{m}_f h_{PR})$ and is largely proportional to $\sqrt{T_0}$ or a_0, so that

$$S \propto \frac{M_0}{\eta_{prop}} \tag{L.25}$$

which means that S worsens as M_0 increases (see Fig. K.8), particularly as $M_0 = 1$ is approached and η_{prop} decreases rapidly. Again, the turboprop is an excellent device at low M_0—in fact the lower the better.

To find the static specific fuel consumption, Eq. (L.24) is differentiated using L'Hospital's rule to yield

$$S|_{M_0=0} = \frac{a_0}{\eta_{TH} h_{PR}(d\eta_{prop}/dM_0)_{M_0=0}} \tag{L.26}$$

Example

Suppose that $\eta_{prop} = 10 M_0 \eta_{prop\,max}$ for $M_0 \leq 0.1$ and $\eta_{prop} = \eta_{prop\,max}$ for $0.1 < M_0 < 0.8$. How do F and S vary with M_0?
From Eq. (L.22)

$$F = \frac{10\eta_{prop\,max} P_{prop}}{a_0} \qquad M_0 \leq 0.1 \qquad \text{(constant)}$$

$$F = \frac{\eta_{prop\,max} P_{prop}}{a_0 M_0} \qquad 0.1 < M_0 < 0.8 \qquad (\sim 1/M_0)$$

From Eq. (L.24)

$$S = \frac{a_0}{10\eta_{prop\,max} h_{PR}\eta_{TH}} \qquad M_0 \leq 0.1 \qquad \text{(constant)}$$

$$S = \frac{a_0 M_0}{\eta_{prop\,max} h_{PR}\eta_{TH}} \qquad 0.1 < M_0 < 0.8 \qquad (\sim M_0)$$

References

[1]Glauert, H., *The Elements of Airfoil and Airscrew Theory*, 2nd ed., Cambridge Univ. Press, Cambridge, England, UK, 1947.

[2]Theodorsen, T., *Theory of Propellers*, McGraw–Hill, New York, 1948.

[3]Theodorsen, T., "Theory of Static Propellers and Helicopter Rotors," American Helicopter Society, Paper 326, May 1969.

[4]Amatt, W., et al., "Structural Analysis and Blade Design," *Summary of Propeller Design Procedures and Data*, Vol. II, USAAMRDL-TR-73-34A, Nov. 1973.

Appendix M
Example Material Properties

Our purpose here is to provide the basis for representative structural properties of materials typically found in aircraft engines for use in component design calculations of Sec. 8.2.3. The amount of information that might be displayed can truly be called bewildering for a number of reasons. To begin with, the material for each separate engine part is carefully selected, taking into account its usage, environment, and required durability. Furthermore, for each part there are many competing materials that have similar capabilities, but different compositions, processing methods, and brand names. Finally, many properties of a candidate material must be known before a confident design can be contemplated, such as allowable tensile and compressive strengths, cyclic strength, creep rates, oxidation, erosion, and corrosion rates, fracture toughness, crack propagation rate, ductility, allowable deformation, hardness, modulus of elasticity, thermal conductivity, thermal growth coefficient, and Poisson's ratio (all as a function of time, temperature, and heat treatment). The permutations are endless.

To cope with this in a textbook, drastic reductions must be made. They are achieved by only including materials for critical parts (see Sec. 8.2.3), giving only one example for each generic application, and, most importantly, concentrating mainly upon allowable creep strength as required by the considerations of Sec. 8.2.3.

Although not used directly in the design examples, special attention is drawn here to the so-called fatigue or cyclic strength of these typical engine materials. This has been done because the life of engine parts is often consumed by fatigue—or at least by a combination of steady-state and cyclic stress. Exactly how this combination is accounted for in practice is usually a proprietary matter. The general nature of the jet engine is such that the major source of cyclic stress at the "cold end" (i.e., fan and compressor) is vibratory excitation, it and therefore occurs at about 1000 cycle/s, whereas at the "hot end" (i.e., burner and turbines) it is a result of pressure and temperature transients and therefore occurs at about 1 cycle/h. Vibratory and pressure or thermal fatigue are therefore often referred to as high-cycle and low-cycle fatigue, respectively. The example material properties gathered here contain fatigue strength data appropriate to the usual application of each material, while illustrating the perplexing behavior of this characteristic.

The information assembled here has been abstracted from the Battelle Memorial Institute's *Aerospace Structural Metals Handbook*.[1] The seven examples are presented more or less as in their usual order of appearance from the inlet to the exit of the engine.

Aluminum 2124 Alloy (ρ = 5.29 slug/ft^3)

This is one of a series of premium aluminum alloys that were developed as a result of studies into the micromechanisms of fracture in high-strength aluminum compositions. It is normally produced in plate form in a thickness range up to 6 in. and has been thoroughly characterized.

Figure M.1 contains traditional yield and ultimate tensile strength data for Al 2124 as a function of test temperature and exposure time. Using yield strength as a design criterion, one would conclude that a part having a required life of 1000 hours while exposed to a temperature of 400°F could withstand tensile stresses up to 25,000 psi. This, however, would not be a conservative design practice because

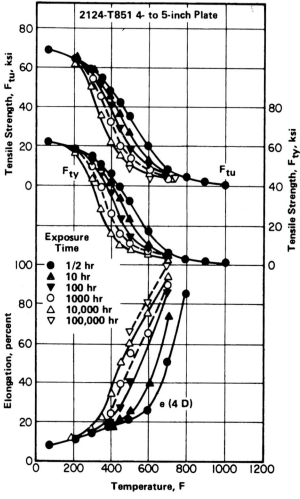

Fig. M.1   Effect of temperature and exposure time on tensile properties of 2124-T851.

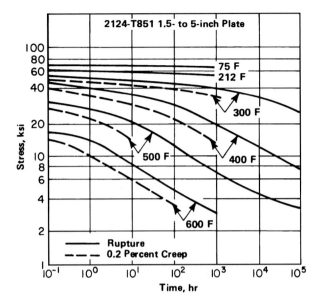

Fig. M.2   Creep and creep-rupture curves at temperatures from 75 to 600°F for 2124-T851 plate.

the part will undergo permanent deformation during the exposure time, which could cause unacceptable distortion and/or interference.

Consequently, it is preferable to base designs on creep and creep-rupture data, such as those shown in Fig. M.2. The common practice is to allow less than 1% creep during the life of the part, which, for the preceding example, would allow a tensile stress of about 15,000 psi. This is generally the more restrictive criterion, and, therefore, no further yield or ultimate strength data will be presented for any material.

Figure M.2 reveals that the useful tensile strength of Al 2124 diminishes rapidly above a temperature of 200°F; thus, it would seldom find engine application above 400°F. It must also be remembered that the value obtained from Fig. M.2 represents an upper limit that cannot be directly used as a design criterion. Reductions must be made to account for cyclic stress, uncertainties in load calculations, property variations, and safety margins. Experience indicates that a reasonable estimate of the "allowable working stress" is 80% of the 0.2% creep value obtained from Fig. M.2.

Some idea of the ability of Al 2124 to tolerate cyclic stress can be found on Figs. M.3 and M.4. A turbine engine part will experience several thousand LCF cycles caused by throttle motions, but literally billions of HCF cycles caused by vibrations. Hence, the so-called "run-out" stress, which the material can apparently withstand forever, becomes an important factor.

Among the conclusions to be drawn from Figs. M.3 and M.4 are that a notch reduces the alternating stress capability of Al 2124 dramatically and that it is less tolerant of bending than longitudinal cyclic stress. The latter point could be critical for cantilevered airfoil applications.

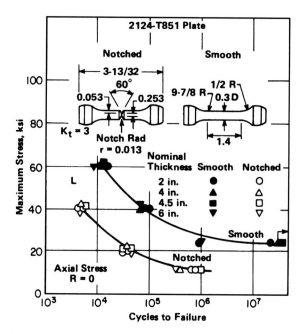

Fig. M.3 Axial-load fatigue curves for longitudinal smooth and notched specimens from 2124-T851 plate.

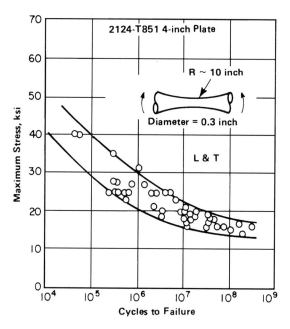

Fig. M.4 Rotational bending fatigue curves for smooth specimens from 4 in 2124-T851 plate.

Table M.1   Variations in creep deformation with different creep exposures

Creep exposure			Time to 0.1% creep, h	Time to 0.2% creep, h	Total plastic deformation, %
Temp, °F	Stress, ksi	Time, h	α–β forged at 1650°F		
750	90	1228	270	840	0.251
750	89	150	——	——	0.101
800	75	504	105	420	0.217
800	85	241	40	210	0.234
800	85	150	——	——	0.180
1000	20	51	6	27	0.246
1000	30	72	2	8	0.760
1000	30	150	——	——	0.820

Form: disc forging, 3 in. thick × 11 in. diameter.

Titanium 6246 Alloy (ρ = 9.08 slug/ft^3)

This alloy was designed to combine long-time, elevated-temperature strength characteristics with markedly improved short-time strength properties at both room and elevated temperatures. It is intended for use in forgings for intermediate-temperature-range sections of gas turbine engines, particularly in disk and rotor airfoil components of the fan and compressor.

Ti-6246 is not thoroughly characterized, but is recommended for gas turbine applications up to 750°F. The data of Table M.1 suggest that the allowable stress based on 1% creep for 1000 hours use at 750°F is about 90,000 psi, whereas at 800°F it is only about 75,000 psi and at 1000°F it is below 20,000 psi.

The data of Fig. M.5, although taken at room temperature, show that Ti-6246 does well with cyclic stress. However, Ti-6246 has poor fracture toughness

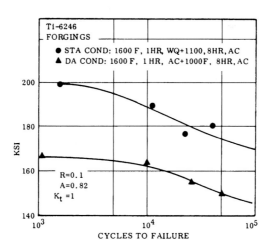

Fig. M.5   Axial fatigue properties of $\alpha - \beta$ forged materials in two heat-treated conditions.

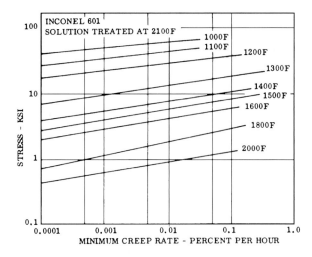

Fig. M.6   Minimum creep rate at various temperatures and stresses.

and is very susceptible to minor damage. Therefore, either a damage-tolerant processed version of Ti-6246 or a slightly different alloy is required for practical applications.

Inconel 601 (ρ = 15.6 slug/ft^3)

This is a general-purpose alloy for applications requiring resistance to both heat and corrosion at temperatures up to about 2100°F. It has been used in burner liners, diffuser assemblies, containment rings, exhaust liners, and burner igniters.

The data of Fig. M.6 may be used to show, for example, that Inconel 601 will creep 1% in 1000 hours at 1600°F if the stress is about 3000 psi. For the higher-temperature applications it must, therefore, be kept unloaded. In stark contrast with Ti-6246, however, it retains much of its room temperature strength well beyond 1000°F.

Because Inconel 601 is not commonly employed where vibrations matter, Fig. M.7 shows that it has more than adequate fatigue strength.

Hastelloy X (ρ = 16.0 slug/ft^3)

This is a nickel-base superalloy with good oxidation resistance at temperatures up to 2200°F and moderately good strength properties up to 1600°F. It has been used in jet engine exhaust nozzles, afterburner components, and structural parts in the burner and turbine components.

Referring to Fig. M.8 and using the 1% creep at 1000 hours criterion, one would conclude that the upper limit to tensile stress at 1200°F is 22,000 psi and at 1500°F is 7000 psi for Hastelloy X.

Because Hastelloy X is generally used in situations where only low-cycle fatigue caused by pressure or thermal cycles matters, its fatigue characteristics are

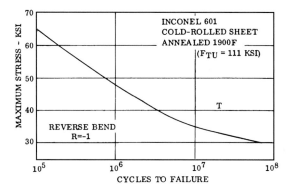

Fig. M.7   Fatigue properties of annealed sheet.

presented in terms of strain range rather than stress range, as in Fig. M.9. This must obviously be obtained from a thermal stress calculation involving at least a knowledge of the coefficient of thermal expansion and modulus of elasticity, given in Figs. M.10 and M.11, respectively. Note that in the 1200–1600°F range the modulus of elasticity is approximately 20 million psi. Consequently, the stress corresponding to a 1% strain range equates approximately to 200,000 psi. This makes it evident that such materials can tolerate only a small fraction of a percent strain.

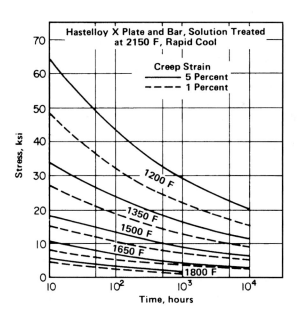

Fig. M.8   Creep-deformation curves for plate and bar at temperatures of 1200–1800°F.

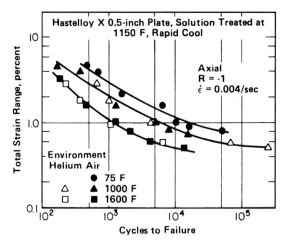

Fig. M.9 Fatigue life of plate at various temperatures in air and impure helium at atmospheric pressure.

Mar-M 509 (ρ = 17.2 slug/ft^3)

This is a high-chromium, carbide-strengthened, cobalt-base superalloy. It was designed for use in the gas turbine industry, primarily as an investment-cast stator airfoil alloy to operate at temperatures of 1800°F. Mar-M 509 has high inherent oxidation and sulfidation resistance and is, therefore, sometimes used without a protective coating. It also has superior thermal shock characteristics.

The most relevant design tensile stress data for Mar-M 509 are given in Fig. M.12. A logical criterion would be 0.5% creep deformation in 500 hours, which would lead to a stress of approximately 9000 psi at 1800°F. No data were given for alternating stress.

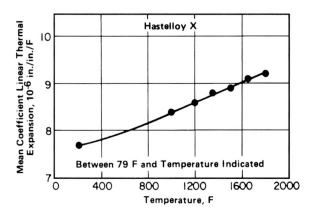

Fig. M.10 Effect of elevated temperature on thermal expansion coefficient.

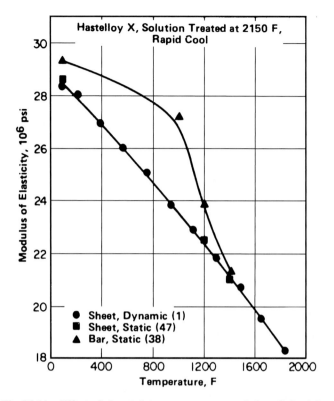

Fig. M.11   Effect of elevated temperature on modulus of elasticity.

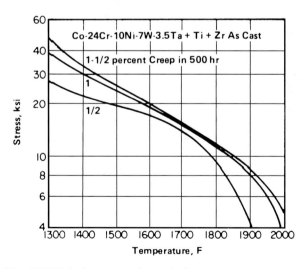

Fig. M.12   Mar M 509 design curves for typical stresses required to produce creep strains of 0.5, 1, and 1.5% in 500 hours at temperatures of 1300–2000°F.

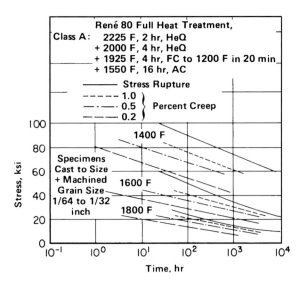

Fig. M.13   Creep strain and creep-rupture curves at 1400, 1600, and 1800°F for fully treated cast alloy.

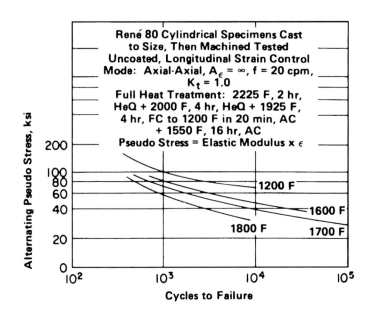

Fig. M.14   Axial low cycle fatigue behavior at 1200–1800°F.

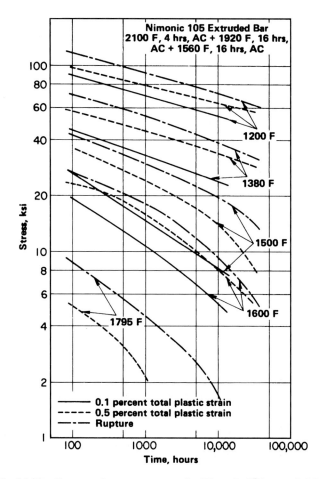

Fig. M.15   Creep and rupture curves for Nimonic 105 extruded bar.

Rene' 80 (ρ = 15.9 slug/ft^3)

This is a cast, precipitation-hardenable, nickel-base superalloy. It has excellent creep-rupture strength up to 1900°F, combined with good elevated temperature ductility and superior hot corrosion resistance. The main use of Rene' 80 is in investment-vacuum-cast turbine stator and rotor airfoils, which are coated for any jet engine applications.

Using the 1% creep deformation at the 1000 hour criterion, Fig. M.13 reveals that Rene' 80 has the remarkably high tensile stress capability of about 32,000 psi at 1600°F and 13,000 psi at 1800°F.

Alternating stress considerations are often important in cooled turbine rotor airfoils, which are usually cantilevered and subject to the aerodynamic buffeting (as a result of both random turbulence and organized wake passage) that produces vibratory loads. It is especially important to avoid resonance between a regular upstream disturbance and a natural frequency of the rotor airfoils.

Thermal stresses can cause low-cycle fatigue failure if the limits given in Fig. M.14 are reached. This means that cooled airfoils must be designed with the greatest care so that no local areas of large thermal stress are created at any time during the normal engine operation. In particular, it can be readily seen that a thin airfoil "skin" with a large temperature difference between coolant and mainstream will not last long.

Nimonic 105 (ρ = 15.5 slug/ft^3)

This is a wrought nickel-cobalt-chromium-base superalloy having creep and oxidation resistances that make it suitable for service at temperatures up to 1750°F. It is used for turbine rotor airfoils, disks, forgings, ring sections, bolts, and fasteners.

The data of Fig. M.15 show that Nimonic 105 falls between Rene' 80 and Hastelloy X in tensile strength. Under the same ground rules, one finds a stress of about 17,000 psi at 1600°F and perhaps 3000 psi at 1800°F. No data were given for the low-cycle fatigue behavior of Nimonic 105.

Reference

[1]*Aerospace Structural Metals Handbook*, Battelle Memorial Inst., Columbus Lab., Columbus, OH, 1984.

Appendix N
Turbine Engine Life Management

N.1 Introduction to the Engine Lifing Process

While performing their intended aerodynamic tasks, the rotating compressor and turbine parts must also be almost certain to last the design lifetime of the engine. The turbine engine lifing (pronounced "life"-ing) process is evolutionary and has been unfolding over the past 50 years. In various degrees it is affected today by many of the factors depicted in Fig. N.1. These factors have all evolved through lessons learned and state-of-the-art changes. Some of the most notable advances that have been made are in the areas indicated by the shaded blocks in Fig. N.1. Some of these include: 1) finite element modeling techniques used in stress analysis; 2) improved materials (strength, temperature capability, life, fracture toughness); 3) engine controls; 4) testing techniques; 5) manufacturing and inspection; 6) surface treatments that instill beneficial residual stresses such as laser shock peening; 7) data recording systems for usage monitoring; and 8) usage tracking systems.

When taken together, all of these advances in the "state of art" have had a very positive effect on the ability to predict engine component life and on safety.

N.2 Engine Life Management

N.2.1 Lessons Learned

Through many development programs (commercial and military) and customer engine problems the following summary of generic lessons learned has been collected:

1) It is dangerous to assume defect-free structures in safety of flight components.

2) Critical parts and potential failure modes must be identified early in development and appropriate control measures implemented.

3) Thermal and vibratory environments must be identified early in engine development.

4) For complex components analytic stresses must be verified by testing.

5) Materials and processes must be adequately characterized (particularly, the fracture properties).

6) Design stress spectra, component test spectra, and full scale engine test spectra must be based on the anticipated service usage of the engine.

7) Potential engine/airframe structural interactions must be defined and taken into account.

8) Closed-loop management procedures must be defined and enforced through the application of realistic inspection and maintenance requirements, individual engine tracking procedures, deficiency reporting, and updates in procedures based on actual usage.

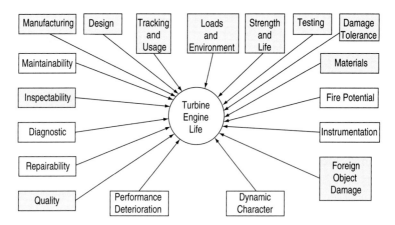

Fig. N.1 Turbine engine lifing factors.

N.2.2 Life Management Scope

Life management is important because its goal is to ensure the safe operation of engines subjected to complex usage. This is accomplished through the calculation of the lives of high-energy rotating and pressurized components, which would not be contained if they were to fail in an engine. The goal of life management is to safely maximize the use of critical parts to minimize ownership costs. The cost of some of these parts, because of the use of high-temperature exotic materials, complex design and manufacture, and rigid quality control, is considerable. Examples of some of these high-energy components would be rotating disks, spools, airfoils, spacers, shafts, and seals and high-pressure cases.

Life management requires the selection of one of the lifing concepts that will be discussed in Sec. N.4, Lifing Concepts, or the lifing concepts may be dictated by the customer and stated in the Request for Proposal (RFP).

For example, a typical commercial engine flight usage shown in Fig. N.2 would lean heavily on the commercial safe life management concept. The stress response of a typical turbine rim from this usage is shown in Fig. N.3. In simple terms, the maximum stress range at the critical location is used to enter the low cycle fatigue (LCF) minimum life material curve at the corresponding operating temperature to give the component minimum life.

In contrast, Fig. N.4 shows engine usage that would be common to a military fighter aircraft. In this case, to life manage would require combining the safe life concept with damage tolerance (required by the military customer in the RFP) and involve a more rigorous thermal, stress, and fatigue and facture analysis to establish minimum life and safe inspection intervals.

In addition to the effects of usage on engine life, the effects of mission mix and the effects of an ambient temperature mix and warm and cold starts would also require an evaluation.

N.2.3 Definitions

N.2.3.1 Damage tolerance approach. The damage tolerance approach is a structural philosophy that recognizes that undetected metallurgical defects

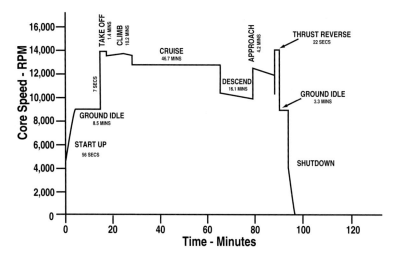

Fig. N.2   Typical commercial mission.

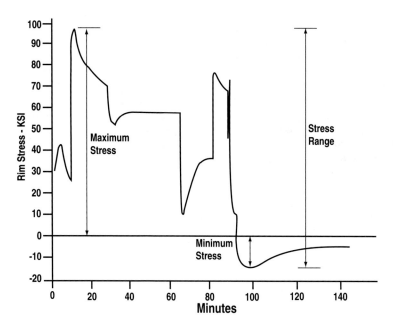

Fig. N.3   Typical turbine rim transient stress analysis.

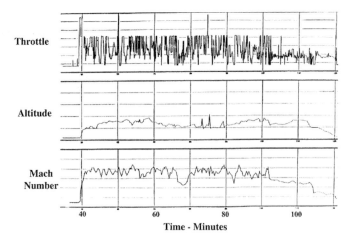

Fig. N.4 Typical F-16 flight recorder data.

and/or manufacturing flaws or damage (knicks, voids, tears, laps, burrs, etc.) can progress to failure. It assumes that damage, in the form of a crack of minimum detectable size, is present at all locations and should not grow to critical size in two inspection intervals for the intended usage.

N.2.3.2 Fracture critical components. Fracture critical components are those whose failure would result in loss of the aircraft, and for single-engine aircraft, prevention of sustained flight. This includes all major rotating structures such as disks, shafts, and rotating seals. For single-engine applications this also includes blades, bearings, and critical external accessories. Damage tolerance requirements are applied only to fracture critical components and not, in general, to durability critical components.

N.2.3.3 Durability critical components. These are components whose cracking or failure could cause significant engine structural damage or performance/reliability/maintainability problems.

N.2.3.4 Hot parts. Hot parts are those parts in the hot gas stream. Usually the life requirement is one-half that of cold parts life.

N.2.3.5 Cold parts. Cold parts are all parts not in the hot gas stream. This includes turbine disks, spacers, etc. Usually the life requirement is the same as that required for the aircraft system in which the engine is to be used.

N.2.3.6 Initial flaw size. Initial flaws are assumed to exist in fracture critical components. Experience has shown that premature cracking occurs at high stressed areas, and initial flaw conditions have included both material and manufacturing related quality variations. Damage tolerance uses a sharp crack initial flaw assumption to characterize these abnormal initial conditions. Assumed initial embedded flaw sizes are based on the intrinsic material defect distribution or the nondestructive evaluation (NDE) methods to be used during manufacture. An inspection reliability of 90% probability of detection (POD) at the lower bound 95%

confidence level (CL) is required for the assumed initial flaw sizes. The basis for these flaw sizes is the data on the various nondestructive evaluation methods.[1]

N.2.3.7   Residual strength.   Residual strength is defined as the load carrying capability of a component at any time during service exposure period considering the presence of damage and accounting for the growth of damage as a function of exposure time. The requirement is to provide limit load or maximum expected service load residual strength capability throughout the service life of the component. One example of this is normal or expected overspeed caused by control system tolerance.

N.2.3.8   Inspection interval.   The inspection interval for damage tolerance considerations should be compatible with the overall engine maintenance plan. It is highly desirable that the inspection interval be equal to the hot part design service life as this is the expected minimum maintenance interval for the engine or module. The damage tolerance inspection interval should be contained in the contract specification or RFP.

N.2.3.9   Flight data recorder.   An in-flight recorder records usage time history of aircraft and engine, is used to sample usage, and is not required on every aircraft.

N.2.3.10   Engine life monitor.   This monitor is an in-flight counter that tracks certain engine parameters for life purposes and is required on every engine.

N.2.3.11   Creep.   Creep is permanent deformation that occurs as the result of the prolonged application of stress. The applied stress is below a level that would be expected to cause plastic deformation. Creep occurs at temperatures that are high relative to the melting point of the metal.

N.2.3.12   Low cycle fatigue (LCF).   LCF is damage that is related to stress cycles that lead to component failure in less than 10,000 cycles.

N.2.3.13   High cycle fatigue (HCF).   HCF is damage that is related to stress cycles that lead to component failure in more than one million cycles, caused primarily by vibration.

N.2.3.14   Stress rupture.   Rupture is failure when a component has been statically loaded at elevated temperature for a long period.

N.2.3.15   Laser shock peening (LSP).   LSP is a new process for using compressive residual stress to desensitize airfoil leading edges to foreign object damage (FOD). This process is available and is in production on some military engines. The process is so effective that retired blades have had leading edges laser shock peened and severely damaged, simulating FOD in a critical area, and when tested have shown remarkable high cycle fatigue strength and life that was even higher than new undamaged blades. The process uses a high-energy pulsed split laser beam to create a high amplitude shock wave on both sides of the blade or vane simultaneously, as shown in Fig. N.5.

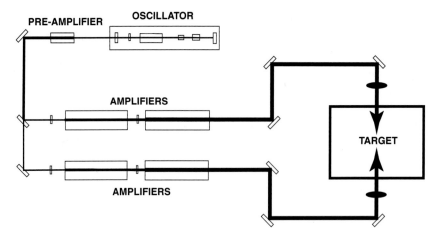

Fig. N.5   Pulsed laser beam used in peening.

Figure N.6 shows the airfoil with ablative material on the area to be laser shock peened with a water curtain flowing over the area to be processed. The laser is focused on the blade surface and when fired passes through the water and quickly vaporizes the ablative material. The rapid vaporization of the ablative material is contained by the water curtain and causes a large spike in pressure, which drives a shock wave into the host material. Yielding of the material occurs on both sides of the airfoil, and deep residual compressive stresses are formed in the spot by the reactive response of the elastic material that surrounds the laser spot.

N.2.3.16   Crack initiation life.   Crack initiation life is used in fatigue analysis to establish a component life based on the attainment of a 0.030-in. crack length used in safe life analysis.

N.2.3.17   Crack propagation life.   This is the cyclic life of a component where a crack from an initial flaw size (usually determined by NDE) grows to a critical size and failure occurs.[2]

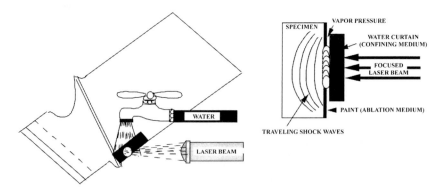

Fig. N.6   Airfoil with ablative material in laser shock peening.

N.3   Engine Failure Modes

Each component of the engine can react differently, from a life standpoint, to the duty cycle to which the engine is subjected. For example, turbine blades and vanes can be critical in creep or stress rupture if the usage requires long periods of time at maximum power. On the other hand, a large number of throttle transients in this duty cycle can alter the failure mode of the same turbine blade and vanes to that of LCF. Because of this sensitivity, engine usage must be monitored for significant changes relative to that assumed for design. Table N.1 shows the failure modes for various components in the engine for typical usage.

N.4   Lifing Concepts

Lifing concepts have evolved and improved since the early period of the gas turbine engine. Early on, passing a 150-h test was the main "pass or fail" criteria used to qualify a new engine design to enter production and service. Engine life development and life prediction techniques evolved mostly in response to durability problems, customer demands, and/or regulatory involvement. The safe life (see Fig. N.7) and damage tolerance concepts have been the two most widely used design methods for producing components to meet life requirements. More recently, however, the combination of both life concepts, as shown in Fig. N.8, is the preferred lifing method for both commercial and military and is required by the military in their engine structural development programs.

N.4.1   Safe Life Criterion

The safe life fatigue design approach is shown in Fig. N.7. Components are designed so that the LCF limit exceeds the required usage interval. The life limit is usually based on minimum or minus 3-sigma value of the material life property curve for crack initiation. The main concern with this safe life concept is that there is no recognition or provision for what effect initial defects can have on component life such as machining errors, burrs, nicks, etc.

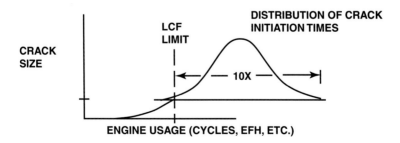

CRITERIA: LOW CYCLE FATIGUE (LCF) LIMIT BASED ON LOWER BOUND
(-3σ OR 1/1000) DISTRIBUTION OF CRACK INITIATION TIME
ACTION: 100% PART REPLACEMENT AT LCF LIMIT

Fig. N.7   Safe life fatigue design.

Table N.1 Failure modes for various turbine components

Engine section	Component	HCF	LCF	Creep	Erosion	Fretting[a]	TMF[b]	Oxidation[c]	Overload	Buckling	Over temp	Wear	Corrosion[d]
Fan and compressor	Blades	X	X	X	X	X	—	—	—	—	—	—	—
	Vanes	X	—	—	X	X	—	—	—	—	—	—	X
	Disks	X	X	X	X	X	X	—	X	—	X	X	—
	Spacers	X	X	X	X	X	X	—	X	—	X	X	—
	Seal teeth	—	X	X	X	X	—	—	—	—	X	X	—
	Shafts	—	X	X	—	X	X	—	X	—	X	X	X
High and low turbine	Blades	X	X	X	X	X	X	X	X	—	X	X	—
	Nozzles	X	—	X	X	—	X	X	—	X	X	X	—
	Disks	X	X	X	—	X	X	—	X	—	X	X	—
	Spacers	X	X	X	X	X	X	X	X	—	X	X	—
	Seal teeth	X	X	—	X	X	X	X	X	X	X	X	—
Cases		X	—	—	—	X	—	—	X	X	X	X	—
Mounts		X	—	—	—	X	—	—	X	—	—	X	X
Nozzles		X	—	X	X	X	X	X	X	X	X	X	—
Combustors	Liners	X	—	X	X	X	X	X	—	X	X	X	—
Frames		X	X	X	X	X	X	—	X	X	X	X	X

[a]Fretting: Material damage from minute movements between two contacting materials.
[b]TMF: Thermomechanical fatigue.
[c]Oxidation: Affects high temperature fatigue, creep and crack propagation rates. Can adversly affect material grain boundaries.
[d]Corrosion: Material interaction with air, water, salt water and hot gases and stresses.

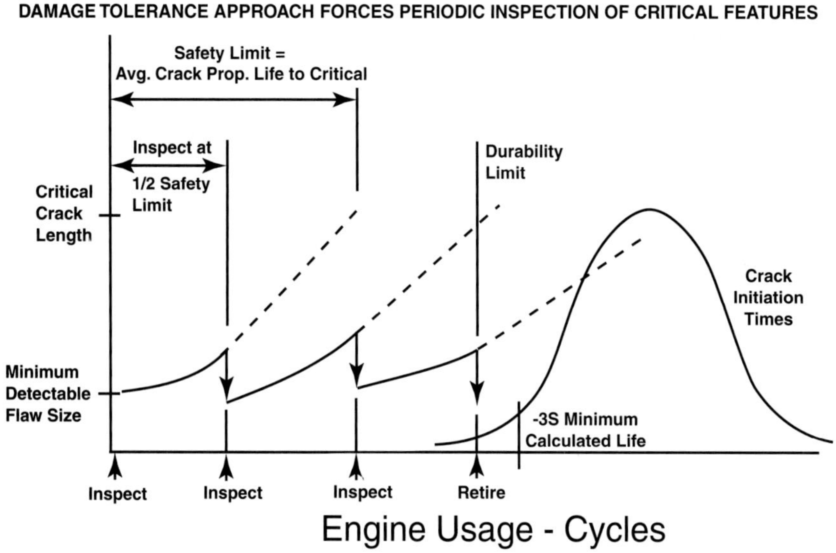

DAMAGE TOLERANCE APPROACH FORCES PERIODIC INSPECTION OF CRITICAL FEATURES

Fig. N.8   Damage tolerance plus safe life.

Implementation of this life philosophy requires that all like components be removed from service upon reaching the minimum life even though, with fatigue life scatter what it is, the component may have 10 times more life remaining. Safe life philosophy[3] is strongly driven by the premise that the material and finished components are free of any defects.

N.4.2   Safe Life Plus Damage Tolerance

The purpose for using damage tolerance with the safe life concept, as shown in Fig. N.8, is to economically provide maximum product safety through regulated focused inspections on critical points of critical parts. It is a safety feature designated to provide protection from numerous uncertainties or rogue flaws that can exist, that is, LCF generated, intrinsic, or induced (handling, machining, etc.) flaws, and for material imbedded flaws. When using damage tolerance in design, components are designed for crack growth using average crack growth material data so that the safety limit exceeds two times the required inspection interval.

Successful application of damage tolerance-based procedures depends on supporting technologies. These technologies include nondestructive inspections, mechanical testing of coupons and components, structural analysis based on a verified thermal environment and gradients, mission profile analysis, and cyclic tracking of components. Extensive material testing at room and elevated temperatures must be performed to obtain crack growth rate data.

The damage tolerance requirement only applies to fracture critical parts and will usually impact component design in the manner as shown in Fig. N.9.

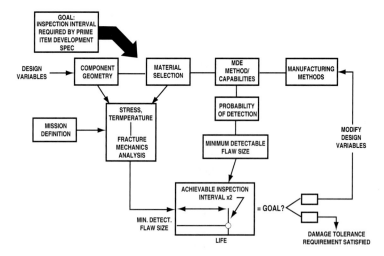

Fig. N.9   Damage tolerance requirement impacts component design.

N.4.3   Retirement-for-Cause

Damage tolerance is used to its fullest extent when the retirement-for-cause (RFC) lifing concept is employed. As shown in Fig. N.10, disks designed to safe life philosophy are typically retired at the time where one disk in 1000 could be expected to have initiated a 0.030-in. fatigue crack. By definition then, 99.9% of the retired disks still have useful life remaining at the time they are removed from service.

Under the retirement-for-cause concept, each of these disks could be inspected and returned to service. The return to service interval is determined by a fracture mechanics calculation of remaining propagation life from the largest crack that

Retirement-for-cause

- **BASED ON CONCEPT THAT RETIRING COMPONENTS AT -3S INITIATION LIFE WASTE SUBSTANTIAL LIFE FOR, SIMPLISTICALL, "999 OUT OF 1000" PARTS**

- **APPROACH CALLS FOR**

    - INSPECTION AT 1/2 AVERAGE CRACK PROPAGATION LIFE

    - OPERATION OF PART UNTIL CRACK IS DETECTED

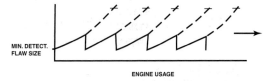

Fig. N.10   Retirement–for-cause applied to disk failure.

could have been missed during inspection. This procedure could be repeated until the disk has incurred measurable damage, at which time it is retired for a cause. Retirement-for-cause, then, is a methodology under which an engine disk would be retired from service when it had incurred quantifiable damage, rather than because an analytically determined minimum design life had been exceeded. Its purpose is not to extend the life of the rotor disk, but to use safely the full life capacity inherent in each part. In many cases, the decision as to whether or not RFC can be applied to a component will be predicated upon the ability of available NDE approaches to detect the initial flaw with sufficient sensitivity and reliability.

N.5   Inspection and PODs

The concept of damage tolerance is strongly based on the ability of fracture mechanics analysis to predict crack growth life with reasonable accuracy coupled with the capability of NDE to reliably find defects. The capability of NDE to reliably find defects is quantified through test data to determine the flaw size defined by a POD of 90% with a CL of 95%. The generation of these data is accomplished for each NDE technique (dye penetrant, eddy-current, ultrasonic, etc.). The technique for generating surface cracks in specimens, with and without original cracks, to be inspected to obtain data is shown in Fig. N.11. The specimens, with and without cracks, are then inspected by trained inspectors, and the hit/missed data are gathered. The estimated POD and CL are determined statistically and plotted, as shown in Figs. N.12 and N.13. Comparison of mean crack detection capabilities of several NDE methods for Titanium 6Al-4V materials is shown in Fig. N.14.

N.5.1   Fluorescent Penetrant Inspection

Liquid penetrant inspection is used to detect small discontinuities that cannot be easily found during simple visual inspection. The method depends on the ability of a highly penetrating liquid to seep, through capillary action, into any discontinuity in the material to which it is applied. It can only be used to detect surface defects and subsurface defects that are open to the surface. There are six critical steps in the penetrant inspection of a part:

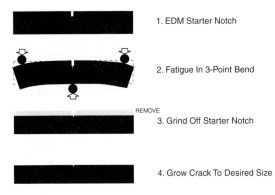

1. EDM Starter Notch

2. Fatigue In 3-Point Bend

REMOVE
3. Grind Off Starter Notch

4. Grow Crack To Desired Size

Fig. N.11   Fatigue crack generation.

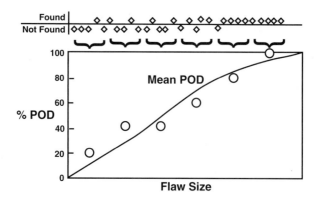

Fig. N.12   Basis for estimating probability of detection.

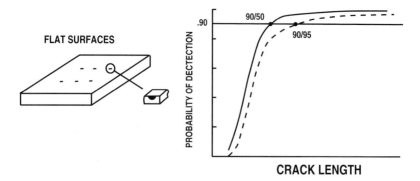

Fig. N.13   Quantified nondestructive evaluation.

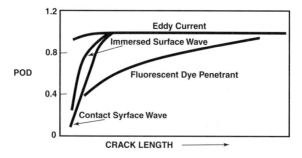

Fig. N.14   Crack detection in titanium 6Al-4V.

1) *Surface preparation*: The part surface must be cleaned of all contaminants (such as rust, scale, oil, paint, plating, etc.) to ensure that any defect is open to the surface of the bare material.

2) *Penetrant application*: A properly selected fluorescent or nonfluorescent penetrant is applied either over the entire part or extending at least 1 in. around a particular area to be investigated.

3) *Removal of excess penetrant*: Excess penetrant is removed to minimize the possibility of false indications.

4) *Developer application*: The developer acts like a blotter and draws the penetrant out of any discontinuity and brings it to the surface. It also spreads out and amplifies the penetrant to make it more readily seen. Because the penetrant is diffused on the surface, the indication will be larger than the real discontinuity.

5) *Inspection*: A true indication occurs when penetrant bleeds back to the surface from a discontinuity.

6) *Post-test cleaning*: Remove residual developer and penetrant for return to service or additional inspection.

N.5.2 Eddy Current Inspection

Eddy current inspection is used to interrogate surface and/or near-surface material for discontinuities in the form of defects or cracks. This method is dependent on the electrical conductivity of the material to be inspected. When electrically conductive material is exposed to an alternating magnetic field that is generated by a coil of wire (transducer) carrying an alternating current, eddy currents are induced on the material surface or in the near-surface material (see Fig. N.15). The effect of eddy currents, generating magnetic fields that interact with the magnetic fields of the transducer to change its electrical impedance, can be measured. These measured changes in the impedance of the transducer can be used to detect surface or near-surface discontinuities that affect the current carrying properties of the test material.

Eddy current inspection has several advantages and disadvantages. The advantages of eddy current are that it 1) can detect both surface and subsurface discontinuities; 2) can be used on ferrous and nonferrous material; 3) is more versatile

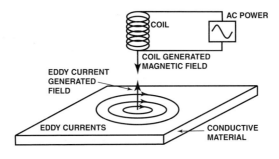

Induced Eddy Currents on Conductive Material

Fig. N.15   Eddy current inspection.

than fluorescent penetrant inspection methods; 4) has adjustable sensitivity, and 5) is portable.

The disadvantages are as follows: 1) the applications are limited to electrically conductive material, 2) they require reference standards and specific operator training, and 3) there is difficulty in some cases in interpreting results.

Very little part preparation is needed for eddy current inspection. The surface of the area to be inspected may need to be cleaned or otherwise exposed so that the eddy current probe has adequate access. The inspection is accomplished in real time, where the probe-sensed variations in impedance are displayed on a meter or computer screen. This allows the inspector to reinspect to confirm the presence of an indication prior to further interpretation.

Eddy current inspection has become a highly reliable method for detecting surface and near-surface defects, and has been used to enhance other surface inspection methods (visual and fluorescent penetrants) in evaluating the presence of defects, or for inspecting areas where visual observation is impracticable. To maintain high reliability in detecting defects, particular care must be taken in the setup of the eddy current system and in the interpretation of displayed signals. It is therefore necessary to ensure that the inspector is properly trained to operate an eddy current system.

N.5.3 Ultrasonic Inspection

Ultrasonic inspection applications include 1) thickness checks, 2) billet inspection for internal defects, 3) forging inspection for internal defects, 4) weld examination, 5) surface defects on blades and engine-run hardware, and 6) composite inspection for delaminations and porosity.

The basis for ultrasonic inspection is the detection of reflected or absorption of acoustic energy. It records amplitude and distance to echo and can be used to find surface and subsurface defects.

High-frequency mechanical vibrations are introduced to the part through a coupling medium, and energy reflected is detected and displayed on a computer screen. Figure N.16 shows ultrasonic signal displays using unfiltered signals as well as the type of signal that is caused by the use of coarse grain material.

N.6 Engine Structural Development Plan

A typical layout of a structural development plan required by the U.S. Air Force Engine Structural Integrity Program (ENSIP[4]) that is included in a military RFP is shown in Fig. N.17. ENSIP is an organized and disciplined approach to the structural design, analysis, development, production, and life management of gas turbine engines. The goal is to ensure engine structural safety, increase service readiness, and reduce life cycle costs through reducing the occurrence of structural durability problems during service operations. The plan would require the type of detail as stated in the following subsections.

N.6.1 TASK I—Design Information

N.6.1.1 Master plan. The contractor shall prepare a time-phased plan for the accomplishment of the required tasks.

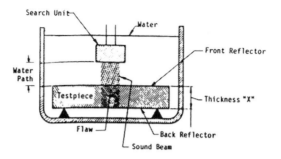

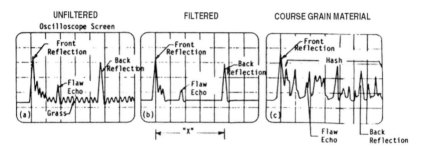

Fig. N.16   Ultrasonic signal analysis.

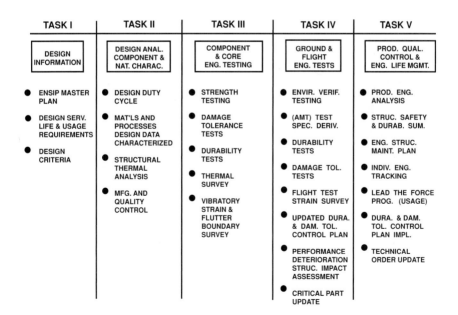

Fig. N.17   Engine structural development plan.

N.6.1.2   Design service life and usage requirement

The design service life.   Cold parts shall be designed to a service life equal to that specified by the customer or of the intended airframe. Estimated test cell and installed ground run time shall be included in the designed life. Hot parts shall be designed to a service life equal to $\frac{1}{2}$ the cold part life.

Usage.   The design usage in terms of mission profiles and mission mix shall be that used in the design of the aircraft. The mission profiles and mission mix shall be supplied by the customer and shall include, as a minimum, estimates of the number of major throttle transients, time at/or above intermediate power settings, number and type of A/B lights, and run time.

N.6.1.3   Design criteria.   Key criteria for safety, durability, maintainability, compatibility, quality, diagnostic, materials, and processes are given in the following:

1) *Safety*: Damage tolerance criteria shall be used for critical parts whose failure would a) result in direct loss of aircraft or b) result in engine power loss preventing sustained flight either by direct part failure or by causing other progressive part failure.

2) *Fracture critical parts*: Design for "slow crack growth" from maximum nondetectable flaw size to critical in two depot inspection periods or two design lifetimes if the part is not inspected at depot.

3) *Field level inspectable parts*: It shall be shown by analysis and test (or test only where analysis is not feasible) that maximum undetectable damage, using the field inspection procedure, shall not grow to critical size in two field inspection intervals.

4) *Durability*: The economic life of the engine structural components shall exceed the design service life. Average engine performance margins and performance deterioration shall be considered in the engine design.

5) *Maintainability*: a) Old parts shall fit and function with new parts; b) depot level repairs shall have a demonstrated life of at least two inspection periods; c) the engine and its components shall be designed for inspectability; and d) structural diagnostics shall be designed into and developed with the engine.

6) *Engine/airframe compatibility*: The engine/airframe shall be compatible from a strength and dynamic standpoint.

7) *Damage tolerance and durability control plans*: These will control the quality of the delivered engine critical parts.

8) *Structural diagnostics*: Diagnostics shall be used in the development program to protect the development engine as well as to build a diagnostic database for production engines.

a) Internal diagnostic sensors shall be designed for external installation and removal from the engine where possible.

b) Structural diagnostic sensors shall include but not be limited to bearing-mounted accelerometers and turbine blade optical pyrometers.

9) *Instrumentation system*: The engine shall be designed to accommodate the development instrumentation system (for example, telemetry).

10) *Materials and process characterization plan*: A comprehensive materials and process characterization plan will be required and contain minimum data requirements and quantity for each engine development.

N.6.2   TASK II—Design Analysis, Component and Material Characterization

N.6.2.1   Design duty cycle.   From the mission profiles, mission mix, and throttle data supplied by the customer, the contractor is to derive a design duty cycle. A sensitivity analysis on engine life shall be prepared on usage variables.

N.6.2.2   Materials and process design data characterized.   Final design data shall consider the full-scale material heats, the correlation of material data with that from the "as produced part," and the effect of special processes on final design properties.

N.6.2.3   Structural/thermal analysis.

1) *Thermal environment*: The thermal environment for steady-state and transient conditions will be analytically determined on major components for key points in the flight envelope. Sensitivity analyses will identify critical cooling circuit leakage points affecting major structural component temperatures.

2) *Component stress/environment spectra*: For each major structural component, a plot of stress and temperature vs time for the design duty cycle shall be developed. Effects of performance deterioration, shutdown, and cooldown shall be included.

3) *Strength analysis*: The engine structure (static and rotating) shall be shown to withstand ultimate internal and external acceptable critical clearances under limit load conditions. Ultimate stress = 1.5 × limit stress except for internally pressurized cases, which shall be 2.0 × max operating stress.

4) *Vibration/flutter analysis*: An analytical dynamic model of the engine and accessories will be used to identify critical system modes, potential forcing functions, resonance, and instability conditions including flutter. Detailed analysis augmented by bench testing shall be made to determine component vibrational mode shapes and frequencies.

5) *Damage tolerance analysis*: This analysis shall protect the safety-of-flight engine structure from deleterious effects of material, manufacturing, and processing defects, through proper material selection and control, control of stress levels, use of fracture-resistant design concepts, manufacturing and process controls, and the use of careful inspection procedures.

Initial flaw or defect sizes that shall be used in these damage tolerance analyses (or tests) shall be established by the contractor based on the results of an evaluation of nondestructive inspection (NDI) capabilities and recognizing the probability of flaw occurrence associated with the specific material and manufacturing processes used. These initial sizes shall be subject to customer approval.

6) *Durability analysis*: The analysis shall ensure that the specified economic life of the engine is attained through addressing the major failure modes of the engines, that is, low-cycle fatigue, high-cycle fatigue, stress rupture, protective coating strain compatibility, creep, salt stress corrosion, etc., when used to the approved designed duty cycle.

7) *Critical parts list*: Each of the safety and durability critical components (and specified critical locations on components) as identified by analysis and/or previous experience shall be listed and categorized with regard to degree of criticality.

8) *Safety fault analysis*: A fault analysis shall be performed to assess the consequences and probability of occurrence of the engine system (for example, oil system, fuel system, control system, etc.) malfunctions on engine structural safety and durability. As a minimum, the following items shall be included: a) oil fire assessment, b) control system malfunctions, c) fuel system malfunctions, d) rotor hot gas inflow margins and sensitivities, e) combustor pattern factor and radial profile variations, f) A/B transient effect on rotor speed, g) low-pressure power turbine shaft failure and consequences, h) HPT nozzle burnout and consequences, and i) titanium fire risk.

9) *Field inspectability analysis*: All parts designed as "field inspectable" per the criteria specified under "Design Criteria" shall be readily inspectable without engine disassembly. For example, a sufficient number of boroscope points shall be designed into the engine.

The capability and limitations of the field inspection equipment (for example, boroscope, visual, penetrant, etc.) shall be established.

10) *Structural diagnostic analysis*: Sensor durability limits will be established, and a built-in test for functionality will be developed.

N.6.2.4 Manufacturing and quality control.

A manufacturing and quality plan shall be prepared showing concepts and procedures. A NDI evaluation and demonstration for field depot and factory use shall be conducted to verify design flaw sizes for damage tolerance analysis.

N.6.3 TASK III—Component and Core Engine Testing

N.6.3.1 Strength testing.

All major structural components (static and rotating) shall be tested to design ultimate strength (for example, design burst speed for bladed disks) with deflections ensured at design limit load. Correlation with analysis shall be accomplished.

N.6.3.2 Damage tolerance tests.

Safety critical parts shall be preflawed and tested as components in rigs and/or spin pits and correlated with analysis prior to any full-scale damage tolerance engine testing.

N.6.3.3 Durability tests.

Component life testing (for example, low-cycle fatigue tests) will be conducted to failure or as a minimum to two design service lives.

N.6.3.4 Thermal survey.

From core engine tests, steady-state and transient temperature profiles shall be determined for critical structural parts. Measured data shall be altered by analysis for full-scale engine conditions and for critical points in the flight envelope. The probable variation in radial profiles and pattern factor between combustors and component temperatures as a function of combustion system variability shall be established.

N.6.3.5 Vibration strain and flutter boundary survey.

Vibration data and flutter boundary investigation will be conducted on the core engine under ram conditions with simulated fan distortion.

N.6.4 TASK IV—Ground and Flight Tests

N.6.4.1 Environmental verification testing

1) *Thermal survey*: An instrumented engine shall determine the steady state and transient temperature profiles for critical parts to correlate with thermal analysis.

2) *Ground vibration strain and flutter verification survey*: An instrumented engine will measure vibratory stress at all critical points in the flight envelope with aircraft simulated inlet distortion in an altitude/ram facility with nominal and off-nominal IGV schedules to ensure sufficient vibratory stress margins. Flutter boundary exploration shall be conducted.

3) *Rotor dynamic survey*: A full-scale engine rotor dynamic test shall be conducted on an instrumented engine with deliberate rotor unbalance. Bowed rotor characteristics with clocked rotor out-of-balance shall be investigated.

4) *Installed vibrations survey*: An installed engine vibration survey shall be conducted to ensure dynamic compatibility between the engine, its accessories, and the airframe. The engine should have each rotor unbalanced to the maximum allowable limit for this test.

5) *External component resonance search test*: A vibration survey shall be conducted on all externally mounted components to identify resonance frequencies. Resonance shall not occur at operating speeds.

6) *Clearance control*: Critical clearances (blade tip clearances and seal clearances) shall be understood through the following test programs: a) high-energy X-ray (HEX) testing, b) installed engine/nacelle thermal survey, c) flight test data from clearance indicators, and d) optimized final green run cycle.

7) *Individual engine vibration characteristics database*: All development engines shall have their vibration signatures characterized. Engine acceptance bands shall be derived from this data.

N.6.4.2 Accelerated Mission Test spectrum derivation. Accelerated Mission Tests (AMT) shall be derived initially based on design mission profiles and mix and continually updated based on real usage from the usage program in Task V (lead the fleet with flight recorder data). When it is necessary, altitude and/or ram testing shall be included. (See Sec. N.7.2 for definition of AMT.)

N.6.4.3 Durability tests

1) *Flight readiness verification tests* (to be completed before first flight): a) overspeed and overtemperature test; b) resonance search and installed vibration survey; and c) a limited AMT test to verify engine durability for the length of the planned flight test program plus incremental running.

2) *Product verification AMT*: Product verification (PV) engine run to one lifetime prior to production release.

3) *Production AMT #1*: Test hard-tooled B/M engine to one lifetime using design mission usage spectra.

4) *Production AMT #2*: Test hard-tooled B/M engine to a minimum of one lifetime with spectra updated to real usage obtained from flight recorder data.

5) *Overhauled engine AMT*: Test random overhauled engine to remaining lifeline.

N.6.4.4 Damage tolerance tests. An instrumented PV configured engine shall be employed for damage tolerance tests of safety critical structure:

1) Critical parts will be preflawed at those critical points judged by analysis and prior component tests to be critical and using the AMT test spectrum shall be tested to one inspection period. Flaw growth will be monitored, fractographically examined subsequent to testing, and correlated with the damage tolerance analysis component tests.

2) FOD, ingestion, and containment tests will be tested to demonstrated compliance with design criteria.

3) All repairs will be tested by AMT methods to two inspection periods.

N.6.4.5 Flight test strain survey. Selected engine components known to be sensitive to installation-induced vibratory stresses (for example, the fan) shall be instrumented, and data shall be taken for ground and flight operational loading conditions, such as gunfire or rocket exhaust gas ingestion, thrust reverse reingestion, cross wind, and high angle of attack.

N.6.4.6 Update durability and damage tolerance control plan. The results of Task III and IV shall be used to update.

N.6.4.7 Performance deterioration, structural impact assessment. One of the most undesirable effects of deterioration is that combustion temperatures must be increased in order to maintain engine thrust, thus reducing hot section parts life.

N.6.4.8 Critical part update.

N.6.5 TASK V—Production Quality Control and Engine Life Management

N.6.5.1 Production engine analysis. The Task II analysis shall be updated to account for redesign components, changes in usage, material properties, and results of TASK III and IV tests. The updated analysis shall form the basis for preparation of the engine structural maintenance plan.

N.6.5.2 A summary report on safety and durability shall be prepared.

N.6.5.3 Engine structural maintenance plan. The structural maintenance plan shall include the inspection requirements for critical parts for both field and depot. Critical part safety and economic life limits shall be supplied for use with the individual engine tracking system. Diagnostic logic and procedures shall be supplied.

N.6.5.4 Individual engine tracking. Damaging events such as significant power transients and time at and above intermediate power levels will be recorded with exceedance-type counters so that inspection and part replacement can be accomplished to preclude structural failures. Critical parts shall be serialized for tracking purposes.

N.6.5.5   Lead the force program (usage).   A "lead the force program" shall be implemented and will provide early maintenance and operational usage data. Usage data shall be recorded on the Service Loads Monitoring Program (SLMP) recorder and shall include at least N1, N2, PLA, T2, and T4 vs time. These data will be used to update analysis and AMT tests.

N.6.5.6   Durability and damage tolerance control plan implementation. The updated durability and damage tolerance control plan shall be implemented on the production program.

N.6.5.7   Technical order update.   Technical orders are the principal means by which changes in logistic and maintenance procedures are implemented in the field. They are essential to solving field problems and improving availability and life.

N.7   Development and Qualification Testing

N.7.1   Historical Perspective—The 150-H Test

From 1950 to 1970 turbine engine structural life qualification/verification was mostly based on engine running tests that involved a 150-h formal qualification test that was, in turn, the legacy of the qualification testing of piston engines. This test, shown in Fig. N.18, was not mission oriented but did put emphasis on the engine hot section by having appreciable time at high power settings to ferret out high temperature-induced creep and stress rupture failure modes. Some partial throttle transients were included but were far too few to drive a low-cycle fatigue-type of failure mode in either the compressor or turbine sections of the engine. Throttle stair steps were added to incite possible high cycle fatigue weakness, but have proven inadequate. The major throttle cycle of "zero to max/mil power to

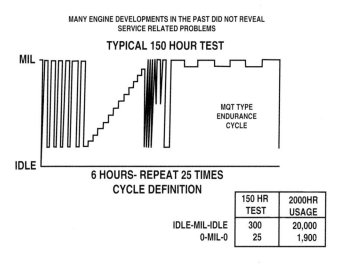

Fig. N.18   Typical 150-h qualification test spectrum.

zero" with some cooldown, which is prevalent in every mission, does contribute substantially to engine low-cycle fatigue damage and was virtually missing. Also shown in Fig. N.18 is a block showing a comparison between the qualification test and the throttle usage of a typical modern fighter for 2000 flight hours.

Recognizing the shortcomings of the formal 150-h test requirement contained in the coordinated Tri-Service Mil Spec 5007C (contains military requirements for development of new turbine engines) written in 1966, the military revised the specification to include additional structural component and engine tests in 1974. This revision was Mil Spec 5007D (Ref. 5), which still retained the 150-h qualification test but also added an engine running mission related low-cycle fatigue test requirement. In addition, this revision also contained a structural program that required structural analysis and component testing along with a usage and tracking system and contained many elements of the early ENSIP Program. This revision, however, did not contain damage tolerance requirements. It was not until 1984 that damage tolerance requirements were introduced through ENSIP (Engine Structural Integrity Program) in the Military Standard 1783. The mission-related test is now known as the AMT, which is a formal engine qualification/verification test to demonstrate full design engine life prior to full scale production.

N.7.2 AMT (Military)

The AMT[6] is a mission-related test that has all the nondamaging throttle cycles and power levels, such as idle and cruise, removed from the mission flight profile as shown in Fig. N.19. This process uses severity analysis tools as shown in Fig. N.20

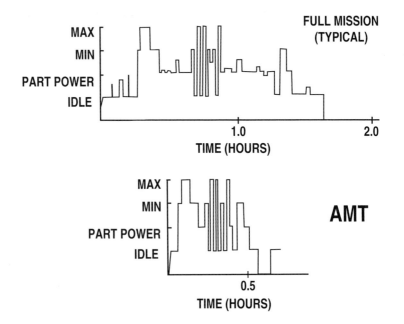

Fig. N.19 Typical AMT for military engine usage.

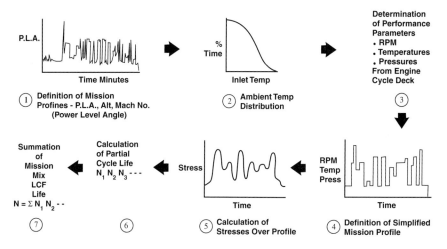

Fig. N.20   Use of severity analysis tools.

in order to reduce the test and calendar time required to reproduce the damage over the life of the engine.

It is possible to balance or adjust the severity of an AMT cycle to better match the most severe mission for each component by adjusting the magnitude of transients and hold time to control thermally induced stresses.[7] This can be done as shown in Fig. N.21 by adjusting hold time at maximum power, or if total time at maximum power needs to be maintained, by altering hold time at idle or subidle.

Certain qualification tests may require the use of ground facilities for running conditions to better simulate the flight envelope, such as duplicating high

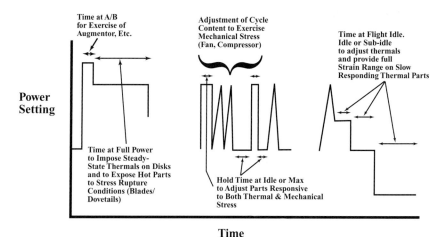

Fig. N.21   Test cycle design.

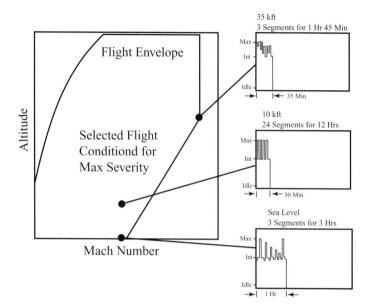

Fig. N.22   Low altitude high speed ram tests.

Mach number at altitude or low-altitude, high-speed ram tests as depicted in Fig. N.22.

The RFP typically may require a series of AMT tests such as Mil Standard 1783 that involve a series of formal tests for flight clearance release points such as the IFR, FFR, ISR, and OCR shown and defined in Fig. N.23.

Component structural special engine testing has also become a formal qualification requirement. The following verification tests and measurements are examples: 1) turbine and compressor over-speed engine running tests usually to 115%; 2) disk bust testing to a minimum of 122% of the maximum allowable steady-state speed; 3) overtemperature of the first stage turbine rotor by 81°F and engine static load tests; 4) low-cycle fatigue and crack testing of critical engine components including high-pressure cases, engine mounts, and spin pit testing of rotors and correlated with analysis; and 5) engine AMT testing is usually accompanied by HCF stair-step tests up and down.

A fighter engine typical AMT structural verification ground test is shown in Fig. N.24. The mission mix is usually dictated by the customer or derived from a usage survey.

N.7.3   1000 Simulated Service Cycle ("C" cycle) Test (Commercial)

Figure N.25 shows an example of two "C" type cycles used as a verification test for engine integrity and reliability that must be passed for commercial engine certification. This test cycle is tailored to fit the expected usage such as time at takeoff,

ENSIP Durability Requirement

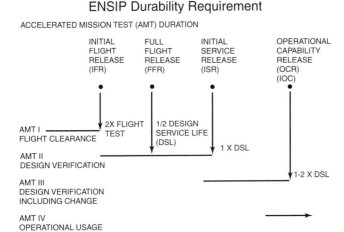

Fig. N.23   Mil Standard 1783 formal test.

reverser throttle transient power levels expected, and cooldown times. A minimum of 1000 cycles is to be generated prior to certification, and in many cases, many more cycles are generated prior to initiation of revenue service. Additional tests are also required for certification such as blade out, blade containment, overtemperature and rotor overspeed tests, bird ingestion tests, and rotor burst speed component tests.

N.8   Summary

The current turbine engine lifing process has evolved over the past 50 years with many of the factors that control life changing based on lessons learned from the engine development programs and customer field problems. Some of the changes were driven by state-of-the-art improvements such as finite element modeling, improved material, engine controls, testing techniques, manufacturing, inspection capability, surface treatments, usage monitoring, and tracking systems. Life management techniques and philosophies have changed, as well, with recent changes involving the addition of damage tolerance lifing concepts. Lifing concepts such as the safe life concept combined with damage tolerance requirements are now being employed, which will ensure safety even in the event of a rogue flaw. In addition, engine design development programs now contain improved design criteria and a better understanding of intended usage, thorough understanding of material characteristics, more specimen and component analysis and testing, and comprehensive engine environmental and formal verification testing.

When taken together, these advances have had a very positive effect on our ability to life manage turbine engine components, even in situations that involve complex usage, which will, through better utilization of engine components, allow the customer to see benefits in the cost of ownership, improved service lives,

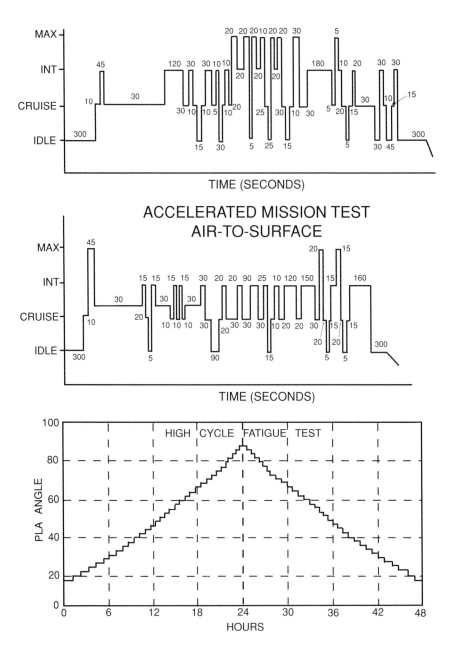

Fig. N.24   Typical accelerated mission test profiles.

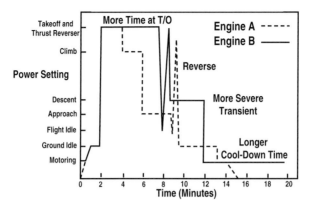

Fig. N.25   Simulated service cycle ("C" cycle).

and on safety. Currently, there is a major, national high-cycle fatigue (HCF) initiative under way that will alter ENSIP so that more emphasis is placed on HCF development.

References

[1]ASM International Handbook Committee, *Metals Handbook*, 9th ed., Vol. 17, Nondestructive Evaluation and Quality Control, ASM International, Metals Park, OH.

[2]Anderson, T. L., "Fracture Mechanics Fundamentals and Applications," CRC Press, Boca Raton, FL, 1991, p. 793.

[3]Miner, M. A., "Cumulative Damage in Fatigue," *Journal of Applied Mechanics*, Vol. 67, 1945, pp. 159–164.

[4]"Engine Structural Integrity Program," U.S. Air Force, MIL-STD-1783, USAF, Wright-Patterson AFB, OH, 30 Nov. 1984.

[5]"Engine, Aircraft, Turbojet and Turbofan," MIL-E-5007D Military Specification, USAF, Wright-Patterson AFB, OH, 15 Oct. 1973.

[6]Taylor, W. R., and Ogg, J. S., "Accelerated Mission Testing of Gas Turbine Engines," AIAA Paper 77-992, 1977.

[7]Turnbull, R. C., "Recent General Electric Engine Development Testing for Improved Service Life," Society of Automotive Engineers, Paper 78-0990, Aerospace Meeting, San Diego, CA, 27–30 Nov. 1978.

Appendix O
Engine Controls

O.1 Control System Requirements

The operation of an aircraft gas turbine engine is certainly complex. It is a mixture of aerodynamic, thermodynamic, chemical, and mechanical processes functioning together as a single unit. The control of these processes can be quite challenging, and the potential for unstable behavior abounds. As an example, consider the operation of the high-pressure compressor, or the fan. In normal operation for these components, the air discharges at a higher pressure. The function can be likened to pushing water uphill—it is forcing the fluid in a direction it does not want to naturally go. The potential for instability exists, and, indeed, it is not uncommon for fan or compressor surges and stalls to occur in operation.

For the purposes of this description of the engine control function, it will be assumed that we are describing the control system for a current state-of-the-art fighter aircraft engine, which is characterized as a low-bypass-ratio, twin-spool, mixed flow, afterburning turbofan engine. The basic principles would also apply to a high-bypass-ratio, nonafterburning engine, as used in a commercial airliner or military transport, as well, with some minor differences.

The primary functions of the engine's control system are to 1) maintain consistent, stable thrust levels; 2) maintain smooth, repeatable performance during transient operation from one requested thrust level to another; 3) maintain stable airflow, internal pressures and temperatures, and rotor speeds within safe operating limits; and 4) avoid stalls and surges, and significant speed, pressure or temperature variations.

In addition to these primary functions, there are secondary functions that the engine control system must perform. These secondary functions include engine startup and shutdown; engine bleed and power extraction; inlet anti-icing; hot gas ingestion protection; and fan and compressor tip-clearance control, among others. These secondary functions will not be described in detail, but it should be noted that they are necessary functions and they can result in significant mechanical complexity.

The first two primary functions of the engine control system focus on maintaining and modulating engine thrust levels. To understand how the engine control system accomplishes these functions, consider the equation for uninstalled engine thrust:

$$F = (\dot{m}_9 V_9 - \dot{m}_0 V_0)/g_c + (P_9 - P_0)A_9 \tag{4.1}$$

The equation contains an element of propulsive force caused by the momentum transfer between the inlet mass flow and the exhaust mass flow and an element of force caused by the pressure differential between the inlet airflow and the exhaust gases acting through the engine exhaust nozzle. An actual measurement of engine thrust in flight is not practical because of the difficulty in directly measuring mass flows within the engine in real time. Consequently, engine thrust levels must be inferred through the known thermodynamic relationships with other measurable parameters within the engine. The regulation of engine thrust through a controller evolved from the discipline of process control, most notably within the chemical industry where chemical processes were difficult to monitor directly. The most practical and repeatable method of "measuring" engine thrust is to relate it to the engine operating line on a fan map (see Fig. O.1a). If the controller is able to regulate the engine's performance to the same corrected mass flow and pressure ratio for a given throttle setting, the engine's thrust will be maintained. It is a fairly simple task to measure the engine's operating condition on a fan or compressor map because the operating environment of the fan is relatively benign. For example,

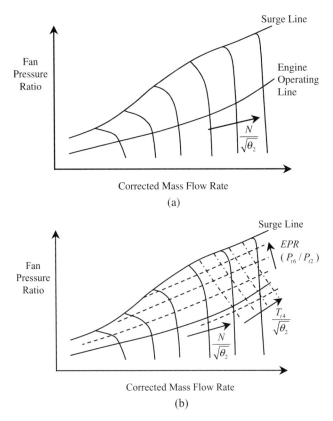

Fig. O.1   Typical fan map and the relationship of engine pressure ratio (*EPR*) and turbine inlet temperature (T_{t4}). a) Typical fan map; b) Relationship of *EPR* and T_{t4}.

mechanical rotor speeds are easily measured by a magnetic pickup located in proximity to a passing gear tooth. The fan rotor speed N_1, corrected for inlet temperature and pressure, correlates very well to engine mass flow. Likewise, a differential pressure measurement within the engine correlates very well with fluid velocities (see Fig. O.1b). As a result, fan rotor speed and engine pressure ratio correlate to the two most significant variables in the equation for uninstalled thrust [Eq. (4.1)]. Hence, reliable thrust setting parameters for the engine control system can be found through the measurements of fan rotor speed N_1 and engine pressure ratio (EPR), and these two parameters can be directly plotted directly on a fan or compressor map. EPR is defined as the tailpipe exhaust pressure P_{t6} divided by engine inlet pressure P_{t2}. This assumption holds under the assumption of choked flow within the turbine, which is the case for most of the engine's normal operation. The exception being for very low-power throttle settings, when the flow in the turbines is not always choked.

This relationship is shown in Fig. O.1b. The engine control system translates the throttle position command from the pilot into a rotor speed command N and an engine pressure ratio (EPR) command as a means of controlling engine thrust levels.

The other primary control functions—maintaining stable airflow, internal pressures, temperatures, and rotor speeds within safe operating limits; and avoiding stalls, surges, and significant speed, pressure or temperature variations—are addressed in a similar manner. In addition to being a good thrust setting parameter, another desirable feature of engine pressure ratio is that lines of constant engine pressure ratio are roughly parallel to the fan stall line. Therefore, using engine pressure ratio as a thrust control variable offers the additional benefit of providing adequate stability margin for the engine. Figure O.1b also shows how values of constant turbine inlet temperature T_{t4} relate to fan inlet corrected airflow and fan pressure ratio. Therefore, using these two parameters in the engine control also offers a means of overtemperature protection.

Of course, corrected fan rotor speed and engine pressure ratio are not the only variables that correlate well to engine thrust. Over the years, many other measured variables have been used as thrust setting parameters. Some other steady-state control modes that have been used are shown in Table O.1. Early control modes

Table O.1   Common engine control modes

Regulated variables	Effectors	Comments
Fan rotor speed—$N1$ Core rotor speed—$N2$	Exhaust area Fuel flow	Requires field trim because of performance shift caused by degradation.
Fan rotor speed—$N1$ EPR—P_{t6}/P_{t2}	Fuel flow Exhaust area	No trim is required; EPR is proportional to fan discharge pressure (for constant bypass ratio).
Fan rotor speed—$N1$ Fan exit Mach no.—$\Delta P/P_{t2}$	Fuel flow Exhaust area	No trim is required; variable cycle engines (variable bypass ratio) require a direct fan measurement of fan exit Mach number.

used the fan and compressor rotor speeds to set engine thrust. Blade tip clearances will expand as a result of bending and flexing of the engine shafts during flight maneuvers, and other wear encountered during normal flight operation will cause the engine's performance to degrade. As a result, using rotor speeds as the control variables will result in a loss of thrust. Periodically, the engine controls would have to be "trimmed" by the maintenance personnel to account for this loss of performance. For high performance fighters, the frequency of these maintenance actions became unbearable. For bomber and transport aircraft these maintenance actions were not as frequent and, therefore, were more tolerable. This lead to the need to develop so-called "trimless" control modes, where engine thrust levels could be maintained in spite of engine degradation. Two of these modes are shown in Table O.1. One is the N_1/EPR mode already discussed. The other is the $N_1/\Delta P/P_{t2}$ control mode. $\Delta P/P_{t2}$ is fan pressure rise divided by fan inlet total pressure, and it is proportional to fan exit Mach number (velocity). This mode is appropriate for variable cycle engines where the engine bypass ratio can be modulated, through the use of internal variable geometry, to a high-bypass-ratio configuration for good fuel economy at cruise, or to a lower bypass ratio for high specific thrust during combat maneuvers. With these trimless control modes thrust regulation will be maintained as the engine degrades, but at the expense of increased fuel burn and increased turbine inlet temperature. As further degradation occurs, a turbine inlet temperature limit will be reached, and the engine will be pulled from service for maintenance—usually a complete overhaul at a maintenance depot.

The fan map depicted in Fig. O.1b offers a glimpse of the permissible operating regime of the engine during transient and steady-state operation with respect to rotor speeds, engine pressure ratio, surge or stall limits, and temperature limits. These limits represent upper thresholds of operation. There are also minimum thresholds for fan pressure ratio, below which combustion cannot occur, and for minimum inlet airflow to sustain continuous operation. Figure O.2 shows, notionally, the complete operating envelope for the engine as it relates to the fan map.

O.1.1 Control Logic and Processing

The engine control system relies on a number of inputs to accomplish its function. Some are input commands from the pilot or flight control system, and others are direct measurements from the aircraft and the engine. Output commands are then sent on to the actuators that control main engine and afterburner fuel flows, exhaust nozzle area, etc. Since the early 1990s, the heart of the military aircraft gas turbine engine control system has been a digital electronic controller. The electronic processor performs all of the control system calculations and logical functions based on sensors located on the aircraft and within the engine. It offers significantly more flexibility in defining control schedules and such compared to previous hydromechanically based control units used up to the early 1970s. A simplified schematic of the engine control system is shown in Fig. O.3. The power lever angle (PLA), or throttle position, command from the pilot is the primary input to the controller. This command is coupled with sensed values of inlet temperature and pressure. The inlet temperature and pressure signals are used to infer information on the aircraft's altitude and Mach number, in addition to providing data to compute corrected rotor speeds, etc. Other inputs may be fed into

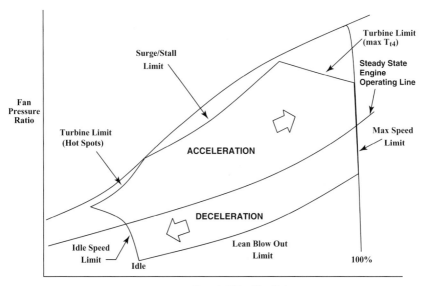

Fig. O.2   Engine operating limits as related to the fan map.

the control system from the aircraft flight control system and flight data system, such as aircraft attitude, air speed, and angle of attack. For example, in certain flight conditions, such as during extreme combat maneuvers, the inlet air to the engine may be highly distorted, and the engine may be more susceptible to stall or surge. With the appropriate information from the flight data system, the engine controller can make the necessary adjustments to the engine's operating condition to accommodate these flight maneuvers.

The input commands from the pilot and flight data system are fed into a control logic function that translates this information into the required operating condition for the engine to produce the thrust requested by the pilot. In the example chosen for this discussion, the output of this logic function would be a required fan rotor speed and a required engine pressure ratio. Table O.2 shows the input variables, output variables, and sensed parameters typically used by the engine controller for this particular steady-state control mode. The engine control system is characterized by open-loop and closed-loop control elements. The position of the variable

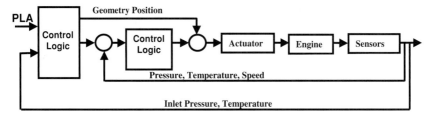

Fig. O.3   Engine control system schematic.

Table O.2 Input variables, output variables, and sensed parameters

Control input variables	Sensed parameters										Controlled variables (outputs)	
	N_1	N_2	P_{t3}	T_{t5}	T_{t2}	P_{t2}	M_{13}	P_{t6}	LOD[a]	PLA		
Main burner fuel flow	X	X	X	X	X	X	—	—	—	X	N_1	Closed loop
Exhaust nozzle thrust area	X	—	—	—	X	X	X	X	—	X	EPR	Closed loop
Fan, HPC variable geometry	X	X	—	—	X	—	—	—	—	X	Vane position	Open loop
Engine bleed	X	X	—	—	X	—	—	—	—	X	Valve position	Open loop
A/B fuel flow	X	—	—	—	X	X	—	X	X	X	Fuel valve	Open loop

[a]LOD = light-off detector.

geometry stator vanes in the fan and compressor are usually open-loop scheduled as a function of the respective corrected rotor speeds to provide the airflow an optimal incidence angle with respect to the leading edge of the blades. This ensures optimal aerodynamic efficiency of these components. Likewise, compressor bleed flow is usually open-loop scheduled as a function of corrected compressor rotor speed to ensure good starting characteristics and good low-speed performance. The most important closed-loop variable is main burner fuel flow. It has the greatest impact over the largest dynamic operating range of any other variable in the engine.

The basic dynamics of the engine are characterized by the polar moment of inertia of each rotor and by the volume of the afterburner tailpipe. Figure O.4 shows a general state-space representation of the principal gas turbine engine dynamics and the corresponding root locus plot in the frequency domain. State-space equations are written in the time domain and are ordinary differential equations describing the physical motion of the engines dynamic elements. Using Laplace transforms, time domain differential equations can be written and analyzed in the frequency domain. Designers may use either time domain methods or frequency domain techniques, or both when designing and analyzing a control system for an engine (see Ref. 1). The root locus plot shows the rotor inertias to be close to the origin, meaning they have the dominant effect on the dynamic response of the engine. The root associated with the tailpipe is higher in frequency and has a limited effect on the overall engine dynamic response. There is a weak, but discernable coupling between the tailpipe pressure and fan rotor speed through the pressure associated with the fan duct and afterburner volume. Because this coupling is weak, the two principal closed-loop control functions can be viewed as being independent of one another. In other words, the main engine fuel flow will control fan rotor speed, and the exhaust nozzle area will control engine pressure ratio. In reality, the coupling

State Space Equations:

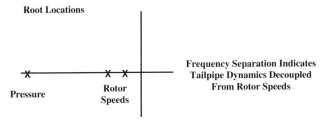

$$\begin{bmatrix} \dot{N}_H \\ \dot{N}_L \\ \dot{P}_{t6} \end{bmatrix} = \begin{bmatrix} -a_H & 0 & 0 \\ C_{HL} & -a_L & C_{PL} \\ 0 & C_{LP} & -a_{P6} \end{bmatrix} \begin{bmatrix} N_H \\ N_L \\ P_{t6} \end{bmatrix} + \begin{bmatrix} b_{FH} & 0 \\ b_{FL} & 0 \\ b_{FP} & b_{AP} \end{bmatrix} \begin{bmatrix} \dot{m}_f \\ A_8 \end{bmatrix}$$

Root Locations

Pressure   Rotor
                  Speeds

Frequency Separation Indicates
Tailpipe Dynamics Decoupled
From Rotor Speeds

Fig. O.4   Governing dynamics of the gas turbine engine.

between fan rotor speed and exhaust nozzle area is accounted for by the control logic.

The rotor inertia, or rotational mass, determines the dynamic response of the engine. For a large diameter, high-bypass-ratio engine, a typical acceleration from a low power setting to a high power setting may take 10 or more seconds. Conversely, for a small diameter, single spool turbojet, an acceleration may take only 1 or 2 s. The excess energy produced by increasing the fuel flow to the combustor is transferred to the rotor through the turbine. The result of this excess torque is a change in rotor speed. To accelerate the engine quickly, the fuel flow input to the engine should be raised quickly. There is an inherent problem with this approach, however. As shown in Fig. O.2, the engine operating line is bounded by various operational limiting conditions. Raising fuel flow too rapidly could cause an engine overtemperature condition or a fan or compressor stall, if not properly regulated. The appropriate operating limits are built into the engine control system in the form of acceleration and deceleration schedules. These acceleration and deceleration schedules come into play when large and sudden changes in thrust are requested. A typical rotor speed/fuel flow control loop logic diagram, showing the appropriate limits for acceleration and deceleration, is depicted in Fig. O.5. Figure O.5 is greatly simplified. The acceleration schedule accounts for multiple limits, as depicted in Fig. O.2. Rapid accelerations require the engine to operate transiently far from the normal operating line very close to the engine stall line. The acceleration limits incorporated in the control system enable the engine to make large, rapid thrust transients safely, without encountering a stall or over temperature condition. During transient operation, the variable geometry vanes in the fan and compressor will be positioned to follow a prescribed schedule as a function of rotor speed. By limiting the variable vanes to track a precise schedule, high frequency aerodynamic instabilities, such as blade flutter, are avoided.

The control logic employed during an engine deceleration is very simple: cut fuel flow to the lowest possible level that will sustain combustion and keep the main

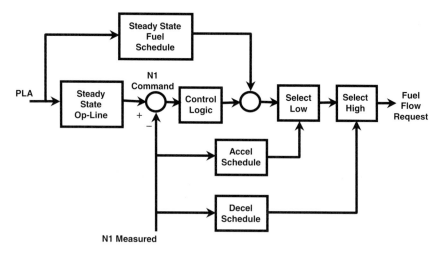

Fig. O.5   Rotor speed control schematic.

burner lit. Acceleration schedules, on the other hand, are more complicated and more sophisticated, because, as shown in Fig. O.2, multiple operation limits are encountered during a large thrust excursion. Just as there were different approaches to defining engine steady-state control modes, there are different approaches to defining acceleration, or transient, control modes. Some of the more common transient control modes and the operational advantages and disadvantages of each are listed here:

1) $\dot{m}_f$ vs rpm: This requires temperature biasing to account for varying ambient conditions and requires accurate measurements.

2) $\dot{m}_f/P_{t3}$ vs rpm: This is a simple concept (fuel flow divided by compressor exit pressure directly relates to fuel-to-air ratio) but tends to increase required performance margins; has potential instability with pressure fluctuations; and has good response to engine stalls. (As compressor discharge pressure drops during a stall, the controller will correspondingly reduce engine fuel flow, which is the safest response to a compressor stall or surge.)

3) T_{t4} vs rpm: Only one biasing parameter is required (inlet temperature); is intolerant to varying fuel type (varying heat content); has consistent accels, but requires high response measurement.

4) $\dot{N}$ vs rpm: Closed-loop accel control provides consistent, repeatable response. It does not *require* biasing parameters, but provides superior performance with temperature and pressure biasing.

From a performance standpoint the $\dot{N}$, or the rotor speed rate of change transient control mode, has evolved to be a preferred choice for military applications. This mode would not have been possible without the advent of digital electronic controls. The principal advantage of this control mode is that is provides repeatable and consistent accelerations over a very broad range of engine operating conditions. Pilots like it for that reason.

O.1.2 Advanced Control Logic

Protection of the engine hardware is one of the primary responsibilities of the control system. This consists of avoiding all of the limits discussed earlier. To avoid reaching these limits, margins (safety factors) that consist of a worst-case stackup of undesirable effects which could cause the engine to exceed one or more of the limits are established. In the case of stall margin, this consists of effects caused by, but not limited to, values associated with inlet distortion, engine transients, tip wear, Reynolds number effects, engine-to-engine variations, and control tolerances. Historically, the amount set aside for design margins has not changed.

It is important to realize that the control system cannot create performance that the engine does not already have built into it. To further improve engine performance from a control viewpoint, the engine design process must be considered. During the engine design process, a design point is selected, and the requirements for each engine component are established. Then, each component proceeds on an independent path until all of the components are assembled into a final engine for test. During the component development program, safety factors are added to the component design for safe operation. The inclusion of these margins reduces potential engine performance.

To understand these concepts, consider Fig. O.6. In this plot, thrust ratio is plotted as a function of temperature ratio. Temperature ratio is defined as the ratio of turbine inlet temperature limit to turbine inlet temperature at stoichiometric temperatures. This axis then shows the growth of turbine engine material limitations and cooling technologies over time (increase in temperature ratio). Thrust ratio is then defined as the thrust produced at a given stall margin and temperature ratio divided by the thrust at no stall margin and stoichiometric temperatures. The line labeled stall line is the line of zero margin, and the one labeled operating line is a line of constant design stall margin. The area between these two curves denotes the performance that is lost as a result of constant design stall margins. The ellipses represent engine

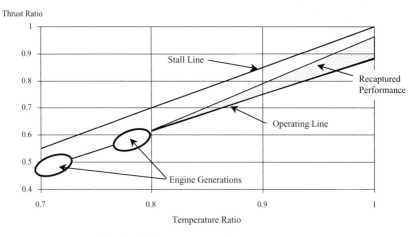

Fig. O.6   Recaptured performance potential.

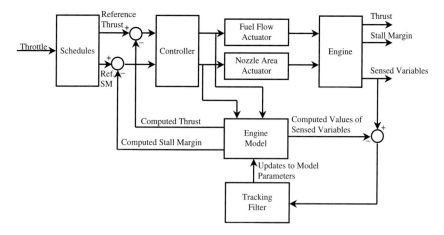

Fig. O.7   Model-based control architecture.

generations or levels of engine technology as time progresses. The wedge labeled recaptured performance is shown to illustrate the effects of the parameters that make up the margin stackup which are not fully understood. As we gain further understanding of the phenomena that reduce stall margin and how they can be controlled, the amount of performance that can be regained will increase.

It is possible for the control to recapture some of this loss performance by actively controlling these margins. To do this, the propulsion control is moving from the classical feedback control that has been used for decades, shown in Fig. O.3, to model-based control that has been used in the process control industry. The model-based control architecture is shown in Fig. O.7. The remainder of this section will discuss model-based control.

During the engine development process, a detailed nonlinear simulation of the engine is created. The control engineer usually starts this work after the simulation is created. He or she first linearizes the model and checks linear model responses against the nonlinear model to ensure they have the same response characteristics. If responses are acceptable, the control design can begin with the linear models. At this point significant benefits can be achieved by rethinking the design. The nonlinear model contains all of the knowledge and expertise available for that engine at that time. However, it is never used for anything more than evaluation of proposed changes to control logic or engine hardware. Model-based control uses this knowledge to regain some lost performance.

The key aspect of model-based control is the addition of the nonlinear model of the engine into the control approach. This model is a reduced order or simplified version of the detailed nonlinear model created during development. This model is fed the same commands from the control as the actual engine, and the sensed engine outputs are then compared to the same outputs computed by the model. Model computed values can now be used for feedback, including values that cannot be directly sensed.

The addition of a model into the control scheme presents some difficult challenges. For example, the model is a nominal or average engine representation that may not match the specific engine in question. To overcome this, a tracking filter is added. The function of the tracking filter is to take comparisons between model outputs and sensor readings and adjust the model parameters so that the model outputs match the sensor readings. The model is then assumed to provide an accurate representation of that engine. The selection of a tracking filter is based upon what you are actually interested in controlling. For example, if you are interested in controlling thrust, then you have a performance tracking filter. Similarly, when controlling stall margin an operability tracking filter may be appropriate, or if interested in extending engine life a life tracking filter may be selected. A multipurpose tracking filter that does well for all cases has not been found. Therefore, if all cases need to be covered, then separate tracking filters and models will be necessary. This is a significant hurdle to overcome as a result of memory and processing limitations in today's FADECs (Full Authority Digital Electronic Controls).

O.2 Control System Components

The preceding discussion on control logic touched on some of the control devices required for implementation. This is to be expected, because the description of a control mode provides strong clues as to the types of components involved. For example, control of engine pressure ratio (P_{t6}/P_{t2}) suggests the need for measuring pressures at engine stations 2 and 6. Common sense tells us that modulation of fuel flow to control rotor speed is a fundamental control system function. Afterburning turbojets and turbofans require the ability to change nozzle throat area A_8. Some of the newest military engines also feature A_9 control to allow optimization of nozzle expansion ratio at various power settings and flight conditions. Most modern engines have variable geometry and bleed valves in the compression system to maintain high efficiency and stability over a wide range of operating conditions. This high-level description of required functions suggests a categorization of engine control system components into one of three primary subsystems—electrical, fuel delivery, or actuation.

O.2.1 Electrical Subsystem

The electrical subsystem consists of power generation components (a gearbox-driven alternator and associated power control circuitry), sensors, ignition exciters and igniters, miscellaneous solenoids, an engine diagnostic computer, and a control computer. Engine electrical subsystems have changed significantly over the years, driven by the evolution from hydromechanical to electrically based analog to digital electronic control. Over the last 30 years, these changes have produced tremendous increases in control system capability that have in turn enabled dramatic improvements in engine performance and operability.

Power for the electrical subsystem, as for the rest of the aircraft, is extracted from the engine. A bull gear on the engine's high spool drives a tower shaft connected to a case-mounted gearbox. The engine accessory gearbox typically has several drive pads for various engine accessories, and one of these is devoted to a 5 kW alternator that supplies the engines electrical needs. The alternator output is fed to ignition exciters and to some type of power conditioning unit. The ignition exciters store electrical energy to drive main combustor and augmentor spark igniters during engine start and augmentor light-off. The power conditioning unit converts the alternator alternating current output to direct current and steps the voltage up or down to meet the needs of the other electrical loads on the engine. Because digital controls require continuous power, modern engines typically bring in an aircraft power bus to serve as backup in case of alternator failure.

A standard engine sensor set includes devices to measure temperatures, pressures, rotor speeds, and actuator positions. Specialized diagnostic sensors (e.g., vibration, lubrication system chip detection) may also be included. The specific temperatures and pressures measured may vary slightly from engine to engine, depending on the engine manufacturer and the control strategies each employs. A typical sensor set for a two-spool turbofan will measure engine inlet temperature and pressure (T_{t2} and P_{t2}), compressor inlet temperature ($T_{t2.5}$), bypass duct pressure (P_{t16}), combustor inlet pressure (P_{t3}), tailpipe temperature (T_{t6}), and position feedbacks from the compression system variable stator actuators, fuel metering valve, and exhaust nozzle actuators. Because of the harsh environment, hot section sensing between the high-pressure turbine inlet and low-pressure turbine exit is generally avoided or limited to a non-intrusive method such as optical pyrometry. Optical pyrometers are not accurate enough to use for control purposes, but are useful as limiters to avoid excessive temperatures in the turbine system.

The heart of the electrical subsystem, indeed of the control system, is the digital electronic controller. Depending on the manufacturer and engine, it may be referred to as a DEC (digital electronic controller), DEEC (digital electronic engine control), DECU (digital electronic control unit), or FADEC (full authority digital electronic control). A typical FADEC (Fig. O.8) consists of a computer running a program that implements the control algorithms described previously, analog sensor signal conditioning circuitry with analog-to-digital converters to feed information into these control algorithms, and output signal conditioning circuitry interfaced to digital-to-analog converters that turn the computed commands into the current and voltage levels necessary to drive valves and actuators to the required positions. A modern FADEC will take readings, compute commands, and adjust actuator and valves settings up to 80 times per second. Because of the critical role the FADEC plays in the operation of the engine, digital control is typically implemented in a redundant architecture. Redundancy is usually limited to the electrical subsystem, since the mechanical portion of the control system is highly reliable. Millions of hours of field experience have demonstrated that dual, or duplex, redundancy raises electrical subsystem reliability to a level commensurate with that of the mechanical components. More recent military engines also have some type of

Fig. O.8   Full authority digital electronic control (FADEC).

health or maintenance diagnostic unit interfaced with the FADEC. Future engines will employ predictive or prognostic sensor and data processing to increase safety and improve logistic support. The level of sophistication ranges from simple data logging (limit exceedances, occasional performance snapshots, cycle counting, time at temperature) to complex health tracking with Fast Fourier Transform (FFT) based vibration analysis, automated failure diagnosis, and continuous performance trending. Although FADECs and diagnostic units are similar in many respects, there is one critical difference. FADECs are flight-critical (sometimes called safety-critical) devices, i.e. loss of FADEC function directly impacts safety of flight. Failure of a diagnostic unit will cause the loss of important maintenance information, but has no bearing on flight safety. Therefore, redundancy requirements are not imposed on the diagnostic system in order to save weight and cost.

O.2.2   Fuel Delivery Subsystem

The fuel delivery subsystem consists of one or more pumps, filters, heat exchangers, valves, and plumbing. Its primary functions are to deliver fuel to the main combustor (and augmentor, for afterburning engines) at the appropriate mass flow rate and to cool, either directly or indirectly, engine or aircraft components. These tasks are complicated by the temperature limit of the fuel, around 350°F for the kerosene-based Jet-A, JP-5, and JP-8 fuels used in commercial and military engines. By the time fuel reaches the engine's main fuel pump from an aircraft tank, it has already cooled various vehicle subsystems (Fig. O.9). Although current design practice is to keep fuel temperature below 200°F at the engine interface, higher temperatures are not uncommon. Between the pump discharge and combustor fuel nozzles, fuel is routed through a heat exchanger to cool engine oil. When the maximum operating temperature of approximately 350°F is exceeded, various compounds precipitate from the fuel. These solids deposit in fuel lines and nozzles, leading to performance deterioration and ultimately engine failure. At certain flight conditions maintaining fuel below this critical temperature at the main combustor nozzles (and augmentor spray bars in afterburning turbofan engines) is extremely difficult. This challenge has become more severe on newer military fighter aircraft, leading to the need for a disciplined systems engineering approach to the design of the aircraft fuel delivery system to ensure that

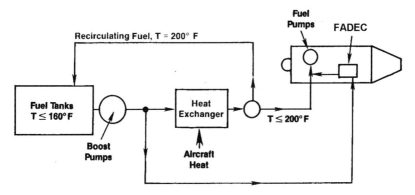

Fig. O.9   Typical aircraft fuel delivery system.

fuel temperature is kept under control at all operating conditions. This has led to the search for fuels that can absorb more heat before destabilizing, as well as endothermic fuel that can absorb additional heat by cracking. Also fuel may be recirculated to the aircraft tanks during periods of high heat rejection (see Fig. O.9). For such systems pump thermal performance, that is, the change in fuel temperature between pump inlet and discharge, is critical. Variable geometry fuel pumps that minimize fuel heating over the entire flow range have been developed to address this critical thermal management issue.

An engine fuel delivery system is required to supply the required mass flow of fuel at sufficient pressure to ensure proper mixing with compressor discharge air in the combustor. The main fuel pump is the critical element in this system. It is responsible for taking low pressure (less than 100 lbf/in.^{2}) fuel from the aircraft fuel delivery system and driving it through the engine fuel system such that it enters the combustor fuel injectors at much higher pressure, often in excess of 1000 lbf/in.^{2} Today's engines use various types of fixed geometry pumps to deliver main fuel flow to their combustors. Gear-type main fuel pumps are the most commonly used because of their simplicity and ruggedness. Centrifugal pumps have also begun to appear in newer engines. A fuel metering valve is located downstream of the pump and is used to vary flow to a manifold that supplies the combustor's individual fuel nozzles. The flow range of the main fuel pump and metering valve is related to the speed range of the pump drive system, contained in the engine accessory gearbox. Because of the relatively small variation in engine core speed, and therefore gearbox drive speed, compared to the huge difference in fuel flow between idle and full power, it is impossible to match delivered fuel flow to required fuel flow at all power settings. Thus, all engine fuel systems include a recirculation loop that takes flow in excess of requirement back either to the pump inlet or to the aircraft tanks. In addition, afterburning engines include a separate loop in their fuel systems to deliver fuel to their augmentors. This loop includes its own pump and plumbing, terminating at a manifold that feeds the augmentor spray bars.

O.2.3 Actuation Subsystem

The actuation system consists of valves and actuators required to manage fuel flows, secondary and bleed airflows, and variable stator positions. Depending on the type of engine, turbine system clearance, nozzle throat area, and thrust vector angle are other potential control parameters of interest. Actuation power is supplied by readily available sources on the engine, usually hydraulic (from the high pressure fuel supply) and occasionally pneumatic (compressor interstage or discharge bleed).

Linear actuators are used to position compression system variable stators and nozzle flaps (for engines with variable area exhaust). This device consists of a servo-valve controlled by a torque motor mounted on a cylinder and piston (Fig. O.10). In certain applications the servovalve may drive more than one cylinder. The servovalve modulates flow of high pressure hydraulic fluid (fuel) to either side of the piston head to control displacement from a predefined null position. Control of the actuated variable is accomplished by changing the position of the piston, which is mechanically linked to the control effector. For example, variable stator position is controlled by displacement of an actuator piston rod that is

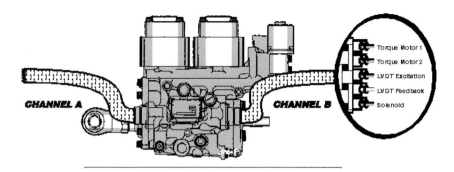

Fig. O.10   Inlet guide vane actuator.

mechanically linked to a "synch" ring. The synch ring is mounted to the outer case of the engine and has individual tabs or levers that are connected to shafts that extend from each stator. Linear displacement of the actuator piston causes rotation of the synch ring, which in turn causes rotation of the variable stators.

Turbine system clearance control, used in some high bypass commercial turbofans, uses an airflow modulation approach as opposed to the direct mechanical positioning method just described. This typically involves using a valve to route "cool" (relative to the turbine section) compression system bleed air across the turbine case to cause it to contract. The contraction reduces airfoil tip clearance, resulting in reduced specific fuel consumption via increased turbine system efficiency. This is done during cruise portions of the mission, where constant throttle settings are the norm for commercial engines.

O.3 Summary

This discussion addressed the basic and fundamental elements of the gas turbine engine control system. Developing control modes and logic for gas turbine engines have evolved over many decades of research and experiment from simple speed governors to more elaborate, multivariable functions. As the application of digital electronic control systems to commercial and military gas turbine engines has become more accepted and widespread, more sophisticated, performance enhancing control modes and logic have, likewise, evolved. The ability to optimize engine performance at various flight conditions is now possible. Adaptive control modes that can optimize engine performance based on a variety of requirements and conditions, such as the particular mission being flown or the health of the engine, are being aggressively pursued.

Reference

[1]D'Azzo, John J., and Houpis, Constantine H., *Feedback Control System, Analysis and Synthesis*, McGraw–Hill, New York, 1966.

Appendix P
Global Range Airlifter (GRA) RFP

This abbreviated Request for Proposal (RFP) is presented as the second design example of this textbook. It is based on anticipated global airlift needs of the Department of Defense and commercial carriers, including passengers and cargo. The solution is carried out in the accompanying supplemental material.

P.1 Background

The C-5 Galaxy was developed in the 1960s to provide strategic airlift needs during the Cold War where the majority of material was prepositioned. The first high-bypass turbofan engine, the General Electric TF39, was developed to power this aircraft. Without aerial refueling, this aircraft can fly about 2,000 n miles with its maximum payload of 290,000 lbf and 6,300 n miles empty.

Recent hostilities such as Desert Storm, Bosnia, and Afghanistan demonstrated that a new Global Range Airlifter (GRA) that could fly without being refueled anywhere in the world from the continental United States was needed. The following section lists specific requirements that will be the basis of the design exercise. Please note that several of the requirements have been imposed in order to allow the GRA to meet civilian flight restrictions, reflecting the modern reality that military aircraft are seldom exempt from peacetime considerations.

P.2 Requirements

1. Maximum gross takeoff weight (GTOW) of 1,000,000 lbf.
2. Minimum payload of 150,000 lbf.
3. Minimum unrefueled range of 10,000 n miles.
4. Maximum fully loaded takeoff distance of 10 kft (no obstacle) at sea level on a hot day (90°F).
5. Maximum landing distance (50% reverse thrust) of 6 kft at sea level on a standard day.
6. Maximum takeoff distance (no payload, return fuel load) of 6 kft at sea level on a hot day (90°F).
7. Maximum one engine out takeoff distance (no payload, 2,000 n miles fuel load) of 6 kft at sea level on a standard day.
8. Maximum fully loaded distance for climb to 35 kft altitude of 200 n miles on a Mil Std 210 hot day.
9. Minimum fully loaded takeoff climb gradient with one-engine out of 3 deg at sea level on a hot day (90°F).
10. Minimum cruise ceiling of 35 kft at 95% GTOW on a standard day.

Appendix Q
About the Software

An extensive collection of supplemental material accompanies this textbook. Most important is the general and specific computational software entitled AEDsys. The programs that make up the AEDsys software suite are described in Secs. 1.10.1 and 1.10.2. Additional material included with the software are comprehensive software user guides, software data files for the Air-to-Air Fighter (AAF) design problem, design solution to the Global Range Airlifter (GRA) design problem, engine digital pictures, other design problems, and textbook supplemental material.

Q.1 Getting Started

To get started, you need a PC-compatible system with Microsoft Windows operating system (XP or later). Download the support material (AEDsys software, user's manuals, etc.) from the AIAA Web site at www.aiaa.org/publications/supportmaterials. Follow the instructions provided and enter the following password: constraint. Save the downloaded file and unpack into the files necessary for installation of the software and other supporting materials.

Run the Setup program within the AEDsys Software folder and the opening installation window is displayed as shown in Fig. Q-1.

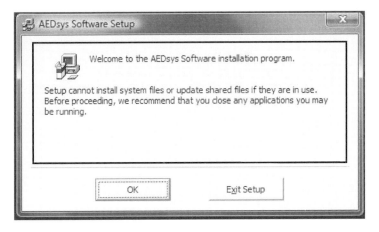

Fig. Q.1   Opening installation window.

Select the OK button and the software destination window is displayed as shown in Fig. Q.2.

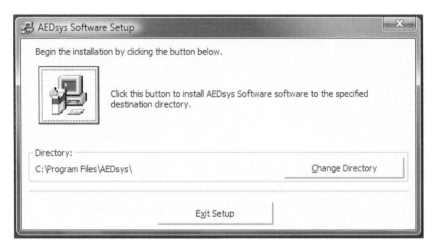

Fig. Q.2   Installation destination window.

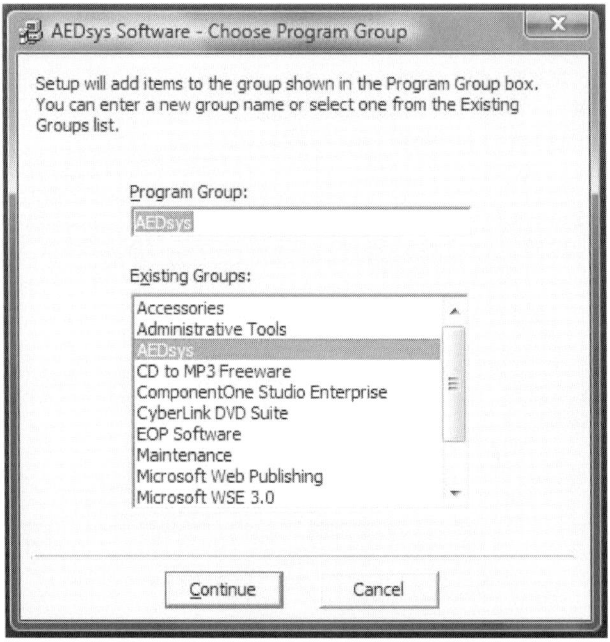

Fig. Q.3   Program group window.

Select the highlighted button in the upper left to install the programs in the default location (C:\Programs Files\AEDsys\). The program group window is displayed as shown in Fig. Q.3. It is recommended that the user uses the default AEDsys program group and press the Continue button. Software installation will then proceed.

Index

685